ATOMIC ORBITAL

p. 2 The region in the space about the nucleus of an atom where an electron is most likely to be found.

CARBOHYDRATES

p. 379 Polyhydroxy aldehydes, or polyhydroxy ketones, or substances that can be hydrolyzed to such aldehydes or ketones.

CARBONYL GROUP

p. 223 The reactive group to be found in aldehydes, ketones, and acyl compounds, i.e.,

$$\overset{O}{\underset{\|}{-C-}}.$$

CARBOXYL GROUP

p. 259 The functional group characteristic of the carboxylic acids, i.e.,

$$\overset{O}{\underset{\|}{R-COH}}.$$

CONFIGURATION

p. 139 The spatial arrangement of atoms in a molecule that may be changed only be breaking and rearranging bonds.

CONFORMATION

p. 40 A spatial arrangement of atoms or groups in a molecule permitted by their rotation around single bonds.

CONJUGATED SYSTEM

p. 81 A system of alternate single and double bonds through which chemical activity may be transmitted from one atom to another.

COVALENCE

p. 7 Bonding through electron pair sharing.

DEXTROROTATORY

p. 143 A term applied to optically active compounds that rotate plane polarized light clockwise or to the right.

DIASTEREOISOMERS

p. 152 Optical isomers that are not enantiomorphs or mirror images.

DIAZOTIZATION

p. 368 A reaction carried out at low temperature between a primary aryl amine and nitrous acid.

ELECTROPHILIC REAGENT

p. 109 A reagent that seeks an unshared pair of electrons, i.e., an acid.

ELECTROVALENCE

p. 5 Bonding between ions of opposite charge.

ENANTIOMORPHS

p. 147 Optical isomers that are mirror images and nonsuperimposable.

ESTERS

p. 278 A general class of acid derivatives in which the ionizable hydrogen has been replaced by a hydrocarbon group.

Continued on back end leaves

Ex Libris

Rebecca Jean
Armentrout

organic chemistry

a brief course
second edition

WALTER W. LINSTROMBERG
Professor of Chemistry
University of Nebraska at Omaha

Under the editorship of
JACOB KLEINBERG
Professor and Chairman
of the Department of Chemistry
University of Kansas

D. C. HEATH AND COMPANY
Lexington, Massachusetts

Illustrator
Winston M. Allen · Boston

preface

The revision of a textbook presents an opportunity to improve it — to eliminate errors, to make changes in emphasis, and to bring the book up to date. In the revision of a brief text all of this must be accomplished without too great an increase in the number of pages. The author of a brief text thus is faced with a hard choice. He must decide what new material to include and what old material to leave out. His judgment in these decisions can be, fortunately, in many instances, reinforced by the comments and suggestions of the many teachers who used the original edition in their classes. The present text, therefore, is a retention of all that was judged good in the first edition, an expansion of certain sections considered too brief, and the addition of new material believed to be necessary.

The basic organization of the first edition, in which compounds were treated as families, has been retained with an integration of aliphatic and aromatic compounds. This treatment has adapted itself especially well to teaching the subject in a brief course. A change in chapter sequence has brought the treatment of stereo-chemistry nearer to the beginning of the text, in order to give students an early feeling for the three-dimensionality of organic molecules, and a clearer insight into and a better interpretation of reaction routes. The attempt to give dimension to structures has not been limited entirely to the chapter on stereochemistry but has been made throughout the text. Graphical representations of molecules are shown in perspective to help the student visualize the geometry of the structures more nearly as they are. Sections dealing with reaction mechanisms have been expanded slightly and then only when it was felt they were part of the explanation due the student. The section dealing with spectroscopy has been taken out of Chapter 14, *Light Absorption by Organic Compounds*, and introduced in Chapter 1 as a technique useful in organic analysis. Accordingly, the residual portion of the chapter on light absorption has been renamed *Color in Organic Compounds, Dyes* and placed next to the last chapter thus bringing the chapters on *Carbohydrates* and *Amino Acids, Peptides*, and *Proteins* nearer to related sections of the text.

A section on oxidation-reduction reactions has been included in the chapter on the alcohols to illustrate to the students that organic reaction equations involving oxidation and reduction can be as easily balanced as those for inorganic reactions.

The utility of the present edition has been extended by additional exercises placed within the body of the text to illustrate concepts as they are introduced. In addition, a number of new exercises and problems have been added to the end of each chapter.

Several new charts have been added and existing ones expanded. As in the first edition, a second color has been generously used to emphasize reaction sites, to indicate reaction pathways, and to illustrate better the geometry of structures.

I wish to thank all the users of the first edition who were so generous in giving of their time to correspond with me. I especially wish to thank Professors Robert L. McKee of the University of North Carolina, Samuel P. McManus of the University of Alabama, Philip H. Davidson of City College of San Francisco, Robert W. Isensee of San Diego State College, Norma Gaillard of Tuskegee Institute, and Jack Powers of Ripon College. Many of the changes incorporated into the present edition have been in response to their suggestions.

I am again indebted to **Dr. Jacob Kleinberg** of the University of Kansas who read the entire revised edition and smoothed many of the rough spots. I also acknowledge with thanks the helpfulness of my colleague Dr. Paul J. Stageman of the University of Nebraska at Omaha whose criticisms were most valuable.

I shall be grateful for continued suggestions for improvement of the text in matters of fact, judgment, and presentation.

Walter W. Linstromberg

contents

vi

introduction

Organic chemistry according to its original definition dealt only with those substances of natural *organic* origin — that is, products of plants or animals. It was thought by early chemists that the production of an organic compound involved the "vital force" of a living organism. The science of chemistry thus was separated into two broad divisions — **inorganic** and **organic.** In 1828, however, the German chemist Friedrich Wöhler[1] heated some ammonium cyanate, NH_4OCN, and obtained urea.

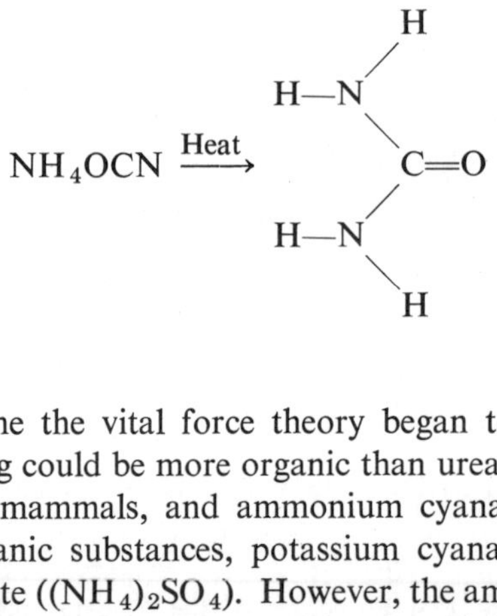

$$NH_4OCN \xrightarrow{\text{Heat}} \begin{array}{c} H \\ H-N \\ \\ C=O \\ H-N \\ H \end{array}$$

For the first time the vital force theory began to be questioned. Certainly nothing could be more organic than urea for it is excreted in the urine of mammals, and ammonium cyanate was prepared from two inorganic substances, potassium cyanate (KOCN) and ammonium sulfate $((NH_4)_2SO_4)$. However, the ammonium cyanate that Wöhler used had been prepared by the calcination of animal bones and for this reason some of his contemporaries still held the vitalistic theory to be valid. It was not until some time later when Kolbe[2] succeeded in converting chloroacetic acid into acetic acid

[1]Friedrich Wöhler (1800–1882). Professor of Chemistry, University of Gottingen.

[2]Adolph Wilhelm Kolbe (1818–1884). Professor of Chemistry, University of Leipzig.

by heating it with zinc that the vital force theory was completely abandoned by chemists and the relationship of the two branches of chemistry clearly recognized. As is often the case, names persist even though they are no longer descriptive. Today, **organic chemistry** is recognized as the study of most **carbon containing compounds.** Hundreds of thousands of these compounds of carbon have been synthesized and studied, and possibly the structures of more than a million are known. The list continues to grow daily. In many instances the organic chemist not only has recreated structures found in nature but has improved upon them as well. Moreover, he has synthesized many compounds which have no counterparts in nature. Indeed, the synthesis of new and useful compounds is one of the most important aspects of organic chemistry. It was thus that we obtained nylon and dacron, novocaine, substitutes for rubber, the sulfa drugs, and DDT, to mention but a few of the more familiar products. Others, that you will read about in later sections of the text, make up a long and impressive list. Thanks to the research chemist, a myriad of wondrous products make our lives more healthful, more comfortable, and more enjoyable.

A working knowledge of organic chemistry is a necessary prerequisite to a clearer understanding of those studies of which it is an integral part — i.e., medicine, nursing, pharmacy, home economics, agriculture, and all their related fields. Our fuels, foods, medicines, and clothing are, for the most part, organic in nature. There is hardly a phase of our daily lives that is not related to or dependent upon this tremendously important and fascinating science.

The need for getting off to a good start in an organic chemistry course cannot be overemphasized. It is in order, therefore, to offer to the student a few suggestions which will make the study of organic chemistry orderly, meaningful, and interesting. Read your assignments carefully. Learn each new concept and term as you come to it. Use the reviews, exercises, and problems which you will find at the end of each chapter. Most important, by the extensive use of scratch pad and pencil apply through practice what you have learned. *This is the only way you will remember the material you study.* Finally, ask questions in class and in the laboratory.

In the beginning it may appear confusing that the laboratory preparation of one class of compounds frequently requires the use of another class not yet studied. Cheer up! It soon will become obvious that in this manner the synthesis of one substance automatically employs a reaction of the other. Inasmuch as the study of organic chemistry involves principally learning the **names, structures, preparation,** and **reactions** of many compounds, the whole scheme of presentation is one of integrating these constituents. As in a jig-saw puzzle, the pieces will fit into place as you proceed through the course.

chapter 1

General Principles

INTRODUCTION

The analysis of any plant or animal product reveals that it always contains carbon and hydrogen and usually also oxygen and/or nitrogen. In many organic compounds sulfur, phosphorus, and the halogens are also to be found. In some cases even a metallic element makes up part of a natural occurring organic structure.[1] It would be correct to say that a very small number of elements (less than a dozen) comprise most organic compounds. This is small indeed when compared to the large number of different elements found in inorganic substances. How is it possible for such a small number of elements to account for a million or more organic compounds? To obtain the answer to this question we need to examine the manner in which the atoms in compounds are held together. It is not enough to know the number and kind of atoms an organic compound contains. We must be able to translate each molecular formula into a structure. When we have done this, we will see that carbon is nearly unique among the elements. Not only does the carbon atom bond to each of the elements cited above, but it shows a predilection for bonding to other carbon atoms. The unique role of the carbon atom in the formation of organic compounds will be understood better after a brief review of atomic structure.

1.2   ATOMIC STRUCTURE

In your introductory course in chemistry you learned that an atom consists of a positively charged nucleus surrounded by negative

---

[1]Iron is present in the hemoglobin of blood to the extent of 0.34%, magnesium comprises about 2.7% of the chlorophyll found in green plants, and cobalt is present in Vitamin B_{12} to the extent of 4.34%.

electrons equal in number to the charge on the nucleus. You also learned that the electrons are distributed around the nucleus in energy levels called **principal quantum shells** designated by the letters K, L, M, N, O, P, and Q, or by numbers 1–7, in each case starting with the shell nearest the nucleus. If n is the number of the principal shell, the number of electrons needed to completely fill that shell with electrons is $2n^2$. Thus, the first shell (K shell) can hold a maximum of two electrons, the second shell (L shell) a maximum of eight electrons, etc. Electrons in the first shell have the lowest energy, the energy increasing with shell number. In addition to principal shells, there are still other spatial categories for electrons.

Principal shells are divided into **subshells** designated by letters in order of filling as s, p, d, and f. The first principal shell has only one subshell, designated as the $1s$. The second principal shell has two subshells designated $2s$ and $2p$ subshells and the third principal shell consists of three subshells, namely $3s$, $3p$, and $3d$. Inasmuch as our present study is limited principally to compounds of carbon formed with elements of low atomic numbers, we need not concern ourselves at this time with higher subshells. The subshells are further divided into **atomic orbitals.** An orbital is not easily defined but may be described as the region in the space surrounding an atomic nucleus which is most likely to be occupied by an electron. Imagine an electron in the s orbital as a point of light capable of being photographed. A time exposure on a photographic film then would reveal a circular cloud, dense toward the center and diffuse at its outer boundary. In other words, the time-average-position of an s electron is a sphere. All s orbitals, or orbitals in s subshells, are spheres, with their centers at the nucleus of the atom (Fig. 1.1). However, the shapes of orbitals vary. The K shell has only the $1s$ orbital. The L shell has, in addition to the $2s$ orbital, which also is spherical but somewhat larger than the $1s$ orbital, three p orbitals. The p orbitals are of equal energy and are dumbbell-shaped with a lobe on either side of the atomic nucleus (Fig. 1.2). The nucleus of the atom is at the node or the point where the line crosses itself in describing the figure-8 shape. The probability of finding an electron at the node is zero. The axes of the p orbitals are perpendicular to each other and the orbitals are differentiated as $2p_x$, $2p_y$, or $2p_z$. The small subscripts refer to the x, y, and z axes. Each orbital regardless of its designation has a maximum capacity of two electrons, and when the orbital is filled the electrons must be oriented in opposite directions, or must have **opposite spin.** Further, in any principal shell electrons occupy orbitals of lower energy first — that is, they occupy s orbitals before p orbitals, p before d, etc. Moreover, an orbital is not occupied by a pair of electrons until orbitals of equal energy are each occupied

■□FIGURE 1.1

THE *s* ORBITAL

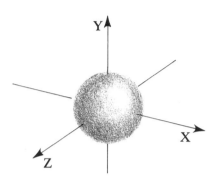

■□FIGURE 1.2

ATOMIC $2p_x$, $2p_y$, AND $2p_z$ ORBITALS WITH AXES MUTUALLY PERPENDICULAR.

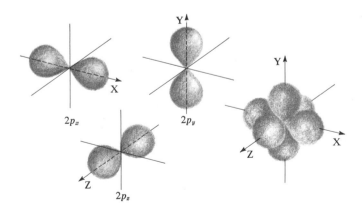

by at least one electron. Table 1.1 shows graphically how electrons are distributed around the nuclei of the first ten elements.

☐■ TABLE 1.1

SCHEMATIC REPRESENTATION OF ELECTRON ORBITALS
FOR THE FIRST TEN ELEMENTS OF THE PERIODIC TABLE*

| | | Normal | | | | | Excited | | | | | Valence |
| | | K-shell | L-shell | | | | K-shell | L-shell | | | | |
Element	At. No.	$1s$	$2s$	$2p_x$	$2p_y$	$2p_z$	$1s$	$2s$	$2p_x$	$2p_y$	$2p_z$	
H	1	↓										1
He	2	↑↓										0
Li	3	↑↓	↓									1
Be	4	↑↓	↑↓	○	○	○	↑↓	↓	↓	○	○	2
B	5	↑↓	↑↓	↓	○	○	↑↓	↓	↓	↓	○	3
C	6	↑↓	↑↓	↓	↓	○	↑↓	↓	↓	↓	↓	4
N	7	↑↓	↑↓	↓	↓	↓						3
O	8	↑↓	↑↓	↑↓	↓	↓						2
F	9	↑↓	↑↓	↑↓	↑↓	↓						1
Ne	10	↑↓	↑↓	↑↓	↑↓	↑↓						0

*The spin of an electron is shown by a small arrow. Since the spins of two electrons occupying the same orbital must be opposite (positive and negative), the arrows representing such electrons are shown pointing in opposite directions. The empty (broken line) circles in the diagram represent orbitals potentially available to electrons of higher energy.

Exercise 1.1   Expand Table 1.1 to include the M, or third principal quantum shell, and show the electron distribution of the next eight elements in the Periodic Table.

Chemical Bonding

The only elements which have a completely filled outermost, or valence, shell belong to the family of elements referred to as the noble gases in Group O of the periodic table.[2] A completely filled outer-most shell appears to represent a stable arrangement, and many elements in their reactions with each other exhibit a tendency to fill their outermost shells through a transfer or sharing of electrons. Either transfers or sharing result in the formation of chemical bonds.

1.3   ELECTROVALENT, OR IONIC BONDS

When sodium and chlorine enter into chemical combination the product, sodium chloride, is a solid compound in which both sodium and chlorine appear as ions, or charged particles. By con-tributing its one outermost (valence) electron to the chlorine atom, sodium is left deficient by one electron and becomes a sodium ion with a charge of plus one. Chlorine, by acquiring the extra electron from sodium, becomes a chloride ion with a charge of minus one.

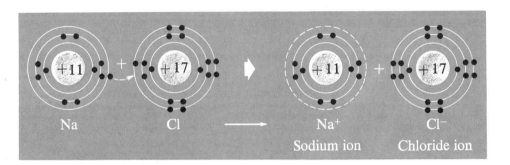

After the transfer of the electron is completed, both sodium and chloride ions have filled outer shells of electrons; the former ion has an electronic configuration equivalent to that of the noble gas (Ne) preceding it in the periodic table, and the chloride ion has the con-figuration of the noble gas (Ar) immediately following (Table 1.2).

In the sodium chloride crystal each sodium ion is surrounded by six chloride ions and each chloride ion is surrounded by six sodium ions in a cubic structure (Fig. 1.3). These ions of opposite charge are held together by strong, attractive electrostatic forces, or **electrovalent bonds.**

---

[2]The outermost (valence) shell is usually regarded as completed when it has eight electrons, that is, filled s and p subshells even though the shell can potentially hold more than eight electrons. Exceptions: hydrogen and helium have a filled outermost shell when it contains two electrons — the 1s subshell.

☐■ TABLE   1.2

AN   ABBREVIATED   PERIODIC   TABLE

	1	2	3	4	3	2	1	0
1	$_1$H							$_2$He
2	$_3$Li	$_4$Be	$_5$B	$_6$C	$_7$N	$_8$O	$_9$F	$_{10}$Ne
3	$_{11}$Na	$_{12}$Mg	$_{13}$Al	$_{14}$Si	$_{15}$P	$_{16}$S	$_{17}$Cl	$_{18}$Ar
4	$_{19}$K	$_{20}$Ca					$_{35}$Br	$_{36}$Kr
5	$_{37}$Rb	$_{38}$Sr					$_{53}$I	$_{54}$Xe
6	$_{55}$Cs	$_{56}$Ba					$_{85}$At	$_{86}$Rn

(The numbers across the top are the usual valences of the elements in that column.)

■☐ FIGURE   1.3

THE SPATIAL ARRANGEMENT OF SODIUM AND CHLORIDE IONS IN
A CRYSTAL OF SODIUM CHLORIDE (COMMON SALT).

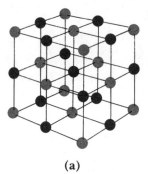

(a) The black circles represent sodium ions,
the green circles chlo-
ride ions;
(b) The small spheres represent sodium ions
and the large spheres
chloride ions.

(a)   (b)

(*Courtesy* Nebergall, Schmidt, Holtzclaw. *General Chemistry*, 3rd ed.,
Lexington, Mass.: D. C. Heath and Co.)

Another example of an ionic compound is lithium fluoride.
The lithium atom, like sodium, also gives up the single electron in its
outermost shell. The lithium ion, with two electrons remaining in its
K shell, thus has the same spatial arrangement of electrons (called
configuration) as helium. Fluorine, on the other hand, attains the
configuration of neon by accepting an electron (see next page). The
compound has the formula Li^+F^-.

Thus, many inorganic compounds are formed by transfers of
electrons between the elements to produce, not molecules, but ag-

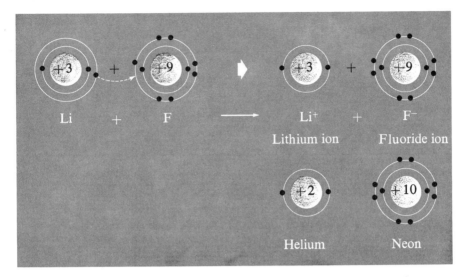

gregates of charged particles. Crystals of inorganic salts usually are hard substances with high melting points, because the electrostatic forces that hold the ions together in the crystal are great and not easily broken. When inorganic salts dissolve in water, the ions present in the crystals dissociate or separate from each other and produce solutions which conduct an electric current. These properties are not generally characteristic of organic compounds.

1.4   COVALENT BONDS

A covalent single bond forms between two atoms through the *sharing* of a pair of electrons. The orbital of one atom overlaps that of another to form a new orbital. In most cases, the orbitals of the atoms undergoing this merger have but single electrons in them and half-filled orbitals available. The orbital which forms from such sharing is called a **molecular orbital** and encompasses the nuclei of both atoms. As in the case of a filled atomic orbital, the electrons in the pair occupying the molecular orbital also must have opposite spin. Now each electron, which before bonding was a "loner" and attracted only to its own nucleus, is also subject to the attraction of a second nucleus. This additional attractive force gives the bond strength and makes for a stable arrangement. Ions are not formed in this type of union since there is no transfer of electrons.

The simplest example of the covalent single bond is found in the hydrogen molecule. Each hydrogen atom with a single electron in its $1s$ orbital can supply one of the shared electron pair which fills the molecular orbital. The shape of the resulting molecular orbital is no longer spherical but, as might be imagined, more sausage-shaped as if two rubber balls had been tightly compressed. The bond formed between the two hydrogen atoms is cylindrically symmetrical about its axis and is called a σ **(sigma) bond.** It is a very strong bond and results in a very stable molecule. The cross sections illustrated in Fig. 1.4 show (a) the region of greatest electron density when $1s$ electrons occupy atomic orbitals about hydrogen nuclei, and (b) the region of greatest electron density when a shared pair of $1s$ electrons occupy a hydrogen molecular orbital.

A number of atoms share more than one pair of electrons. Nitrogen, for example, is capable of mutually sharing three electrons to form three covalent bonds. In the nitrogen molecule, N_2, each nitrogen atom supplies three electrons to a common linkage. In ammonia, NH_3, nitrogen shares each of its three unpaired electrons ($2p_x$, $2p_y$, $2p_z$) with those of three hydrogen atoms. Oxygen is capable of providing two electrons (and two half-filled orbitals) for two shared electron pairs, as in H_2O and CO_2.

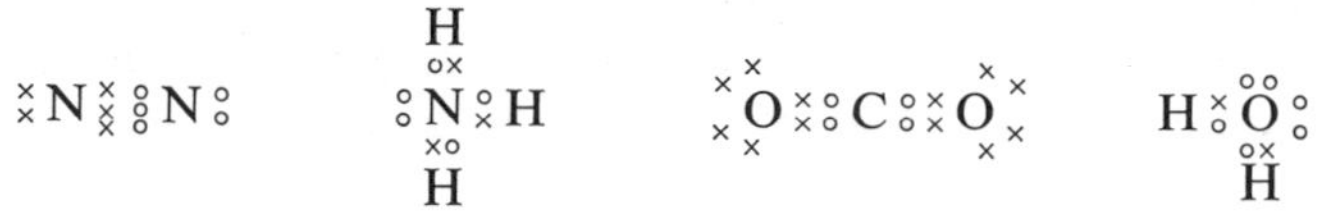

Nitrogen	Ammonia	Carbon dioxide	Water

Since electrons are the same regardless of their origin, we can use a short line (—) to represent the shared electron pair (or covalent single bond), double lines for two shared pairs (covalent double bonds), and triple lines for three shared pairs (covalent triple bonds).

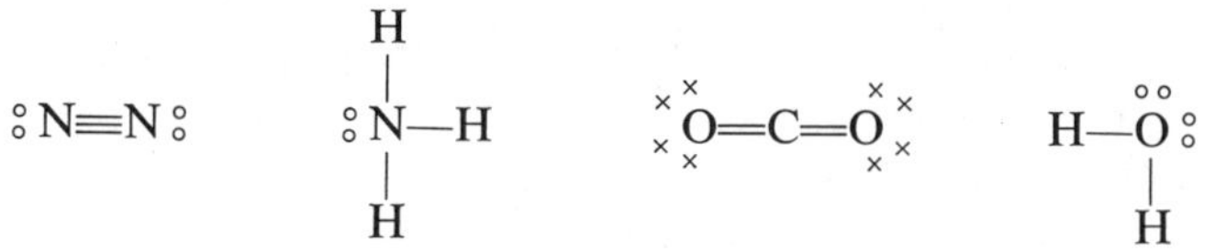

Nitrogen	Ammonia	Carbon dioxide	Water

■☐FIGURE   1.4

ATOMIC AND MOLECULAR ORBITALS OF HYDROGEN.

(a) Atomic orbitals   (b) Molecular orbital

Exercise 1.2   Using dots and small asterisks to represent electrons, show the electronic structures for: (1) Hydrogen peroxide, H_2O_2, (2) Chlorine, Cl_2, (3) Phosgene, $COCl_2$.

In our discussion of the covalent bond we have emphasized the idea of electron pair sharing as a give-and-take proposition in which each atom sharing in the bond makes an equivalent contribution. Frequently structures are formed in which both electrons comprising the shared pair of a covalent bond come from only one of the atoms. Such an arrangement is possible when one atom has an empty valence orbital and the orbital of the other contains an unshared pair of electrons. This type of bond is called a **coordinate covalent, or semipolar bond.** An excellent illustration of the coordinate covalent bond is found in the boron hydride–ammonia complex. Using dots to represent the valence electrons of boron, small circles for the five outermost electrons of nitrogen, and asterisks for the electrons of hydrogen, we can show how B, N, and H are bonded to each other in this structure.

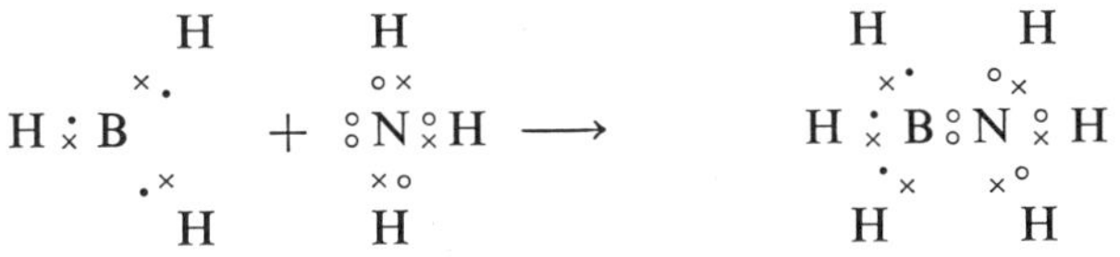

Boron hydride   Ammonia   Boron hydride-ammonia complex

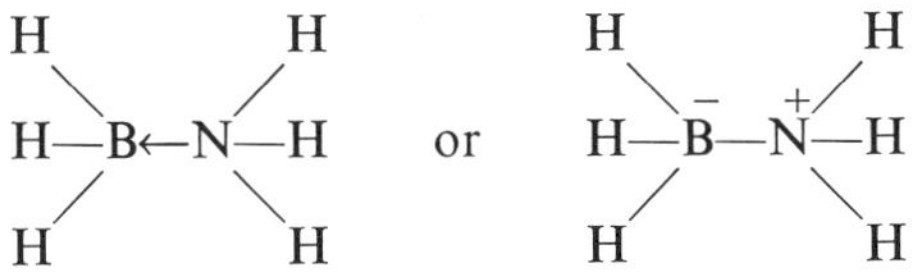

The bond with an arrowhead indicates a coordinate covalent, or semipolar, bond between nitrogen and boron, with nitrogen as the donor of the electron pair and boron as the acceptor. Since nitrogen has, in effect, bestowed upon boron a charge almost equivalent to one electron and lost a corresponding amount, the donation also may be indicated by placing a plus sign on nitrogen and a minus sign on boron. All other bonds shown in the structure are of the ordinary covalent type.

> **Exercise 1.3**   Trimethylamine oxide has the electron con-
> figuration shown. Redraw this structure using a different color
> or symbolism to indicate the origin of all electrons. Are any
> bonds of the coordinate covalent type?
>
> $$
> \begin{array}{c}
> \text{H} \\
> \overset{\circ\circ}{} \\
> \text{H} \overset{\circ}{} \text{C} \overset{\circ}{} \text{H} \\
> \text{H} \qquad \overset{\circ\circ}{} \\
> \text{H} \overset{\circ}{} \text{C} \overset{\circ\circ}{} \overset{\circ}{} \text{N} \overset{\circ}{} \text{O} \overset{\circ}{} \\
> \text{H} \qquad \overset{\circ\circ}{} \\
> \text{H} \overset{\circ}{} \text{C} \overset{\circ}{} \text{H} \\
> \overset{\circ\circ}{} \\
> \text{H}
> \end{array}
> $$

Nearly all bonds which bind atoms together to form organic
compounds are of the covalent type. The unit particles in most
organic compounds are molecules, not ions of opposite charge as in
inorganic salts. Since the attractive forces between molecules are
much weaker than those between ions in salts, many organic substances are liquids with low boiling points. They ordinarily have low
melting points if crystalline solids. Organic substances, for the most
part, are only slightly soluble or insoluble in water. If slightly
soluble, their aqueous solutions seldom conduct an electric current,
unless they are the salts of organic acids or salts of organic bases.
Reactions between organic molecules are usually slow and take place
only when molecules collide with sufficient kinetic energy to break,
rearrange, or form new bonds. For this reason organic reactions
frequently require long periods of heating and the presence of a
catalyst before any appreciable changes occur. For example, a covalently bound halogen atom shows no tendency to precipitate as silver
halide when merely shaken with a silver nitrate solution. On the other
hand, the reaction of an ionic halide with silver nitrate is immediate.

The Covalence of Carbon

1.5   HYBRIDIZED ORBITALS

Since the covalence which an element generally exhibits usually
is determined by the number of unpaired electrons in half-filled
orbitals in its valence shell, the case of carbon deserves special mention. In nearly all compounds containing carbon it exhibits a covalence of four. How can this be when Table 1.1 shows carbon has

but two unpaired electrons in its outer shell? To answer this question we must imagine that a covalence of four for carbon may be attained by promoting one of the $2s$ electrons to a vacant, higher energy $2p$ orbital and mathematically mixing s and p orbitals to give an excited atom with *four equivalent orbitals*. These four blended orbitals are said to be *hybridized* and are called sp^3 (pronounced s-p-three) orbitals. Chemical theory predicts that the four sp^3 hybrid orbitals should be directed from the carbon atom toward the corners of a tetrahedron (Fig. 1.5).

■ □ FIGURE 1.5

HYBRIDIZED sp^3 ORBITALS.

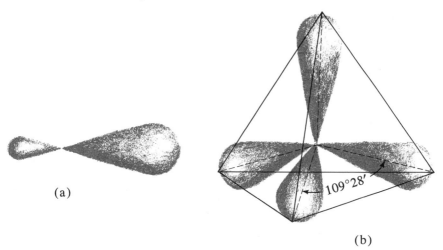

(a)

(b)

(a) A HYBRIDIZIED sp^3 ORBITAL, (b) FOUR TETRAHEDRAL sp^3 ORBITALS OF THE CARBON ATOM.

Experimental data are in agreement with this prediction. Thus, for example in methane, CH_4, the principal constituent of natural gas, the four covalent C—H bonds, are directed toward the vertices of a regular tetrahedron (Fig. 1.6).[3] With carbon in the center, these four sigma bonds make angles of 109° 28′ with each other. They

[3]A regular tetrahedron is easily constructed by drawing a cube and connecting all nonadjacent corners.

■□FIGURE 1.6

STRUCTURAL REPRESENTATIONS OF METHANE.

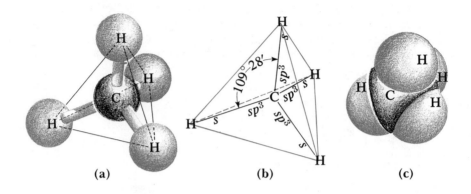

(a)   (b)   (c)

(a) BALL AND STICK MODEL IN REGULAR TETRAHEDRON, (b) TET-
RAHEDRAL STRUCTURE SHOWING ELECTRONS INVOLVED IN BOND-
ING AND BOND ANGLES, (c) STUART MODEL.

are of the same length (1.09 Å).[4] The energy required to break any
one of them is the same (102 kcal).[5] The bonds, therefore, *must* be
equivalent.

Hybridization likewise can be considered to take place in the
case of boron to give three hybridized sp^2 orbitals, and with beryllium to yield two hybridized sp orbitals. Were it not for such
hybridization, one would expect the covalence of carbon to be two
and that of boron one; beryllium would have no electrons available
for chemical combination. This, we know, is contrary to fact.

Exercise 1.4   If the boron atom uses three sp^2 hybridized
orbitals for bonding with fluorine, and each B—F bond is separated from the other by a maximum distance, what is the value
of the bond angle? What is the geometry of the boron tri-
fluoride molecule?

---

[4]The Angstrom (Å) is equal to 10^{-8} centimeter.
[5]The *kilocalorie* (kcal) is equal to 1,000 calories.

1.6   POLAR COVALENT BONDS

In molecules in which the bonded atoms are idential, as in the hydrogen or chlorine molecules (H—H, Cl—Cl), the bonding electrons are equally shared. However, were hydrogen to be substituted for either of the chlorine atoms or chlorine for either of the hydrogen atoms in the above examples, then the shared pair of electrons binding the two atoms in each instance would be drawn somewhat closer to the chlorine atom. Such displacement, however small, results in a polar bond and confers upon the more electronegative (electron-attracting) element — chlorine, in this case — a partial negative charge (delta minus) and leaves the other part of the molecule with a partial positive charge (delta plus).

$$ \text{H} \overset{..}{\underset{..}{\underset{\times}{:}}} \text{Cl} : \qquad\qquad \text{H}^{\delta+} \longmapsto \text{Cl}^{\delta-} $$

This slight shift in electron density is indicated by an arrow directed toward the more electronegative element. Opposite the arrowhead the shaft is crossed by a short vertical bar as in a plus sign.

A rough determination of the relative electronegativities of elements may be obtained from their position in the periodic chart. Electronegativities increase as we proceed from left to right or from bottom to top through the periodic arrangement. This establishes fluorine as the most electronegative of the elements. The polarity of a molecule, as you will discover later, frequently determines its behavior in the course of a chemical reaction. For this reason you should have some knowledge of electronegativities.

> **Exercise 1.5**   In which of the hydrogen halides will the bond between the hydrogen and the halogen atom be most polar? Least polar?

Analysis of Organic Compounds and Calculation of Formulas

1.7   EMPIRICAL FORMULAS

The symbols for the elements present in a substance expressed in the simplest atomic ratio in whole numbers is called the **empirical formula.** The ratio in which the atoms of elements are present in an organic compound is found from the percentage composition of the compound. Since most organic substances contain carbon, hydrogen, and oxygen,'they usually will burn to produce carbon dioxide and water. These gases may be collected and weighed. The presence of nitrogen, sulfur, and the halogens in an organic substance is revealed by fusion of a sample with molten sodium: nitrogen yields sodium cyanide, $NaCN$; sulfur yields sodium sulfide, Na_2S; and the halogens yield the sodium halides, $NaCl$, $NaBr$, or NaI. An analysis for these inorganic, water-soluble, fusion products easily shows whether nitrogen, sulfur, or the halogens are present in the sample.

Let us determine the empirical formula of a white, crystalline, water-soluble compound which burns but gives negative tests for nitrogen, sulfur, and the halogens. If a carefully weighed sample is heated in a combustion tube while a stream of oxygen is passed over it, the hydrogen will be oxidized to H_2O and the carbon to CO_2. These gases may be collected in two separate absorption tubes. One tube is filled with anhydrous magnesium perchlorate, $Mg(ClO_4)_2$, which collects the water, and the other is filled with sodium hydroxide which collects the carbon dioxide. These absorption tubes are carefully weighed before and after combustion and their gain in weight is taken equal to the amount of each gas collected.

Let us suppose that the sample taken weighed 0.1800 g, the CO_2 collected 0.264 g, and the H_2O 0.108 g.

$$\text{Weight of sample} = 0.1800 \text{ g}$$
$$\text{Weight of } CO_2 = 0.264 \text{ g}$$
$$\text{Weight of } H_2O = 0.108 \text{ g}$$

Since carbon comprises 12 g of the total gram molecular weight of carbon dioxide and hydrogen accounts for 2 g of the gram molecular weight of water, the percentages of carbon, hydrogen, and oxygen in the sample may be calculated (using rounded atomic weights) as follows:

$$\% \text{ Carbon} = \frac{0.264 \times 12/44}{0.1800} \times 100 = 40$$

$$\% \text{ Hydrogen} = \frac{0.108 \times 2/18}{0.1800} \times 100 = 6.6$$

$$\% \text{ Oxygen} = 100 - (40 + 6.6) = 53.4$$

The simplest gram-atom ratio is found by dividing the percentage of each constituent by its gram atomic weight:

$C_{40/12}H_{6.6/1}O_{53.4/16}$, which may be reduced to $C_{3.3}H_{6.6}O_{3.3}$

Further reduction to a simple whole number gives an atomic ratio of CH_2O, which is the empirical formula for the unknown.

The only substance with this simple ratio in its molecular structure is formaldehyde — a gas; the sample was a solid. In order to determine the **molecular formula** of the sample we must know its molecular weight.

1.8   MOLECULAR FORMULAS

Since the compound in the problem of the previous section was described as water-soluble, it might occur to you that its molecular weight could be determined by dissolving a weighed amount in a known quantity of pure water and noting the freezing point of the solution. The cryoscopic constant, K_f, is the freezing point depression produced by a gram molecular weight of a soluble, un-ionized substance in 1,000 g of a given solvent. If the solvent is water, the value for K_f is $1.86°C$. To determine the freezing point depression of a solution, Δt (delta-tee), we multiply the cryoscopic constant of the solvent by two factors: (1) the number of gram molecular weights (moles) dissolved, and (2) a solvent factor relative to 1,000 g of solvent.

$$\Delta t = K_f \times \frac{\text{weight in grams of material dissolved}}{\text{M.W. of material dissolved}} \times \frac{1,000}{\text{weight in grams of solvent}}$$

Let us suppose that 6 grams of the solid whose empirical formula was found to be CH_2O lowered the freezing point to $-1.24°C$ when dissolved in 50 grams of water. To find the molecular weight of the solid, we rearrange the above equation, substitute the values given, and have

$$\text{M.W.} = \frac{1.86 \times 6 \times 1000}{1.24 \times 50} = 180$$

$$CH_2O \text{ formula weight} = 30$$

$$(CH_2O)_n = 180; \quad n = 6$$

The correct molecular formula for the solid is $C_6H_{12}O_6$.

The example just taken illustrates but one method for molecular weight determination. Actually, for two reasons, water is not a good solvent to employ for molecular weight determinations of organic compounds. One, its cryoscopic constant is so small that even the slightest error in the freezing point determination will give a meaningless result. Second, few organic substances are very soluble in water. Camphor, with a freezing-point depression constant of

40°C, is a much better solvent to employ for molecular weight determination of organic compounds. More elegant instrumental methods are now available to the chemist for the determination of molecular weights. These involve the use of electronic devices and to describe them here in detail is beyond the scope of this text.

To determine the molecular weight of a liquid, a weighed quantity may be converted to vapor. When the volume of vapor produced is measured and corrected to standard conditions of temperature and pressure, the gas laws you learned in beginning chemistry may be applied to calculate the molecular weight. This method can be illustrated by the following example.

Example

A liquid hydrocarbon was found to contain 92.4% carbon and 7.6% hydrogen. When a sample weighing 0.139 g was converted to vapor, it occupied 56 ml at a temperature of 100°C and a barometric pressure of 740 mm of mercury. What is the molecular formula for this hydrocarbon?

First step. Correct the volume of vapor to standard conditions:

$$\text{Volume (STP)} = \frac{56 \text{ ml} \times 740 \times 273}{760 \times 373} = 40 \text{ ml}$$

Second step. Find the molecular weight:

$$\frac{0.139}{40} \text{ g/ml} \times 22,400 \text{ ml/mole} = 78 \text{ g/mole}$$

Third step. Find the simplest gram-atom ratio:

$$C_{92.4/12}H_{7.6/1} = C_{7.7}H_{7.6} = (CH)_n$$
$$CH = 13; \quad n = 6$$

The correct molecular formula is C_6H_6 and corresponds to that for the aromatic hydrocarbon benzene (Chapter 4).

Exercise 1.6   A gaseous hydrocarbon has a molecular weight of 30. It contains 80% carbon and 20% hydrogen. What is its molecular formula?

1.9 STRUCTURAL FORMULAS AND ISOMERISM

As was stated in the introductory section it is not enough simply to determine the number and kinds of elements comprising an organic compound. Let us illustrate this point. We have already encountered methane whose molecular formula is CH_4 and have learned that in methane the four hydrogens are bonded to a central carbon atom. Now the gaseous hydrocarbon butane has the formula C_4H_{10}. How can the four carbon and ten hydrogen atoms be arranged so that each carbon has four bonds and each hydrogen only one? We discover that there are two possibilities. In one structure, no carbon would be bonded to more than *two* others, whereas in the second structure, one carbon could be attached to *three* others:

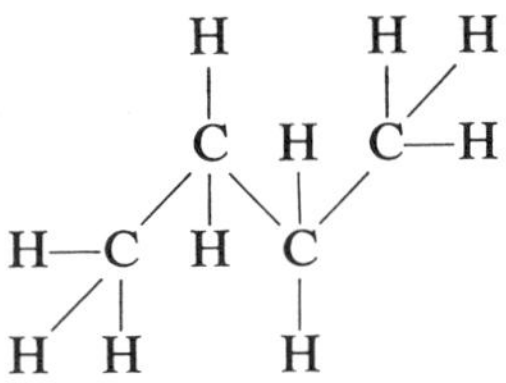

Normal butane, B.P., 0.5°C (a continuous "straight" chain structure)

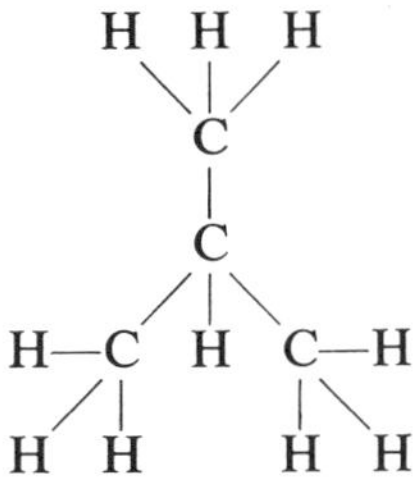

Isobutane (Methylpropane) B.P., −11.7°C (a branched chain structure)

In order to draw these two structures, we simply have allowed the sp^3 hybrid orbitals of carbon atoms to overlap those of other carbons, as well as with *s* orbitals of hydrogen atoms, to form the four sigma bonds that each carbon is entitled to. (See also page 18.)

Although both compounds have the *same molecular formula*, they have *different structures* and are called **isomers.** (Gr. *isos*, same; *meros*, part.)

■□FIGURE 1.7

BALL AND STICK MODELS OF (a) *n*-BUTANE, AND (b) ISOBUTANE.

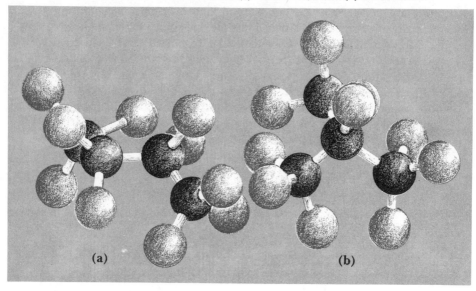

(a)   (b)

■□FIGURE 1.8

MOLECULAR AND SCALE MODELS OF (a) *n*-BUTANE AND
(b) ISOBUTANE.

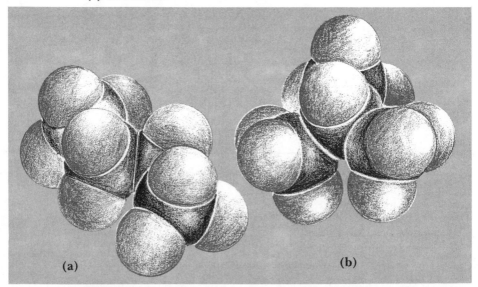

(a)   (b)

(CARBON ATOMS ARE INDICATED IN BLACK, HYDROGEN ATOMS
IN GREEN.)

Exercise 1.7   Is there more than one structure possible for dicloromethane, CH_2Cl_2, if its geometry is tetrahedral? Would more than one structure be possible if its structure were pyramidal with carbon at the apex and hydrogen and chlorine atoms at the corners of the base?

Another gaseous hydrocarbon has the molecular formula C_4H_8. By following the rules of valence for these two elements and bonding the carbon atoms in a continuous cyclic arrangement we are able to draw two different C_4H_8 structures.

Cyclobutane, B.P., 13.0°C   Methylcyclopropane, B.P., 4.0°C

In Chapter 3 you will discover that this same molecular formula will permit four additional structures. While the bonds involved in these structures will not all be of the sigma type as in the previous examples, the six compounds represented by the molecular formula will all be isomers, nevertheless.

You can see from the preceding examples that carbon is capable of sharing an electron-pair not only with hydrogen and other elements, but also with another carbon atom. You also have seen that it is capable not only of forming "straight" and branched chain structures, but cyclic ones as well. The tetrahedral nature of the carbon atom and its ability to bond to other carbons makes possible a great number of organic compounds by the combination of a relatively few different atomic species. If the number of carbon atoms is increased from four to ten as in the compound $C_{10}H_{22}$, we could draw *seventy-five* different structures for this molecular formula. It has been calculated that the molecular formula of tetracontane, $C_{40}H_{82}$, would permit the formation of 62,491,178,805,831 different structures! Of course, this number of compounds with the molecular formula $C_{40}H_{82}$ are not all known, and it is doubtful that more than a few even exist. The point is exaggerated simply to show that the structural formula, or graphic representation, of a compound is necessary to show the geometric arrangement of the atoms.

The determination of a structure for an unknown organic compound may, at first thought, appear to be a formidable task. Quite often it is. However, in recent years the availability of sophisticated instruments for measuring certain physical properties has made it much easier for the organic chemist to classify a compound and to determine its structure. In addition he also obtains from these physical measurements some idea as to its chemical properties, and a clue to its synthesis, as well.

One of the most generally useful instrumental methods employed by present day organic chemists in the analysis of compounds is infrared absorption spectroscopy. We will explain and illustrate the application of this method in Section 1.11.

1.10   FUNCTIONAL GROUPS

Chemical reactions involving organic compounds center, for the most part, about some unique structural feature known as a **functional group.** This group not only bestows a characteristic behavior upon the molecule, but also identifies it as belonging to a certain family of compounds or **homologous series.** For example, methyl alcohol, or methanol, (used extensively at one time as radiator antifreeze) has the structure

The next higher member, or *homolog*, in this series is ethyl alcohol, the alcohol of beverages, which has the structure

It is clear from their structures that a feature common to both alcohols is the **hydroxyl group**, —OH, which is the functional group that characterizes the alcohol family. Simply by increasing the length of the hydrocarbon chain each time by an increment of —CH$_2$—

we can write formulas for other members of the series. The size and geometry of the unreactive portion of the structure may modify, but usually does not alter the reactions characteristic of the functional group. This greatly simplifies the study of organic chemistry. In the following chapters you will learn how to build into a structure the desired functional group, how to replace it by another, and in some cases, how to eliminate it entirely. Table 1.3 lists the principal families, or classes, of compounds encountered in organic chemistry, the corresponding functional groups, and a common example within each class.

Exercise 1.8 The molecular formula of a compound is $C_4H_{10}O$. See if you can incorporate these fifteen atoms into seven different structures. What classes of compounds are represented by these structures?

□■ TABLE 1.3

CLASSES OF COMPOUNDS AND THEIR FUNCTIONAL GROUPS

Class Name	Functional Group	General Formula*	Common Example
Alcohols	—O—H	R—O—H	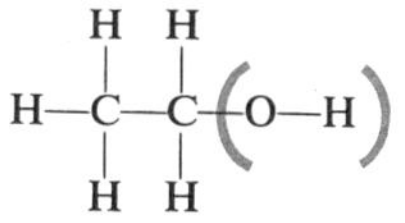 Ethyl alcohol
Ethers	C—O—C	R—O—R	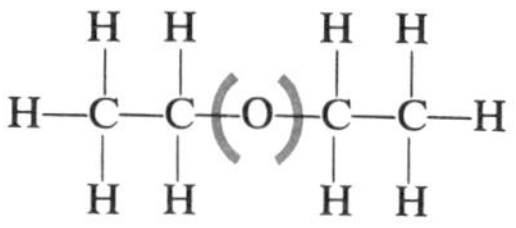 Diethyl ether
Aldehydes	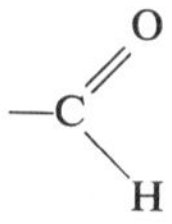	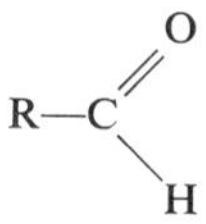	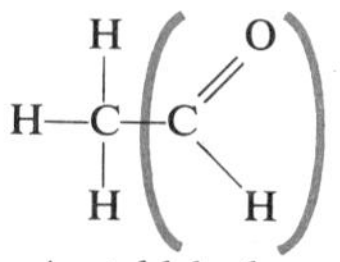 Acetaldehyde

(*Table 1.3 continued on page 22.*)

☐■TABLE 1.3 — *Continued.*

CLASSES OF COMPOUNDS AND THEIR FUNCTIONAL GROUPS

Class Name	Functional Group	General Formula*	Common Example
Ketones	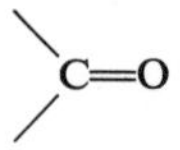 C=O	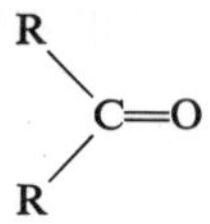 $\begin{array}{c} R \\ \diagdown \\ C=O \\ \diagup \\ R \end{array}$	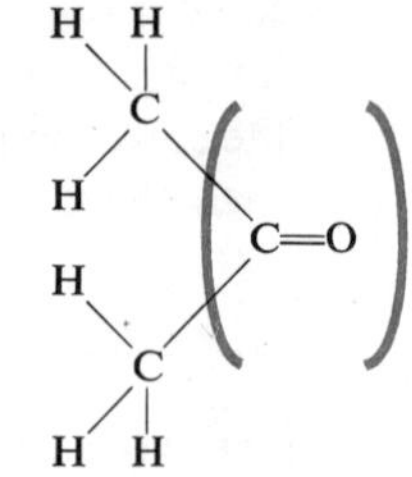 Acetone
Carboxylic Acids	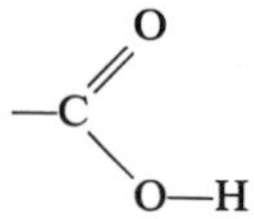 $-C\overset{O}{\underset{O-H}{}}$	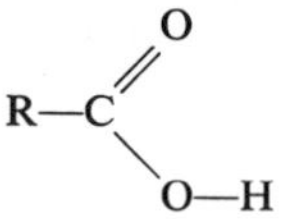 $R-C\overset{O}{\underset{O-H}{}}$	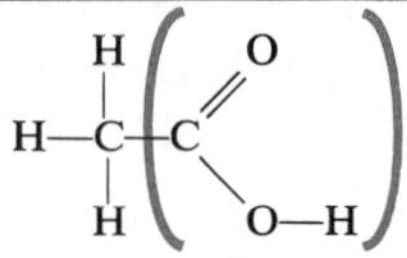 Acetic Acid
Amines	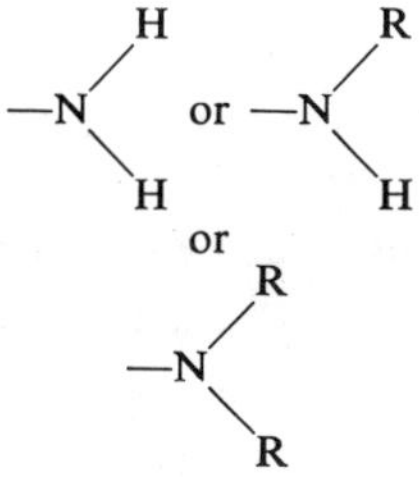 $-N\overset{H}{\underset{H}{}}$ or $-N\overset{R}{\underset{H}{}}$ or $-N\overset{R}{\underset{R}{}}$	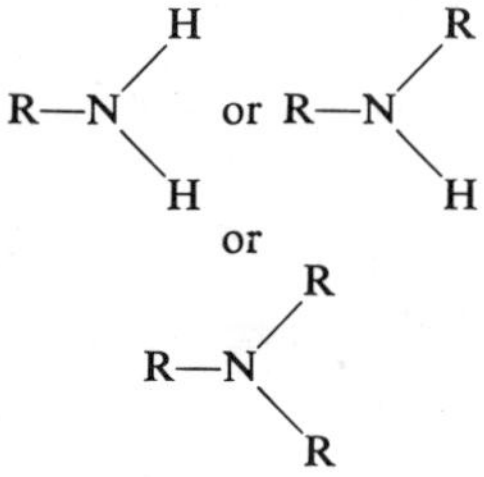 $R-N\overset{H}{\underset{H}{}}$ or $R-N\overset{R}{\underset{H}{}}$ or $R-N\overset{R}{\underset{R}{}}$	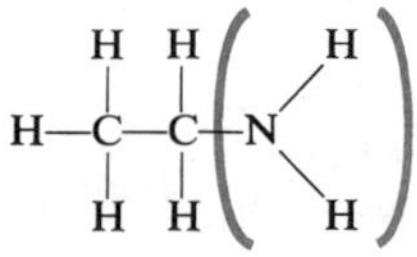 Ethyl Amine

*The R used in a general formula refers to that portion of the molecule other than the functional group. In most cases $R=C_nH_{2n+1}$.

Example:

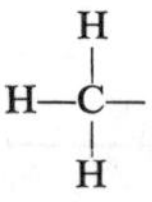

$$H-\underset{H}{\overset{H}{C}}-$$
methyl

$$H-\underset{H}{\overset{H}{C}}-\underset{H}{\overset{H}{C}}-$$
ethyl

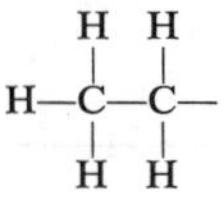

1.11   INFRARED SPECTRA AND ORGANIC ANALYSIS

All light travels at the same velocity[6] and possesses energy whether it be in the visible, in the ultraviolet, or in the infrared regions. When light strikes organic molecules some of its energy is

---

[6]Wavelength $\times$ frequency = velocity ($\lambda \times \nu = c$).

absorbed, and the molecules are affected in different ways. The changes which occur when molecules absorb light that is in the visible region of the electromagnetic spectrum (3,800–7,800 Å) may be seen as color. The dyestuffs used to impart the many beautiful colors now seen in the market place are organic molecules that absorb within this region. Changes which occur in the molecule when absorption of light takes place outside the visible region do not result in color but may be detected by instruments called **spectrophotometers.**

The infrared region which extends over the range of 2.5–15 μ[7] (25,000–150,000 Å) is of special interest to the organic chemist. In this region the functional groups in organic molecules absorb at characteristic frequencies[8] and can be "seen" by the infrared spectrometer. The energy absorbed at infrared frequencies appears to be converted into energy of molecular vibration — a rhythmic stretching and bending of bonds. Some idea regarding the manner in which bonds are able to stretch and bend is indicated by the following drawings where bonds have been portrayed as small coil springs.

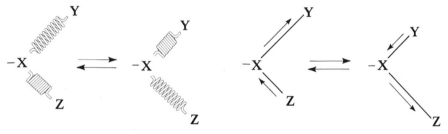

Unsymmetrical

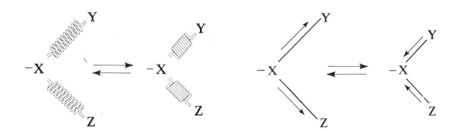

Symmetrical

[7] μ = micron (one-millionth meter); mμ = millimicron (one-thousandth micron) = 10 Å. Wavelengths in the infrared region are more conveniently expressed in microns than in Angstrom units.

[8] Frequencies are expressed in *wave numbers*, cm^{-1}, or reciprocal centimeters.

Bending Vibrations

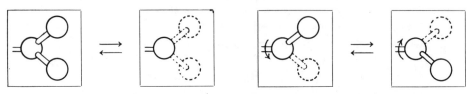

Scissoring (in-plane bending)

Wagging (in and out of plane)   Twisting (in and out of plane)

The spectrophotometer is able to detect and record the infrared absorption that results from these changes in the bonds. Examination of the spectra of a great number of compounds has made it possible to assign characteristic absorption frequencies to certain functional groups. Some of these absorption frequencies and the bonds within the functional group responsible for them are listed in Table 1.4. Note that the absorption frequencies of the hydroxyl group are revealed in the spectra of the alcohols and also in the spectra of the acids (Fig. 1.9). The ethers and ketones, on the other hand, would give spectra in which the O—H frequencies are lacking. However, the acids and the ketones both would show a strong C=O absorption value. You can see from an inspection of Table 1.4 and Figure 1.9 that the same type of bond will absorb within the same IR region regardless of the class of compounds in which the bond appears.

Infrared spectroscopy, with the exception of nuclear magnetic resonance spectrometery (which locates the various hydrogen atoms within a molecule), is one of the most useful single techniques available for the determination of molecular structure and the qualitative identification of unknown organic materials. Few other analytical methods enable the organic chemist to determine the identity of a molecular structure without destroying it or laboriously converting it into some other identifiable derivative.

■□FIGURE 1.9

INFRARED SPECTRA OF (1) ETHYL ALCOHOL, (2) ACETONE, AND
(3) ACETIC ACID.

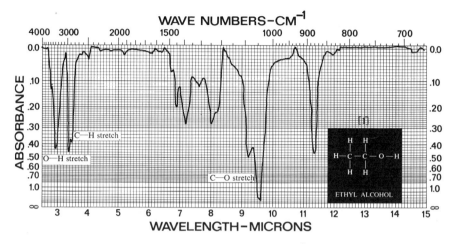

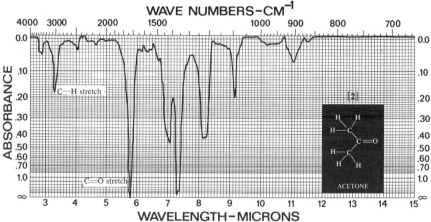

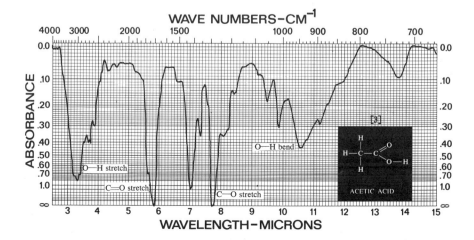

□■ TABLE   1 . 4

SOME CHARACTERISTIC INFRARED ABSORPTION FREQUENCIES

Type of Bond	Class of Compound	Frequency (cm^{-1})*	Intensity of Absorption
O—H	Alcohols, Phenols	3500–3650	Variable, sharp
O—H	Carboxylic acids	2500–3000	Variable, broad
O—H	Hydrogen-bonded** Alcohols and Phenols	3200–3400	Strong, broad
C—O	Alcohols, Ethers, Carboxylic acids, and Esters	1080–1300	Strong
C=O	Aldehydes. Ketones, Carboxylic acids, and Esters	1690–1750	Strong
C—H	Alkanes	2850–2950	Strong
N—H	Amines	3300–3500	Medium

*Absorbed radiation in the infrared region may be defined by its wavelength (λ) in *microns*, μ ($1\mu = 10^{-4}$ cm or 10^4 Å), or by its frequency (ν). The preferred method for expressing frequencies is not in cycles per second, but in *wave numbers*, cm^{-1}, called reciprocal centimeters. The wavenumber is the reciprocal of the wavelength in centimeters, or when the wavelength is in microns, the wavenumber is $\frac{1}{\mu} \times 10^4$.

**See Sec. 8.4.

□□ *SUMMARY*

[1]   Carbon, which has four electrons available for bonding, has a great tendency to self-link. It may bond to itself in straight chain, branched chain, and cyclic structures.

[2]   The covalent bond involves a pair of shared electrons between two atoms. This type of bond predominates in organic compounds.

[3]   When carbon is bonded to four other atoms or groups, it does so through four sp^3 hybridized orbitals. The bonds so formed are directed to the vertices of a tetrahedron. (If the bonded groups are identical, it will be a regular tetrahedron.)

[4]   Empirical and molecular formulas are determined by qualitative tests and quantitative measurements.

[5]   Formulas of organic compounds reveal little unless written as structures.

[6] Compounds having the same molecular formula, but different structures, are isomers.

[7] Organic reactions nearly always involve some structural feature known as a functional group.

[8] Instrumental methods, especially IR spectroscopy, play an important role in the analysis of unknown organic compounds.

□□ NEW TERMS

[1] Atomic orbitals

[2] Covalence

[3] Electronegativity

[4] Empirical formula

[5] Functional group

[6] Homologous series

[7] Hybridized orbitals

[8] Isomers

[9] Molecular formula

[10] Molecular orbitals

[11] Polar bond

[12] Sigma bond

[13] Spectroscopy

[14] Tetrahedral angle

■ □ SUPPLEMENTARY EXERCISES
▼ AND PROBLEMS

[1] Using only the outermost (valence) electrons and employing dots, asterisks or any other symbolism, write electronic structures for the following.

(a) H_2SO_4
(b) HCN
(c) ethane, C_2H_6
(d) methyl alcohol
(e) N_2O_5
(f) chloroform, $CHCl_3$
(g) chloromethane, CH_3Cl
(h) dimethyl ether, C_2H_6O
(i) BF_3
(j) carbon tetrachloride, CCl_4

[2]   Contrast the physical properties of common salt with those of naphthalene (moth flakes), $C_{10}H_8$, with specific reference to: (a) solubility in water; (b) solubility in gasoline; (c) formation of electrolytic solutions; (d) flammability; (e) melting points; (f) vapor pressure. Which of the above properties makes naphthalene a good larvacide?

[3]   What unique characteristics of carbon make possible the formation of the great number of organic compounds?

[4]   Draw all possible structures permitted by the following molecular formulas.

(a) C_3H_8 (e) C_5H_{12}
(b) C_3H_7Cl (f) CH_5N
(c) C_3H_8O (g) C_2H_3N
(d) $C_2H_4Cl_2$ (h) C_3H_7N

[5]   In the structure CCl_4 what is the maximum number of chlorine atoms which may lie in the same plane? (*Hint: See Fig. 1.6*)

[6]   In which of the following substances does the molecule contain polar bonds? Which ones are polar molecules?

(a) CH_4 (f) C_2H_6
(b) CH_3Br (g) CCl_2F_2
(c) CCl_4 (h) BF_3
(d)   HI   (i) CH_3OH
(e) CO_2 (j)   diethyl ether, $C_2H_5OC_2H_5$

[7]   Calculate the percentage composition of each element in the following.

(a) CH_4O (d) CH_4N_2O
(b) CH_5N (e) $C_{12}H_{22}O_{11}$
(c) CH_3I

[8]   A volatile organic liquid contains only carbons, hydrogen, and bromine. The vapor produced by 1.25 g of the liquid measures 150 ml when corrected to STP. What is the molecular weight of the compound?

The percentage of bromine in the compound is 85%. What is the molecular formula?

Does this formula permit more than one structure? If so, draw them.

[9]   A colorless, volatile liquid was found to contain carbon (65%), hydrogen (13.5%), and oxygen. Its molecular weight was determined to be 74 ± 1. What is its molecular formula? How many possible structures can be drawn from this combination of elements?

[10] Combustion of a 0.060 g sample of an organic substance containing C, H, N, and O yielded 0.044 g of CO_2 and 0.036 g of H_2O. In a separate determination a sample of the same size yielded 22.4 ml of nitrogen gas when corrected to STP. What is the empirical formula of the compound?

[11] The molecular formula of the compound whose IR spectrum is shown is $C_4H_{10}O$. With the aid of Table 1.4 determine the class of compounds to which it belongs. Draw a structural formula for the compound.

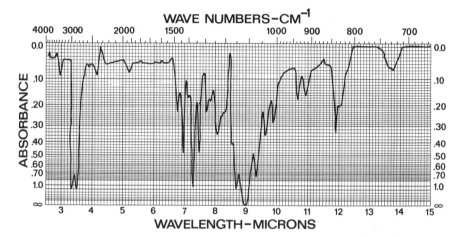

chapter 2

The Saturated Hydrocarbons, or Alkanes

INTRODUCTION

> The hydrocarbons, as the name suggests, are compounds containing only carbon and hydrogen. The various structural forms, which a combination of these two elements permit, provide us the simplest introduction to the study of organic chemistry. These useful compounds are isolated from petroleum. Not only is petroleum our principal fossil fuel, but it is also a source material for benzene, toluene, xylene, and innumerable other useful compounds, all of which are generally referred to as petrochemicals. Organic chemistry — indeed, the American economy — is dependent to a great extent upon the petroleum industry.

2.2   STRUCTURE AND FORMULAS OF THE ALKANES

Saturated hydrocarbons, or alkanes, are compounds composed of carbon and hydrogen in which each carbon atom is covalently linked to four other atoms by single electron pair bonds. The alkanes also are frequently referred to as the **paraffins** (L. *parum*, little; *affinis*, affinity) because of their relative inertness.

The molecular formulas for the alkanes are easily obtained from the general formula C_nH_{2n+2}, where n is the number of carbon atoms present. Each member of a family, or homologous series, differs from its immediate relatives by a methylene group, $-CH_2$. However, the structures for compounds which have the same molecular formula, as we have already noted (Sec. 1.9), may, in some cases, be written in different ways. Table 2.1 lists the formulas and structures of the alkanes containing one to five carbon atoms.

☐■ TABLE 2.1

FORMULAS OF THE ALKANES

n	No. of Isomers	Molecular Formula	Projection Formula and Name	Condensed Formula
1	None	CH_4	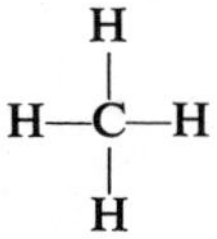 H | H—C—H | H Methane	CH_4
2	None	C_2H_6	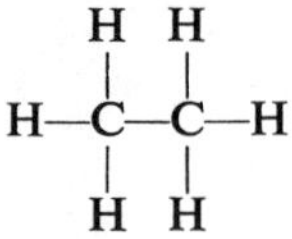 H H | | H—C—C—H | | H H Ethane	CH_3CH_3
3	None	C_3H_8	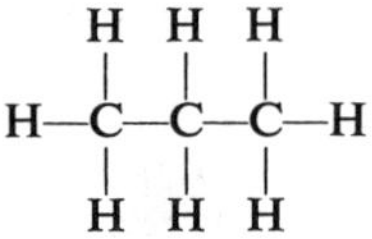 H H H | | | H—C—C—C—H | | | H H H Propane	$CH_3CH_2CH_3$
4	2	C_4H_{10}	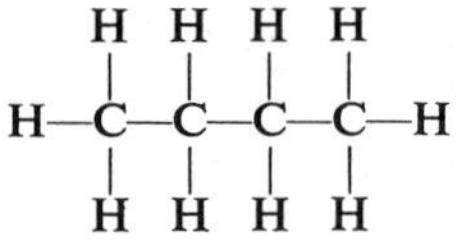 H H H H | | | | H—C—C—C—C—H | | | | H H H H Normal butane	$CH_3(CH_2)_2CH_3$
			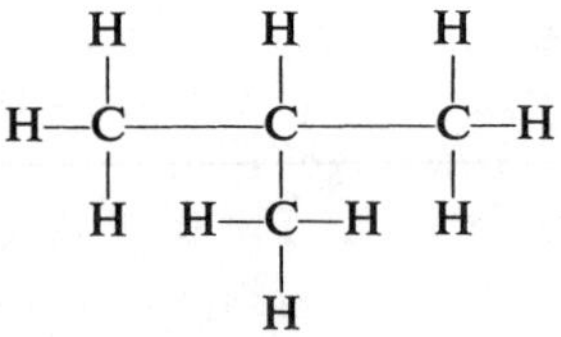 H H H | | | H—C C C—H | | | H H—C—H H | H Isobutane	$(CH_3)_2CHCH_3$
5	3	C_5H_{12}	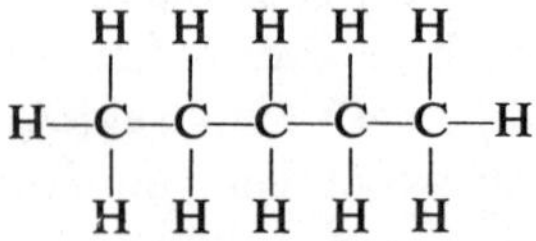 H H H H H | | | | | H—C—C—C—C—C—H | | | | | H H H H H Normal pentane	$CH_3(CH_2)_3CH_3$

■ TABLE   2.1 — *Continued.*

FORMULAS OF THE ALKANES

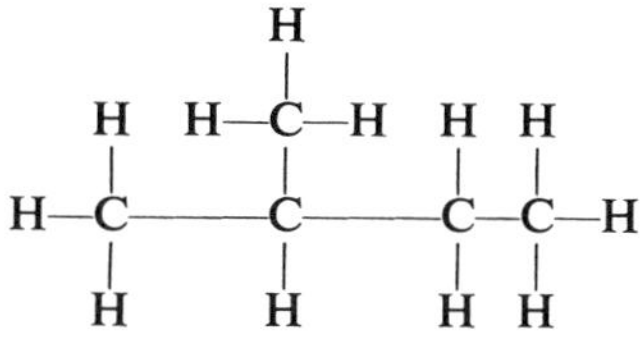

$$
\begin{array}{c}
\text{H} \\
|\\
\text{H}\quad \text{H—C—H}\quad \text{H}\quad \text{H}\\
|\qquad\quad |\qquad\; |\;\; |\\
\text{H—C}\quad\quad\quad \text{C}\quad\quad\quad \text{C—C—H}\\
|\qquad\quad |\qquad\; |\;\; |\\
\text{H}\qquad\quad \text{H}\qquad\; \text{H}\;\; \text{H}\\
\text{Isopentane}
\end{array}
$$

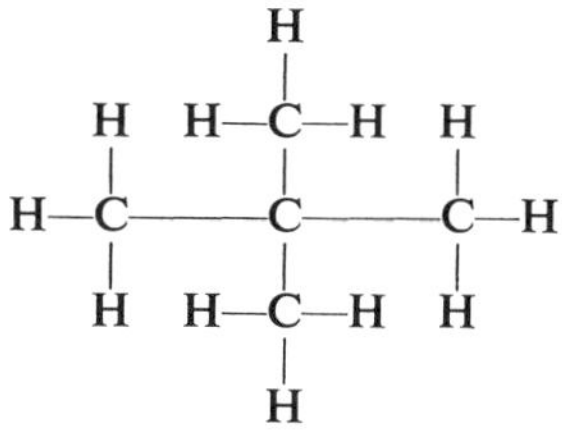

$(CH_3)_2CHCH_2CH_3$

$$
\begin{array}{c}
\text{H}\\
|\\
\text{H}\quad \text{H—C—H}\quad \text{H}\\
|\qquad\quad |\qquad\; |\\
\text{H—C}\quad\quad\quad \text{C}\quad\quad\quad \text{C—H}\\
|\qquad\quad |\qquad\; |\\
\text{H}\quad \text{H—C—H}\quad \text{H}\\
|\\
\text{H}\\
\text{Neopentane}
\end{array}
$$

$C(CH_3)_4$

2.3   NOMENCLATURE OF THE ALKANES

Names of the first four members of the alkane family have no simple derivation and must be memorized. However, naming the higher members of the series does follow a system and learning them is relatively easy. The number of carbon atoms present in a continuous chain is indicated by a Greek prefix which is followed by the suffix *-ane:*

Penta = 5; C_5H_{12} is **pentane**

Hexa = 6; C_6H_{14} is **hexane,** etc.

The unbranched, or continuous chain is called **normal** and must be indicated in the name as a prefix, *n-*, to differentiate it from its branched chain isomers:

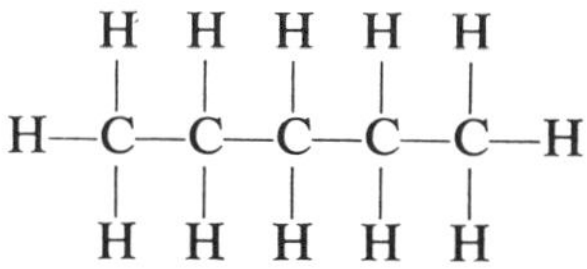

n-Pentane

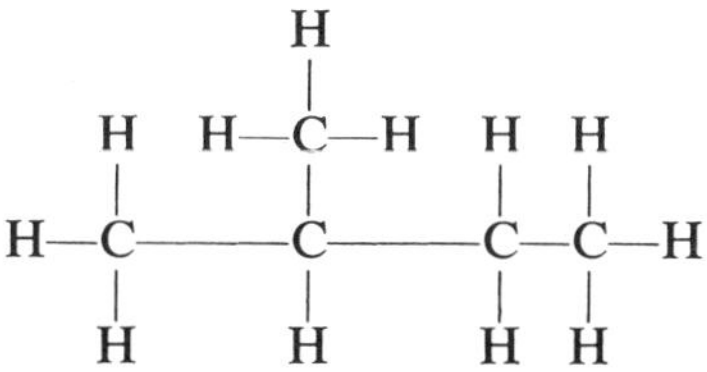

Isopentane, or 2-Methylbutane

$$
\begin{array}{c}
\text{H} \\
| \\
\text{H} \quad \text{H—C—H} \quad \text{H} \\
| \qquad\quad | \qquad\quad | \\
\text{H—C} \text{———} \text{C} \text{———} \text{C—H} \\
| \qquad\quad | \qquad\quad | \\
\text{H} \quad \text{H—C—H} \quad \text{H} \\
| \\
\text{H}
\end{array}
$$

Neopentane, or 2, 2-Dimethylpropane

In the sections which follow we will learn how to name highly branched structures, but before this can be done we first must learn the names of some of the "branches."

2.4   ALKYL GROUPS

Alkyl groups, as such, have no independent existence but are simply structural derivatives useful in the naming of compounds.

Removal of one of the hydrogen atoms of an alkane produces an alkyl group. The residual group then is named by replacing the -*ane* suffix of the parent hydrocarbon by -*yl:*

$$
\begin{array}{c}
\text{H} \\
| \\
\text{H—C—H}
\end{array}
\text{ becomes }
\begin{array}{c}
\text{H} \\
| \\
\text{H—C—}
\end{array}
\text{ or more simply written as } CH_3\text{—}
$$

Methane   Methyl

$$
\begin{array}{c}
\text{H} \quad \text{H} \\
| \quad | \\
\text{H—C—C—H}
\end{array}
\text{ becomes }
\begin{array}{c}
\text{H} \quad \text{H} \\
| \quad | \\
\text{H—C—C—}
\end{array}
\text{ or simply } C_2H_5\text{—}
$$

Ethane   Ethyl

For the third member of the series, propane, there is only one structure as a saturated hydrocarbon, but there are two different **propyl groups.** This is possible because the two end carbons are attached to only *one* other carbon while the middle carbon is attached to *two* others.

$$
\begin{array}{c}
\text{H} \quad \text{H} \quad \text{H} \\
| \quad | \quad | \\
\text{H—C—C—C—H} \\
| \quad | \quad | \\
\text{H} \quad \text{H} \quad \text{H}
\end{array}
$$

Propane

A carbon bonded to only one other carbon is called **primary,** one bonded to two carbons is called **secondary** (*sec*) and to three carbons, **tertiary** (*tert*). Hydrogens bonded to these carbons are designated according to the types of carbons to which they are attached. Thus, a primary carbon has bonded to it *three* primary hydrogens and *one* alkyl group. A secondary carbon has *two* secondary hydrogens and *two* alkyl groups. A tertiary carbon is bonded to only *one* tertiary hydrogen, but to *three* alkyl groups.

The six primary hydrogens shown bounded by solid lines in the formula for propane are all equivalent. Removal of any one of these six hydrogen atoms gives the **normal propyl** group

$$
\begin{array}{ccc}
H & H & H \\
| & | & | \\
H-C-C-C-, \\
| & | & | \\
H & H & H
\end{array}
\quad \text{or} \quad CH_3-CH_2-CH_2-, \quad \text{or} \quad n\text{-}C_3H_7-
$$

Note that for brevity the normal propyl group can be shown simply as $n\text{-}C_3H_7-$. Removal of one of the secondary hydrogens shown within the dotted circles in the formula for propane gives the **isopropyl** group

$$
\begin{array}{ccc}
H & H & H \\
| & | & | \\
H-C-C-C-H \\
| & & | \\
H & & H
\end{array}
\quad \text{or} \quad (CH_3)_2CH- \quad \text{or} \quad iso\text{-}C_3H_7-
$$

Obviously the general formula for an alkyl group is C_nH_{2n+1}. The number of different alkyl groups that can be produced from any alkane depends upon how many different primary, secondary, or tertiary hydrogen atoms can be replaced. We can illustrate this very easily using the two isomeric butanes.

Removal of any one of the six primary H atoms outlined (solid) produces the *n*-butyl group.

$$
\begin{array}{cccc}
H & H & H & H \\
| & | & | & | \\
H-C-C-C-C- \\
| & | & | & | \\
H & H & H & H
\end{array}
$$

n-Butyl group

n-Butane

Removal of any one of four secondary H atoms outlined (dotted) produces the *sec*-butyl group.

$$
\begin{array}{ccc}
H & H & H \\
| & | & | \\
H-C-C-C- \\
| & | & | \\
H & H & CH_3
\end{array}
$$

sec-Butyl group

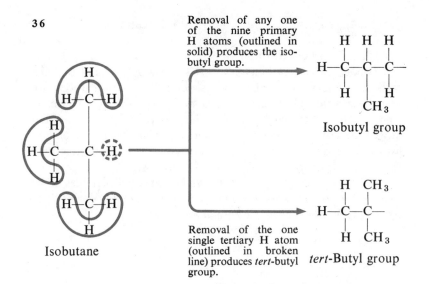

Removal of any one of the nine primary H atoms (outlined in solid) produces the iso-butyl group.

Isobutyl group

Isobutane

Removal of the one single tertiary H atom (outlined in broken line) produces *tert*-butyl group.

tert-Butyl group

An *iso* compound is one that has a methyl substituent on the next to last carbon atom. The isopropyl group is the only example of an *iso* group which at the same time is also a secondary group.

□■ TABLE 2.2

COMMONLY USED ALKYL GROUPS

Hydrocarbon	Group	Example of Common Usage
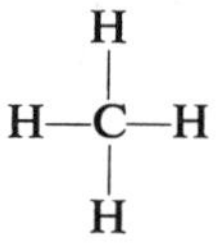 Methane	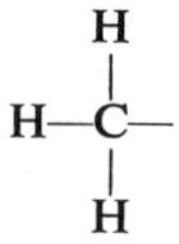 Methyl	CH_3I Methyl iodide (Iodomethane)
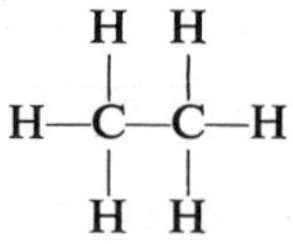 Ethane	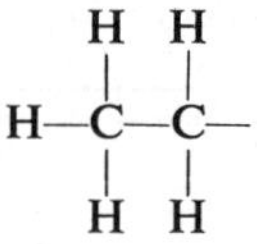 Ethyl	C_2H_5OH Ethyl alcohol (Ethanol)
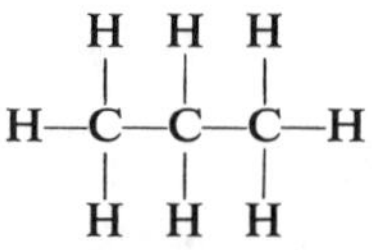 Propane	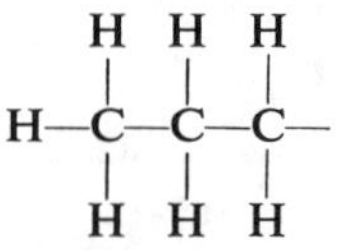 *n*-Propyl	$CH_3CH_2CH_2Br$ *n*-Propyl bromide (1-Bromopropane)

□ ■ TABLE 2.2 — *Continued*

COMMONLY USED ALKYL GROUPS

	$CH_3-\overset{\overset{\displaystyle H}{\mid}}{\underset{\mid}{C}}-CH_3$ Isopropyl	$CH_3-\overset{\overset{\displaystyle H}{\mid}}{\underset{\underset{\displaystyle OH}{\mid}}{C}}-CH_3$ Isopropyl alcohol (2-Propanol)
$H-\overset{\overset{\displaystyle H}{\mid}}{\underset{\underset{\displaystyle H}{\mid}}{C}}-\overset{\overset{\displaystyle H}{\mid}}{\underset{\underset{\displaystyle H}{\mid}}{C}}-\overset{\overset{\displaystyle H}{\mid}}{\underset{\underset{\displaystyle H}{\mid}}{C}}-\overset{\overset{\displaystyle H}{\mid}}{\underset{\underset{\displaystyle H}{\mid}}{C}}-H$ *n*-Butane	$CH_3CH_2CH_2CH_2-$ *n*-Butyl	$CH_3CH_2CH_2CH_2-Cl$ *n*-Butyl chloride (1-Chlorobutane)
	$CH_3-\overset{\overset{\displaystyle H}{\mid}}{\underset{\underset{\displaystyle H}{\mid}}{C}}-\overset{\overset{\displaystyle H}{\mid}}{C}-CH_3$ sec-Butyl	$CH_3-\overset{\overset{\displaystyle H}{\mid}}{\underset{\underset{\displaystyle H}{\mid}}{C}}-\overset{\overset{\displaystyle H}{\mid}}{\underset{\underset{\displaystyle CH_3}{\mid}}{C}}-Br$ sec-Butyl bromide (2-Bromobutane)
$H-\overset{\overset{\displaystyle H}{\mid}}{\underset{\underset{\displaystyle H}{\mid}}{C}}-\overset{\overset{\displaystyle H}{\mid}}{\underset{\underset{\displaystyle CH_3}{\mid}}{C}}-\overset{\overset{\displaystyle H}{\mid}}{\underset{\underset{\displaystyle H}{\mid}}{C}}-H$ Isobutane	$CH_3-\overset{\overset{\displaystyle H}{\mid}}{\underset{\underset{\displaystyle CH_3}{\mid}}{C}}-CH_2-$ Isobutyl	$CH_3-\overset{\overset{\displaystyle H}{\mid}}{\underset{\underset{\displaystyle CH_3}{\mid}}{C}}-CH_2-Br$ Isobutyl bromide (1-Bromo-2-methylpropane)
	$CH_3-\overset{\overset{\displaystyle CH_3}{\mid}}{\underset{\underset{\displaystyle CH_3}{\mid}}{C}}-$ tert-Butyl	$CH_3-\overset{\overset{\displaystyle CH_3}{\mid}}{\underset{\underset{\displaystyle CH_3}{\mid}}{C}}-Br$ tert-Butyl bromide (2-Bromo-2-methylpropane)

Branched-chain hydrocarbons which contain six or more carbon atoms have so many isomeric structures that to attempt to characterize them by simple prefixes such as *iso, sec, tert*, and the like is hopeless. It soon became apparent to chemists throughout the world that with the growing number of compounds some better system of naming was necessary.

In order to cope with the problem of standardizing nomenclature an international committee of chemists met at Geneva, Switzerland in 1892 to develop and adopt a systematic method for the naming of organic compounds. A commission from the International Union of Chemists (IUC) met in Liege, Belgium in 1930 and again as the International Union of Pure and Applied Chemistry (IUPAC) at Amsterdam in 1949. Rules originally adopted and subsequently modified by these groups of chemists have given us an orderly system of nomenclature known first as the **Geneva system,** or the **IUC system,** but more recently as the **IUPAC system.** Common, or trivial names, still are used for relatively simple structures and must be learned. However, the name of any compound, and most certainly that of a complex structure, is unmistakable if the IUPAC system is followed.

2.5   RULES FOR NAMING THE ALKANES

A. Determine the longest continuous carbon chain in the compound and name it as an alkane. The name of this chain is the basic part of the name.

B. Number the carbon atoms in the chain from one end or the other to locate substituent alkyl groups by the smallest possible number.

C. The position of each substituent is designated by the number of the carbon atom to which it is attached. Hyphens are used to separate numbers from names of substituents.

D. If identical groups appear more than once, the number of the carbon to which each is bonded is given each time. If identical groups appear on the same carbon, the number is repeated. Numbers are separated from each other by commas. The number of identical groups is indicated by prefixes *di, tri, tetra*, etc.

E. The last alkyl group named becomes one word with the parent hydrocarbon.

F. Substituent groups are named in alphabetical order (*ethyl* before *methyl*, etc.) and placed before the name of the parent structure.

Let us apply these rules of nomenclature to a few examples:

$$CH_3-\underset{\underset{CH_3}{|}}{\overset{\overset{CH_3}{|}}{C}}-CH_3 \qquad CH_3-\underset{\underset{H}{|}}{\overset{\overset{CH_3}{|}}{C}}-CH_2-CH_3$$

(1)   (2)   (3)   (4)

2, 2-Dimethylpropane   2-Methylbutane
(Neopentane)   (Isopentane)

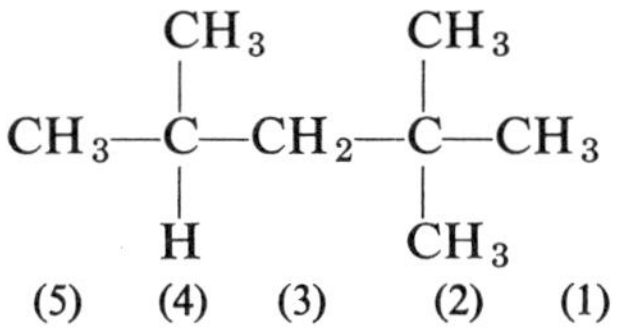

$$CH_3-\underset{\underset{\overset{|}{H}}{|}}{\overset{\overset{CH_3}{|}}{C}}-CH_2-\underset{\underset{\overset{|}{CH_3}}{|}}{\overset{\overset{CH_3}{|}}{C}}-CH_3$$

(5) (4) (3) (2) (1)

2, 2, 4-Trimethylpentane

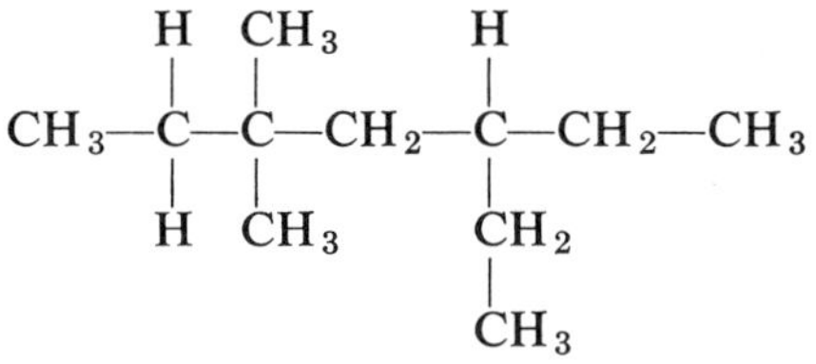

$$CH_3-\underset{\underset{\overset{|}{H}}{|}}{\overset{\overset{H}{|}}{C}}-\underset{\underset{\overset{|}{CH_3}}{|}}{\overset{\overset{CH_3}{|}}{C}}-CH_2-\underset{\underset{\overset{|}{CH_3}}{\underset{\overset{|}{CH_2}}{|}}}{\overset{\overset{H}{|}}{C}}-CH_2-CH_3$$

3, 3-Dimethyl-5-ethylheptane

Exercise 2.1   Five different structures may be drawn for the molecular formula C_6H_{14}. One isomer has a continuous chain of six carbons, two have continuous chains of five carbons, and two have continuous chains of four carbons. Draw structures for all five structures and name them according to IUPAC rules.

Examples of substituents other than (or in addition to) alkyl groups:

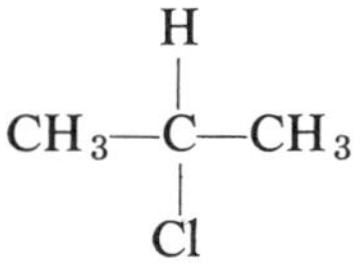

$$CH_3-\underset{\underset{\overset{|}{Cl}}{|}}{\overset{\overset{H}{|}}{C}}-CH_3$$

2-Chloropropane
(Isopropyl chloride)

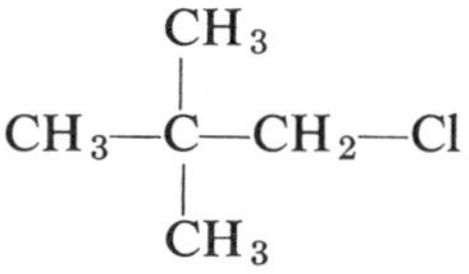

$$CH_3-\underset{\underset{\overset{|}{CH_3}}{|}}{\overset{\overset{CH_3}{|}}{C}}-CH_2-Cl$$

1-Chloro-2,
2-dimethylpropane
(Neopentyl chloride)

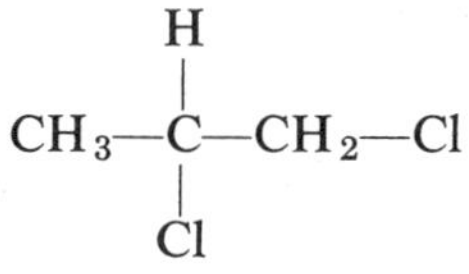

$$CH_3-\underset{\underset{\overset{|}{Cl}}{|}}{\overset{\overset{H}{|}}{C}}-CH_2-Cl$$

1, 2-Dichloropropane
(Propylene chloride)

Exercise 2.2   A student named the structure below incorrectly as 1-chloro-2-ethyl-2-methylpropane.

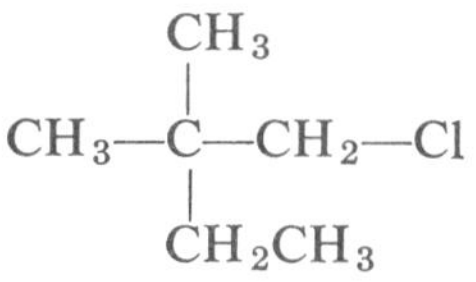

$$CH_3-\underset{\underset{\overset{|}{CH_2CH_3}}{|}}{\overset{\overset{CH_3}{|}}{C}}-CH_2-Cl$$

Tell why this name is objectionable and assign a correct name to the compound.

The single bond between carbon atoms in a molecule permits rotation of these atoms as if the shared pair of electrons were a pivot point between two tetrahedra (Fig. 2.1).

■ □ FIGURE 2 . 1

BALL AND STICK MODEL OF ETHANE SHOWING ARRANGEMENT OF ATOMS IN (a) SKEW, AND (b) ECLIPSED CONFORMATIONS.

Frequently, this ability to revolve around the line joining two carbons is called **free rotation.** How free or easy it is depends upon the nature of the atoms or groups occupying the other three corners of each tetrahedron. If these groups are large or bulky, free rotation not only may be inhibited, but prevented entirely. Again, if groups on adjacent carbons are of high electron density such as chlorine or bromine, they will tend to repel each other and therefore will occupy positions as far from each other as possible. The different spatial arrangements made possible by rotation about a single bond are called **conformations.** The conformational isomers possible for 1, 2-dichloroethane are shown in Figure 2.2. We must be careful to distinguish between such structural arrangements and those made possible by breaking and rearranging bonds.

Free rotation about singly-bonded carbons permits hydrocarbons in a continuous chain to be anything but "straight." They may zig-zag, turn corners, spiral, and even cyclize in a head-to-tail arrangement. Note the near cyclic form normal pentane (Fig. 2.3) can assume when carbon atoms numbered (2) and (3) are each rotated through an angle of 109°28′. For this reason we must inspect

■ □ FIGURE 2.2

SCALE MODELS SHOWING (a) STAGGERED, (b) SKEW, AND
(c) ECLIPSED CONFORMATIONS OF 1, 2-DICHLOROETHANE.

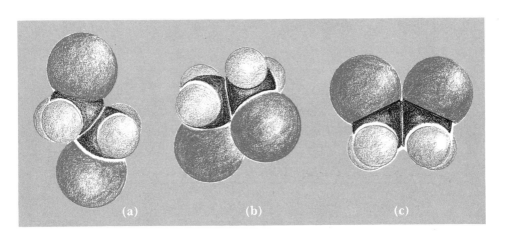

■ □ FIGURE 2.3

BALL AND STICK MODELS OF *n*-PENTANE.

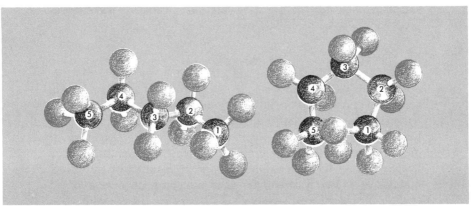

THE MODEL AT THE RIGHT SHOWS THE "HEAD-TO-TAIL" ARRANGE-
MENT POSSIBLE BECAUSE OF SINGLY-BONDED CARBONS.

a carbon chain carefully before numbering it. The longest chain
need not necessarily be the horizontal one.

Exercise 2.3   Conformational isomers often are shown by "dotted line-wedge" drawings in which the dotted line is the bond below, the wedge the bond above, and the solid line the bond within the plane of the paper. Consider the structure below a representation of *n*-butane.

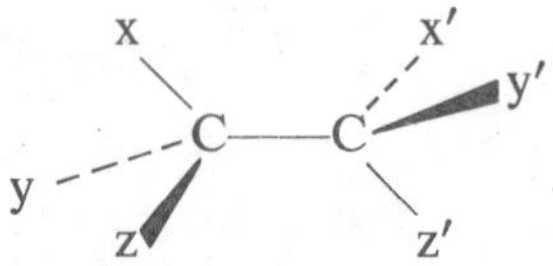

Where should methyl groups be placed to give (a) the staggered conformation; (b) the skew or gauche conformation? Which conformation is most likely for *n*-butane? Why?

2.7   PHYSICAL PROPERTIES OF THE ALKANES

The first four members of the alkane family are gases. Those containing five to seventeen carbon atoms are liquids at room temperature, while those members having eighteen or more carbon atoms are solids. All hydrocarbons are insoluble in water but dissolve easily in most organic solvents. They are colorless and tasteless. When pure they are odorless. The odor of natural gas is not that of methane, its principal constituent, but that of a contaminant purposely added to allow for the detection of leaks. Table 2.3 summarizes properties of some representative members of the alkane series.

2.8   PREPARATION OF THE ALKANES

The alkanes are isolated from petroleum and usually are consumed as mixtures. It is seldom necessary to synthesize a hydrocarbon. Rather, if one is required alone, it is separated from its homologs by one of several laboratory techniques. A number of organic compounds, when properly treated, do react to produce hydrocarbons. In order to illustrate the preparation of an alkane, however, it will be necessary for us to use compounds we have yet to meet in subsequent chapters.

A.   The Wurtz Reaction.   In 1855 Adolph Wurtz[1] discovered that when metallic sodium reacts with an alkyl halide, the sodium

---

[1]Charles Adolph Wurtz (1817–1884). French chemist best known for his early work with chlorinated hydrocarbons.

☐■ TABLE 2.3

PHYSICAL PROPERTIES OF SOME NORMAL SATURATED
HYDROCARBONS

Name	Formula	M.P., °C	B.P., °C	Specific Gravity	Normal State
Methane	CH_4	−182.6	−161.4	–	gas
Ethane	C_2H_6	−172.0	−88.3	–	gas
Propane	C_3H_8	−187.1	−44.5	–	gas
n-Butane	C_4H_{10}	−135.0	−0.5	–	gas
n-Pentane	C_5H_{12}	−129.7	36.2	0.6264	liquid
n-Hexane	C_6H_{14}	−94.0	69	0.6594	liquid
n-Heptane	C_7H_{16}	−90.5	98.4	0.6837	liquid
n-Octane	C_8H_{18}	−56.8	124.6	0.7028	liquid
n-Decane	$C_{10}H_{22}$	−32	175	0.730	liquid
n-Pentadecane	$C_{15}H_{32}$	10	271	0.772	liquid
n-Octadecane	$C_{18}H_{38}$	28	308	0.77	solid

salt of the halogen is formed. He performed the reaction with methyl iodide hoping to produce the *free methyl radical*[2] according to the following equation.

$$\underset{\substack{\text{Methyl} \\ \text{iodide}}}{\text{H}-\overset{\displaystyle \text{H}}{\underset{\displaystyle \text{H}}{\text{C}}}:\text{I}} + \underset{\text{Sodium}}{\text{Na} \cdot} \longrightarrow \underset{\substack{\text{Sodium} \\ \text{iodide}}}{\text{Na}^+\text{I}^-} + \underset{\substack{\text{Free methyl} \\ \text{radical}}}{\text{H}-\overset{\displaystyle \text{H}}{\underset{\displaystyle \text{H}}{\text{C}}} \cdot}$$

However, the only product Wurtz obtained, other than the inorganic salt, was ethane. The free methyl radical, if formed, was presumed to have coupled immediately with another similar radical, the odd electrons pairing.

---

[2]A free radical is a structure which has an odd, or unpaired, electron. It is ordinarily a very reactive species and has only a transient existence as an intermediate in a chemical reaction. A free radical should not be confused with an alkyl group or with an ion.

$$
\begin{array}{c}
\underset{\displaystyle H}{\overset{\displaystyle H}{H-C}} \cdot + \cdot \underset{\displaystyle H}{\overset{\displaystyle H}{C-H}} \longrightarrow \underset{\displaystyle H\ H}{\overset{\displaystyle H\ H}{H-C:C-H}}
\end{array}
$$

Ethane

More recent evidence indicates that the Wurtz reaction involves the formation of alkyl sodium compounds as intermediates. For example,

$$CH_3CH_2I + 2\,Na \longrightarrow CH_3CH_2{}^-Na^+ + NaI$$

Ethyl iodide   Ethylsodium

$$CH_3CH_2{}^-Na^+ + CH_3CH_2I \longrightarrow NaI + CH_3CH_2CH_2CH_3$$

n-Butane

The net result, however, of treating an alkyl halide with metallic sodium is the coupling of two alkyl groups to produce a symmetrical alkane of an even number of carbon atoms. The general equation for the **Wurtz reaction** is[3]

$$2\,R-X + 2\,Na \longrightarrow 2\,NaX + R-R$$

The Wurtz reaction as a preparative method is of limited value and works best with primary halides.

B.   Reduction of Alkyl Halides (via the Hydrolysis of a Grignard Reagent).   In 1901 Victor Grignard[4] discovered one of the most useful of all chemical reactions. He prepared methylmagnesium iodide, an organometallic compound, by treating methyl iodide with fresh magnesium turnings in anhydrous ether (diethyl ether, the hospital variety). In the organometallic compound formed, the alkyl group is united to the metal.

---

[3]R is a general designation for an alkyl group, C_nH_{2n+1}; X is a general designation for a halogen. These symbols are used throughout the text.

[4]Victor Grignard (1871–1935). French chemist and winner of the Nobel Prize in chemistry (1912) for the discovery and development of the reaction that bears his name.

$$\underset{\substack{\text{Methyl}\\\text{iodide}}}{\text{H}\overset{\displaystyle \text{H}}{\underset{\displaystyle \text{H}}{-\text{C}-}}\text{I}} + \text{Mg} \xrightarrow[\text{ether}]{\text{Anhydrous}} \underset{\substack{\text{Methylmagnesium}\\\text{iodide}}}{\text{H}\overset{\displaystyle \text{H}}{\underset{\displaystyle \text{H}}{-\text{C}-}}\text{MgI}}$$

The over-all equation for the preparation of alkylmagnesium halides, or Grignard reagents, as they came to be known, can be written

$$\text{R}-\text{X} + \text{Mg} \xrightarrow{\text{Ether}} \text{RMgX}$$

The reaction also proceeds satisfactorily with higher molecular weight alkyl iodides, bromides, or chlorides. Grignard reagents are extremely reactive and, when hydrolyzed (reacted with water), are easily converted into alkanes.[5] Methylmagnesium iodide, on hydrolysis, yields methane; ethylmagnesium bromide, when hydrolyzed, gives ethane.

$$\text{CH}_3\text{MgI} + \text{H}_2\text{O} \longrightarrow \text{CH}_4 + \text{HO}-\text{Mg}-\text{I}$$

$$\text{C}_2\text{H}_5\text{MgBr} + \text{H}_2\text{O} \longrightarrow \text{C}_2\text{H}_6 + \text{HO}-\text{Mg}-\text{Br}$$

In practice, hydrolysis usually is accomplished by the use of dilute hydrochloric acid which converts the basic magnesium halide, $\text{HO}-\text{Mg}-\text{X}$, to the water-soluble magnesium halide, MgX_2.

2.9   CHEMICAL PROPERTIES OF THE ALKANES

The only reactions the saturated hydrocarbons are capable of undergoing without a rupture of carbon–carbon bonds are reactions in which hydrogen of the parent hydrocarbon is replaced by some other atom or group. Such replacements are called **substitution reactions.** Generally, the hydrocarbons are unreactive toward most reagents but are attacked by halogens and oxygen under certain conditions. Reactions with halogens are substitution reactions; attack by oxygen results in the breaking of carbon–carbon and carbon–hydrogen bonds. When alkanes are heated to extreme tem-

---

[5]Because Grignard reagents are easily hydrolyzed, glassware used in their preparation must be dry and reagents used must be anhydrous. Unless these precautions are taken, Grignard reagents will not form.

peratures in the absence of air (a treatment referred to as *pyrolysis*, or *cracking*), the carbon–carbon and the carbon–hydrogen bonds are also ruptured to give a variety of fragmentary products. Catalytic cracking of long chain hydrocarbons as carried out in the petroleum industry (Chapter 5) makes possible the production of great quantities of motor fuel.

A.   Oxidation (Combustion)   Alkanes are resistant to ordinary chemical oxidizing reagents such as potassium permanganate, $KMnO_4$, and potassium dichromate, $K_2Cr_2O_7$, but may be oxidized to carbon dioxide and water when ignited in the presence of an excess of oxygen. Great quantities of heat energy are released, and it is this reaction which makes hydrocarbons so useful as fuels.

$$CH_4 + 2\,O_2 \longrightarrow CO_2 + 2\,H_2O + 211\ kcal$$

$$C_2H_6 + 3\tfrac{1}{2}\,O_2 \longrightarrow 2\,CO_2 + 3\,H_2O + 368\ kcal$$

$$C_3H_8 + 5\,O_2 \longrightarrow 3\,CO_2 + 4\,H_2O + 526\ kcal$$

Incomplete combustion of alkanes results in the formation of carbon (soot) and the very dangerous carbon monoxide.

$$2\,CH_4 + 3\,O_2 \longrightarrow 2\,CO + 4\,H_2O$$

$$CH_4 + O_2 \longrightarrow C + 2\,H_2O$$

Although both of the preceding reactions are to be avoided if we are to heat our homes safely and economically, the reaction that produces soot (carbon black) is of vital importance to our tire and rubber industry.

B.   Substitution (Halogenation)   At ordinary temperatures, and in the absence of light, chlorine does not react with saturated hydrocarbons. At elevated temperatures and in the presence of sunlight or unltraviolet light, the hydrogen atoms are replaced by one or more chlorine atoms. A substitution of hydrogen by chlorine is known as a **chlorination** reaction. The reaction pathway by which chlorine substitutes for hydrogen in a hydrocarbon has been well established as one involving the formation of **free radicals.** A free radical in its reaction with another molecule can lead each time to the production of another free radical. The reaction is thus a self-propagating chain reaction which continues until all materials are consumed or until two free radicals meet and unite. A reaction pathway followed in this manner is referred to as a **free radical chain mechanism.** The first steps in the chlorination of methane may be shown as follows:

$$Cl : Cl \xrightarrow{\text{Sunlight}} 2\ Cl \cdot$$

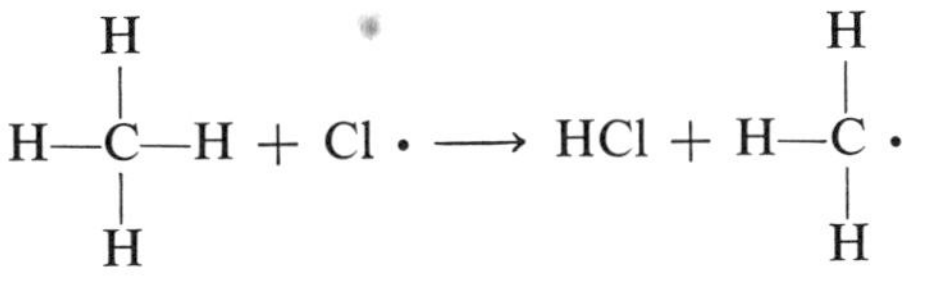

$$H{-}\underset{\displaystyle H}{\overset{\displaystyle H}{\underset{|}{\overset{|}{C}}}}{-}H + Cl \cdot \longrightarrow HCl + H{-}\underset{\displaystyle H}{\overset{\displaystyle H}{\underset{|}{\overset{|}{C}}}}\cdot$$

Methyl radical

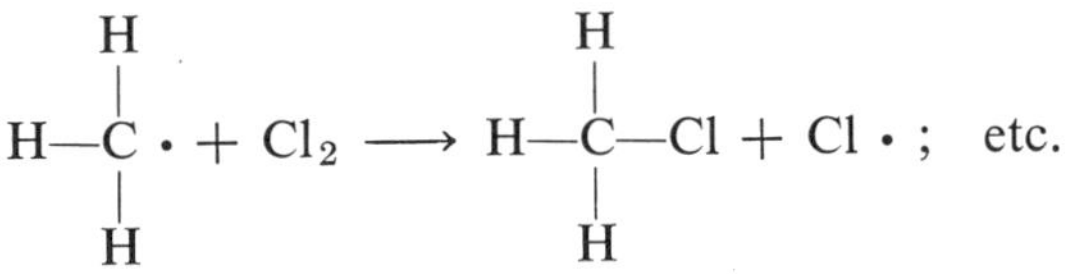

$$H{-}\underset{\displaystyle H}{\overset{\displaystyle H}{\underset{|}{\overset{|}{C}}}}\cdot + Cl_2 \longrightarrow H{-}\underset{\displaystyle H}{\overset{\displaystyle H}{\underset{|}{\overset{|}{C}}}}{-}Cl + Cl \cdot\ ;\quad \text{etc.}$$

Chloromethane
(Methyl chloride)

The chlorination of methane is not restricted to the exclusive conversion of all methane to methyl chloride but proceeds until all four hydrogen atoms (on at least some) of the methane molecules have been substituted. The chlorination of a hydrocarbon therefore may result in a mixture of products.

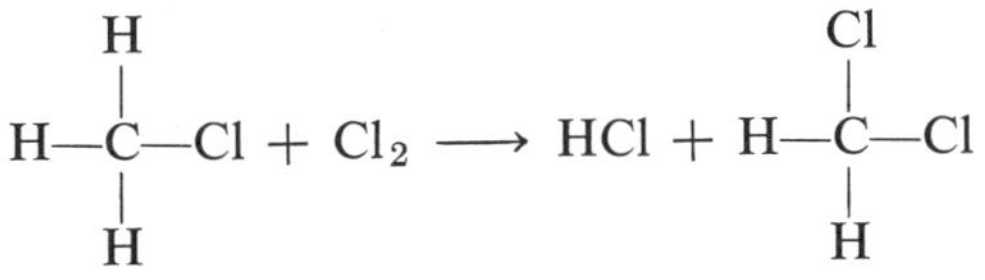

$$H{-}\underset{\displaystyle H}{\overset{\displaystyle H}{\underset{|}{\overset{|}{C}}}}{-}Cl + Cl_2 \longrightarrow HCl + H{-}\underset{\displaystyle H}{\overset{\displaystyle Cl}{\underset{|}{\overset{|}{C}}}}{-}Cl$$

Chloromethane   Dichloromethane
(Methyl chloride)   (Methylene chloride)

$$H{-}\underset{\displaystyle H}{\overset{\displaystyle Cl}{\underset{|}{\overset{|}{C}}}}{-}Cl + Cl_2 \longrightarrow HCl + H{-}\underset{\displaystyle Cl}{\overset{\displaystyle Cl}{\underset{|}{\overset{|}{C}}}}{-}Cl$$

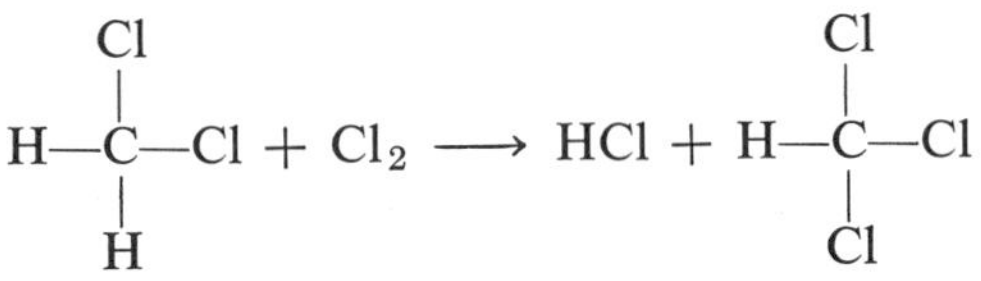

Trichloromethane
(Chloroform)

$$H\overset{\overset{\displaystyle Cl}{|}}{\underset{\underset{\displaystyle Cl}{|}}{C}}Cl + Cl_2 \longrightarrow HCl + Cl\overset{\overset{\displaystyle Cl}{|}}{\underset{\underset{\displaystyle Cl}{|}}{C}}Cl$$

Tetrachloromethane
(Carbon tetrachloride)

The chlorination of either methane or ethane in which only one hydrogen atom has been replaced can result in only one mono-chlorinated product because all hydrogen atoms in these two alkanes are of the primary type. Propane, on the other hand, can yield two different monochlorinated products because it has secondary hydrogen as well as primary hydrogen atoms which may be replaced (Sec. 2.4). This being the case, a question arises as to which propyl chloride would we obtain if propane is chlorinated. Actually, both *n*-propyl chloride and isopropyl chloride are produced but not in equal amounts.

$$H\overset{\overset{\displaystyle H}{|}}{\underset{\underset{\displaystyle H}{|}}{C}}\overset{\overset{\displaystyle H}{|}}{\underset{\underset{\displaystyle H}{|}}{C}}\overset{\overset{\displaystyle H}{|}}{\underset{\underset{\displaystyle H}{|}}{C}}H + Cl_2$$

Propane

$$\xrightarrow{\text{UV}} \quad H\overset{\overset{\displaystyle H}{|}}{\underset{\underset{\displaystyle H}{|}}{C}}\overset{\overset{\displaystyle H}{|}}{\underset{\underset{\displaystyle H}{|}}{C}}\overset{\overset{\displaystyle H}{|}}{\underset{\underset{\displaystyle H}{|}}{C}}Cl \quad + \quad H\overset{\overset{\displaystyle H}{|}}{\underset{\underset{\displaystyle H}{|}}{C}}\overset{\overset{\displaystyle H}{|}}{\underset{\underset{\displaystyle Cl}{|}}{C}}\overset{\overset{\displaystyle H}{|}}{\underset{\underset{\displaystyle H}{|}}{C}}H$$

1-Chloropropane   2-Chloropropane
(*n*-Propyl chloride)   (Isopropyl chloride)
45%   55%

Generally speaking, a tertiary hydrogen is more readily replaced than a secondary one, and a secondary more readily than a primary hydrogen.

Bromine also reacts with the alkanes when the reaction is catalyzed by high frequency radiation, but does so much more slowly than chlorine. Iodine fails to react when catalyzed in this manner, but fluorine reacts with explosive violence. The reasons for this difference in the reaction behavior among members of the same family is a matter of energy relationships between reactants and products. To understand these relationships we need to know what energy requirements must be met in order for molecules to meet and react.

2.10   BOND ENERGIES AND HEATS OF REACTION

In order for two molecules to react they must collide in a certain way with sufficient energy to break existing bonds and to form new ones. The breaking of a chemical bond requires energy. Conversely, the formation of a new bond yields energy. It would seem, then, that if the formation of bonds in the products were to yield a greater amount of energy than that expended in the breaking of bonds in the reactants, the reaction should proceed spontaneously. This is not the case, however. Consider the following analogy: Your automobile is on a plateau on the western side of the continental divide, at a higher elevation than Missouri, and thus possesses potential energy. But the ride to Kansas City is not simply one of coasting downhill. Some energy must be expended to climb over the divide as well as to overcome the intervening hills. Thus it is with chemical reactions. The energy necessary to get over the "hump" is called the **activation energy.** The net heat change for the overall reaction in going from reactants to products is called the **heat of reaction** and is symbolized by ΔH, the capital Greek delta signifying *change.* The heat of reaction for many chemical reactions can be

□■ TABLE 2.4

BOND DISSOCIATION ENERGIES (kcal/mole at 25°)

H—H	104	F—F	37	O=O	119
H—F	135	Cl—Cl	58	O—H	111
H—Cl	103	Br—Br	46	C=O[a]	192
H—Br	87	I—I	36	H₃C—H	102
H—I	71				
		H		H	
		|		|	
H₃C—F	108	CH₃C—Cl	83	CH₃C—H	97
		|		|	
		H		H	
		H		H	
		|		|	
H₃C—Cl	81	CH₃CH₂C—Cl	77	CH₃CH₂C—H	97
		|		|	
		H		H	
		H		H	
		|		|	
H₃C—Br	67	(CH₃)₂C—Cl	73	(CH₃)₂C—H	94
H₃C—I	53	(CH₃)₃C—Cl	75	(CH₃)₃C—H	91

[a]CO₂

calculated from a knowledge of bond dissociation energies. The
dissociation energies for a number of different bonds are given in
Table 2.4.

The following example illustrates how Table 2.4 may be used.

Problem: Calculate ΔH for the monochlorination of methane.

Solution: (1) Write the equation to show exactly which bonds
are to be broken and which new bonds are to be formed.

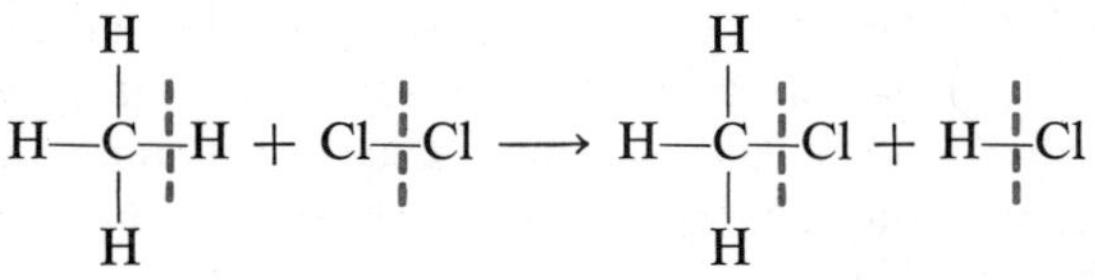

$$\underset{\text{H}}{\overset{\text{H}}{\text{H---C---H}}} + \text{Cl---Cl} \longrightarrow \underset{\text{H}}{\overset{\text{H}}{\text{H---C---Cl}}} + \text{H---Cl}$$

$$102 \quad + \quad 58 \qquad\qquad 81 \quad + \quad 103 \quad \text{(kcal)}$$

(2) Add bond energies on both sides of the equation. Breaking
the C—H bond and the Cl—Cl bond requires 160 kcal; formation of the C—Cl and the H—Cl bonds yields a total of
184 kcal.

(3) Subtract the heat liberated through bond formation from
the heat expended in bond dissociation. The difference is ΔH
for the reaction.

$$\Delta H = 160 \text{ kcal} - 184 \text{ kcal} = -24 \text{ kcal.}$$

The sign is negative when the net result is *exothermic*.
The sign is positive when the net result is *endothermic*.

Potential energy changes involved in the monochlorination of
methane may be illustrated graphically by means of a diagram such
as that shown in Figure 2.4. The height of the hump represents the
activation energy or the minimum energy needed to get the reaction
to "go."

Exercise 2.4   Calculate ΔH for the following reaction:

$$\text{CH}_3\text{---H} + \text{Br---Br} \longrightarrow \text{CH}_3\text{---Br} + \text{H---Br}$$

Answer: −6 kcal.

■□FIGURE 2.4

POTENTIAL ENERGY CHANGES DURING THE PROGRESS
OF AN EXOTHERMIC REACTION.

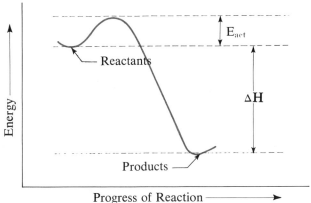

2.11   CYCLOALKANES

The cycloalkanes are saturated hydrocarbons that have ring
structures. The general formula for this class of hydrocarbons is
C_nH_{2n}.

Cyclopropane   Cyclobutane   Cyclopentane

(chair form)   (boat form)

Cyclohexane

Only the ring carbons are counted in naming the cycloalkanes
and, as in open chain structures, they are numbered in order to
designate substituents by the smallest numbers. The alkyl sub-

stituent also becomes one word with the name of the parent cycloalkane.

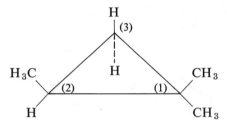

1, 1, 2-Trimethylcyclopropane

The cyclic paraffins of lower molecular weight may be prepared
by a Wurtz-type synthesis using a dihalogen substituted alkane.

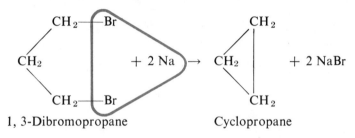

1, 3-Dibromopropane   Cyclopropane

Although the general formula of the cycloalkanes is the same
as that of the alkenes (next chapter), their chemical behavior generally
is more like that of the alkanes than that of the alkenes. Cyclopropane and cyclobutane are exceptions to this general rule, for
reasons explained in the next section.

Exercise 2.5   How many cyclic structures of formula
C_5H_{10} can you draw and name?

2.12   RING STRUCTURE AND THE BAEYER STRAIN THEORY

In order to bring the terminal carbons of propane together and
form a bond between them, the tetrahedral angle of 109°28′ between
carbon-carbon bonds (Sec. 2.6) must be changed to 60°, which is the
value for the angles in an equilateral triangle. Each valence bond in
cyclopropane thus is distorted from the normal tetrahedral angle by
1/2(109°28′ − 60°) or 24°44′. A bond angle deviation of this mag-
nitude places the ring structure of cyclopropane under considerable

strain and makes it more reactive than propane. With bromine substitution does not occur. Instead, the ring is opened and the bromine adds at each end of the chain.

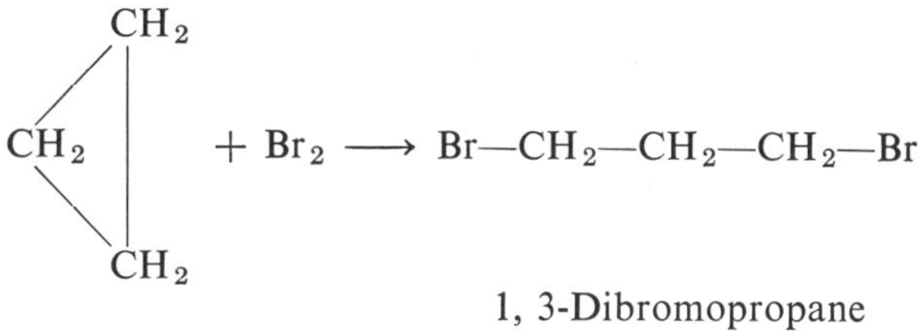

$$
\underset{CH_2}{\overset{CH_2}{\triangle}} \quad + Br_2 \longrightarrow Br{-}CH_2{-}CH_2{-}CH_2{-}Br
$$

1, 3-Dibromopropane

Other reagents that react with carbon-carbon double bonds (Sec. 3.7–3.9) may also cause the ring to open.

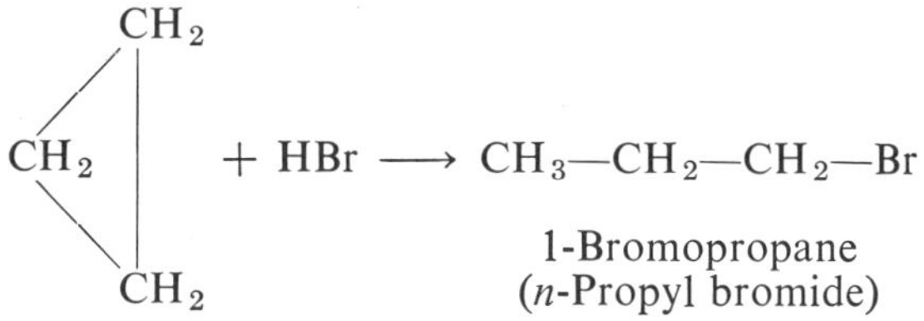

$$
\underset{CH_2}{\overset{CH_2}{\triangle}} \quad + HBr \longrightarrow CH_3{-}CH_2{-}CH_2{-}Br
$$

1-Bromopropane
(n-Propyl bromide)

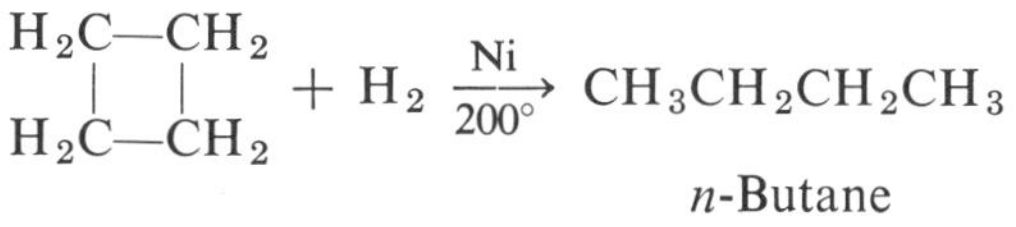

$$
\begin{array}{c} H_2C{-}CH_2 \\ |\quad\quad| \\ H_2C{-}CH_2 \end{array} + H_2 \xrightarrow[200^\circ]{Ni} CH_3CH_2CH_2CH_3
$$

n-Butane

In 1885 von Baeyer[6] advanced the theory that rings larger or smaller than five or six carbon atoms would possess too much strain to be stable. His theory, based on the assumption that all carbons within the ring lie in the same plane, is correct insofar as small rings are concerned, but not true for larger rings. Rings of six carbons or more do not have to lie flat with all carbon atoms in the same plane, but can pucker to retain the unstrained tetrahedral angle. Any strain within the ring is thus easily relieved. This is illustrated in Figure 2.5 and Figure 2.6 with the known conformations, the boat and chair forms, of cyclohexane.

Although both boat and chair forms are possible cyclohexane conformations that are free of angle strain, chemical evidence has revealed that of these two, the chair conformation appears to be the

---

[6]Adolph von Baeyer (1835–1917). One of the greatest German chemists of his time. A prolific researcher and outstanding teacher. Professor of chemistry, University of Munich. Winner of the Nobel Prize in chemistry 1905.

■ ☐ FIGURE   2.5

BOAT CONFORMATION OF CYCLOHEXANE. COMPARE THE BALL
AND STICK MODEL WITH THE STRUCTURE AT THE RIGHT.

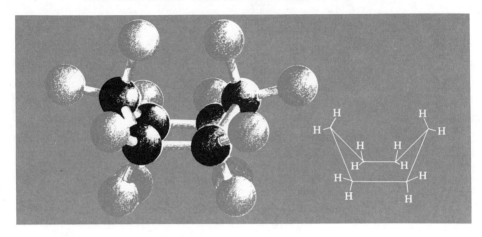

■ ☐ FIGURE   2.6

CHAIR CONFORMATION OF CYCLOHEXANE. COMPARE THE BALL
AND STICK MODEL WITH THE STRUCTURE AT THE RIGHT.

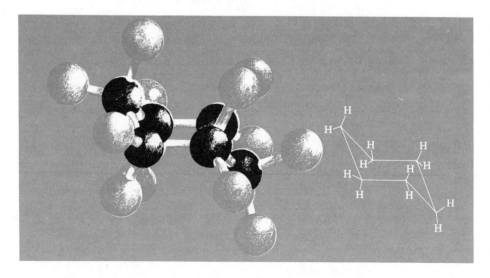

more stable. The chair conformation enables us to bond hydrogen
atoms (or other substituents) in two kinds of position. In one position six bonds lie roughly in the plane of the ring, or "equatorial

■□FIGURE 2.7

EQUATORIAL AND AXIAL BONDS IN CYCLOHEXANE.

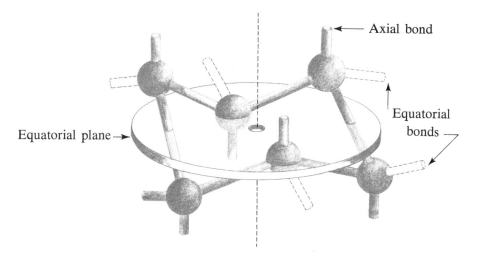

belt," and are called **equatorial bonds.** The other six bonds point in a direction parallel to an axis drawn perpendicular to the plane of the ring and are called **axial bonds** (Figure 2.7). Substituents on adjacent carbon atoms of the 6-atom ring will show less interference with each other — that is, will have more space to occupy, when in equatorial positions.

□□ *SUMMARY*

[1] The alkanes, or saturated hydrocarbons, contain only carbon and hydrogen. They are also called paraffins. All carbon atoms in alkanes are singly bonded to four other atoms.

[2] The **general formula for an alkane** is C_nH_{2n+2}.

[3] The names for the alkanes end in *"ane."* Alkanes may be named unambiguously by the IUPAC system.

[4] The **general formula for an alkyl group** is C_nH_{2n+1}. Groups are named after the parent hydrocarbon by changing the suffix *ane* to *yl*. The prefixes *iso, sec, tert* are used depending upon which hydrogens have been removed from the parent compound.

[5] Saturated hydrocarbons may have straight (that is, in a continuous chain), branched, or cyclic structures.

[6] Alkanes may be prepared by:

   a.   Coupling of alkyl groups *via* a Wurtz synthesis.

$$2\,R{-}X + 2\,Na \longrightarrow R{-}R + 2\,NaX$$

   b.   Reduction of an alkyl halide via a Grignard reagent.

$$R{-}X + Mg \longrightarrow RMgX \xrightarrow[\text{(HX)}]{\text{Hydrolysis}} R{-}H + MgX_2$$

[7] Chemically, the alkanes are relatively inert. The only reactions which occur without rupture of the carbon-carbon bond are those of substitution. Typical reactions include:

   a.   Oxidation (combustion)

$$C_nH_{2n+2} + \frac{(3n + 1)}{2}\,O_2 \longrightarrow nCO_2 + (n + 1)\,H_2O$$

   b.   Halogenation

$$R{-}H + X_2 \xrightarrow[\text{light}]{\text{UV}} R{-}X + HX$$

[8] Chemical reactions occur when properly oriented molecules collide with sufficient energy to break existing bonds and form new bonds. The energy required to break a chemical bond is called its **dissociation energy.** The same amount of energy is released when the bond is reformed.

[9] The heat of reaction, ΔH, is the difference in the energy content of reactants and products. ΔH is negative when the reaction is exothermic; positive when endothermic.

[10] Cycloparaffins are ring compounds of general formula C_nH_{2n}. Small rings are strained. Rings of six or more carbon atoms permit a puckered structure and are strain-free.

□□ *NEW TERMS*

[a]	activation energy	[h]	free radical
[b]	alkyl group	[i]	free rotation
[c]	axial bonds	[j]	Grignard reagent
[d]	bond dissociation energy	[k]	heat of reaction
[e]	conformation	[l]	paraffins
[f]	"cracking"	[m]	"strained" rings
[g]	equatorial bonds		

■ □SUPPLEMENTARY EXERCISES
▼ AND PROBLEMS

[1] Name each of the following structures according to IUPAC rules. Also assign common names to each.

(a) 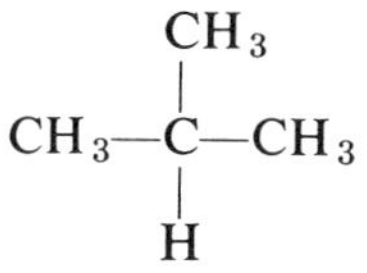 $CH_3-\overset{\overset{\displaystyle CH_3}{|}}{\underset{\underset{\displaystyle H}{|}}{C}}-CH_3$

(b) $CH_3-\overset{\overset{\displaystyle H}{|}}{\underset{\underset{\displaystyle Cl}{|}}{C}}-CH_3$

(c) $CH_3-\overset{\overset{\displaystyle CH_3}{|}}{\underset{\underset{\displaystyle H}{|}}{C}}-CH_2-CH_2-CH_3$

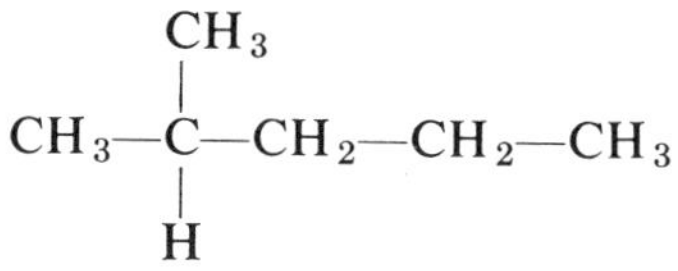

(d) 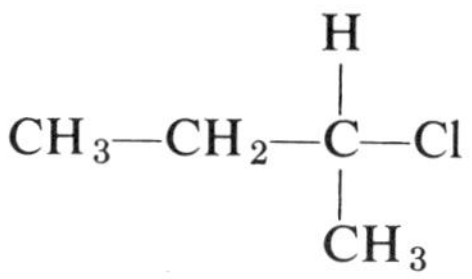 $CH_3-CH_2-\overset{\overset{\displaystyle H}{|}}{\underset{\underset{\displaystyle CH_3}{|}}{C}}-Cl$

(e) 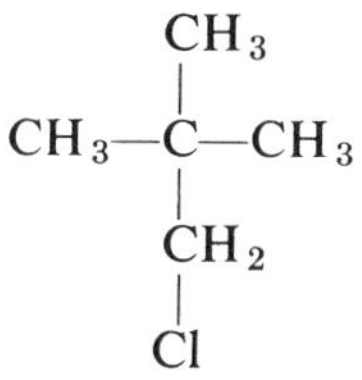 $CH_3-\overset{\overset{\displaystyle CH_3}{|}}{\underset{\underset{\underset{\underset{\displaystyle Cl}{|}}{CH_2}}{|}}{C}}-CH_3$

(f) 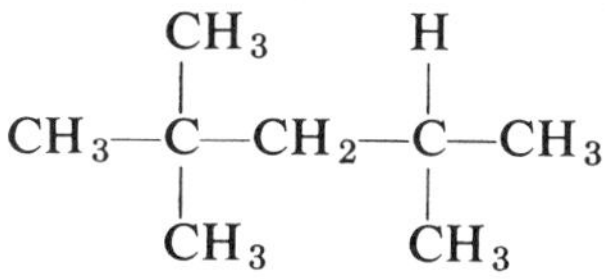 $CH_3-\overset{\overset{\displaystyle CH_3}{|}}{\underset{\underset{\displaystyle CH_3}{|}}{C}}-CH_2-\overset{\overset{\displaystyle H}{|}}{\underset{\underset{\displaystyle CH_3}{|}}{C}}-CH_3$

[2] Which of the following structures are the same? What are their IUPAC names?

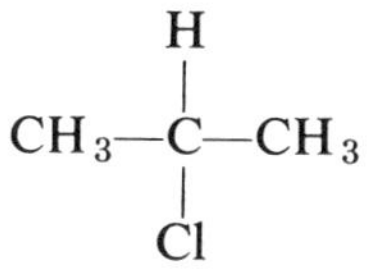

(a) 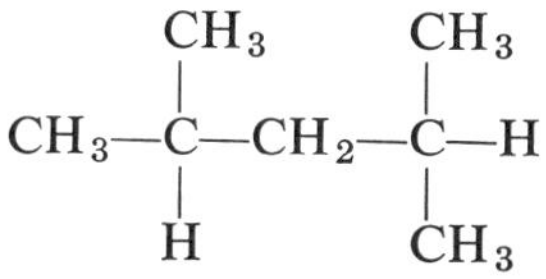 $CH_3-\overset{\overset{\displaystyle CH_3}{|}}{\underset{\underset{\displaystyle H}{|}}{C}}-CH_2-\overset{\overset{\displaystyle CH_3}{|}}{\underset{\underset{\displaystyle CH_3}{|}}{C}}-H$

(b) $CH_3-\overset{\overset{\overset{\overset{\displaystyle CH_3}{|}}{CH_2}}{|}}{\underset{\underset{\displaystyle H}{|}}{C}}-CH_2-CH_3$

(c) $CH_3-\overset{\overset{\displaystyle H}{|}}{\underset{\underset{\displaystyle CH_3}{|}}{C}}-CH_2-\overset{\overset{\displaystyle CH_3}{|}}{\underset{\underset{\displaystyle H}{|}}{C}}-CH_3$

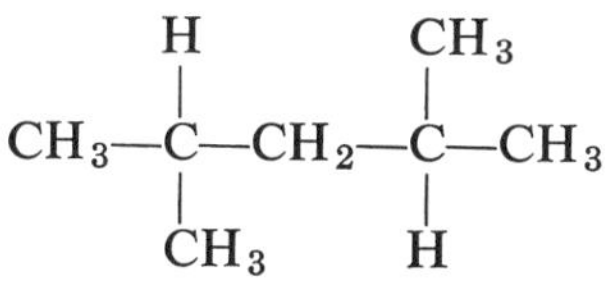

(d) 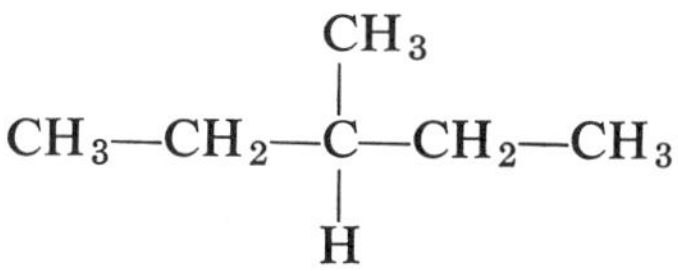 $CH_3-CH_2-\overset{\overset{\displaystyle CH_3}{|}}{\underset{\underset{\displaystyle H}{|}}{C}}-CH_2-CH_3$

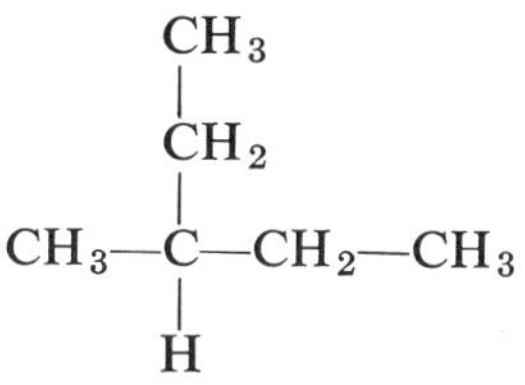

(e) 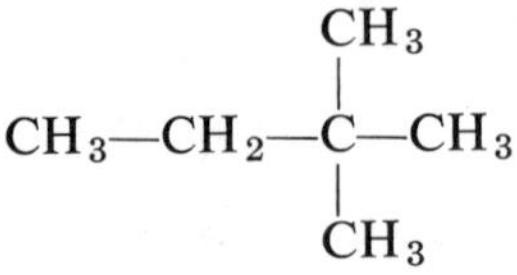 $CH_3-CH_2-\underset{\underset{\displaystyle CH_3}{|}}{\overset{\overset{\displaystyle CH_3}{|}}{C}}-CH_3$

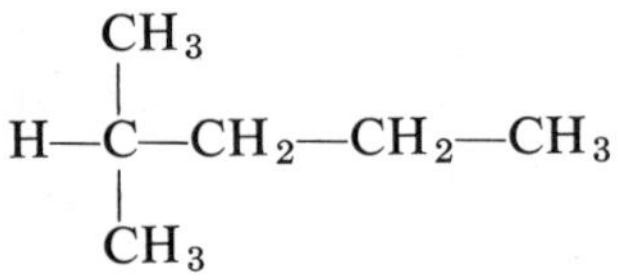

(f) 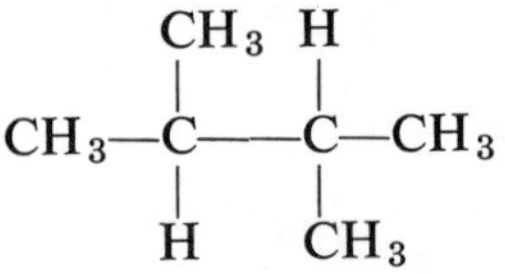 $CH_3-\underset{\underset{\displaystyle H}{|}}{\overset{\overset{\displaystyle CH_3}{|}}{C}}\ \underset{\underset{\displaystyle CH_3}{|}}{\overset{\overset{\displaystyle H}{|}}{C}}-CH_3$

(g) $H-\underset{\underset{\displaystyle CH_3}{|}}{\overset{\overset{\displaystyle CH_3}{|}}{C}}-CH_2-CH_2-CH_3$

(h) $CH_3-CH_2-\underset{\underset{\displaystyle CH_3}{|}}{\overset{\overset{\displaystyle CH_3}{|}}{C}}-CH_2-CH_3$

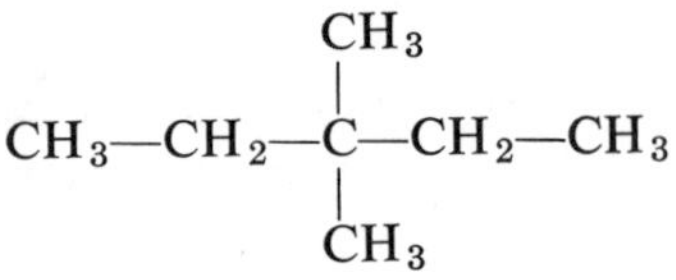

[3]   The following names are incorrect. In each case tell why the name is wrong and give the correct form.

(a)   2-methyl-3-ethylbutane   (d)   2-isopropyl chloride
(b)   4-methylpentane   (e)   3-methyl-4-chloropentane
(c)   3, 5, 5-trimethylhexane   (f)   1, 3-dimethylcyclopropane

[4]   Write structural formulas for the following.   Also assign systematic names to compounds (c–f).

(a)   2-methylbutane   (e)   isobutyl chloride
(b)   2, 2, 4-trimethylhexane   (f)   chloroform
(c)   neopentyl chloride   (g)   1, 3-dibromopropane
(d)   *tert*-butyl chloride   (h)   3-ethyl-2-methylpentane

[5]   Draw all hydrocarbon structures possible for the molecular formula, C_5H_{12}.   Identify the primary, secondary, and tertiary hydrogen atoms in these structures. How many monochlorinated products of formula $C_5H_{11}Cl$ are possible?

[6]   Give all structures possible for $C_3H_6Cl_2$. Name each according to the IUPAC system.

[7]   Complete the following reactions: (These should be balanced)

(a) $C_2H_5Br + Mg \xrightarrow{\text{Anhydrous ether}}$

(b) $CH_3CH_2I + Na \longrightarrow$

(c) $CH_3MgI + H_2O \xrightarrow{H^+}$

(d) C_3H_8 (bottled gas) $+ O_2 \longrightarrow$

(e) $CH_4 + Cl_2 \xrightarrow{\text{Sunlight}}$

[8]   Using structural formulas, show all products possible when a mixture of methyl and ethyl iodides is treated with metallic sodium.

[9]   A hydrocarbon was shown by analysis to contain 83.3% carbon and 16.7% hydrogen. A liter of the vapor at standard conditions weighed 3.21 g. When treated with chlorine in the presence of

sunlight, the compound gave only one monosubstituted product. What is the structure of the hydrocarbon?

[10] During a certain winter month a home furnace consumed 169 cu. ft. of natural gas. What volume of air (20% oxygen) was required to burn this gas if we assume it to be 80% methane plus noncombustible material? How many liters of water were produced? (1 cu. ft. = approximately 28.2 liters)

[11] Calculate ΔH for the following reactions: (*Consult Table 2.4*)

(a) $2 H_2 + O_2 \longrightarrow 2 H_2O$
(b) $C_2H_6 + Cl_2 \longrightarrow C_2H_5Cl + HCl$
(c) $C_3H_8 + Cl_2 \longrightarrow (CH_3)_2CHCl + HCl$

[12] Draw and properly identify each part of an energy diagram similar to that shown in Figure 2.4 for the reaction in Exercise 2.4. E_{act} for the bromination of methane is approximately 18 kcal.

chapter 3

The Unsaturated Hydrocarbons— Olefins and Acetylenes

INTRODUCTION

> The unsaturated hydrocarbons include two classes of compounds. In one class are hydrocarbons that contain carbon-carbon double bonds,
>
> —C=C—, and are known as **olefins,** or **alkenes.** The second class of unsaturated hydrocarbons include those that contain carbon-carbon triple bonds, —C≡C—, and are known as **acetylenes,** or **alkynes.** Both classes are described as unsaturated because they do not contain the maximum possible number of hydrogen atoms. They are not as "filled up" or saturated with hydrogen as they could be and potentially are capable of bonding to additional atoms. Unlike the saturated hydrocarbons, more than one pair of electrons is shared between two carbon atoms in these unsaturated compounds, As a result of such unsaturation both the olefins and the acetylenes are much more reactive than the alkanes. They combine readily with other compounds (or with themselves) and yield many useful products.

Part I: The Olefins (Alkenes)

As just pointed out, the olefins, or alkenes, are characterized by the presence of double bonds between adjacent carbon atoms. The general formula C_nH_{2n} corresponds to an open chain olefin if only *one* double bond is present in the molecule. The same general formula also represents a cycloalkane. In the first, or simplest member of the series, $n = 2$, and the formula C_2H_4 is that for ethylene, or ethene.

As a class these compounds are commonly referred to as the olefins (L., *oleum*, oil; *ficare*, to make). The name originated because ethene, in its reaction with chlorine, forms 1, 2-dichloroethane, an oily liquid.

$$
\underset{\text{Ethene}}{H-\overset{\displaystyle\overset{H}{|}}{C}=\overset{\displaystyle\overset{H}{|}}{C}-H} + Cl_2 \longrightarrow \underset{\text{1, 2-Dichloroethane}}{H-\overset{\displaystyle\overset{H}{|}}{\underset{\displaystyle\underset{Cl}{|}}{C}}-\overset{\displaystyle\overset{H}{|}}{\underset{\displaystyle\underset{Cl}{|}}{C}}-H}
$$

The name alkene is used in systematic nomenclature when referring to the olefins. Both common and systematic names will be used in the present chapter.

3.2   FORMULAS AND NOMENCLATURE

Systematic names for members of the olefin family are formed by replacing the suffix *ane* of the corresponding alkane with *ene*. Common names usually are employed to name the simplest members of the alkenes. Such common names are formed by replacing the suffix *ane* of the corresponding alkane with *ylene*. The following are examples of both systems of nomenclature.

$$
\underset{\substack{\text{Ethene}\\\text{(Ethylene)}}}{H-\overset{\overset{H}{|}}{C}=\overset{\overset{H}{|}}{C}-H} \qquad \underset{\substack{\text{Propene}\\\text{(Propylene)}}}{CH_3-\overset{\overset{H}{|}}{C}=\overset{\overset{H}{|}}{C}-H} \qquad \underset{\substack{\text{2-Methylpropene}\\\text{(Isobutylene)}}}{\overset{\displaystyle CH_3}{\underset{\displaystyle CH_3}{>}}C=\overset{\overset{H}{|}}{C}-H}
$$

The IUPAC rules for naming the alkenes follow those for the alkanes, except for the following modifications:

(1) Instead of simply numbering the longest carbon chain, the longest chain *which includes the functional group* is numbered. In the case of the olefins the functional group is the carbon-carbon double bond, $-\overset{\overset{H}{|}}{C}=\overset{\overset{H}{|}}{C}-$. Change the *ane* of the corresponding alkane to *ene*.

(2) Numbering begins from the end of the chain that will confer upon the carbon atom holding the functional group the smaller number. Since the double bond in an olefin appears between two carbons, only the carbon atom with the lower

number need be designated. This number precedes and is separated from the name by a hyphen.

(3) The functional group is located by a number each time it appears. The prefixes *di*, *tri*, etc. appear before *ene* in olefins with more than one double bond and are incorporated within the name.

A few examples will help make these points clear.

$$\underset{\text{2-Butene}}{CH_3-\overset{\overset{H}{|}}{C}=\overset{\overset{H}{|}}{C}-CH_3}$$

$$\underset{(4)\quad(3)\quad(2)\quad(1)}{\underset{\text{1-Butene}}{CH_3-CH_2-\overset{\overset{H}{|}}{C}=CH_2}}$$

$$\underset{(3)\quad(2)\quad(1)}{\underset{\text{2-Methylpropene}}{CH_3-\overset{\overset{CH_3}{|}}{C}=CH_2}}$$

$$\underset{(1)\quad(2)\quad(3)\quad(4)}{\underset{\text{1, 3-Butadiene}}{H-\overset{\overset{H}{|}}{C}=\overset{\overset{H}{|}}{C}-\overset{\overset{H}{|}}{C}=\overset{\overset{H}{|}}{C}-H}}$$

$$\underset{\text{3-Methyl-2-pentene}}{CH_3-\overset{(3)}{C}=\overset{(2)}{\underset{\underset{H}{|}}{C}}-CH_3 \quad (1)}$$

(5) CH_3
(4) CH_2

$$\underset{(5)\quad(4)\quad(3)\quad(2)\quad(1)}{\underset{\text{2, 4-Dimethyl-1-pentene}}{CH_3-\overset{\overset{CH_3}{|}}{CH}-CH_2-\overset{\overset{CH_3}{|}}{C}=CH_2}}$$

$$\underset{\text{1, 3-Cyclopentadiene}}{\begin{array}{c} H-C \text{———} C-H \\ \|\,(2)\ (3)\,\| \\ H-\overset{}{C}\,(1)\ (4)\,C-H \\ \diagdown\,(5)\,\diagup \\ C \\ H_2 \end{array}}$$

Exercise 3.1   Draw three different structures for C_5H_{10} in which the continuous chain is four carbons long. Name each compound according to IUPAC rules.

3.3   THE DOUBLE BOND

A double bond represents two pairs, or four electrons shared between two carbon atoms. Although our simple structural formulas show these as two equivalent covalent bonds, actually they are not. As described in Section 1.5, each carbon atom on promotion of a

$2s$ electron to a higher energy $2p$ orbital has available for bonding more than the two electrons ordinarily found in the $2p$ orbitals. You have learned that when one of the $2s$ electrons hybridizes with three $2p$ orbitals, four sp^3 hybridized orbitals result. However, if hybridization takes place with only two $2p$ orbitals, then three sp^2 hybrid orbitals are formed and one $2p$ orbital is left. This is the situation for each carbon atom in ethene. The three sp^2 orbitals formed all lie in the same plane and tend to form angles of 120° with each other. The remaining p electron of each carbon is brought into an orbital perpendicular to the plane of the molecule. Here the electrons overlap and encompass both carbon nuclei by circulating as a cloud above and below the plane of the molecule to form the fourth bond (Figs. 3.1 and 3.2). A bond formed in this manner is called a **pi** (π) bond, to distinguish it from the ordinary covalent or **sigma** (σ) bond. A double bond is, therefore, made up of one sigma C—C bond and one pi C—C bond.

■□FIGURE 3.1

THE π-BOND OF ETHENE IN PERSPECTIVE.

■□FIGURE 3.2

END VIEW OF THE ETHENE MOLECULE.

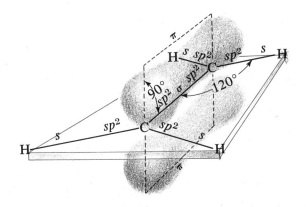

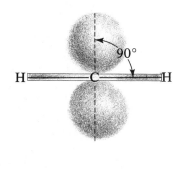

The effect of such double bonding is threefold. One is that two carbon atoms are nearer each other when joined by a double bond than when joined by a single bond; the distance between two doubly-bonded carbon atoms is 1.34 Å compared to 1.54 Å for the C—C single bond. Second, carbon atoms doubly-bonded and the atoms attached to them are now held more or less rigidly *in the same plane*. Free rotation around the bond joining the two carbon atoms is no longer possible, because considerable energy is required to break the *pi* bond. This restriction in a plane bestows upon the double bond a kind of flatness, and the molecule at this site has an upper and lower side. A variation in the space arrangements of groups attached to the carbon atoms makes possible a type of isomerism called **cis** and **trans,** or **geometrical isomerism** (Sec. 6.2). The *cis* isomer has like groups on the same side of the molecule and the *trans* isomer has like groups on opposite sides of the molecule (Figs. 3.3, 3.4, 3.5). Thus, beginning with C_4H_8, a greater number of isomers is possible for any member of the olefin family than was possible for the corresponding alkane, C_4H_{10}, not simply because the position of the double bond in the carbon chain may vary, but also because the groups attached to it may be *cis* or *trans*.

■□FIGURE 3.3

STRUCTURAL REPRESENTATION OF *trans*-2-BUTENE.

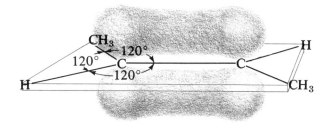

■□FIGURE 3.4

STRUCTURAL REPRESENTATION OF *cis*-2-BUTENE.

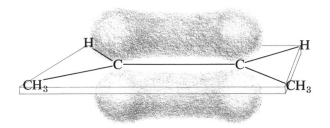

A third effect manifest in doubly-bonded carbon compounds is that the *pi* electrons are not as firmly held as those comprising the sigma bond, but are more mobile and readily available to an electrophilic (electron-seeking) reagent. This mobility on the part of *pi* electrons accounts for the greater reactivity of the olefins when compared to that of the paraffins, or alkanes.

■□FIGURE 3.5

STRUCTURAL REPRESENTATION OF 1-BUTENE. (*Cis-trans* ISOMERISM NOT POSSIBLE.)

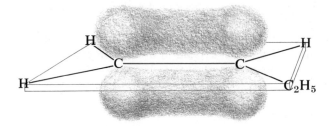

Exercise 3.2   Draw three different structures for C_5H_{10} in which the continuous chain is five carbons long. Name each according to IUPAC rules.

Preparation of the Alkenes

The double bond usually is introduced into a molecule by some type of **elimination reaction** in which groups or atoms are removed from two adjacent carbons.

$$-\overset{|}{\underset{|}{C}}-\overset{|}{\underset{|}{C}}- \rightarrow AB + -\overset{|}{C}=\overset{|}{C}-$$
$$AB$$

In the petroleum industry the elimination of hydrogen atoms from an alkane is accomplished by pyrolysis (Sec. 5.5). Both continuous and branched chain olefins are produced by this cracking process. In a laboratory preparation of an olefin the double bond usually is introduced by eliminating a small molecule such as water, hydrogen halide, or ammonia. Such elimination reactions usually are catalyzed by ions such as H^+, for the removal of water, and OH^-, for the elimination of hydrogen halide, but the double bond also may result from the pyrolytic decomposition of certain ammonium salts (Sec. 13.5-B). Many reactions of both types are known, but we shall consider here only two of the most general procedures for the preparation of olefins.

DEHYDRATION OF ALCOHOLS

Elimination of the elements of water from adjacent carbon atoms of an alcohol will lead to the formation of an olefin. Industrially, water is eliminated from an alcohol by passing the alcohol vapor over heated alumina, Al_2O_3.

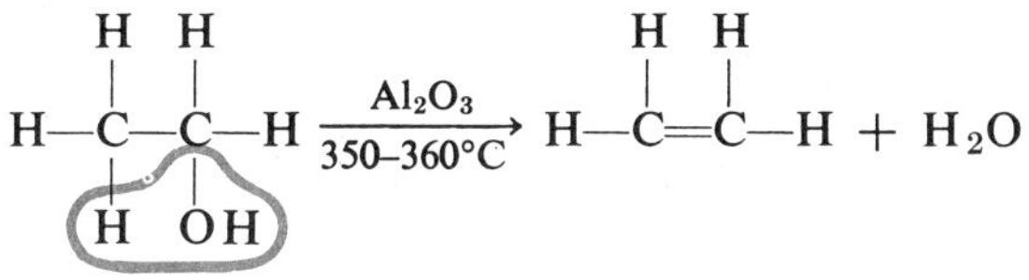

$$H-\underset{\underset{H}{|}}{\overset{\overset{H}{|}}{C}}-\underset{\underset{OH}{|}}{\overset{\overset{H}{|}}{C}}-H \xrightarrow[350-360°C]{Al_2O_3} H-\overset{\overset{H}{|}}{C}=\overset{\overset{H}{|}}{C}-H + H_2O$$

Ethyl alcohol   Ethene

In the laboratory, dehydration of an alcohol usually is accomplished by heating it either with concentrated sulfuric or phosphoric acid. The reaction is thought to take place in the following manner. In the first stage of the reaction, the acid (shown here as the hydrogen ion) protonates the electron-rich hydroxyl group of the alcohol molecule to form an alkyl substituted oxonium ion.[1]

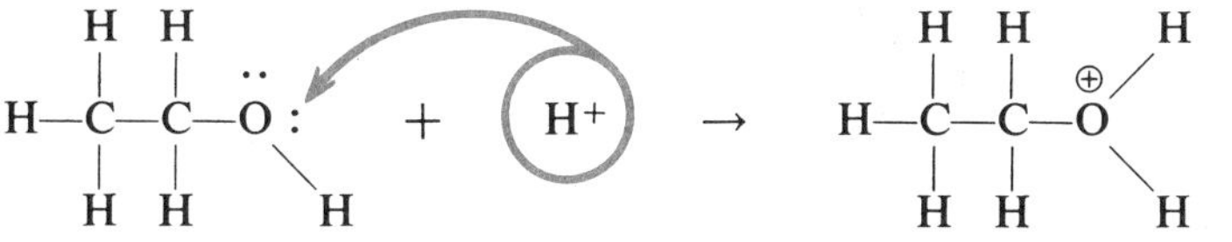

$$H-\underset{\underset{H}{|}}{\overset{\overset{H}{|}}{C}}-\underset{\underset{H}{|}}{\overset{\overset{H}{|}}{C}}-\overset{..}{O}: \quad + \quad H^+ \quad \rightarrow \quad H-\underset{\underset{H}{|}}{\overset{\overset{H}{|}}{C}}-\underset{\underset{H}{|}}{\overset{\overset{H}{|}}{C}}-\overset{\oplus}{O}\diagdown_H^H$$

An alkyl oxonium ion

Next, the protonated alcohol dissociates into water and a carbonium ion.[2]

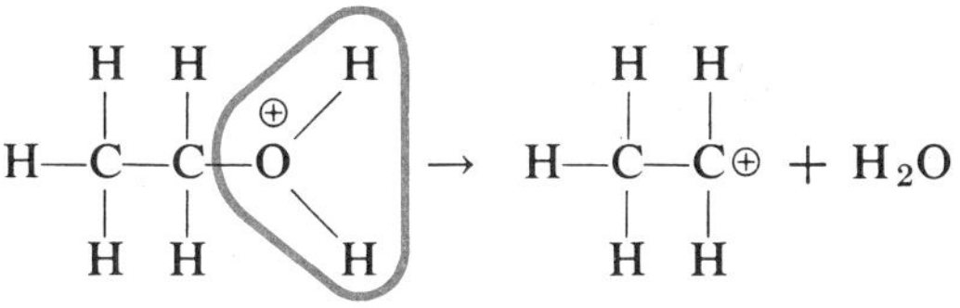

$$H-\underset{\underset{H}{|}}{\overset{\overset{H}{|}}{C}}-\underset{\underset{H}{|}}{\overset{\overset{H}{|}}{C}}-\overset{\oplus}{O}\diagdown_H^H \quad \rightarrow \quad H-\underset{\underset{H}{|}}{\overset{\overset{H}{|}}{C}}-\underset{\underset{H}{|}}{\overset{\overset{H}{|}}{C}}\oplus + H_2O$$

Carbonium ion

[1] A positively charged species in which the charge may be considered to reside on an oxygen atom.

[2] A positively charged species in which the charge may be considered to reside on a carbon atom.

In the last phase of the reaction a proton, H^+, is eliminated from the carbon atom adjacent to the one bearing the positive charge. The elimination of the proton is accompanied by a simultaneous shift of the electron pair.

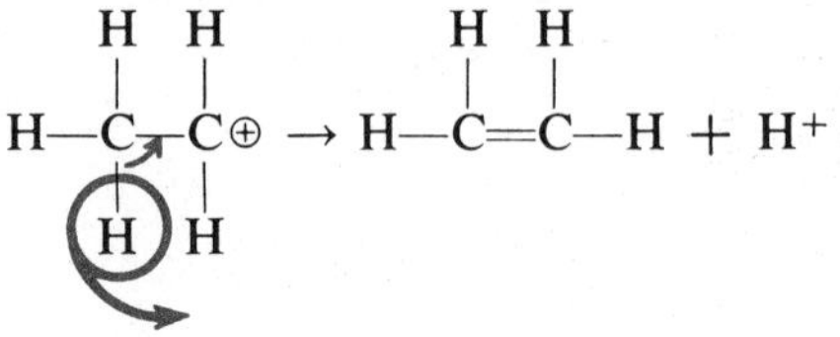

$$H-\underset{\underset{H}{|}}{\overset{\overset{H}{|}}{C}}-\underset{H}{\overset{\overset{H}{|}}{C}}\oplus \rightarrow H-\underset{}{\overset{\overset{H}{|}}{C}}=\underset{}{\overset{\overset{H}{|}}{C}}-H + H^+$$

From these equations it would appear that the acid need be present only in catalytic amounts. Actually, the powerful desiccating action of sulfuric acid takes up the water eliminated from the alcohol. Removal of the water and the volatility of the alkene are both factors that favor the equilibrium to the right. Unless removed, the olefin could react with sulfuric acid to reform the alcohol as illustrated in Sec. 3.9-C. The net effect of heating an alcohol with sulfuric acid may be shown by the following equation for the over-all reaction.

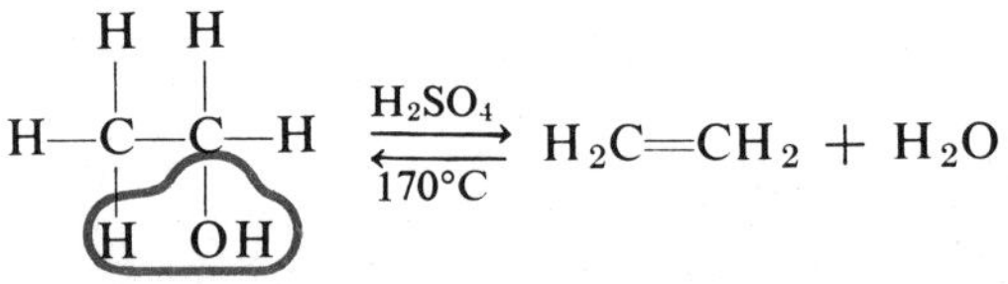

$$H-\underset{\underset{H}{|}}{\overset{\overset{H}{|}}{C}}-\underset{OH}{\overset{\overset{H}{|}}{C}}-H \xrightleftharpoons[170°C]{H_2SO_4} H_2C{=}CH_2 + H_2O$$

Ethanol   Ethene

Cyclohexene may be prepared from the cyclic alcohol, cyclohexanol, in a similar manner.

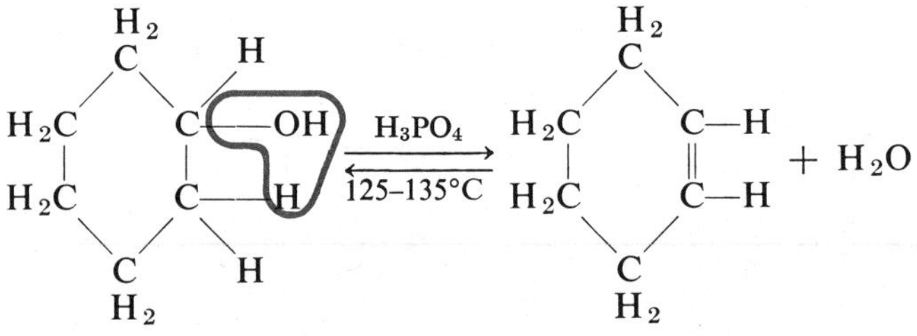

Cyclohexanol   Cyclohexene

DEHYDROHALOGENATION OF ALKYL HALIDES

The elimination of the elements of hydrogen halide (HX) from adjacent carbons is called **dehydrohalogenation.** This reaction is another common method that leads to the preparation of an olefin.

$$\underset{\text{Bromoethane}}{\overset{\displaystyle \overset{H}{\underset{\displaystyle \boxed{H \quad Br}}{\overset{|}{C}}} \overset{H}{\overset{|}{\underset{|}{C}}}}{H-C-C-H}} + KOH \xrightarrow[\text{solution}]{\text{Alcoholic}} \underset{\text{Ethene}}{H-\overset{H}{\overset{|}{C}}=\overset{H}{\overset{|}{C}}-H} + KBr + H_2O$$

Inasmuch as the alkyl halides are insoluble in water, the dehydrohalogenation usually is carried out in a concentrated solution of potassium hydroxide in alcohol. The elimination of hydrogen halide appears to take place in the following manner.

Hydrogen (as a proton) is removed from the β carbon[3] atom by a strong base (shown in the equation as the hydroxide ion). At the same time, the halogen on the α carbon atom moves off as a halide ion assisted by its attraction to the solvent (alcohol) molecules. This migration is accompanied by a simultaneous shifting of an electron pair.

$$\text{OH}^- \qquad H-\overset{H}{\underset{\underset{\displaystyle H \; Br}{\beta| \quad \alpha}}{\overset{|}{C}}}-\overset{H}{\overset{|}{C}}-H \xrightarrow{\;C_2H_5OH\;} H-\overset{H}{\overset{|}{C}}=\overset{H}{\overset{|}{C}}-H + Br^- + H_2O$$

Dehydrohalogenation is thus a concerted reaction in which the carbon-hydrogen and the carbon-halogen σ bonds are broken at the same time the new carbon-carbon π bond is formed.

When either of two β carbon atoms can supply the hydrogen to be eliminated with the halogen atom, obviously two isomeric olefins are possible. If such is the case and a choice of hydrogen atoms is offered, tertiary hydrogen is removed more readily than secondary, and secondary hydrogen more readily than primary. The alkene most likely to result will be the more stable one. This appears to be the one with the greater number of alkyl groups attached to the doubly-bonded carbons. Thus, for example, two olefins are possible when 2-bromobutane is heated with alcoholic potassium hydroxide, but the amount of one isomer produced exceeds that of the other in a ratio of 4:1.

---

[3]The carbon atom bonded to the functional group (halogen in the above example) is designated α, adjacent carbons β, next γ, etc.

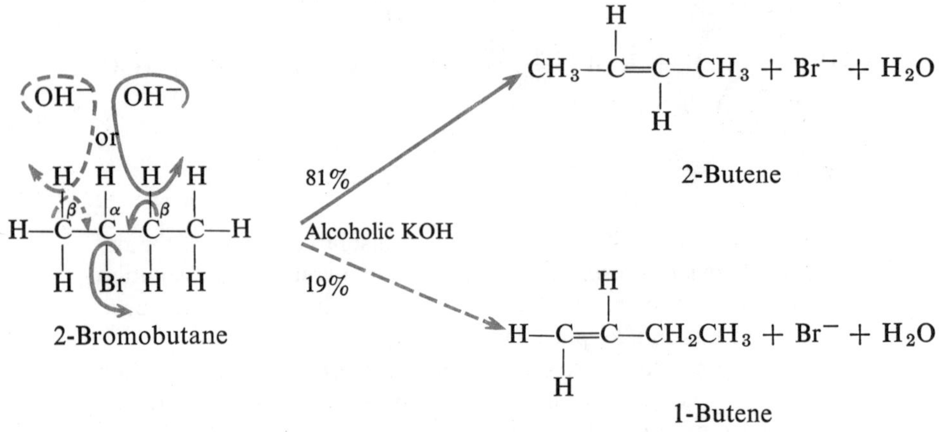

$$CH_3-\overset{\overset{\displaystyle H}{|}}{C}=\overset{\overset{\displaystyle}{|}}{C}-CH_3 + Br^- + H_2O$$

2-Butene

81%

Alcoholic KOH

19%

$$H-\overset{\overset{\displaystyle H}{|}}{C}=\overset{\overset{\displaystyle}{|}}{C}-CH_2CH_3 + Br^- + H_2O$$

1-Butene

(OH⁻) (OH⁻)
or

$$\overset{H}{\underset{H}{{}^{\beta}}}\ \overset{H}{\underset{Br}{{}^{\alpha}}}\ \overset{H}{\underset{H}{{}^{\beta}}}\ \overset{H}{\underset{H}{{}}}$$
H—C—C—C—C—H
  H Br H H

2-Bromobutane

Exercise 3.3   Two isomeric olefins are produced when 2-chloro-2-methylbutane is heated with alcoholic KOH. The yield of one is 86%, the other 14%. Give the name and structure of the isomer produced in greater amount.

3.6   PROPERTIES OF THE ALKENES

The physical properties of the alkenes are not too unlike those of the corresponding alkanes. The lower members of the alkene series are gases while the higher members are liquids and solids. The alkenes have slightly higher densities than the alkanes (Table 3.1).

Reactions of the Alkenes

The chemical behavior most characteristic of the alkenes is the ability to form derivatives by addition to the double bond.

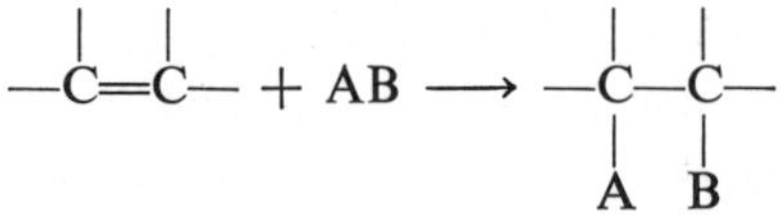

$$-\overset{|}{C}=\overset{|}{C}- + AB \longrightarrow -\overset{|}{\underset{|}{C}}-\overset{|}{\underset{|}{C}}-$$
$$A\ B$$

In such reactions the addition of hydrogen, the halogens (Cl_2, Br_2, I_2), the halogen acids (HCl, HBr), the hypohalous acids (HOCl, HOBr), sulfuric acid, and water all result in the formation

□■ TABLE 3.1

PHYSICAL CONSTANTS OF THE ALKENES

Name	Formula	M.P., °C	B.P., °C	Density as liquid
Ethene	$H_2C{=}CH_2$	−169.4	−103.8	0.566
Propene	$CH_3CH{=}CH_2$	−185.2	−47.7	0.609
1-Butene	$CH_3CH_2CH{=}CH_2$	−130	−6.5	0.625
2-Butene	$CH_3CH{=}CHCH_3$	−127	1.4	0.630
2-Methylpropene (Isobutylene)	$CH_3{-}\overset{\displaystyle CH_3}{\underset{\displaystyle \vert}{C}}{=}CH_2$	−140.7	−6.9	0.594
1, 3-Butadiene	$CH_2{=}CH{-}CH{=}CH_2$	−113	−4.5	0.650
2-Methyl-1, 3-butadiene (Isoprene)	$CH_2{=}\overset{\displaystyle CH_3}{\underset{\displaystyle \vert}{C}}{-}CH{=}CH_2$	−120	35	0.681
1-Pentene	$CH_2{=}CH(CH_2)_2CH_3$	−138	30.1	0.641
1-Hexene	$CH_2{=}CH(CH_2)_3CH_3$	−141	64.1	0.673

of saturated compounds. In such reactions the *pi* bond plays the role of an electron pair donor. The principal reactions of the alkenes are discussed in the following sections.

3.7   ADDITION OF HYDROGEN

Hydrogenation.   Olefins add hydrogen under pressure and in the presence of a catalyst to produce saturated hydrocarbons.

$$\underset{\text{Ethene}}{H{-}\overset{\displaystyle\overset{H}{\vert}}{C}{=}\overset{\displaystyle\overset{H}{\vert}}{C}{-}H} + H_2 \xrightarrow[\text{Pressure, heat}]{\text{Ni}} \underset{\text{Ethane}}{H{-}\overset{\displaystyle\overset{H}{\vert}}{\underset{\displaystyle\underset{H}{\vert}}{C}}{-}\overset{\displaystyle\overset{H}{\vert}}{\underset{\displaystyle\underset{H}{\vert}}{C}}{-}H}$$

A hydrogenation carried out in this manner is called **catalytic hydrogenation.** Without a catalyst the rate of hydrogenation is negligible even though the addition of hydrogen to the double bond is an exothermic reaction. The function of the catalyst appears to be that of providing a common ground on which the hydrogen and the double bond can meet. Both hydrogen atoms add simultaneously to the double bond and from the same side — that is, either from above or from below the plane of the molecule. This mode of

■ □ FIGURE 3.6

SCHEMATIC REPRESENTATION OF THE HYDROGENATION OF
1, 2-DIMETHYLCYCLOPENTENE.

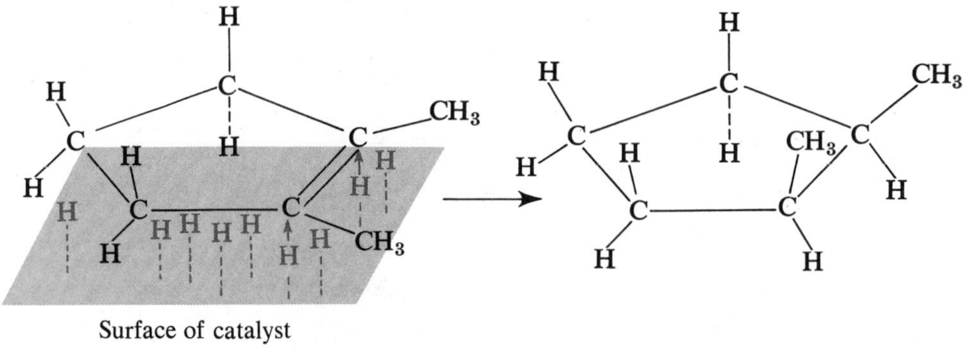

Surface of catalyst

1,2-Dimethylcyclopentene   *cis*-1,2-Dimethylcyclopentane

addition is called *cis* addition and results in the formation of only
the *cis*-isomer if isomeric products are possible. For example, the
hydrogenation of 1, 2-dimethylcyclopentene yields only *cis*-1, 2-
dimethylcyclopentane.

The best catalysts for hydrogenation of unsaturated compounds
are palladium and platinum. Nickel catalysts are also good (and
less expensive), but temperatures higher than those needed with
palladium and platinum are sometimes necessary.

Hydrogenation of unsaturated compounds is a useful and a
commonly employed reaction and one that has a number of important industrial applications. One of these is the hydrogenation of
highly unsaturated liquid vegetable oils to solid, butterlike fats
called **margarines.**

3.8   ADDITION OF HALOGENS

A.   Bromination.   An olefin, when treated with bromine, adds
the halogen across the double bond to place one bromine atom on
each carbon. The olefin usually is added to a carbon tetrachloride
solution of bromine. The reddish color of bromine in carbon tetrachloride disappears as the bromine adds to the olefin. The reaction
thus is a test reaction if the presence of the double bond in an unknown compound is suspected. The mechanism by which bromine
adds to ethene may be explained as follows.

Ethene, although a nonpolar molecule, may, because of the
mobility of the π electrons, cause a polarization of the bromine
molecule — that is, a displacement of the pair of electrons joining the

bromine atoms toward one of the atoms. One bromine with six electrons is abstracted by the *pi* electrons of ethene to produce a positively charged intermediate which may be either a carbonium ion, (a) or (c), or a bromonium ion, (b).

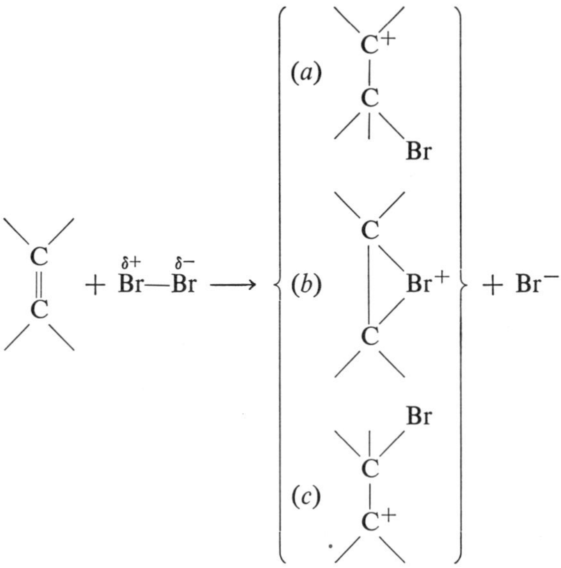

The negative bromide ion then combines with the positively charged intermediate. Experimental studies show that the bromide ion approaches from a direction most remote from the bromine already bonded. The existence of the intermediate bromonium ion or the carbonium ion has been established by the fact that addition of bromine to an olefin in the presence of other negative ions results in a mixture of products.

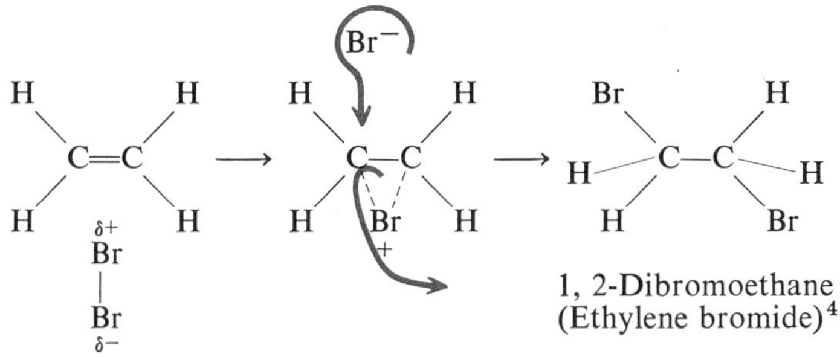

1, 2-Dibromoethane
(Ethylene bromide)[4]

[4]The ethylene group is —C—C—. It would be redundant to say ethylene dibromide.

$$\underset{H}{\overset{H}{\diagdown}}C=C\underset{H}{\overset{H}{\diagup}} + 2\,Br_2 + Cl^- \longrightarrow \underset{Br}{\overset{H}{\diagup}}H\diagdown C-C\diagup\overset{Br}{\underset{H}{\diagdown}}H + \underset{Br}{\overset{H}{\diagup}}H\diagdown C-C\diagup\overset{Cl}{\underset{H}{\diagdown}}H + Br^-$$

1-Bromo-2-chloroethane

This mode of addition is called *trans*-addition and gives the *trans* isomer when isomeric products are possible. The *trans* addition of bromine to the double bond of cyclopentene is illustrated schematically in the following drawings.

■☐FIGURE 3.7

SCHEMATIC REPRESENTATION OF THE BROMINATION OF CYCLOPENTENE.

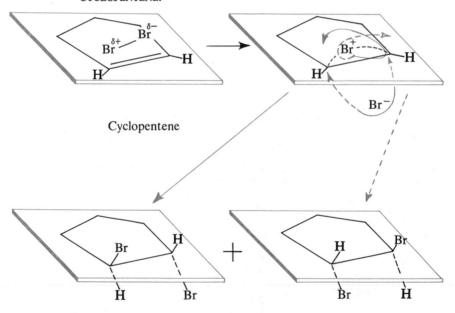

Cyclopentene

trans-1,2-Dibromocyclopentane

Exercise 3.4   A liquid hydrocarbon whose molecular formula was determined to be C_6H_{12} was shaken with bromine-carbon tetrachloride solution without any noticeable result. To what class of compounds does this hydrocarbon belong?

3.9   ADDITION OF ACIDS TO UNSYMMETRICAL OLEFINS
(*Markovnikov's Rule.*)

A.   Addition of Hydrogen Halide.   Hydrogen halides add readily to olefins to produce alkyl halides, R–X. Thus, hydrogen bromide adds to ethene to produce ethyl bromide according to the following equation.

$$
\begin{array}{ccc}
\text{H} & \text{H} & \\
| & | & \\
\text{H—C=C—H} + \text{HBr} & \longrightarrow & \text{H—C—C—Br} \\
\end{array}
$$

Ethene   Ethyl bromide

In this particular reaction there is only one way in which the halogen acid can add across the double bond and therefore only one product is obtainable. This is not the case with an unsymmetrical olefin in which the groups bonded to the unsaturated carbon atoms are different. For example, hydrogen bromide adds to propene to produce *mainly* isopropyl bromide.

Propene   2-Bromopropane
(Isopropyl bromide)
B.P. 59.4°

Note that in this reaction the bromide ion seeks the central rather than the terminal carbon atom. The Russian chemist Markovnikov in 1871 formulated an empirical rule regarding this mode of addition. The rule simply states: *"In the addition of acids to unsymmetrical olefins, the negative portion of the species added will seek the carbon atom holding the fewer hydrogen atoms."* Alkyl groups (especially methyl) appear to be electron donors and in an unsymmetrical olefin such as propene the π electrons are shifted in a direction *away from the alkyl group.* The positive portion of the addend (hydrogen ion) seeks the center of highest electron density which, in this case, is the end carbon atom. The positive charge of the hydrogen ion is conferred upon the central carbon atom, to give a carbonium ion which then becomes neutralized by the negative bromide ion.

Inasmuch as the stability of a carbonium ion has been found to increase with the number of alkyl substituents on it, the secondary carbonium ion with two methyl groups on it is formed as an intermediate more readily than the primary carbonium ion bearing only one ethyl group.

$$CH_3\overset{H}{\underset{+}{\overset{|}{C}}}CH_3 \qquad\qquad CH_3CH_2\overset{H}{\underset{H}{\overset{|}{\underset{|}{C^+}}}}$$

A secondary   A primary
carbonium ion   carbonium ion

Markovnikov's rule can thus be rationalized in terms of energy relationships and stabilities, and the products of an acid addition to olefins predicted with a high degree of accuracy. However, a phenomenon which puzzled chemists for many years was that in some instances hydrogen bromide molecules added to an olefin in an *anti*-Markovnikov manner. This mystery was finally resolved by Professors Kharasch and Mayo of the University of Chicago who in 1933 discovered that the presence of peroxides in the reaction mixture would reverse the Markovnikov mode of addition. Obviously, the manner in which the HBr molecule adds to the double bond in this case is not like that according to Markovnikov's Rule. The *anti*-Markovnikov mode of addition of HBr was explainable in terms of a free radical mechanism. Indicating the peroxide involved simply as R—O : O—R, we may show the different steps in the "peroxide effect" as follows:

$$R-O\,\text{:}\,O-R \longrightarrow 2\,R-O\,\cdot$$

$$R-O\,\cdot + HBr \longrightarrow R-OH + Br\,\cdot$$

$$CH_3-\overset{H}{\underset{}{\overset{|}{C}}}=\overset{H}{\underset{}{\overset{|}{C}}}-H + \cdot Br \longrightarrow CH_3-\overset{H}{\underset{\cdot}{\overset{|}{C}}}-\overset{H}{\underset{H}{\overset{|}{C}}}-Br$$

Propene

$$CH_3-\overset{H}{\underset{\cdot}{\overset{|}{C}}}-\overset{H}{\underset{H}{\overset{|}{C}}}-Br + HBr \longrightarrow CH_3CH_2CH_2Br$$

1-Bromopropene
(*n*-Propyl bromide)
B.P. 71°

The relative stabilities of free radicals, we see, parallels that of carbonium ions, namely, *tertiary* > *secondary* > *primary*.

The peroxide-catalyzed addition of hydrogen halide to an olefin, while a useful reaction, unfortunately works only with hydrogen bromide.

Exercise 3.5   Two alkyl halides are possible when isobutylene, $(CH_3)_2C$=CH_2, is treated with HBr. Which one will predominate? Why?

B.   Addition of Hypohalous Acids.   Markovnikov's rule may be extended to cover the addition of other acids. The addition of chlorine or bromine to an olefin, when carried out in the presence of water, has the net result of adding a hypohalous acid, HOX. The reaction results in the formation of *halohydrins*. Halohydrins have a hydroxyl group and a halogen atom on adjacent carbons. The addition of an aqueous solution of chlorine to propene produces propylene chlorohydrin.

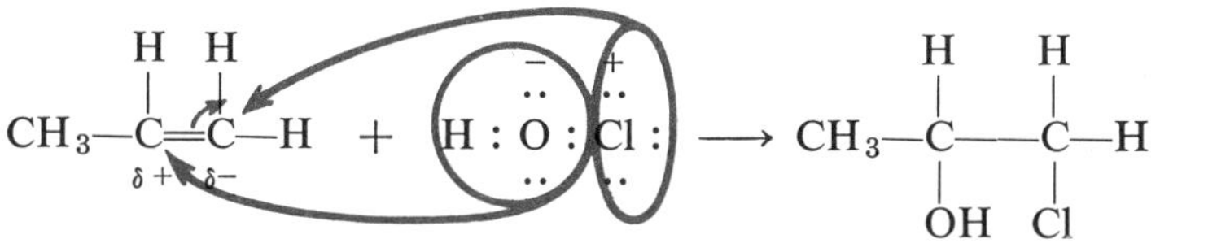

Propene   1-Chloro-2-propanol
                                           (Propylene chlorohydrin)

In this addition, you will note, chlorine is the positive part of the species added.

C.   Addition of Sulfuric Acid (Hydration of Olefins).   Olefins react with sulfuric acid to produce alkyl hydrogen sulfates which, on hydrolysis, yield alcohols. Hydration (addition of water) of an olefin is thus accomplished indirectly in this manner and is an important commercial process for the preparation of alcohols from petroleum products.

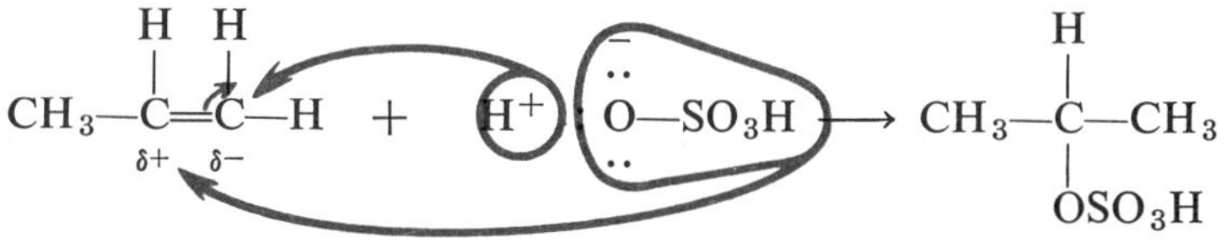

                                           Isopropyl
                                           hydrogen sulfate

$$CH_3-\underset{\underset{OSO_3H}{|}}{\overset{\overset{H}{|}}{C}}-CH_3 + O-H \longrightarrow CH_3-\underset{\underset{OH}{|}}{\overset{\overset{H}{|}}{C}}-CH_3 + H_2SO_4$$

2-Propanol
(Isopropyl alcohol)

3.10   OXIDATION

A.   The Baeyer Test.   Olefins, when oxidized with cold dilute potassium permanganate, form glycols.   In the absence of other easily oxidizable groups (which also react with $KMnO_4$), this reaction serves as an easily recognizable test for olefins because as the oxidant is consumed its bright purple color disappears.   The reaction is the basis for the Baeyer Test for unsaturation.

$$3H-\overset{\overset{H}{|}}{C}=\overset{\overset{H}{|}}{C}-H + 2KMnO_4 + 4H_2O \rightarrow 3H-\underset{\underset{OH}{|}}{\overset{\overset{H}{|}}{C}}-\underset{\underset{OH}{|}}{\overset{\overset{H}{|}}{C}}-H + 2MnO_2 + 2KOH$$

1, 2-Ethanediol
(Ethylene glycol)

B.   Oxidation with Rupture of the Double Bond.   Vigorous oxidation of an olefin with potassium permanganate at elevated temperatures results in a cleavage of the double bond.   The glycol intermediate formed is destroyed and each of the carbon atoms which comprised the carbon-carbon double bond becomes completely oxidized.   A terminal doubly-bonded carbon is oxidized by this treatment to CO_2, a doubly-bonded carbon atom bearing one alkyl group is oxidized to the carboxyl group $\left(-C\overset{\overset{O}{\parallel}}{\underset{OH}{\diagdown}}\right)$, and one bearing two alkyl groups is oxidized to the carbonyl group, $\left(\diagdown C=O\right)$.

$$3\,CH_3-\underset{\underset{CH_3}{|}}{C}=CH_2 + 8\,KMnO_4 \longrightarrow 3\,CH_3-\underset{\underset{CH_3}{|}}{C}=O + 3\,K_2CO_3$$

Isobutylene   Acetone

$+\ 8\,MnO_2 + 2\,KOH + 2\,H_2O$

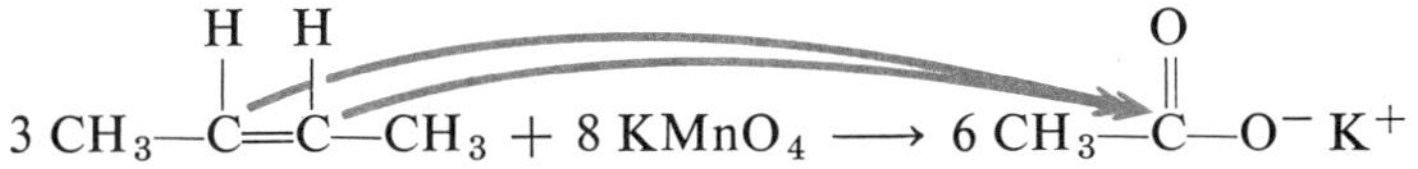

$$3 \, CH_3\!-\!\overset{\displaystyle H}{\underset{\displaystyle |}{C}}\!=\!\overset{\displaystyle H}{\underset{\displaystyle |}{C}}\!-\!CH_3 + 8 \, KMnO_4 \longrightarrow 6 \, CH_3\!-\!\overset{\displaystyle O}{\overset{\displaystyle \|}{C}}\!-\!O^- K^+$$

2-Butene   Potassium acetate

$$+ \, 8 \, MnO_2 + 2 \, KOH + 2 \, H_2O$$

C.   Oxidation with Ozone (O₃).   Most alkenes react with ozone to form cyclic peroxide intermediates called **ozonides.** Ozonides are explosive compounds and thus are not isolated but are directly decomposed with water and zinc metal. The **ozonolysis** of an olefin yields two products, each with a doubly-bonded oxygen where originally the doubly-bonded carbon atom had been. Examination of the reaction products thus establishes the location of the double bond. The ozonolysis reaction has its greatest value as a diagnostic procedure, not as a preparative one.

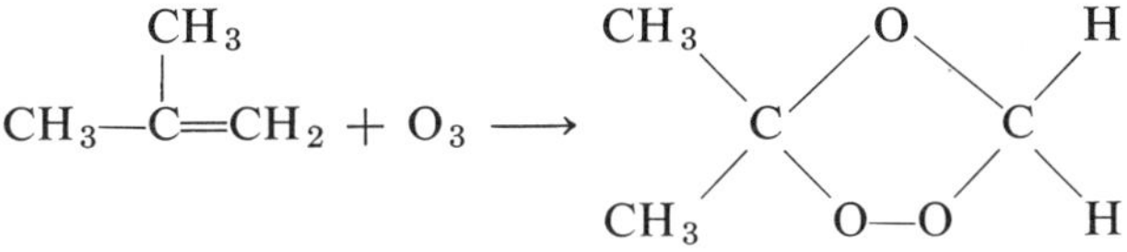

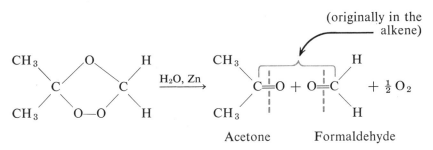

2-Methylpropene   An ozonide
(Isobutylene)

Acetone   Formaldehyde

3.11   POLYMERIZATION

Many simple olefinic substances may undergo self-addition to form huge molecules composed of many basic units. Such high molecular weight structures are called **polymers** (Gr., *poly,* many;

meros, part), and the reaction by which they are formed is called **polymerization.** Polyethylene, polypropylene, Teflon (Sec. 7.4), Orlon (Sec. 3.18), and synthetic rubbers (Sec. 3.21) are examples of familiar polymeric products formed in this manner. One type of polymerization reaction can be initiated by a free radical. The free radical often produced from peroxide, R—O—O—R, combines in the first step with a monomer, that is, with one molecule of the olefin to produce a new free radical. The chain continues to grow by repeated free radical formation. The following series of reactions illustrate the *initiation, propagation,* and *termination* steps in the free radical polymerization of ethylene.

Initiation: Free radicals are produced by an initiator.

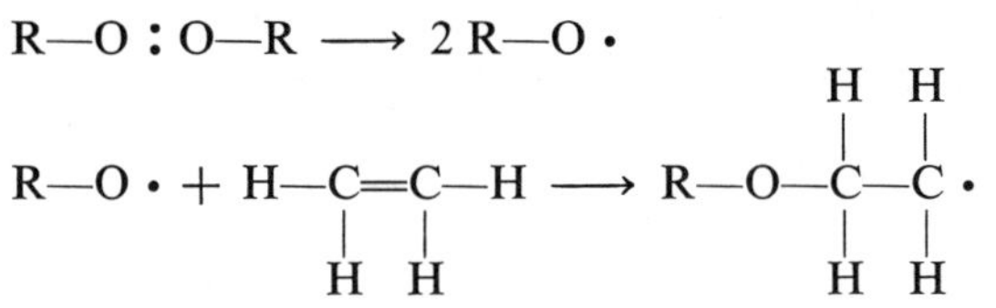

$$\text{R—O}:\text{O—R} \longrightarrow 2\,\text{R—O}\cdot$$

$$\text{R—O}\cdot + \text{H—C}{=}\text{C—H} \longrightarrow \text{R—O—C—C}\cdot$$

Ethylene

Propagation: Continued addition of olefin produces a larger free radical.

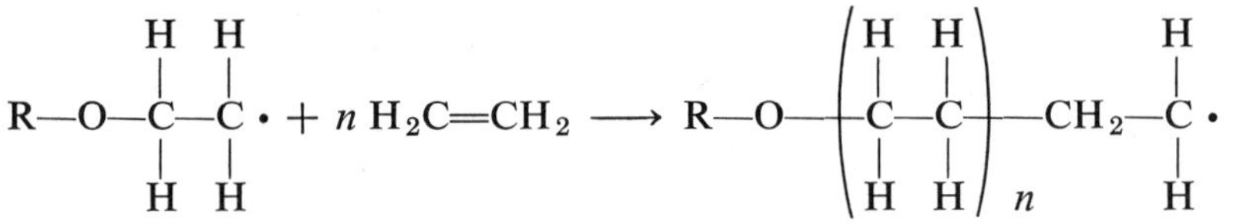

$$\text{R—O—C—C}\cdot + n\,\text{H}_2\text{C}{=}\text{CH}_2 \longrightarrow \text{R—O}\!\left(\!\text{C—C}\!\right)_{\!n}\!\text{—CH}_2\text{—C}\cdot$$

Termination: Two free radicals finally combine.

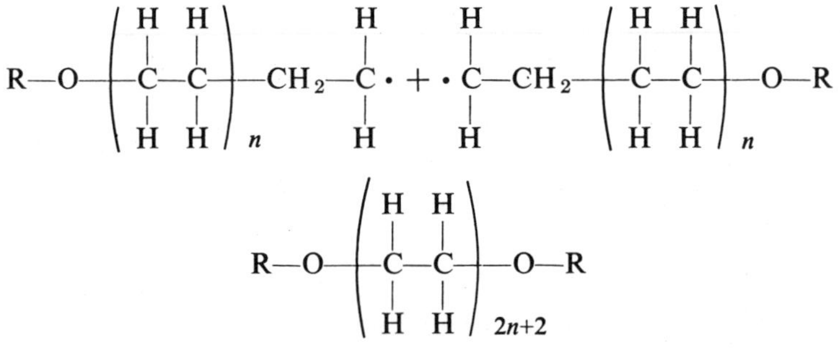

$$\text{R—O}\!\left(\!\text{C—C}\!\right)_{\!n}\!\text{—CH}_2\text{—C}\cdot + \cdot\text{C—CH}_2\!\left(\!\text{C—C}\!\right)_{\!n}\!\text{—O—R}$$

$$\text{R—O}\!\left(\!\text{C—C}\!\right)_{\!2n+2}\!\text{—O—R}$$

Polyethylene

Many polymeric products are tough, flexible, and unreactive to most chemical reagents. Some have a waxy feel and are insoluble in most solvents. Others, with excellent thermal and electric properties, are useful insulating materials. The simple olefins are used to make several polymeric products, as we have seen, but the double bond in many compounds other than the olefins is the functional group which makes possible a great number of wonderful polymeric products. Synthetic polymers of the type described not only have revolutionized the packaging industry and the textile industry but also have made possible the creation of new industries.

3 . 1 2   DIENES AND POLYENES

Extremely reactive functional groups often are a part of organic structures. One can be reasonably certain that *simple* compounds containing highly reactive centers do not occur naturally, but are synthetic products. This is the case with the lower members of the olefin series — ethene, propene, and the butenes. Aside from these simple structures, olefins occur widely in nature in a variety of complex forms. Isoprene, $CH_2=C(CH_3)-CH=CH_2$ (2-methyl-1, 3-butadiene), is a **diene** structure which occurs as the building unit in a number of natural products. Isoprene units appear over and over again in a class of natural compounds called the terpenes (Sec. 17.14). Common examples of the terpenes are camphor, rosin, turpentine, natural rubber, and the coloring matter of certain plants, including edible ones. In each of such natural products some multiple of the isoprene unit may be found. An excellent example, illustrating the repeated addition of isoprene units, is β-carotene, the yellow coloring matter of carrots.

β-Carotene

A system of alternate double and single bonds in a carbon chain such as that in β-carotene is called a **conjugated** system. The simplest conjugated system possible is 1, 3-butadiene. It also is one of the most important of the dienes for it is used in the production of synthetic rubber.

Contradictory as it may seem, a conjugated diene is more stable and at the same time more reactive than a simple olefin. The stability of a conjugated diene is inherent in its structure. For example, when we show 1, 3-butadiene as

$$
\begin{array}{cccc}
\text{H} & \text{H} & \text{H} & \text{H} \\
| & | & | & | \\
\text{H}-\text{C}&=&\text{C}-\text{C}&=&\text{C}-\text{H}
\end{array}
$$

we are showing its structure as if the two π bonds were independent of each other. Actually, they are not. If we redraw butadiene more nearly as it is, we can see that the electrons comprising the π bonds at each end of the molecule can migrate or delocalize to overlap also between carbons 2 and 3. Each pair of π electrons thus is attracted, not by two, but by all four carbon nuclei. The delocalization of the π electrons adds greatly to the stability of the molecule.

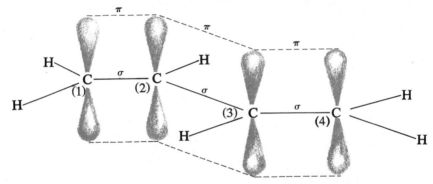

To illustrate the greater reactivity of butadiene we will redraw its structure as it might appear when the molecule is excited and then examine possible reactions of the compound with bromine.

(1) (2) (3) (4)

$$
\text{H}-\text{C}=\text{C}-\text{C}=\text{C}-\text{H} \longleftrightarrow \text{H}-\overset{..}{\text{C}}-\overset{+}{\text{C}}-\text{C}=\text{C}-\text{H} \xrightarrow{\text{Br}_2} \text{H}-\text{C}-\text{C}-\text{C}=\text{C}-\text{H}
$$

(I)

3, 4-Dibromo-1-butene

(1) (2) (3) (4)

$$
\text{H}-\text{C}=\text{C}-\text{C}=\text{C}-\text{H} \longleftrightarrow \text{H}-\overset{..}{\text{C}}-\text{C}=\text{C}-\overset{+}{\text{C}}-\text{H} \xrightarrow{\text{Br}_2} \text{H}-\text{C}-\text{C}=\text{C}-\text{C}-\text{H}
$$

(II)

trans-1, 4-Dibromo-2-butene

The addition of bromine to a structure such as (I) would yield 3, 4-dibromo-1-butene. Addition of bromine to a structure such as (II) would yield *trans*-1, 4-dibromo-2-butene. The mode of addition to structure I is called **1, 2-addition;** that to structure (II) is called **1, 4-addition.** The fact that a mixture of both products is obtained lends credibility to the mechanism as we have tried to show it.

When two or more electronic arrangements can be drawn for the same substance with no variation in the position of the atoms, as we have done here for the butadiene molecule, no single structure is likely to describe the substance accurately. Each of the structures shown is said to be a contributing structure and a double-headed arrow is shown between them to indicate that several structures better describe the substance than any one structure alone. There-fore, any formula used to represent such a substance is but one of a number contributing to a hybrid of them all. We refer to this state of affairs as **resonance** and call the butadiene molecule, in this case, **a resonance hybrid.** Resonance is an important concept in organic chemistry and, while not easy to interpret mathematically, goes far toward explaining phenomena that otherwise would be very difficult to understand.

Part II: The Acetylenes (Alkynes)

The acetylenes, or alkynes, are unsaturated hydrocarbons which contain a triple bond or three pairs of shared electrons be-tween adjacent carbon atoms. The general formula for an acetylene is C_nH_{2n-2} if only one triple bond is present in the structure. The same general formula fits that of an open chain diene. The first member of the alkyne family is acetylene itself, C_2H_2, the structure of which may be written

$$H—C\equiv C—H \quad \text{or} \quad H \overset{\times}{} C \overset{.}{.} \overset{.}{.} C \overset{\times}{} H$$

Exercise 3.7 Draw electronic representations for (a) CS_2 (b) HCN and (c) $BeCl_2$. In what respect are these structures like that of acetylene?

3.13   FORMULAS AND NOMENCLATURE

The acetylenes are named systematically by the same rules of nomenclature that were used to name the olefins. The triple bond is indicated by the suffix *yne* and is located by number in the longest chain which contains it. The alkyl derivatives of acetylene, in which one or both of the singly-bonded hydrogens of acetylene have been replaced by alkyl groups, are named simply as alkyl acetylenes. A few examples will help make this clear.

$$H—C≡C—H$$

Ethyne
(Acetylene)

$$CH_3—C≡C—H$$

Propyne
(Methylacetylene)

$$CH_3—C≡C—CH_3$$

2-Butyne
(Dimethylacetylene)

$$\overset{(1)}{CH_3}—\overset{(2)}{C}≡\overset{(3)}{C}—\overset{(4)}{CH_2}—\overset{(5)}{CH_3}$$

2-Pentyne
(Methylethylacetylene)

$$\overset{(5)}{CH_3}—\overset{(4)}{CH_2}—\overset{(3)}{CH}—\overset{(2)}{C}≡\overset{(1)}{C}—H$$
$$|$$
$$CH_3$$

3-Methyl-1-pentyne
(*sec*-Butylacetylene)

$$\overset{(4)}{CH_2}=\overset{(3)}{CH}—\overset{(2)}{C}≡\overset{(1)}{C}—H$$

3-Butene-1-yne
(Vinylacetylene)[5]

3.14   THE CARBON–CARBON TRIPLE BOND

Carbon atoms attached to only two other atoms hybridize one *s* and one *p* orbital to give two *sp* orbitals. These form the sigma bonds and leave two *p* orbitals at right angles to each other to form π bonds. Now, instead of a planar structure as in the case of the

■☐FIGURE 3 . 6

SCHEMATIC REPRESENTATIONS OF ACETYLENE.

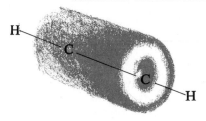

[5]$H—\overset{H}{\overset{|}{C}}=\overset{H}{\overset{|}{C}}$—is the vinyl group. E.g., $H—\overset{H}{\overset{|}{C}}=\overset{H}{\overset{|}{C}}—Cl$ is vinyl chloride.

olefins with a cloud of electrons above and below the plane of the molecule, we have a linear structure with not only a cloud above and below, but in front and behind the axis as well. Here the π electrons overlap and blend into a cylindrical sleeve about the axis of the molecule (Fig. 3.6).

3.15   OCCURRENCE AND PROPERTIES OF THE ACETYLENES

The acetylenes are somewhat more reactive than the olefins and, generally, are not to be found as natural products. Although the lower molecular weight members are not found in nature, the triple bond does occur as a structural feature in some natural substances. An example is the antibiotic *mycomycin*, which has the remarkable structure

$$
\begin{array}{c}
\quad\quad\;\; H \quad\;\; H\; H\; H\; H\; H\; H \quad\quad O \\
\quad\quad\;\; | \quad\;\;\; |\; |\; |\; |\; |\; | \quad\quad \nearrow \\
H-C{\equiv}C-C{\equiv}C-C{=}C{=}C-C{=}C-C{=}C-CH-C \\
(13)\,(12)\,(11)\,(10)\,(9)\,\;(8)\;\;(7)\;\;(6)\;\;(5)\;\;(4)\;\;(3)\;\;(2)\;\;\;\,(1)\;\;\backslash \\
\quad\quad\quad\quad\quad\quad\quad\quad\quad\quad\quad\quad\quad\quad\quad\quad\quad OH
\end{array}
$$

Mycomycin

It has the rather impressive name **3, 5, 7, 8-tridecatetraene-10, 12-diynoic acid.** An unusual group of similar highly unsaturated, linear compounds are secreted by various species of fungi. These compounds are straight chain polyacetylenes of eight to fourteen carbon atoms in length with one or more oxygen-containing functional groups.

The chemical properties of the alkynes, with some exceptions, are very similar to those of the corresponding alkenes. The reactions are largely those of addition. One exception is notable, however. *Hydrogen bonded to an acetylenic carbon atom is acidic in character and can be replaced by certain metals to form salts.* Why should a hydrogen attached to a triple-bonded carbon be acidic? If you will consider the orbital hybridization of acetylene (Sec. 3.14) you will see that three pairs of electrons are confined between two carbon nuclei in the linear structure of an acetylenic bond. The repulsion against the single C—H electron pair is less than it would be in the tetrahedral arrangement of alkanes. The pair of electrons between the carbon and hydrogen thus can move a little closer to the carbon atom than it would be able to in a saturated hydrocarbon. As a result, the acetylenic hydrogen is left slightly more positive and easily removed by a strongly basic reagent.

Preparation of the Alkynes

The alkynes are prepared in the laboratory by reactions very much like those employed for the preparation of alkenes. Obviously, *two simple molecules* must be eliminated from adjacent carbons in a saturated compound in order to introduce the triple bond into the molecule.

3.16   PREPARATION OF ACETYLENE

Acetylene (ethyne), C_2H_2, is one of the most important of industrial organic raw materials. It may be prepared by reaction between calcium carbide and water. Calcium carbide is prepared by heating a mixture of coke and limestone in an electric furnace.

$$CaCO_3 \xrightarrow{\text{Heat}} CaO + CO_2$$

$$3\,C + CaO \xrightarrow{2000°C} CaC_2 + CO$$
$$\text{Calcium}$$
$$\text{carbide}$$

$$CaC_2 + 2\,H_2O \longrightarrow H\text{—}C\equiv C\text{—}H + Ca(OH)_2$$
Acetylene   Calcium
                   hydroxide

3.17   PREPARATION OF HIGHER ALKYNES

Higher members in the series may be prepared by one of two general methods: (1) elimination of two molecules of hydrogen halide from adjacent carbon atoms in a saturated compound, or (2) replacement of acetylenic hydrogen on an existing carbon atom by an alkyl group.

(a) **Elimination of Halogen Acid from *Vicinal* Dihalides.**[6]

$$\begin{array}{cc} \text{H} & \text{Br} \\ | & | \\ CH_3\text{—}C\text{—}C\text{—}H + KOH \\ | & | \\ \text{Br} & \text{H} \end{array} \xrightarrow[\text{solution}]{\text{Alcoholic}} \begin{array}{cc} \text{H} & \text{Br} \\ | & | \\ CH_3\text{—}C\text{=}C\text{—}H + KBr + H_2O \end{array}$$

1, 2-Dibromopropane   1-Bromo-1-propene
                                       (a vinyl halide)

[6]Vicinal (L., *vicinalis*, neighboring). Vicinal dihalides have halogen atoms on adjacent carbon atoms.

Notice that the product of the first HBr elimination is a substituted vinyl bromide. The vinyl halides are unreactive compounds and a stronger base ($NH_2{}^-$) is used to remove the second HBr molecule.

$$CH_3-\overset{\overset{\displaystyle H \quad Br}{|\qquad|}}{C}=C-H + NaNH_2 \longrightarrow CH_3-C\equiv C-H + NaBr + NH_3$$

Propyne
(Methylacetylene)

(b) Replacement of Acetylenic Hydrogen by an Alkyl Group.

The first step in this synthesis is the preparation of the sodium salt of acetylene by reaction with sodium metal. The sodium acetylide then is coupled with an alkyl halide.

$$2\ H-C\equiv C-H + 2\ Na \xrightarrow{\text{Liquid }NH_3} 2\ H-C\equiv C : {}^-Na^+ + H_2$$

Sodium acetylide

$$H-C\equiv C : {}^-Na^+ + C_2H_5I \longrightarrow H-C\equiv C-CH_2CH_3 + Na^+I^-$$

Ethyl iodide   1-Butyne

The second acidic hydrogen, if available, also may be replaced by repeating the process. An alkyne of known structure thus can be synthesized.

$$H-C\equiv C-CH_2CH_3 + Na \xrightarrow[\substack{NH_3}]{\text{Liquid}} Na^+ : {}^-C\equiv C-CH_2CH_3 + \tfrac{1}{2}H_2$$

$$C_2H_5Br + \overset{+}{Na} : {}^-C\equiv C-CH_2CH_3 \longrightarrow CH_3CH_2-C\equiv C-CH_2CH_3 + NaBr$$

3-Hexyne

3.18   REACTIONS OF THE ALKYNES

The chemical reactions of the acetylenes, like those of the olefins, are largely reactions of addition. The mode of addition of hydrogen halides to unsymmetrical acetylenes, you will note, also follows Markovnikov's rule.

A.   Addition of Br_2, HBr, and H_2 to Acetylenes.

$$CH_3-C\equiv C-H + 2\ Br_2 \rightarrow CH_3-\underset{\underset{Br}{|}}{\overset{\overset{Br}{|}}{C}}-\underset{\underset{Br}{|}}{\overset{\overset{Br}{|}}{C}}-H$$

Propyne

1, 1, 2, 2-Tetra-
bromopropane

$$CH_3-C\equiv C-H + 2\ HBr \rightarrow CH_3-\underset{\underset{Br}{|}}{\overset{\overset{Br}{|}}{C}}-\underset{\underset{H}{|}}{\overset{\overset{H}{|}}{C}}-H$$

2, 2-Dibromopropane

$$CH_3-C\equiv C-H + 2\ H_2 \xrightarrow{\text{Catalyst}} CH_3CH_2CH_3$$

Propane

B.   Addition Reactions NOT Given by Olefins.   Acetylene,
unlike the olefins, is sufficiently reactive to add hydrogen cyanide
when the addition is carried out under the influence of acid catalysts.
The product, acrylonitrile, is the important industrial chemical from
which the synthetic fiber "Orlon" is made.

$$H-C\equiv C-H + (H^+) \quad (:CN^-) \xrightarrow[\text{NH}_4\text{Cl-HCl}]{\text{CuCl,}} H-\underset{\underset{}{}}{\overset{\overset{H}{|}}{C}}=\underset{\underset{}{}}{\overset{\overset{H}{|}}{C}}-CN$$

$\delta-\quad\delta+$

Acrylonitrile
(Vinyl cyanide)

Acetylene also will add water or acetic acid directly. These useful
reactions are catalyzed by mercuric sulfate, the addition of water
being effected in an acidic medium. Presumably, reaction with
water proceeds through the intermediate formation of vinyl alcohol,
$H_2C=CHOH$, a product which has never been isolated. If formed,
vinyl alcohol immediately rearranges to acetaldehyde.

$$H-C\equiv C-H + H_2O \xrightarrow[\text{H}_2\text{SO}_4]{\text{HgSO}_4,} \left[H-\overset{\overset{H}{|}}{C}=\overset{\overset{H}{|}}{C}-O(H) \right] \rightarrow CH_3-\overset{\overset{H}{|}}{C}=O$$

Acetaldehyde

$$H-C\equiv C-H + CH_3-\overset{\overset{\textstyle O}{\|}}{C}-OH \xrightarrow[75°C]{Hg^{2+},} CH_2=CH-O-\overset{\overset{\textstyle O}{\|}}{C}-CH_3$$

Vinyl acetate

Higher acetylenes that still possess an acidic hydrogen may

be hydrated to yield methyl ketones, $CH_3-\overset{\overset{\textstyle O}{\|}}{C}-R$.

$$H-C\equiv C-CH_2CH_3 + H_2O \xrightarrow[H_2SO_4]{Hg^{2+},} \left[H-\overset{\overset{\textstyle H}{|}}{C}=\overset{\overset{\textstyle}{\underset{\underset{\textstyle O-H}{}}{}}}{C}-CH_2CH_3 \right]$$

1-Butyne

$$\longrightarrow H-\overset{\overset{\textstyle H}{|}}{\underset{\underset{\textstyle H}{|}}{C}}-\overset{\overset{\textstyle}{}}{\underset{\underset{\textstyle O}{\|}}{C}}-CH_2CH_3$$

2-Butanone
(Methyl ethyl ketone)

3.19   REPLACEMENT OF ACETYLENIC HYDROGEN BY A METAL
(SALT FORMATION)

The principal difference between the chemical behavior of the
acetylenes and that of the olefins, as was pointed out previously, is
due to the acidic character of the hydrogen atom bonded to an acetylenic carbon. Acetylenic hydrogen atoms can be replaced by metals
to produce salts called acetylides. (See Sec. 3.17(b) for reaction of
acetylene with sodium in liquid ammonia.) Acetylene, when passed
through ammoniacal solutions of cuprous chloride and silver nitrate
forms the acetylides of these metals.

$$H-C\equiv C-H + 2\,Cu(NH_3)_2Cl \rightarrow Cu-C\equiv C-Cu + 2\,NH_4Cl + 2\,NH_3$$

Copper acetylide

$$H-C\equiv C-H + 2\,Ag(NH_3)_2NO_3 \rightarrow Ag-C\equiv C-Ag + 2\,NH_4NO_3 + 2\,NH_3$$

Silver acetylide

Heavy metal salts of acetylene such as silver acetylide are extremely
sensitive to shock when dry and may explode violently.

3.20   OXIDATION OF ACETYLENE (COMBUSTION)

Acetylene burns in an atmosphere of pure oxygen to produce extremely high temperatures (ca. 3000°C). This reaction makes possible the common oxyacetylene torch so useful for the welding and cutting of metals.

$$2\ H\!-\!C\!\equiv\!C\!-\!H + 5\ O_2 \rightarrow 4\ CO_2 + 2\ H_2O + 619.7\ kcal.$$

3.21   POLYMERIZATION

Acetylene can add to itself to yield a *dimer* when treated with cuprous chloride in aqueous ammonium chloride solution.

$$H\!-\!C\!\equiv\!C\!-\!H + H\!-\!C\!\equiv\!C\!-\!H \xrightarrow{\text{CuCl, NH}_4\text{Cl}} H\!-\!C\!\equiv\!C\!-\!\underset{\displaystyle\overset{|}{H}}{C}\!=\!CH_2$$

3-Butene-1-yne
(Vinylacetylene)

The vinylacetylene thus produced will add hydrogen chloride to give 2-chloro-1, 3-butadiene or "chloroprene."

$$H\!-\!C\!\equiv\!C\!-\!\underset{\displaystyle\overset{|}{H}}{C}\!=\!CH_2 + HCl \rightarrow H_2C\!=\!\underset{\displaystyle\overset{|}{Cl}}{C}\!-\!\underset{\displaystyle\overset{|}{H}}{C}\!=\!CH_2$$

2-Chloro-1, 3-butadiene
(Chloroprene)

Chloroprene can be polymerized through a 1, 4-addition (see below) of diene units into a synthetic rubber called "neoprene." Using R· to represent the free radical which initiates the polymerization, the propagation of the chain reaction may be illustrated as follows: (Note that each time a molecule is added, a new double bond is formed at the 2, 3-position.)

$$R\cdot + H\!-\!\underset{(1)}{\overset{\displaystyle\overset{|}{H}}{C}}\ \ \underset{(2)}{\overset{\displaystyle\overset{|}{Cl}}{C}}\ \ \underset{(3)}{\overset{\displaystyle\overset{|}{H}}{C}}\ \ \underset{(4)}{\overset{\displaystyle\overset{|}{H}}{C}}\!-\!H \longrightarrow R\!-\!CH_2\!-\!\underset{\displaystyle\overset{|}{}}{\overset{Cl}{C}}\!=\!\underset{}{\overset{H}{C}}\!-\!\underset{\displaystyle\overset{|}{H}}{\overset{H}{C}}\cdot$$

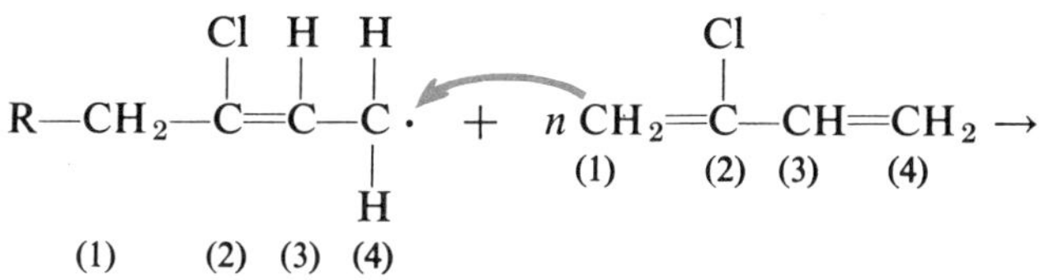

$$R-CH_2-\overset{\overset{\displaystyle Cl}{|}}{C}=\overset{\overset{\displaystyle H}{|}}{C}-\overset{\overset{\displaystyle H}{|}}{\underset{\underset{\displaystyle H}{|}}{C}}\cdot \;\;+\;\; n\;CH_2=\overset{\overset{\displaystyle Cl}{|}}{C}-CH=CH_2 \;\rightarrow$$

(1)   (2) (3) (4)   (1)   (2) (3)   (4)

1, 4-addition

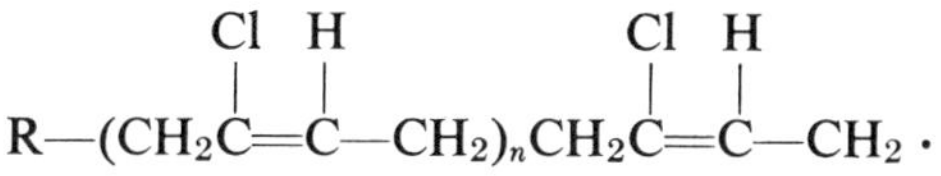

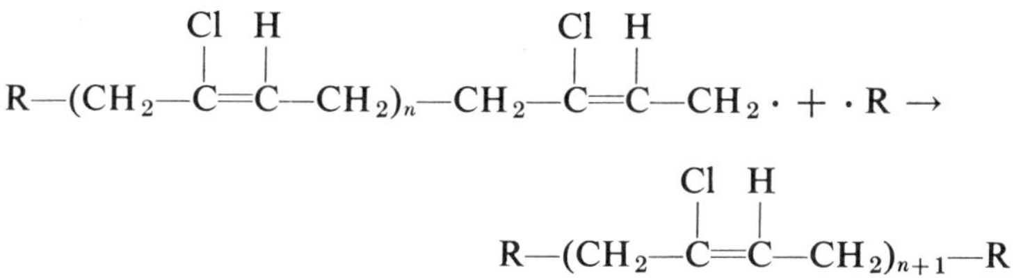

$$R-(CH_2\overset{\overset{\displaystyle Cl}{|}}{C}=\overset{\overset{\displaystyle H}{|}}{C}-CH_2)_n CH_2\overset{\overset{\displaystyle Cl}{|}}{C}=\overset{\overset{\displaystyle H}{|}}{C}-CH_2 \cdot$$

$$R-(CH_2-\overset{\overset{\displaystyle Cl}{|}}{C}=\overset{\overset{\displaystyle H}{|}}{C}-CH_2)_n-CH_2-\overset{\overset{\displaystyle Cl}{|}}{C}=\overset{\overset{\displaystyle H}{|}}{C}-CH_2\cdot\;+\;\cdot R\;\rightarrow$$

$$R-(CH_2-\overset{\overset{\displaystyle Cl}{|}}{C}=\overset{\overset{\displaystyle H}{|}}{C}-CH_2)_{n+1}-R$$

Neoprene, unlike natural rubber, is resistant to attack by greases and oils and finds numerous uses in the automotive industry. It is used primarily as insulation and in sheathing for wires and cables, in hose and hydraulic lines, and in many other rubber components that are likely to come into contact with lubricants.

☐☐ *SUMMARY* PART I:

[1]   Unsaturated hydrocarbons with double bonds are called olefins or alkenes. The general formula for a continuous chain olefin with one double bond is C_nH_{2n}.

[2]   The double bond makes possible *cis-trans* isomerism.

[3]   Pi electrons are mobile and are easily polarized. For this reason olefins are more reactive than the alkanes.

[4]   Olefins are prepared by removing the elements of a simple molecule from adjacent carbon atoms by: (a) the dehydration of an alcohol; (b) the dehydrohalogenation of an alkyl halide.

[5]   Reactions of the olefins are principally those of addition. Markovnikov's rule is followed in the addition of hydrogen halides with the exception of HBr addition in the presence of peroxides.

   a.   Addition takes place with: halogen, hydrogen, hydrogen halides, sulfuric acid, and hypochlorous acid.

   b.   Mild oxidation yields glycols; vigorous oxidation yields cleavage products — carboxylic acids, ketones, and CO_2.

   c. Oxidation with ozone results in cleavage of the double bond to yield two carbonyl $\left(\text{C=O} \right)$ compounds.

   d. Olefins may be polymerized to produce macromolecules called polymers.

[6] A system of alternate single and double bonds is a conjugated system. Butadiene, the simplest example of a conjugated system, may add reagents by 1, 2- or 1, 4-addition.

[7] A conjugated system is stabilized by resonance.

☐☐ SUMMARY PART II:

[1] Unsaturated hydrocarbons with triple bonds are called acetylenes or alkynes. The general formula for a continuous chain alkyne with one triple bond is C_nH_{2n-2}.

[2] The principal feature that distinguishes the acetylenes from the olefins is the acidic hydrogen on the triple-bonded carbon atom.

[3] Acetylenes are prepared by: (a) elimination of two simple molecules from adjacent carbon atoms; (b) replacement of the hydrogen on an existing acetylene by an alkyl group. Acetylene itself is prepared from calcium carbide.

[4] The reactions of the acetylenes are the following.
   a. Addition (halogens, hydrogen, HCN, H_2O, acetic acid).
   b. Oxidation (combustion); a highly exothermic reaction.
   c. Salt formation. The sodium salt is an important intermediate. The heavy metal salts are explosive when dry.
   d. Dimerization to produce vinylacetylene, chloroprene, and synthetic rubber.

☐☐ NEW TERMS

[1]	1, 2- and 1, 4-addition	[10]	hydrolysis
[2]	Baeyer test for unsaturation	[11]	Markovnikov's Rule
[3]	carbonium ion	[12]	oxonium ion
[4]	catalytic hydrogenation	[13]	ozonolysis
[5]	conjugated system	[14]	pi electrons
[6]	dehydrohalogenation	[15]	polymerization
[7]	dimer	[16]	resonance
[8]	geometric isomers	[17]	unsaturation
[9]	hydration	[18]	vicinal dihalide

■ □SUPPLEMENTARY EXERCISES
▼   AND PROBLEMS

[1]   Write a structural formula and give another acceptable name for each of the following.

(a)   propylene
(b)   ethylene bromide
(c)   isoprene
(d)   isobutylene
(e)   3-heptyne

[2]   Name the following structures according to IUPAC rules.

(a) $CH_3CH=CH—CH_2—CH_2—CH_3$
(b) $CH_3CH(Cl)CH=CHCH_3$
(c) $CH_3—CH_2—C≡C—CH_3$
(d) $CH_3—C(Br)=C(Br)—CH_3$
(e) $(CH_3)_2C=C(Br)—CH_3$
(f) $(CH_3)_2CH—CH=CH_2$

(g)

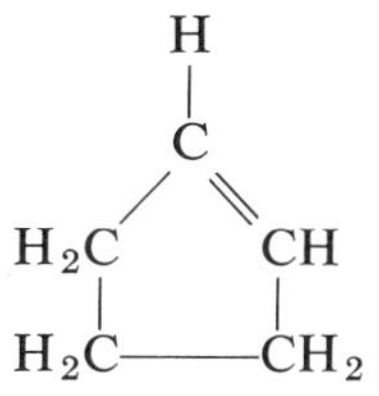

$$
\begin{array}{c}
\overset{\displaystyle H}{\underset{\displaystyle |}{C}} \\
H_2C \diagup \quad \diagdown CH \\
H_2C —— CH_2
\end{array}
$$

(h)

$$
\begin{array}{c}
CH(CH_3) \\
H_2C \diagup \quad \diagdown CH(CH_3) \\
H_2C —— CH_2
\end{array}
$$

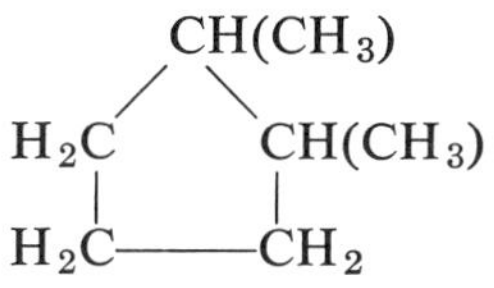

(i)

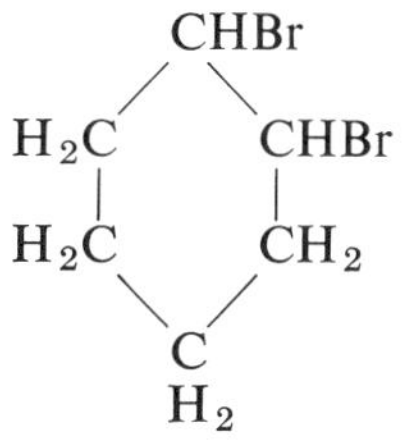

$$
\begin{array}{c}
CHBr \\
H_2C \diagup \quad \diagdown CHBr \\
H_2C \qquad CH_2 \\
\diagdown \quad \diagup \\
C \\
H_2
\end{array}
$$

(j)

$$
\begin{array}{c}
H \quad H \\
C=C \\
H—C \diagup \qquad \diagdown C—H \\
\| \qquad \qquad \| \\
H—C \diagdown \qquad \diagup C—H \\
C=C \\
H \quad H
\end{array}
$$

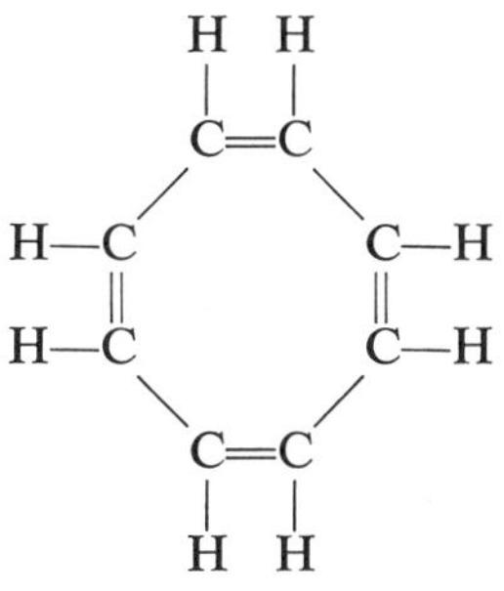

[3]   Which of the structures in exercise [2] may show geometric (*cis-trans*) isomerism?

[4]   Beginning with ethyl alcohol, CH_3CH_2OH, as your only starting material and using any other reagent you may require, show how you would prepare:

(a)   ethene
(b)   bromoethane
(c)   *n*-butane
(d)   ethylmagnesium bromide
(e)   ethane
(f)   acetylene
(g)   3-hexyne

(h)   1, 1-dibromoethane
(i)   1, 2-dibromoethane
(j)   acrylonitrile
(k)   vinylacetylene
(l)   vinyl chloride
(m) chloroprene

[5]   Give structures and names for the organic products resulting from the following reactions.

(a) $CH_3-CH=CH_2 + Br_2$ in $CCl_4 \longrightarrow$

(b) $CH_3-CH=CH_2 + HBr \longrightarrow$

(c) $CH_3-CH=CH_2 + H_2SO_4 \xrightarrow{\text{(Followed by hydrolysis)}}$

(d) $CH_3-CH=CH_2 + HBr \xrightarrow{H_2O_2}$

(e) $CH_3CH(Br)CH_2CH_3$ + alcoholic KOH $\longrightarrow$

(f) $CH_3CH=CHCH_3 \xrightarrow[\text{heat}]{\text{Conc. KMnO}_4}$

(g) $CH_2=CH_2$ + dilute $KMnO_4 \xrightarrow{5\%Na_2CO_3}$

(h) $H-C\equiv C-H \xrightarrow[\text{H}_2\text{SO}_4]{\text{H}_2\text{O, Hg}^{2+}}$

(i)   1, 2-Dimethylcyclopentene $\xrightarrow[\text{pressure}]{\text{H}_2, \text{Ni}}$

(j)   Cyclopentene + $Br_2 \longrightarrow$

[6]   For each of the structures below draw two isomeric alkyl halides which, on dehydrohalogenation, would produce the olefin shown. In each case predict which of the two halogen compounds would react more readily to produce the unsaturated compound.   Give reasons for your choice.

(a) $CH_3CH=CH_2$

(b) $(CH_3)_2C=CHCH_3$

(c) $CH_3CH=CHCH_2CH_3$

[7]   The identifying label on a cylinder of compressed gas unfortunately has been obliterated. The gas is combustible and believed to be either (a) propane, (b) cyclopropane, or (c) acetylene. Design a simple test which will identify the gas.

[8]   A gaseous hydrocarbon was shown by analysis to contain 85.7% carbon and 14.3% hydrogen. It was found that 900 ml of

the dry gas weighed 1.68 g at STP. What is its molecular formula? Write two plausible structures for this formula.

[9]   In the preceding problem how would each compound react with (a) Br_2; (b) HBr; (c) dilute $KMnO_4$?

[10] The hydrocarbon in problem [8] after treatment with hot, concentrated alkaline potassium permanganate followed by acidification, gave acetic acid, CH_3COOH, as the only organic product. What was the structure of the original compound?

[11] A hydrocarbon, C_4H_8, neither decolorized a bromine-carbon tetrachloride solution nor reacted with HBr. When heated to 200° with hydrogen in the presence of a nickel catalyst a new hydrocarbon, C_4H_{10}, was formed. What was the original unknown?

[12] A hydrocarbon, C_5H_8, absorbed two moles of hydrogen when catalytically hydrogenated. Upon ozonolysis the hydrocarbon gave the following products.

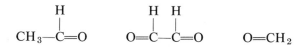

What is the structure and name of the hydrocarbon?

chapter 4

The Aromatic Hydrocarbons, or Arenes

INTRODUCTION

The aromatic hydrocarbons are ring hydrocarbons structurally related to benzene, C_6H_6. Although the formula of benzene indicates unsaturation, neither it nor its related compounds are olefinic in behavior. The aromatic hydrocarbons are found in the black, viscous, pitchlike material called coal tar, which is formed as a by-product when bituminous coal is converted to coke. Although coal tar itself is a vile smelling substance, it is a treasure-trove of aromatic hydrocarbons some of which are of rather pleasant odor — hence the name "aromatic." While the term is not descriptive insofar as many of these compounds are concerned, it has come into common usage to classify organic compounds which have as a common structural feature one or more 6-carbon benzene structures. Compounds in this category generally are named **arenes.** Some of these valuable chemicals are now obtainable in large volume from petroleum. From both sources, coal and petroleum, are harvested the basic materials for many pharmaceuticals, dyes, plastics, pesticides, explosives, and a host of other useful, everyday commodities.

4.2   THE STRUCTURE OF BENZENE

The discovery of benzene and the elucidation of its structure comprises an interesting and significant chapter in organic chemistry. This remarkable substance first was isolated in 1825 by Michael Faraday. He discovered benzene in the residual, oily condensate which collected in the illuminating gas lines of London. He established its empirical formula as (CH) and called it "carburetted hydrogen." The molecular formula of benzene subsequently was established as C_6H_6 by Mitscherlich, who in 1834 prepared it by heating gum benzoin with lime. For the next thirty years, determination of the structure of benzene posed a problem which occupied the serious attention of the best scientific minds of the time.

Since the molecular formula for benzene provided only one hydrogen atom per carbon, the molecule was expected to be unsaturated and, therefore, very reactive. On the contrary, it appeared to be remarkably stable. Benzene neither decolorized dilute potassium permanganate (the Baeyer test for unsaturation), nor did it add bromine readily, as one would expect an olefin to do. When treated with bromine in the presence of bright sunlight, one gram molecular weight of benzene *added* three gram molecular weights of bromine to yield benzene hexabromide. Obviously, each carbon in the benzene molecule has the potential for bonding to one more atom.

$$C_6H_6 + 3\ Br_2 \xrightarrow{\text{Bright sunlight}} C_6H_6Br_6$$

When treated with bromine in the presence of iron, benzene formed a mono-bromo *substitution* product, a behavior remarkably different from that noted above.

$$C_6H_6 + Br_2 \xrightarrow{\text{Fe}} C_6H_5Br + HBr$$

The fact that only one bromobenzene and no isomeric products were obtained indicated to the German chemist Kekulé[1] that each hydrogen atom of benzene must be equivalent to every other hydrogen. In 1865 he proposed a structure for benzene that was in accord with its chemical behavior. The structure Kekulé proposed was a cyclic hexagonal, planar structure of six carbon atoms with alternate double and single bonds. Each carbon atom was bonded to only one hydrogen atom. The Kekulé structure for benzene (shown below) was widely accepted by his contemporaries and still is used today.

---

[1]Friedrich August Kekulé (1829–1896), professor of chemistry successively at Heidelberg, Ghent, and finally at Bonn. Kekulé was an active researcher and a noted teacher but is best remembered for his formulation of the structure of benzene.

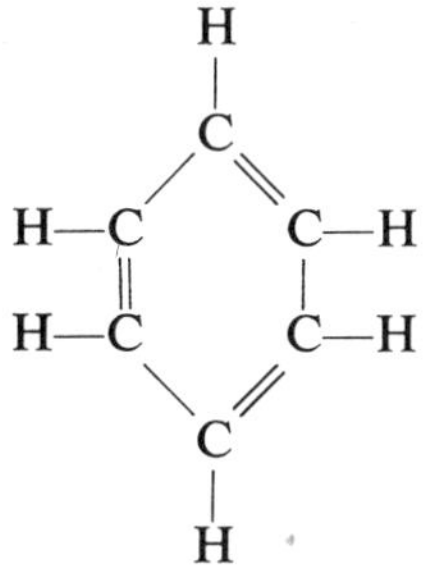

Benzene

The proposed structure for benzene made possible **three** iso-meric disubstituted derivatives. In one isomer, adjacent or **ortho** positions could be occupied by the two substituents. In the second isomer, alternate or **meta** positions could be occupied, and in the third isomer, hydrogens bonded to the carbon atoms opposite or **para** to each other in the ring could be substituted.

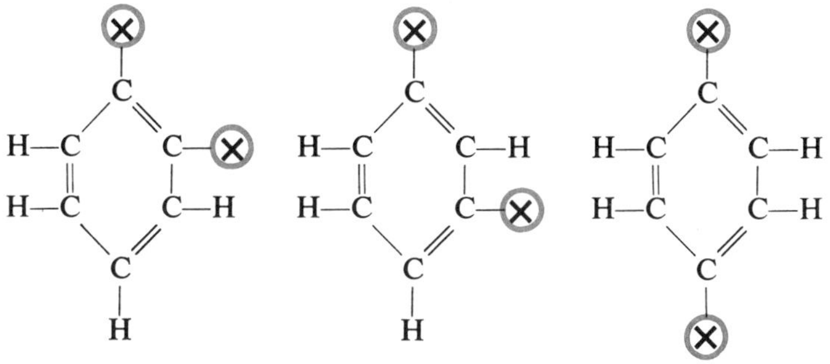

ortho positions   *meta* positions   *para* positions

If Kekulé's formula for benzene were correct, his critics argued, it would appear that **two** *ortho* isomers would be possible. In one *ortho* isomer, the carbon atoms holding the substituents would be separated by a double bond as shown in structure (a). In the other *ortho* isomer, substituents would be separated by a single bond as shown in structure (b)

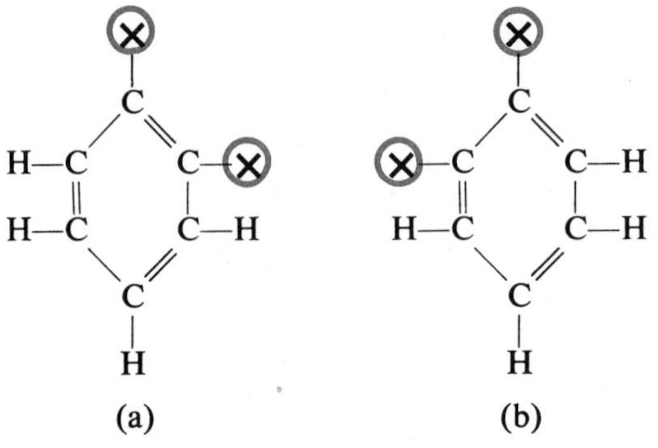

(a)   (b)

Kekulé reconciled the fact that two *ortho* isomers had not been found by stating that the system of alternate double and single bonds in the benzene ring was not a fixed system, but a dynamic one. He suggested that the structure of benzene could be either that of (a) or (b) and that each structure could alternate with the other.

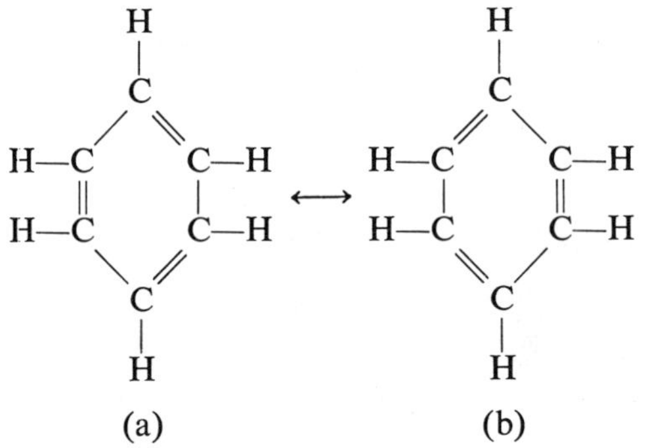

(a)   (b)

Today we consider the structure of benzene to be that of a resonance hybrid intermediate between structures (a) and (b). Although both structures indicated above are contributing forms, the correct structure of benzene must lie somewhere in between these two extremes.

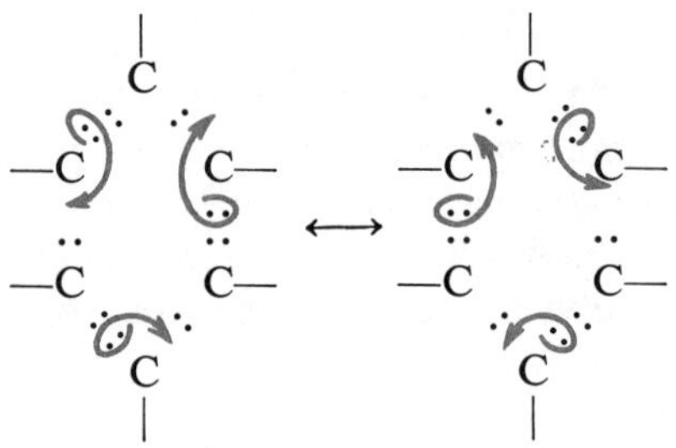

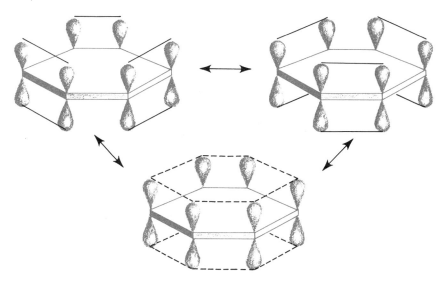

The six π electrons which appear to be part of the three double bonds between alternate carbons in each of the above Kekulé structures actually encompass all six carbon atoms. They may, like the π-electrons in the butadiene molecule (Sec. 3.12), delocalize and overlap with the π-electrons of neighboring carbons either to right or left.

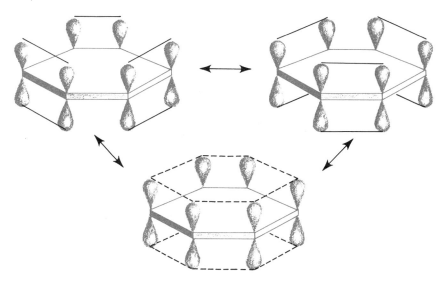

They thus appear as a cloud above and below the plane of the ring much like two hexagonal doughnuts with all six carbon and hydrogen atoms sandwiched in between. (See page 102.)

4.3   THE AROMATIC SEXTET AND AROMATIC CHARACTER

Any compound that contains a sextet of π electrons in a cyclic cloud above and below the plane of the molecule such as that proposed for benzene is classified as "aromatic." Aromaticity, when used to describe an organic compound, usually implies a high degree

■□FIGURE 4.1

STRUCTURAL REPRESENTATION OF BENZENE SHOWING OVERLAP OF SIX π ELECTRONS.

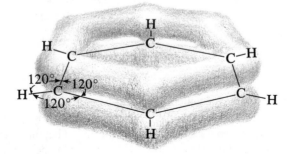

■□FIGURE 4.2

MOLECULAR MODELS OF BENZENE. (a) SCALE MODEL, (b) BALL AND STICK MODEL.

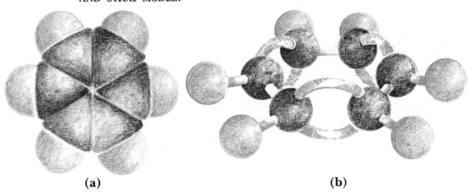

(a)   (b)

of stability. The π electrons above and below the plane of the molecule are able to participate in the formation of more than one bond. The result is strong bonds and a stable molecule. The additional stability possessed by benzene is called **stabilization energy** and the benzene structure is said to be **stabilized by resonance.** The high degree of stability conferred upon the benzene structure by resonance may be illustrated by comparing its heat of hydrogenation with that of an unsaturated 6-carbon ring structure in which little or no resonance occurs. For example, we might reasonably expect the heat of hydrogenation for a ring structure with three double bonds to be three times that of a compound such as cyclohexene which has only one double bond. The heat evolved when cyclohexene is hydrogenated is 28.6 kcal.

Cyclohexene   Cyclohexane $\Delta H = -28.6$ kcal

If benzene were simply a cyclohexatriene, its heat of hydrogenation should be three times 28.6 kcal or 85.8 kcal. Actually, the heat of hydrogenation of benzene is 49.8 kcal.

Benzene $\Delta H = -49.8$ kcal

85.8 kcal (expected heat) — 49.8 kcal (experimental heat)

= 36 kcal

= stabilization energy

Benzene, therefore, gives up 36 kcal less energy than the expected amount because it must contain less energy. This means that benzene is more stable by 36 kcal than the hypothetical cyclohexatriene would be.

A frequently used graphic formula for benzene which embodies all the concepts of π-bonding, resonance, and aromaticity is a regular hexagon with an inscribed circle.

The hexagon represents the six σ bonds between adjacent carbon atoms and the inner circle represents the π-electron cloud. Each corner of the hexagon is understood to be occupied by one carbon with an attached hydrogen atom. All carbon and hydrogen atoms lie in the same plane and the bonds between them describe angles of 120°. Although the hexagon-inscribed-circle notation is a simple one to draw and use in writing the reactions of benzene, for pedagogical reasons we shall more often use the Kekulé representation in our discussion, with the same features being implied. Further, when any hydrogen atoms have been replaced, we shall show only the substituents with the understanding that the other hydrogens remain.

The naming of aromatic compounds may be done in several
different ways. As in the aliphatic[2] or open chain systems, aromatic
compounds also have both trivial and systematic names. Compounds with one or more hydrogen atoms of benzene replaced by
other atoms or groups may be named as substituted benzenes. Examples of such substitutive names are the following:

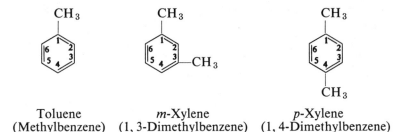

Ethylbenzene   Bromobenzene   Nitrobenzene

Trivial, or common names, usually of early origin, offer no clue
to the nature of the substituent. However, such common names are
so frequently used that they must be learned. When two substituents
appear on the benzene ring, their relative positions must be designated. This is done either by using the prefixes (*ortho* (*o*-), *meta* (*m*-),
and *para* (*p*-) as previously described (Sec. 4.2), or by locating substituents on the ring by numbers. A few examples will illustrate these
rules.

Toluene   *m*-Xylene   *p*-Xylene
(Methylbenzene)   (1, 3-Dimethylbenzene)   (1, 4-Dimethylbenzene)

When a common or trivial name is used, the group which is responsible for the name, i.e., methyl in the case of toluene, or hydroxyl in
the case of phenol, is considered to be on carbon 1. When a trivial
name is not used, as in the case of *p*-chloronitrobenzene, the nitro
group, being the group named just preceding the name of the parent
hydrocarbon, is considered to be on carbon 1.

[2]Gr., (*aleiphatos*, fat). Many of the first open chain structures studied
were derived from fatty acids. In present usage, aliphatic pertains to noncyclic
carbon compounds, or to carbon compounds other than aromatic.

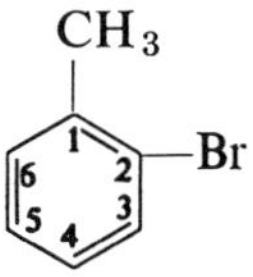

CH₃

—Br

o-Bromotoluene
(2-Bromotoluene)

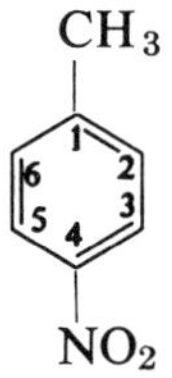

CH₃

NO₂

p-Nitrotoluene
(4-Nitrotoluene)

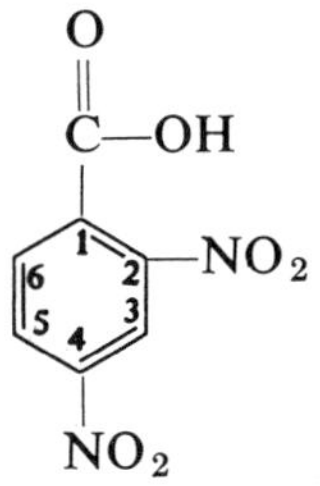

O
‖
C—OH

—NO₂

NO₂

2, 4-Dinitrobenzoic
acid

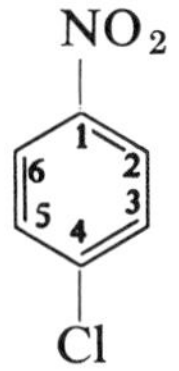

NO₂

Cl

p-Chloronitrobenzene
(4-Chloronitrobenzene)

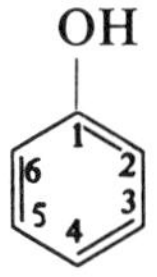

OH

Phenol
(Hydroxybenzene)

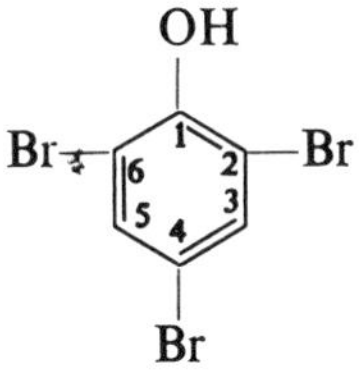

OH

Br—   —Br

Br

2, 4, 6-Tribromophenol

The order of naming usually is alphabetical when three different substituents occupy positions upon the ring.

CH₃

—NO₂

Br

4-Bromo-2-nitrotoluene

CH₃

—Br

NO₂

2-Bromo-4-nitrotoluene

Exercise 4.1   Assign an acceptable name to each of the
following compounds:

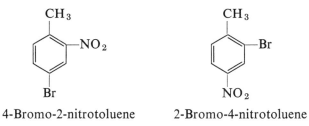

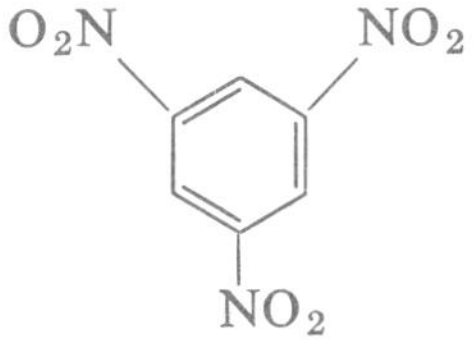

O₂N   NO₂

NO₂

(a)

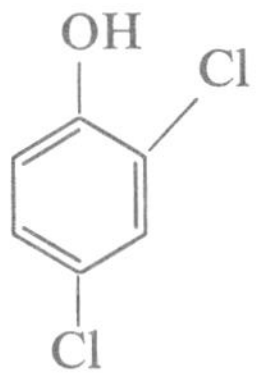

OH
    Cl

Cl

(b)

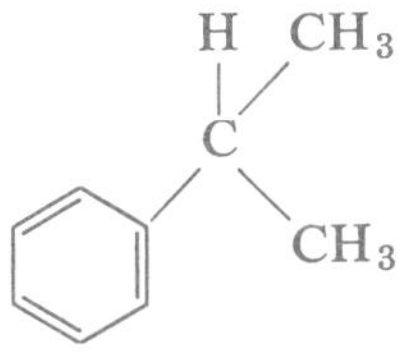

H CH₃
 \ /
  C
     \
      CH₃

(c)

4.5   POSITION ISOMERISM

A disubstituted benzene, as you have already learned, may be one of three isomeric forms — *ortho*, *meta*, and *para*. If both substituents in each of these three isomeric forms are identical, a third similar group, if substituted in the ring, also makes possible three isomers — **vicinal** (*vic*), **asymmetric** (*asym*), and **symmetric** (*sym*). Thus, the vicinal, asymmetric, and symmetric trimethyl benzenes are produced when a third methyl group is substituted into each of the three isomeric xylenes. Ring positions available in each xylene molecule, relative to the methyl groups already on the ring, are designated by *o*, *m*, and *p*. For example, the four positions on *p*-xylene open to an incoming methyl group are all the same. Each open position is *ortho* to one methyl group and *meta* to the other, and is labeled (*o, m*).

All open positions equivalent

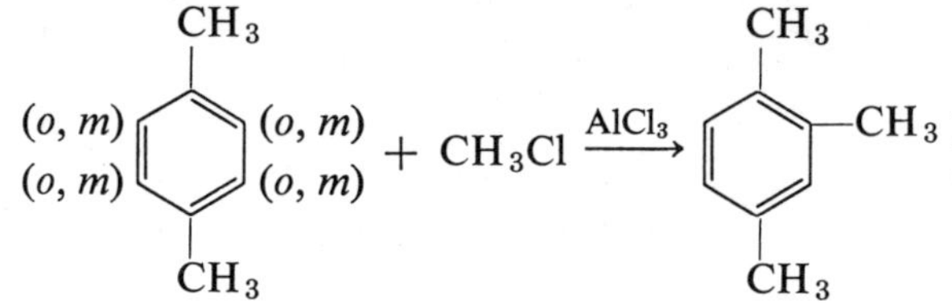

(o, m) (o, m) (o, m) (o, m) + CH_3Cl $\xrightarrow{AlCl_3}$ Isomer (A) (asymmetric)

p-Xylene

CH_3 CH_3

1, 2, 4-Tri- methylbenzene

Two different positions open

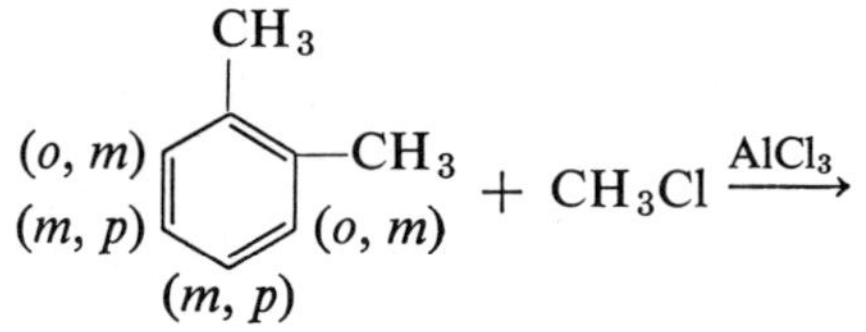

(o, m) (m, p) (m, p) (o, m) + CH_3Cl $\xrightarrow{AlCl_3}$ Isomer (A)

o-Xylene

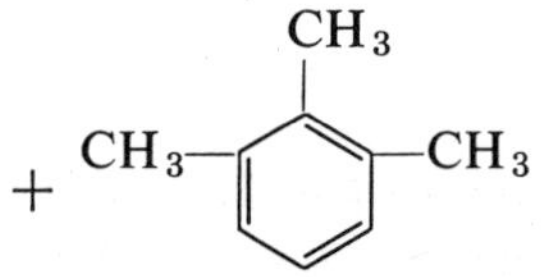

+ CH_3 CH_3 CH_3 Isomer (B) (vicinal)

1, 2, 3-Trimethylbenzene

Three different positions open

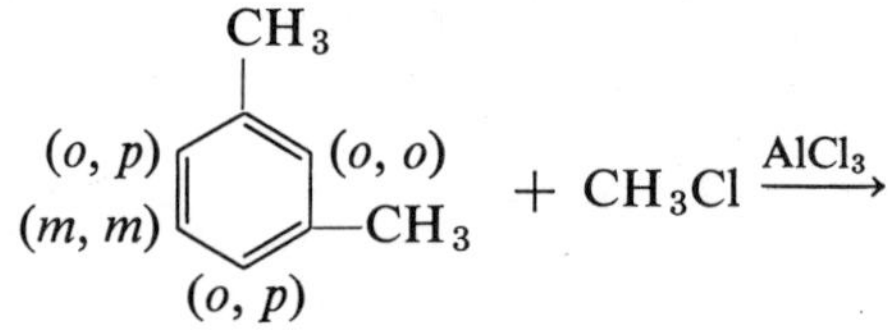

(o, p) (m, m) (o, o) (o, p) + CH_3Cl $\xrightarrow{AlCl_3}$ Isomer (A) + Isomer (B)

m-Xylene

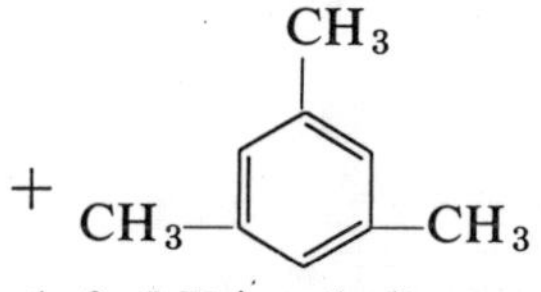

+ CH_3 CH_3 CH_3 Isomer (C) (symmetric)

1, 3, 5-Trimethylbenzene (Mesitylene)

Exercise 4.2   Draw Kekulé structures for the six isomeric products possible if a bromine atom were introduced into each of the three xylenes as a third ring substituent.

Exercise 4.3   Albert Ladenburg[3] in 1869 proposed the prism structure shown to account for the one monosubstitution product and the three disubstituted products found for benzene. Where would the *ortho, meta,* and *para* positions be on the Ladenburg structure?

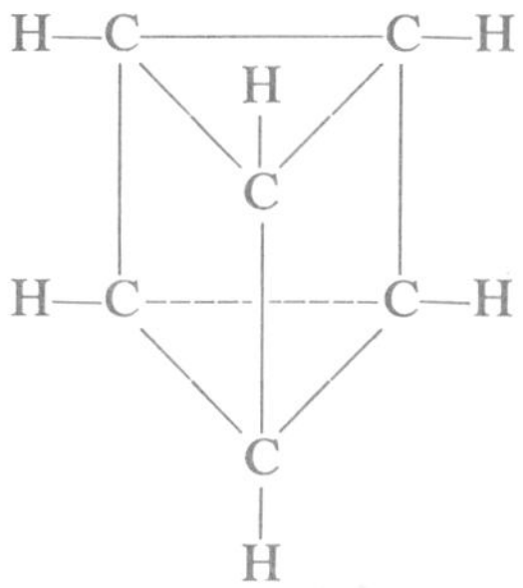

4.6   OTHER AROMATIC HYDROCARBONS

Common aromatic hydrocarbons, other than the alkyl substituted benzenes, include a number of polycyclic systems. In these systems the rings may be either condensed — that is, share a side in common or be separate but joined through carbon-carbon bonds. Many of these hydrocarbons, like benzene, also are coal tar derivatives. The following structures, along with their numbering systems, are those which appear most frequently as part of polycyclic organic molecules.

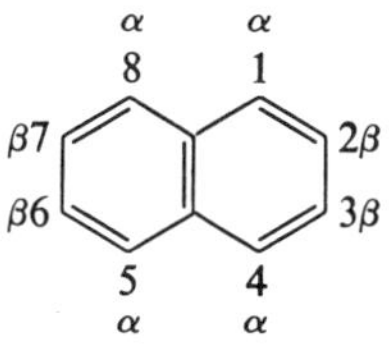

Naphthalene 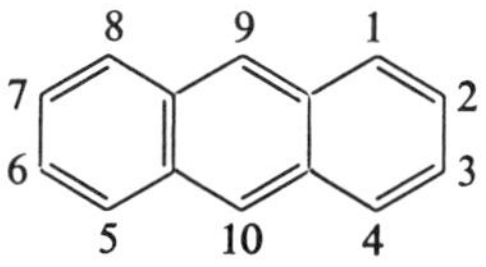   Anthracene

[3]Albert Ladenburg (1842–1911), professor of chemistry at Kiel (1873–1889); at Breslau (1889–1911).

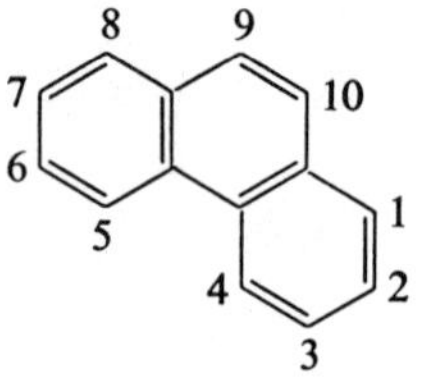

Phenanthrene

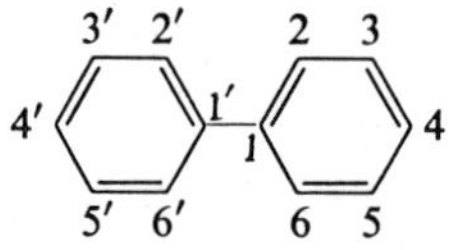

Biphenyl 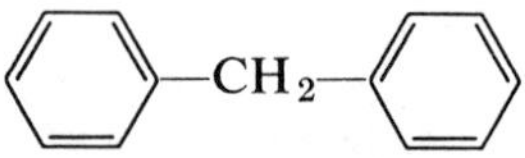   Diphenylmethane

4.7   AROMATIC GROUPS

The removal of a hydrogen atom from an aromatic hydrocarbon, or arene, produces an **aryl group** (Ar). The use of such group
names is limited largely to benzene and naphthalene derivatives. The
phenyl group, C_6H_5—, stems from *phene*, an early name for benzene.
Table 4.1 gives the structures and names of the most commonly used
aryl groups.

☐■ TABLE 4.1

COMMON ARYL GROUPS

Structure	Name of Group	Example of Usage	Name of Example
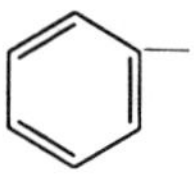	Phenyl	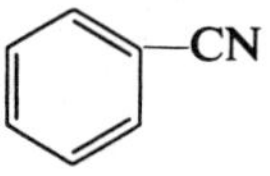 —CN	Phenyl cyanide
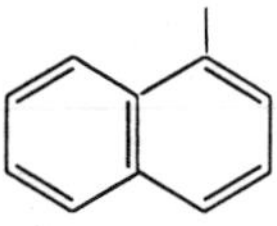	α-Naphthyl	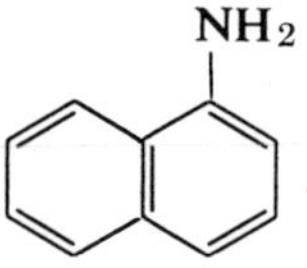 NH$_2$	α-Naphthylamine
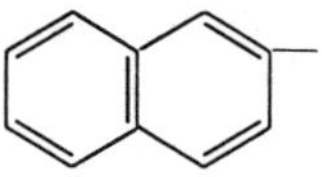	β-Naphthyl	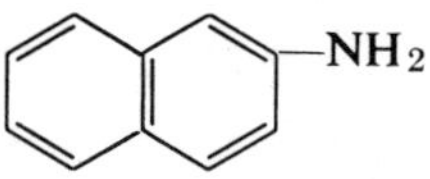 —NH$_2$	β-Naphthylamine
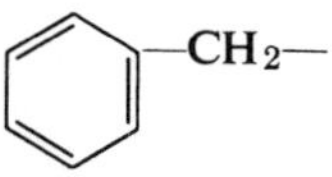 —CH$_2$—	Benzyl	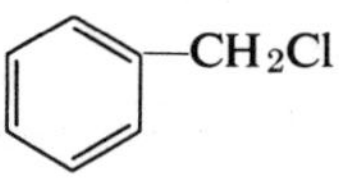 —CH$_2$Cl	Benzyl chloride
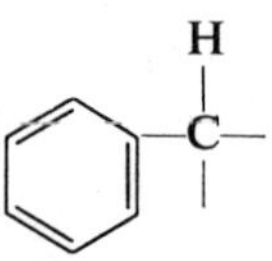 Benzal	Benzal	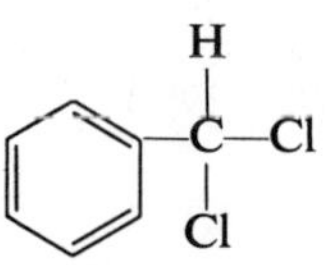 —C—Cl	Benzal chloride

> **Exercise 4.4**   How many mono-substituted products are
> possible for naphthalene? How many di-substituted products?

4.8   REACTIONS OF THE AROMATIC HYDROCARBONS

The reactions of benzene and other aromatic hydrocarbons are mainly reactions of substitution in the aromatic ring. Substitution reactions involving the aromatic ring, unlike those of the alkanes, are controllable and much more useful. The benzene ring is attacked in nearly every case by an electrophilic (electron-loving) reagent which may be either a cation or a neutral but polarized molecule. The electron-deficient group, by sharing in an electron pair supplied at one of the ring carbons, first forms with the benzene ring a cationic intermediate in which the positive charge is distributed among the remaining carbon atoms. In the second step a proton is lost to regenerate the more stable aromatic ring.

Catalysts often are necessary to generate the electrophile. Such catalysts, as you will see in the following sections, often are Lewis acids, each of which lacks an electron pair. The result of attracting a pair of electrons from the substituting reagent by the catalyst is the formation .of either a positive ion or a polarized molecule. In either case, the positive ion or the positive part of the molecule is the ring-attacking group. The mechanics of electrophilic aromatic substitution may be illustrated by the following.

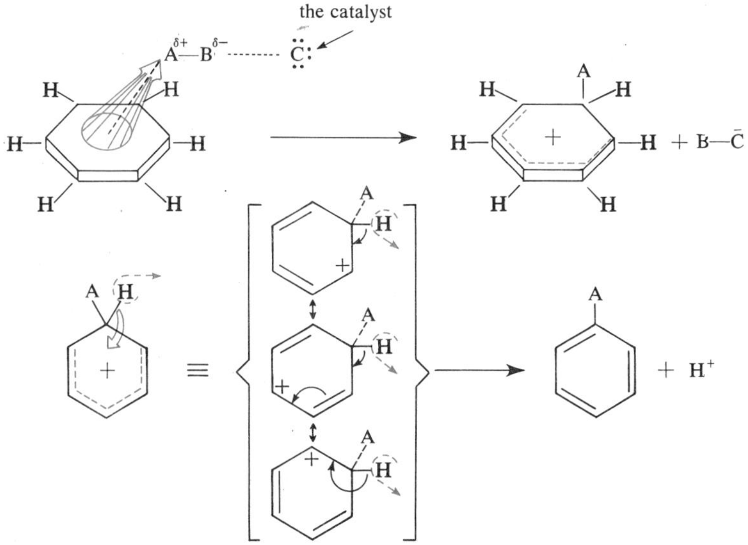

$$H^+ + B-\bar{C} \longrightarrow H-B + C$$

The principal reactions of benzene are described in the follow-ing sections.

A.   Halogenation.   Halogenation of the aromatic ring may be illustrated by bromination. Bromine attacks the aromatic ring in a manner analogous to its attack upon the double bond of an olefin, except that a catalyst is necessary to assist in the polarization of the bromine molecule. Iron, usually in finely divided form, is used for this purpose.   Presumably, ferric bromide, $FeBr_3$, is the actual catalyst and this could form as shown in the first of the equations representing the bromination of benzene.

$$3\,Br_2 + 2\,Fe \longrightarrow 2\,FeBr_3$$

Ferric
bromide

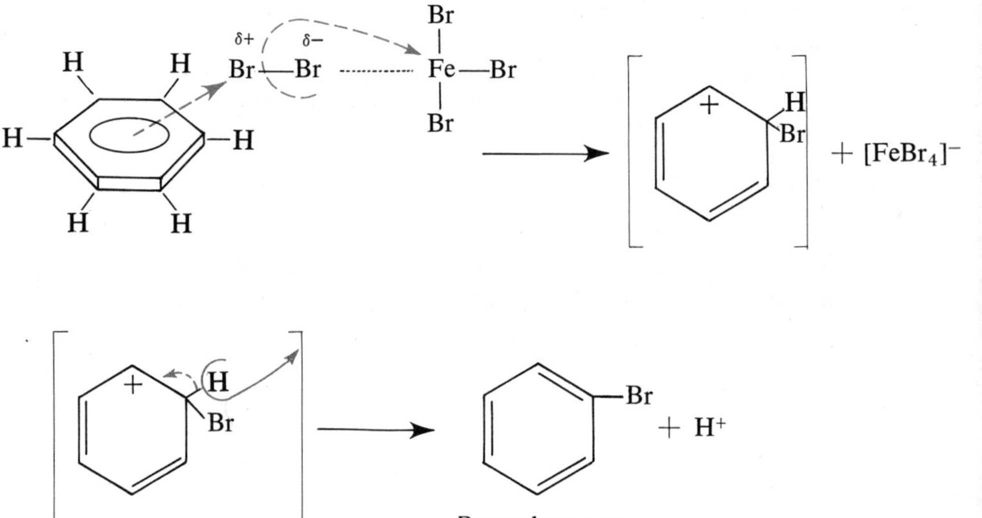

$$H^+ + FeBr_4^- \longrightarrow FeBr_3 + HBr$$

Although we have indicated the bromination of benzene as a series of discrete steps, the net equation for the over-all reaction may be written simply as

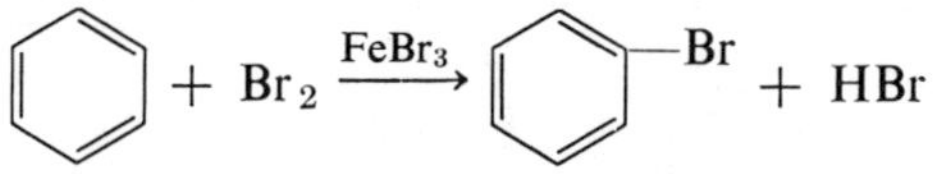

Bromobenzene

Substitution of benzene by chlorine also may be accomplished in a manner similar to that shown for the bromination reaction. As before, a catalyst is necessary. Anhydrous aluminum chloride, $AlCl_3$, is an excellent catalyst for the chlorination reaction. If iron is used, the catalyst presumably is $FeCl_3$.

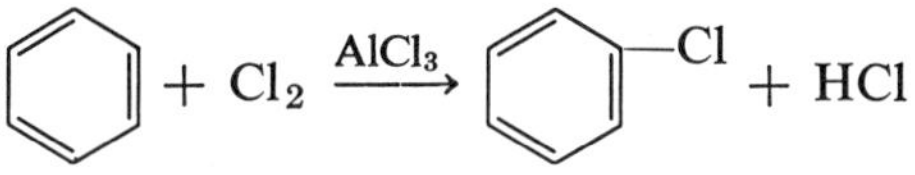

Chlorobenzene

Chlorination of benzene, if carried out in bright light and without a catalyst results in *addition* of chlorine to produce a saturated 6-carbon ring.

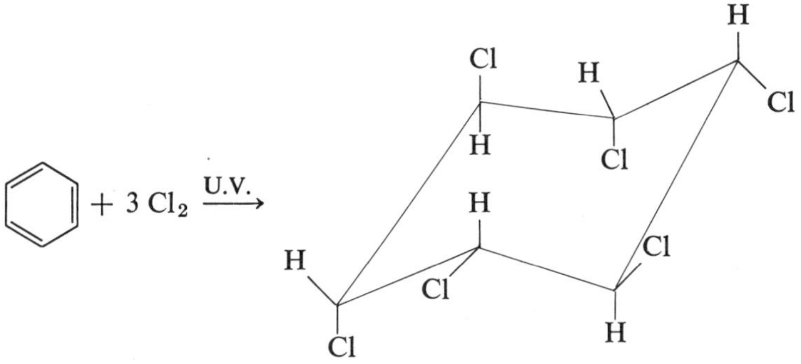

Benzene hexachloride

B.   Nitration of Benzene.   Nitration of the aromatic ring is a very important reaction and produces a number of useful compounds unobtainable in any other way. Nitration usually is accomplished by treating benzene with a mixture of concentrated nitric and sulfuric acids. A mixture of these two acids is referred to as a nitrating mixture. The electrophilic species in the nitration of benzene appears to be the nitronium ion, $^+NO_2$, which may be formed from nitric acid by the action of sulfuric acid. The mechanism usually given for the nitration of benzene is illustrated by the following sequence of reactions.

$$\text{HO—N}\overset{\nearrow O}{\underset{\searrow O}{}} + 2\,H_2SO_4 \longrightarrow 2\,HSO_4^- + H_3O^+ + \oplus N\overset{\nearrow O}{\underset{\searrow O}{}}$$

Nitronium ion

$$\text{⟨benzene⟩} + \oplus N\overset{\nearrow O}{\underset{\searrow O}{}} \longrightarrow \left[\text{⟨intermediate⟩}\begin{array}{c} H \\ NO_2 \end{array} \right] \longrightarrow \text{⟨benzene⟩}-NO_2 + H^+$$

Nitrobenzene

The net equation for the over-all reaction may be written

$$\text{⟨benzene⟩} + HNO_3 \xrightarrow{H_2SO_4} \text{⟨benzene⟩}-NO_2 + H_2O$$

Nitrobenzene

C.   Alkylation of Benzene.   The simple alkyl benzenes such as toluene (methylbenzene) and the xylenes (dimethylbenzenes) are readily available from petroleum.   On occasion, however, it may be necessary or desirable to introduce an alkyl group into the benzene ring.   One method for accomplishing this substitution is a reaction known as the **Friedel-Crafts** reaction.[4] In the Friedel-Crafts reaction an alkyl group is attached to the ring by treating benzene with an alkyl halide in the presence of anhydrous aluminum chloride, $AlCl_3$.   The electrophilic reagent which attacks the ring in the alkylation reaction appears to be a carbonium ion.   Inasmuch as olefins (equation 2) and alcohols (equation 3) also are capable of forming carbonium ions (Sec. 3.4), they, too, can be used to alkylate the benzene ring.   The mechanics of the Friedel-Crafts reaction are illustrated in the following equations for the preparation of iso-propylbenzene.

[4]Charles Friedel (1832–1899), a French chemist, known mainly for his discovery, in collaboration with an American chemist, James M. Crafts (1838–1917), of a convenient method of synthesis of aromatic ketones.

(1) The reaction of isopropyl chloride with aluminum chloride:

$$\text{(1)}\quad \underset{\substack{|\\ \text{H}}}{\overset{\substack{\text{CH}_3\\ |\\ \text{C}}}{\text{CH}_3 \diagup \diagdown \text{Cl}}} + \underset{\substack{|\\ \text{Cl}}}{\overset{\text{Cl}}{\text{Al—Cl}}} \longrightarrow \underset{\text{H}\quad \text{CH}_3}{\overset{\text{CH}_3}{\oplus \text{C}}} \cdots \overset{(-)}{\text{Cl—Al—Cl}}_{\substack{|\\ \text{Cl}}}$$

Isopropyl
chloride

$$\text{H}^+ + \overset{(-)}{\text{AlCl}_4} \longrightarrow \text{AlCl}_3 + \text{HCl}$$

Isopropylbenzene
(Cumene)

$$\text{(2)}\quad \text{CH}_3 \overset{\delta+}{-}\underset{\substack{|\\ \text{H}}}{\overset{\text{H}}{\text{C}}}\overset{\delta-}{=}\text{CH}_2 + \text{HCl} + \text{AlCl}_3 \longrightarrow \text{CH}_3 -\underset{\underset{\oplus}{\substack{|}}}{\overset{\substack{\text{H}\\ |}}{\text{C}}}-\text{CH}_3 + \overset{(-)}{\text{AlCl}_4}$$

$$\text{(3)}\quad \text{CH}_3 -\underset{\substack{|\\ \text{OH}}}{\overset{\substack{\text{H}\\ |}}{\text{C}}}-\text{CH}_3 + 2\,\text{H}_2\text{SO}_4 \longrightarrow \text{CH}_3 -\underset{\underset{\oplus}{\substack{|}}}{\overset{\substack{\text{H}\\ |}}{\text{C}}}-\text{CH}_3 + \text{H}_3\overset{+}{\text{O}} + 2\,\text{HSO}_4{}^-$$

Isopropyl alcohol

The isopropyl cation then combines with the aromatic ring in the same manner as indicated in the second equation above.

The Friedel-Crafts reaction, although useful, has the disadvantage of giving not only polysubstituted products, but also rearranged products if the group to be substituted into the benzene ring is unbranched and larger than ethyl. For example, if benzene is treated with n-propyl chloride and aluminum chloride, the product obtained is largely isopropylbenzene, or cumene.   Only small amounts of the normal isomer are obtained. Formation of the more highly branched secondary carbonium ion which may be accomplished by a rearrangement of a hydrogen atom and a pair of electrons appears to be favored because it represents a more stable intermediate than the primary carbonium ion.

$$
CH_3-\underset{\underset{H}{\overset{..}{|}}}{\overset{\overset{H}{|}}{C}}-\underset{\oplus}{\overset{H}{C}}-H \longrightarrow CH_3-\underset{\oplus}{\overset{\overset{H}{|}}{C}}-CH_3
$$

$$
\bigcirc + CH_3CH_2CH_2Cl \xrightarrow{AlCl_3} \bigcirc-\underset{CH_3}{\overset{CH_3}{C}}-H + HCl
$$

Isopropylbenzene
(Cumene)

D.   Sulfonation of Benzene.   Benzenesulfonic acid is produced when benzene is heated with concentrated sulfuric acid. The ring-attacking group in the sulfonation reaction is not a positive ion as was the case in the previous reactions. Instead, it appears to be the electron-deficient sulfur trioxide molecule produced by the reaction of two molecules of sulfuric acid.

$$
2\,H_2SO_4 \rightleftharpoons H_3O^+ + \quad \overset{\overset{..}{:}\overset{..}{O}:}{\underset{:\overset{..}{O}:}{S:\overset{..}{\underset{..}{O}}:}} + HSO_4^-
$$

The sulfonation of aromatic compounds is a very important reaction, especially in the preparation of dyestuffs. Sulfonation of the aromatic ring is a convenient method for making aromatic compounds water soluble, because many of the sulfonic acids form water-soluble metal salts, and many aromatic sulfonic acids are themselves quite soluble in water.

$$
\bigcirc + H_2SO_4 \longrightarrow \bigcirc-\underset{O}{\overset{O}{S}}-OH + H_2O
$$

Benzenesulfonic acid

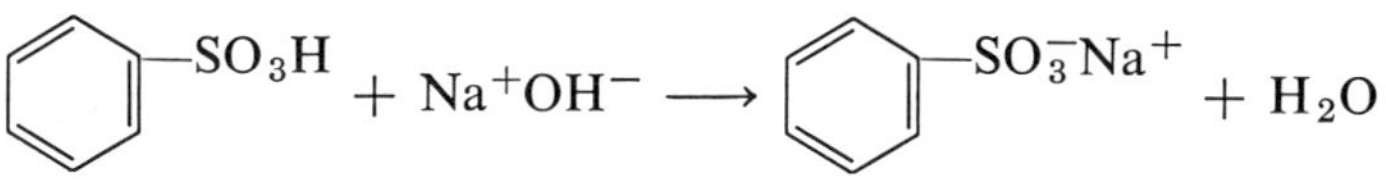

Sodium benzenesulfonate

E. Oxidation of Aromatic Hydrocarbons. Neither benzene nor polycyclic aromatic compounds are reactive to the usual oxidizing reagents such as potassium permanganate ($KMnO_4$) or potassium dichromate ($K_2Cr_2O_7$). However, the benzene ring can be ruptured and oxidized when treated with oxygen in the presence of vanadium pentoxide at high temperatures. The anhydride of maleic acid, a dicarboxylic acid (Sec. 12.2), may be produced in this manner.

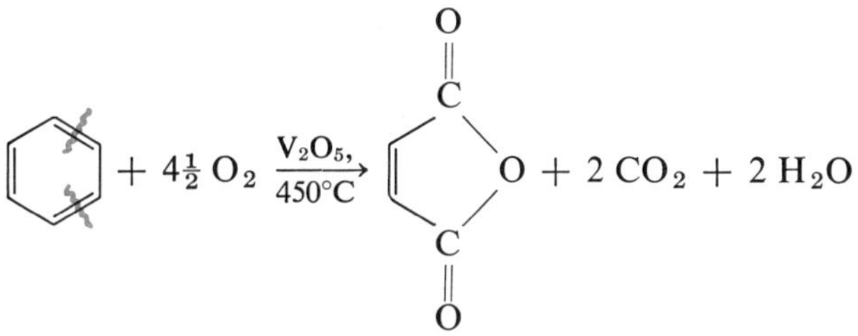

Maleic
anhydride

Naphthalene also is oxidized under these same conditions. One benzene ring appears to facilitate the oxidation of the other. The anhydride of *ortho*-phthalic acid, an important industrial chemical used in the preparation of the glyptal resins and Dacron (Sec. 12.5), is produced from naphthalene in this manner.

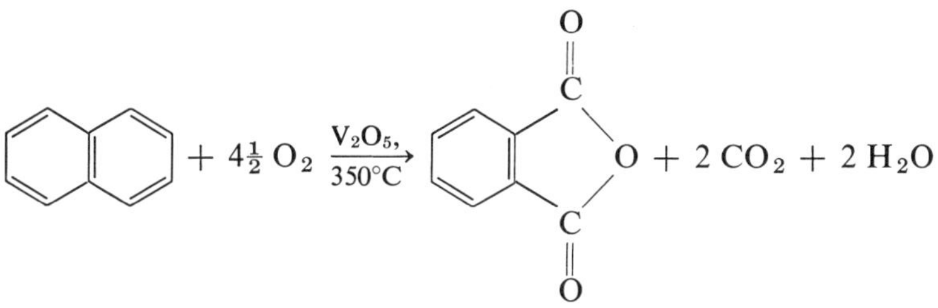

Naphthalene   Phthalic anhydride

Other reactions of naphthalene are similar to those shown for benzene. In nearly every instance the substituting group exhibits a predilection for the **alpha** positions (Sec. 4.6).

4.9   OXIDATION OF ALKYL BENZENES

An alkyl group attached to the benzene ring undergoes oxidation quite readily. Regardless of its length, the carbon *side chain* is degraded to the last ring-attached carbon atom. The ring-attached carbon is converted to a carboxyl group, —**COOH**. All other carbon atoms in the chain are oxidized to carbon dioxide. Hot potassium permanganate or potassium dichromate in sulfuric acid usually is used for the oxidation of side chains.

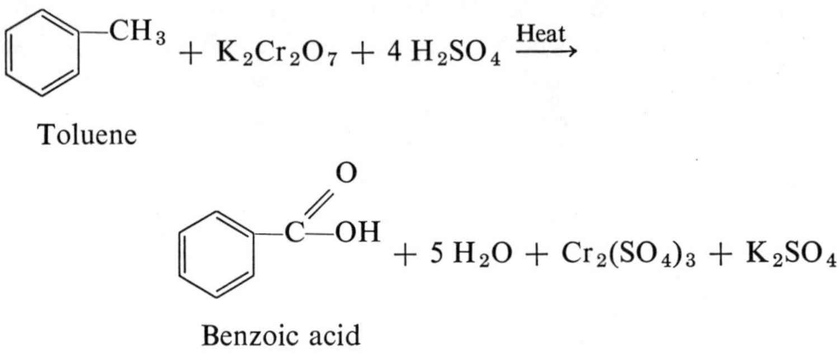

$$\text{C}_6\text{H}_5\text{—CH}_3 + \text{K}_2\text{Cr}_2\text{O}_7 + 4\,\text{H}_2\text{SO}_4 \xrightarrow{\text{Heat}}$$

Toluene

$$\text{C}_6\text{H}_5\text{—C(=O)—OH} + 5\,\text{H}_2\text{O} + \text{Cr}_2(\text{SO}_4)_3 + \text{K}_2\text{SO}_4$$

Benzoic acid

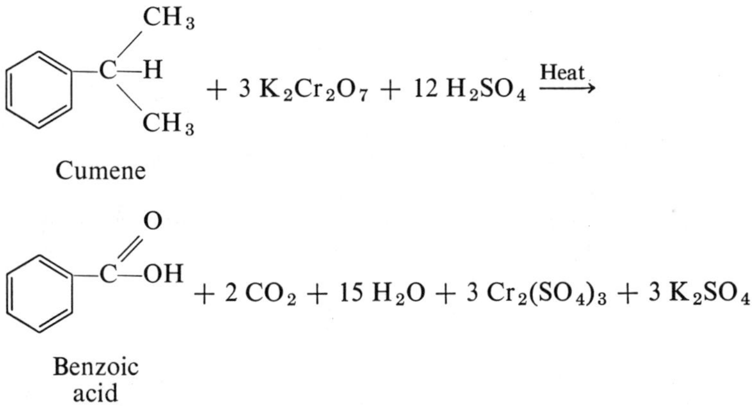

$$\text{C}_6\text{H}_5\text{—CH(CH}_3)_2 + 3\,\text{K}_2\text{Cr}_2\text{O}_7 + 12\,\text{H}_2\text{SO}_4 \xrightarrow{\text{Heat}}$$

Cumene

$$\text{C}_6\text{H}_5\text{—C(=O)—OH} + 2\,\text{CO}_2 + 15\,\text{H}_2\text{O} + 3\,\text{Cr}_2(\text{SO}_4)_3 + 3\,\text{K}_2\text{SO}_4$$

Benzoic
acid

Exercise 4.5   Write a balanced equation for the oxidation of ethylbenzene with potassium dichromate and sulfuric acid.

4.10   DIRECTIVE INFLUENCE OF RING SUBSTITUENTS

A substituent, once positioned on the ring, influences control not only upon the facility with which a second group enters, but also determines the position the group will occupy. If the substituent has one or more pairs of nonbonded electrons on the atom that is directly attached to the benzene ring, the group may serve as an electron-pair donor and have an **activating effect** upon the ring. In this event the ring becomes more reactive than benzene. This increased reactivity results from an increased electron density at both the *ortho* and *para* positions of the ring. Substitution at these sites is enhanced and very little, if any, substitution will occur at the *meta* position. Groups capable of orienting other substituents to *ortho* or *para* positions in this manner are called **ortho-para directors.** The hydroxylic group of phenol with nonbonded electrons on the ring-attached oxygen atom is a very strong electron-pair donor and therefore a strong *ortho-para* director. The resonance forms (I–IV) contributing to the phenol structure illustrate how the electron density at the *ortho* and *para* positions may be *increased* to make these positions especially susceptible to electrophilic attack.

I   II   III   IV

A substituent, if an electron-attracting one, **deactivates** the ring and makes it less reactive than benzene. Such substituents usually are groups in which the ring-attached atom is multiple-bonded to others of greater electronegativity. Substitution at the *ortho* and *para* positions will be inhibited because the electron availability at these positions will be diminished. A second substituent, if it bonds to the ring at all, must take next best and affix itself to one of the *meta* carbons. Groups capable of orienting other substituents to *meta* positions are called **meta directors.** The nitro group is a very strong electron attractor, deactivates the ring, and is a *meta* director. The deactivating power of the nitro group is sufficiently strong to prevent nitrobenzene from entering into a Friedel-Crafts reaction. Nitrobenzene, because of its unreactivity, frequently is used as the solvent for the Friedel-Crafts reaction. The resonance forms (V–VIII) contributing to the nitrobenzene structure show an electron *deficiency* at the ortho and para positions.

☐■ TABLE 4.2

TABLE OF *ortho-para* AND *meta* DIRECTING GROUPS

Ortho-Para Directors (Activating)	Representative Compounds	Meta Directors (Deactivating)	Representative Compounds
—OH	Phenol, 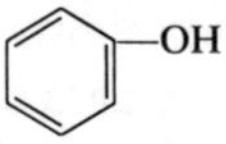 —OH	$-\overset{+}{N}H_3$	Anilinium chloride, 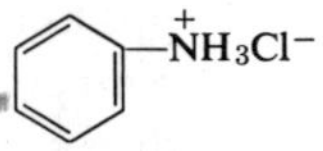 $-\overset{+}{N}H_3Cl^-$
—NH₂	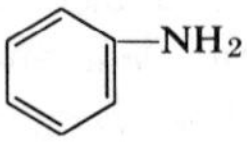 Aniline, —NH₂	—N→O ‖ O	Nitrobenzene, 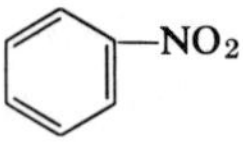 —NO₂
—OCH₃	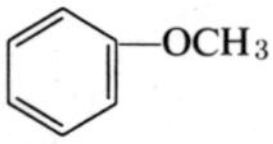 Anisole, —OCH₃	—C≡N	Benzonitrile, 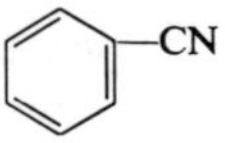 —CN
H O | ‖ —N—C—CH₃	Acetanilide,	O ‖ —S—OH ‖ O	Benzenesulfonic acid, —SO₃H
O ‖ —O—C—CH₃	Phenyl acetate, 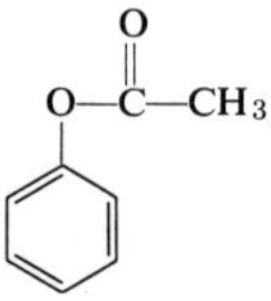	O ‖ —C—CH₃	Acetophenone, 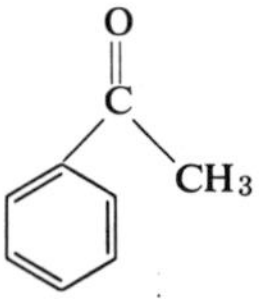
—CH₃	Toluene, —CH₃	O ‖ —C—H	Benzaldehyde, 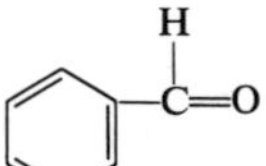
—Cl, —Br, —I*	Bromobenzene, 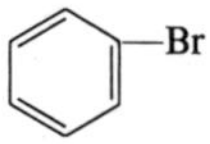 —Br	O ‖ —C—OH	Benzoic acid, 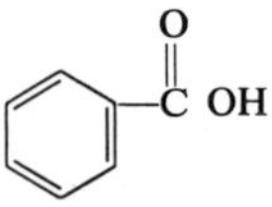

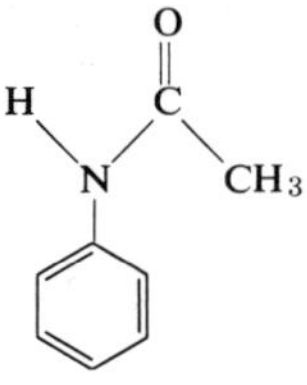

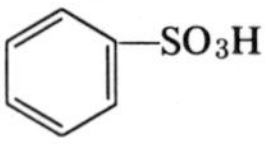

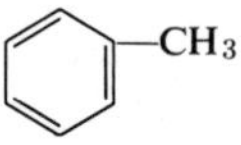

*The halogens are *ortho-para* directing but also are electrophilic. The second influence overshadows the first to deactivate the ring.

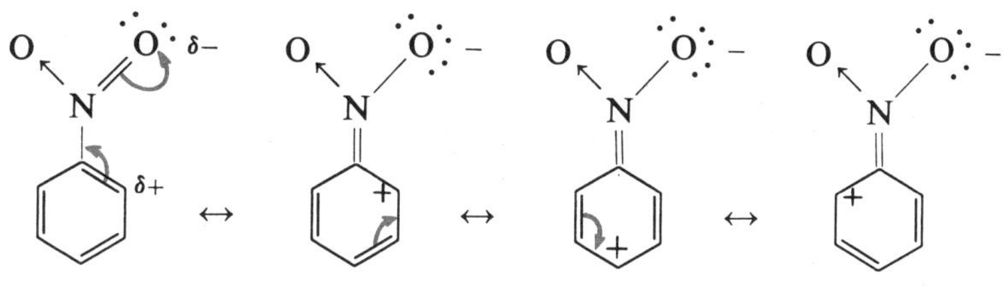

| V | VI | VII | VIII |

Table 4.2 lists the common *ortho-para*, and *meta* directors in approximate order of diminishing directive power.

The directive power of substituents must be considered in any synthetic route which leads to a polysubstituted aromatic ring. For example, if *m*-nitrobromobenzene is to be prepared, one should not attempt to nitrate bromobenzene, but instead, should brominate nitrobenzene.

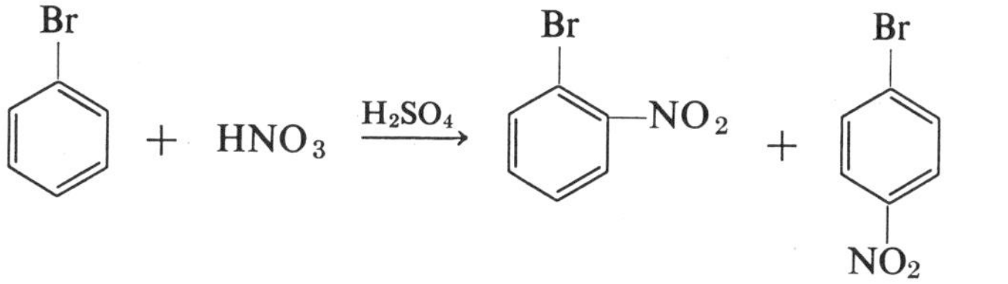

Bromobenzene   + HNO₃ $\xrightarrow{H_2SO_4}$

o-Nitro-
bromobenzene
(38%)

p-Nitro-
bromobenzene
(62%)

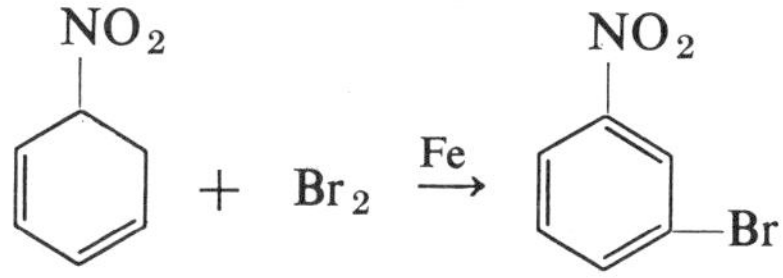

Nitrobenzene   + Br₂ $\xrightarrow{Fe}$

m-Nitro-
bromobenzene
(nearly 100%)

□□ *SUMMARY*

[1] Aromatic hydrocarbons are derived from coal tar and petroleum. They are cyclic, relatively stable systems containing one or more six-carbon benzenoid structures.

[2] Aromatic hydrocarbons may be homologs of benzene or polycyclic systems. The latter may be either fused or isolated rings.

[3]   The benzene structure is a resonance hybrid.

[4]   Aromatic compounds may be named by trivial names or as derivatives of benzene. Relative positions of substituents must be indicated.

[5]   Reactions of benzene include
   a.   halogenation
   b.   nitration
   c.   alkylation (Friedel-Crafts)
   d.   sulfonation
   e.   oxidation of the side chain.

[6]   Substituents already on the ring govern the ease of further substitution and possess a directive influence upon the ring position which entering groups assume.

[7]   *Ortho-para* directors activate the ring and enhance further substitution; *meta* directors deactivate the ring and inhibit further substitution.

□□ *NEW TERMS*

[1]   alkylation   [6]   *ortho-para* director
[2]   aromaticity   [7]   ring-activating group
[3]   Friedel-Crafts reaction   [8]   ring-deactivating group
[4]   *meta* director   [9]   side chain
[5]   nitrating mixture   [10] stabilization energy

■ □ SUPPLEMENTARY EXERCISES
▼   AND PROBLEMS

[1]   Assign an acceptable name to each of the following:

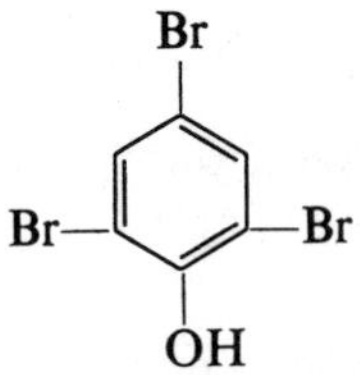

(a) 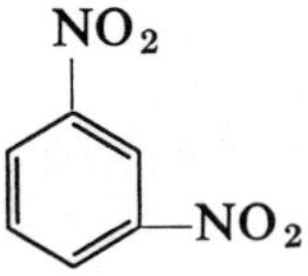   (b) 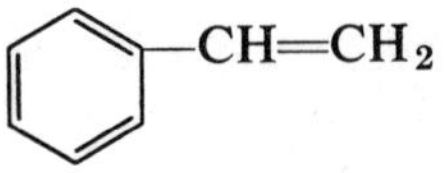   (c) 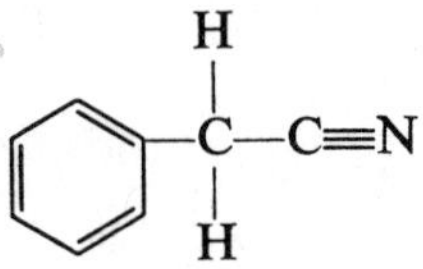   (d)

(e)   (f)   (g)

[2]   Draw structural formulas for the following useful substances:
(a)   T.N.T. (2, 4, 6-trinitrotoluene, a high explosive)
(b)   Salicyclic acid (o-hydroxybenzoic acid, a pharmaceutical)
(c)   Pentachlorophenol (a wood preservative and fungicide)
(d)   p-Dichlorobenzene (a moth repellent and larvicide)

[3]   Draw structures for all isomeric homologs of benzene with the formula C_9H_{12}. Assign an acceptable name to each.

[4]   In the bromination of benzene iron filings were used as a "carrier." Explain by what mechanism iron could promote the formation of an electrophilic ring-seeking bromine atom, when halogens are by nature such strong electronegative elements.
        Do you think that $AlCl_3$ could serve as a catalyst in the bromination reaction?

[5]   Write structural formulas for:
(a)   A compound, C_8H_{10}, which can give only one theoretically possible monobromo ring substitution product.
(b)   A compound, C_9H_{12}, which can give only one theoretically possible mononitro ring substitution product.

[6]   If ethylbenzene were treated with chlorine in the presence of bright sunlight, where would substitution most likely occur? (*Hint: See Section 2.9-B*).

[7]   An unidentified liquid is thought to be either benzene, cyclohexene, or cyclohexane. What simple chemical test will identify it?

[8]   Using toluene or benzene as your only organic starting material and any other reagents you may require, devise synthetic routes which will lead to the following products.
(a)   o-nitrobenzoic acid
(b)   m-bromonitrobenzene
(c)   p-bromobenzoic acid
(d)   p-toluenesulfonic acid
(e)   cumene (isopropylbenzene)

[9]   Show the probable mono-nitrated products when each of the following is treated with a nitrating mixture.

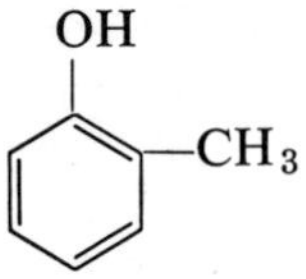

(a)

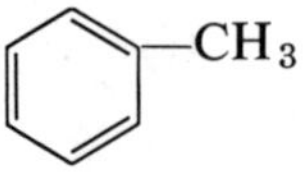

(b)

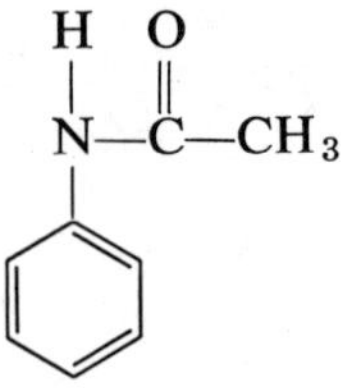

(c)

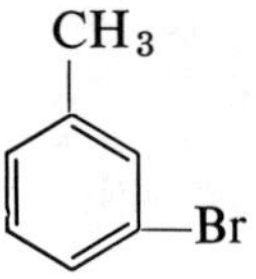

(d)

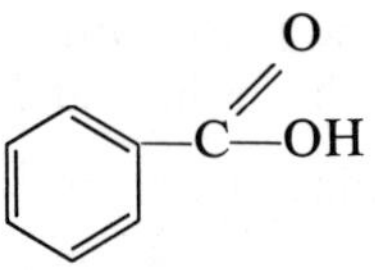

(e)

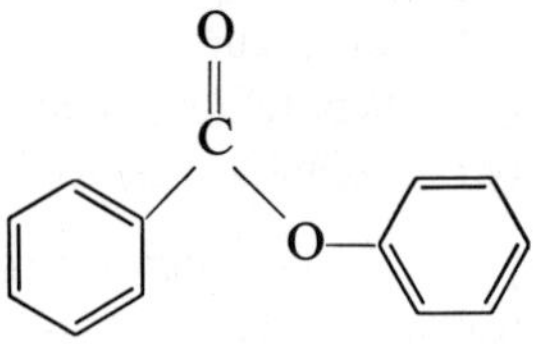

(f)

[10] Complete the following expressions, showing the principal products, if any, expected in each.

(a) 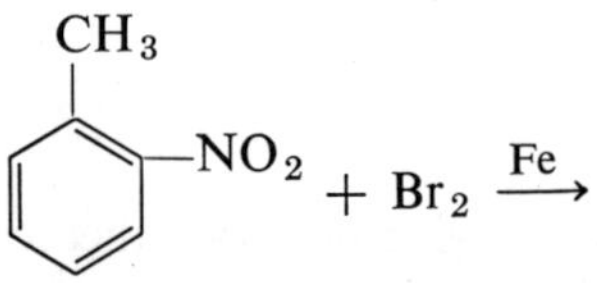 $+ Br_2 \xrightarrow{Fe}$

(b) 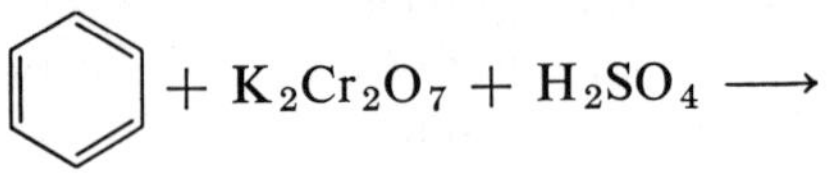 $+ K_2Cr_2O_7 + H_2SO_4 \longrightarrow$

(c) 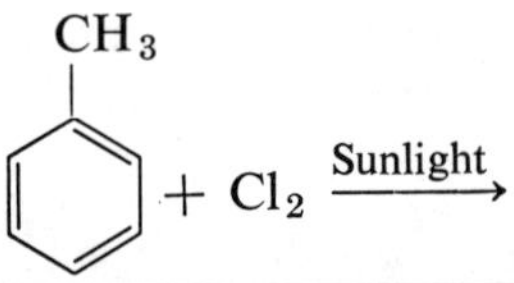 $+ Cl_2 \xrightarrow{Sunlight}$

(d) 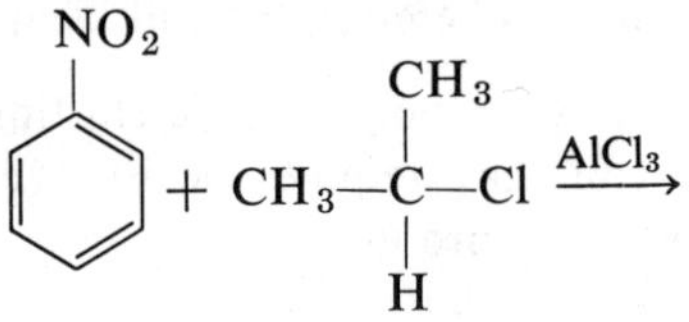 $+ CH_3-\overset{CH_3}{\underset{H}{C}}-Cl \xrightarrow{AlCl_3}$

(e) 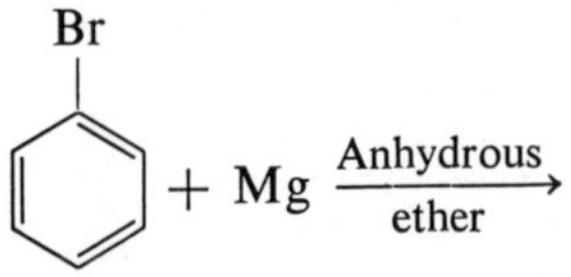 $+ Mg \xrightarrow[\text{ether}]{\text{Anhydrous}}$

(f)  $+ H_2SO_4 \longrightarrow$

[11] A hydrocarbon of the formula C_8H_{10} yields two monobromo derivatives. On strong oxidation it gave an acid isomeric with the oxidation product of naphthalene. What was the original hydrocarbon?

chapter 5

Natural Gas, Petroleum, and Petrochemicals

5.1 INTRODUCTION

> Drilling the first oil well at Titusville, Pennsylvania, in 1859 gave birth not only to a mammoth new industry but also to a new way of life. The discovery of a vast new source of fuels and lubricants ushered in the machine age. These important products, now more in demand than ever before, are supplied not only in greater quantity but in better quality. However, the production of fuels and lubricants from crude oils no longer remains the only function of the petroleum industry. Petroleum provides us with much more. Today, not only the high octane fuel which powers our automobiles, but the upholstery, the dozens of plastic components built into the car, much of the rubber in the tires on the wheels — indeed, the asphalt roadway beneath them, all have this common origin. Although the petroleum industry is still the principal supporting industry for all modes of transportation, every facet of our economy is in some measure dependent upon petroleum.

5.2 NATURAL GASES

According to one theory, petroleum resulted from the decomposition of plant and animal matter of marine origin. This appears to be borne out by the high percentages of nitrogen and carbon dioxide found in gas samples from certain oil fields. Natural gas, other than these noncombustible components, is largely methane with lesser amounts of lower alkanes. The composition of a natural gas varies according to the source from which it is taken. Some natural gases have a carbon dioxide content as high as 30% or more. Other natural gases contain high percentages of nitrogen, hydrogen sulfide, and some helium. Obviously, any gas sold as fuel cannot contain such high percentages of nonfuel components. The latter must be removed by chemical means or by fractionation. Analysis of a representative gas sample supplied as fuel to the consumer has an approximate percentage composition shown in Table 5.1.

□■ TABLE 5.1

COMPOSITION OF NATURAL GAS SOLD AS FUEL*

Component	Percent
Methane	78–80
Nitrogen	10–12
Ethane	5.9
Propane	2.9
n-Butane	0.71
Isobutane	0.26
C_5-C_7 hydrocarbons	0.13
Carbon dioxide	0.07

*Courtesy of Northern Natural Gas Company, Omaha, Nebraska

5.3   LIQUEFIED PETROLEUM (L. P.) GASES

Certain of the low molecular weight gaseous hydrocarbons are found dissolved in crude oil and also occur as by-products of gasoline manufacture. These low-boiling hydrocarbons (largely propane), after removal by distillation, are compressed until liquefied and then "bottled" in steel cylinders. The liquefied gas reverts to gaseous form when the pressure is released. It is a common sight to see such cylinders of L. P. gas in rural areas, on house trailers, at lakeside cabins, and wherever the convenience of piped natural gas is desired but not available.

5.4   COMPOSITION OF CRUDE OIL

Crude oil, with the exception of the very volatile and easily removed gaseous fractions, is an extremely complex mixture made up of hundreds of compounds. A sample of mid-continent crude oil taken from an oil field in Oklahoma and analyzed over a forty-year period (1926–1967) yielded 295 different hydrocarbons. These, altogether, make up but approximately 50% of the volume of the petroleum sample analyzed. The 295 hydrocarbons isolated and identified thus far have been the "easy" ones leaving half of the sample still to be resolved and identified. Table 5.2 lists the classes of hydrocarbons and the number of compounds within each class that have been found in the sample. The number of hydrocarbons within any particular class will, of course, vary according to the geographical location of the producing area. Table 5.3 shows the principal hydrocarbon fractions into which petroleum is separated, the approximate boiling range of each fraction, and their principal uses.

☐■ TABLE 5.2

HYDROCARBONS FOUND IN CRUDE OIL*

Class of Hydrocarbon	Type of Compounds within Each Class	Number of Compounds within Each Class
Alkanes	Saturated, straight-chain hydrocarbons	33
	Saturated, branched-chain hydrocarbons	52
Cycloalkanes	Cyclopentane derivatives	27
	Cyclohexane derivatives	25
	Other cycloparaffins	31
Aromatic	Benzene derivatives	40
	Aromatic cycloparaffins	12
	Naphthalene and poly-nuclear aromatic hydro-carbons	67
	Oxygen-containing compounds	4
	Sulfur-containing compounds	4

*Source: American Petroleum Institute

☐■ TABLE 5.3

PETROLEUM FRACTIONS

Fractions	Approx. Composition	Approx. Boiling Range, °C	Principal Uses
Gas	$C_1–C_4$	0–20	fuel
Gasoline	$C_6–C_9$	69–150	motor fuel, solvent naphtha
Kerosine	$C_{10}–C_{16}$	175–300	jet fuel, fuel oil, diesel fuel
Gas-oil	$C_{16}–C_{18}$	300 up	diesel fuel, fuel oil, cracking stock*
Wax-oil	$C_{18}–C_{20}$	–	lubricants, mineral oils, cracking stock
Paraffin wax	$C_{21}–C_{40}$	–	packaging (wax paper), candles
Residuum	–	–	roofing, water-proofing, road building materials.

*See Sec. 5.5 for a discussion of cracking.

5.5   THE CRACKING, OR PYROLYSIS, OF PETROLEUM

The appearance of the automobile created an immediate demand for a high energy, volatile, liquid fuel. The supply of **straight-run gasoline** (the $C_6–C_9$ fraction obtained by simple fractional distillation of petroleum) soon became inadequate for the number of automobiles. Moreover, straight-run gasoline is a low quality motor fuel unsuitable for use in the present-day, high compression automobile engine.

In order to increase the supply of high octane gasoline, it was found necessary to break down, or "crack," high molecular weight hydrocarbons not suitable for motor fuel into smaller molecules. A number of the lower molecular weight members that result from this treatment fall within the gasoline range. Cracking of petroleum usually is accomplished by heating hydrocarbons to high temperatures in the presence of certain catalysts. This treatment, called **catalytic cracking,** yields not only lower alkanes, but alkenes and hydrogen as well. These various fragmentary products then are combined, rearranged, or in some other manner used in the synthesis of high grade gasoline. Certain of the methods used to make gasoline are illustrated in Section 5.7. Figure 5.1 shows schematically the separation and refinement of petroleum fractions.

■□FIGURE 5.1

A SCHEMATIC FLOW DIAGRAM OF AN OIL REFINERY'S PRINCIPAL PROCESSING UNITS. (COURTESY OF TEXACO, INC.)

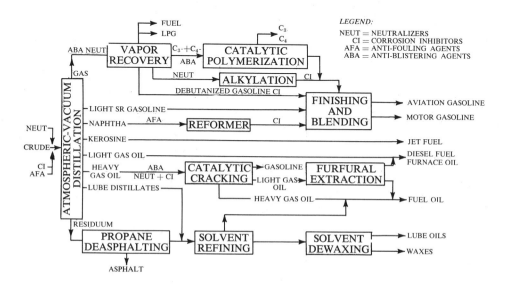

5.6   GASOLINE. OCTANE NUMBER

The ability of a gasoline to perform well in an internal combustion engine is given by its **octane number.** In order to standardize the performance of a gasoline, 2, 2, 4-trimethylpentane, $(CH_3)_3C-CH_2CH(CH_3)_2$, a very fine motor fuel with no tendency to premature explosion under high compression, is assigned an octane number of 100. Normal heptane, $CH_3CH_2CH_2CH_2CH_2CH_2CH_3$, an extremely bad "knocker," is assigned a value of zero. The octane number of any fuel is determined from a comparison of its performance to that of a blend of 2, 2, 4-trimethylpentane and *n*-heptane. Both the fuel in question and the prepared blend are tested in a specially instrumented engine. The percent of 2, 2, 4-trimethylpentane in the blend that gives the same performance as the fuel in question establishes the octane number of the latter. Motor fuels can be prepared that have octane numbers well in excess of 100, that is, they will perform even better as motor fuels than 2, 2, 4-trimethylpentane.

Octane ratings of motor fuels have been improved further by the use of certain additives. These agents improve the performance of a gasoline largely by preventing "knocking" caused by premature explosions. Among the first compounds to be employed as anti-knock agents was tetraethyl lead (TEL), $(C_2H_5)_4Pb$ (Sec. 7.7). Note the improvement in the octane ratings of certain hydrocarbons that results when less than one part per thousand of tetraethyl lead (TEL) is added (Table 5.4). Tetramethyl lead (TML), $(CH_3)_4Pb$, a more recently produced lead alkyl, is used for the same purpose.

□■ TABLE 5.4

OCTANE RATINGS (NUMBER) OF SOME HYDROCARBONS*

Hydrocarbon	Formula	ml TEL**/gallon	
		0.0	3.0
Methane	CH_4	>120	–
Ethane	C_2H_6	118.5	–
Propane	C_3H_8	112.5	–
n-Butane	C_4H_{10}	93.6	101.6
n-Pentane	C_5H_{12}	61.7	88.7
2-Methylbutane (Isopentane)	C_5H_{12}	92.6	102.0
n-Hexane	C_6H_{14}	24.8	65.3
Methylcyclopentane	C_6H_{12}	91.3	105.3
n-Heptane	C_7H_{16}	**0.0**	43.5
Methylcyclohexane	C_7H_{14}	74.8	88.2
Methylbenzene (Toluene)	C_7H_8	103.2	111.8
n-Octane	C_8H_{18}	−19.0	25.0
2, 2, 4-Trimethylpentane (Isooctane)[1]	C_8H_{18}	**100.0**	115.5
2, 4, 4-Trimethyl-2-pentene	C_8H_{16}	103.5	105.7
Isopropylbenzene (Cumene)	C_9H_{12}	113.0	116.7
1, 3, 5-Trimethylbenzene (Mesitylene)	C_9H_{12}	>120	–

*Courtesy of Ethyl Corporation   **Tetraethyl lead
[1]2, 2, 4-Trimethylpentane is sometimes incorrectly named "isooctane."

In order to carry away the lead that otherwise would be deposited in the engine and cause fouling, ethylene bromide, $BrCH_2CH_2Br$, and ethylene chloride, $ClCH_2CH_2Cl$, are added to ethyl fluid as lead scavengers. The lead dibromide ($PbBr_2$) or dichloride ($PbCl_2$) formed at the operating temperature of the engine are carried away with the exhaust. Many additives in addition to "anti-knock" agents are also used in today's motor fuels, each for a specific purpose. Some prevent carburetor icing and fuel line freeze-up. Others prevent spark plug fouling, protect the engine from corrosion, and provide detergent action against deposits. In addition to such materials, antioxidants also are added to inhibit the deterioration of the tetraethyl lead as well as the hydrocarbons which comprise the fuel.

5.7   METHODS USED IN GASOLINE PRODUCTION

The presence of branched-chain aliphatic, olefinic, and aromatic hydrocarbons in gasoline greatly increases its octane number (see Table 5.4). Accordingly, processes known as **reforming** or **isomerization** have been developed for the rearrangement of straight-chain molecules to branched-chain structures. Small branched-chain alkanes and alkenes then may be combined by a process called **alkylation** to produce larger molecules which fall within the gasoline range. Another process referred to as **aromatization** causes straight-chain saturated and unsaturated hydrocarbons of sufficient length to become cyclized and dehydrogenated into aromatic hydrocarbons. For example, 1-heptene, when formed into a ring compound and "aromatized," produces toluene. Other examples of how gasoline may be "tailor-made" by employing modern industrial techniques are shown by the following series of equations.

Cracking

$$C_{15}H_{32} \xrightarrow[\text{heat}]{\text{Catalyst,}} C_8H_{18} + C_7H_{14}$$

$$C_8H_{18} \xrightarrow[\text{heat}]{\text{Catalyst,}} CH_3CH_2CH_2CH_3 + CH_3\!-\!\!\overset{\displaystyle H}{\underset{}{C}}\!\!=\!\!\overset{\displaystyle H}{\underset{}{C}}\!-\!CH_3$$

    n-Butane   2-Butene

or $CH_3\!-\!CH_2\!-\!CH\!\!=\!\!CH_2$,

1-Butene

Reforming

$$n\text{-}C_4H_{10} \xrightarrow[\text{heat}]{\text{Catalyst,}} CH_3\!-\!\underset{\displaystyle \underset{}{CH_3}}{\overset{\displaystyle H}{C}}\!-\!CH_3 \text{ (or Butene)} + H_2$$

Isobutane

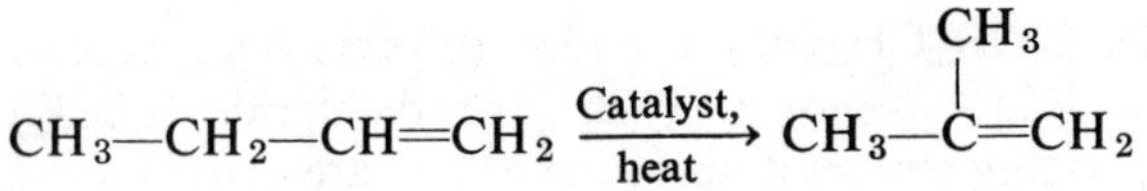

$$CH_3-CH_2-CH=CH_2 \xrightarrow[\text{heat}]{\text{Catalyst,}} CH_3-\underset{\displaystyle CH_3}{C}=CH_2$$

1-Butene   Isobutene

Alkylation

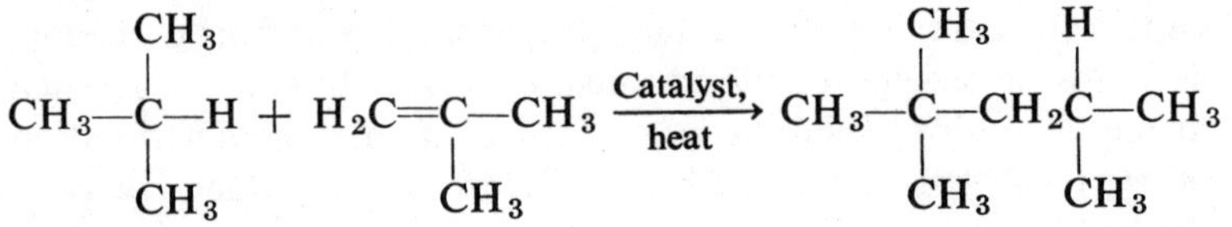

$$CH_3-\underset{\displaystyle CH_3}{\overset{\displaystyle CH_3}{C}}-H + H_2C=\underset{\displaystyle CH_3}{C}-CH_3 \xrightarrow[\text{heat}]{\text{Catalyst,}} CH_3-\underset{\displaystyle CH_3}{\overset{\displaystyle CH_3}{C}}-CH_2\underset{\displaystyle CH_3}{\overset{\displaystyle H}{C}}-CH_3$$

Isobutane   Isobutene   2, 2, 4-Trimethylpentane

Aromatization

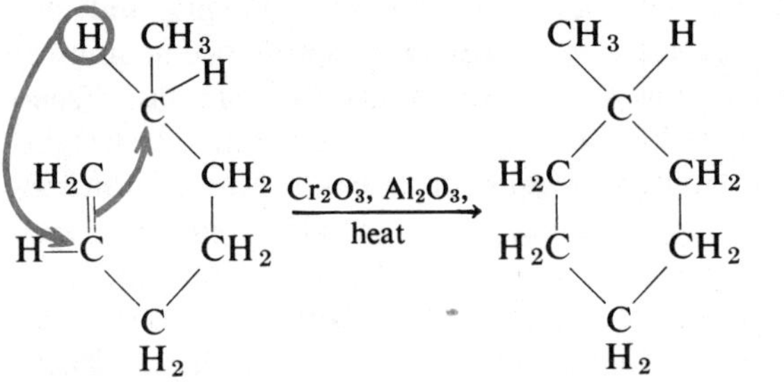

1-Heptene   Methylcyclohexane

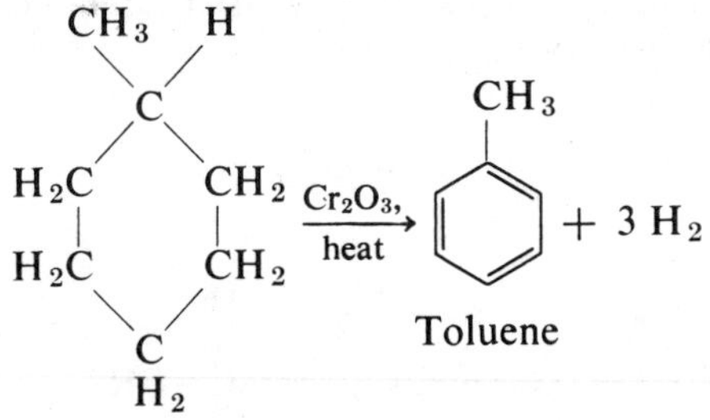

Toluene

5.8   SYNTHETIC LIQUID FUELS

The absence of petroleum deposits in Germany led to the development of two processes for the production of liquid fuels from coal. One of these, the **Fischer-Tropsch Process,** produces carbon monoxide and hydrogen from coke and steam. Hydrogen in excess then is combined with the carbon monoxide to yield hydrocarbons suitable as liquid fuels. The reaction is carried out at high temperatures and pressures and in the presence of catalysts.

$$C + H_2O \xrightarrow{300°C} CO + H_2$$

$$n\,CO + (2n + 1)\,H_2 \xrightarrow[250°C]{ThO_2,} C_nH_{2n+2} + n\,H_2O$$

Another method, known as the **Bergius Process,** hydrogenates coal directly by combining hydrogen and carbon under high pressures and temperatures. In practice, hydrogen under pressure is injected into a heavy asphaltic paste of pulverized coal. The hydrogen required for the reaction is obtained from methane and water by the following series of reactions.

$$CH_4 + H_2O \xrightarrow[750°C]{Catalyst,} CO + 3\,H_2$$

$$CO + H_2O \xrightarrow[750°C]{Catalyst,} CO_2 + H_2$$

Coal, pulverized in a ball mill, is mixed with the residuum of the previous run to provide the heavy viscous paste. A general equation for the process may be written.

$$n\,C + (n + 1)\,H_2 \xrightarrow[\substack{700 \text{ atmospheres,} \\ 400°C}]{Fe_2O_3,\ MoO_2,} C_nH_{2n+2}$$

The Bergius process is a versatile one which yields hydrocarbons that fall within the diesel fuel and jet fuel, as well as within the gasoline range. During World War II Germany produced approximately 70% of its aviation fuel by this method. The U.S. Bureau of Mines in 1949, as an experiment, produced the first synthetic gasoline in this country by the Bergius process. The cost of gasoline when produced synthetically from coal is now not competitive with that produced from petroleum. The two processes described probably will have no place in the American economy as long as there are sufficient petroleum reserves.

5.9   PETROCHEMICALS

The name petrochemicals is one usually assigned to compounds, found in or derived from petroleum, that are used in the manufacture of commodities other than fuels. The hydrocarbons used as fuels and lubricants are mixtures or blends of many compounds. Although these products have a common origin with petrochemicals, the term usually is reserved to describe compounds isolated from petroleum in a high state of purity. Such compounds serve as indispensable raw materials in the plastics, rubber, and synthetic fibers industries. New developments in the manufacture of paints, pesti-

PETROCHEMICALS OBTAINED FROM PETROLEUM

Hydrocarbons	Derived Products and Uses

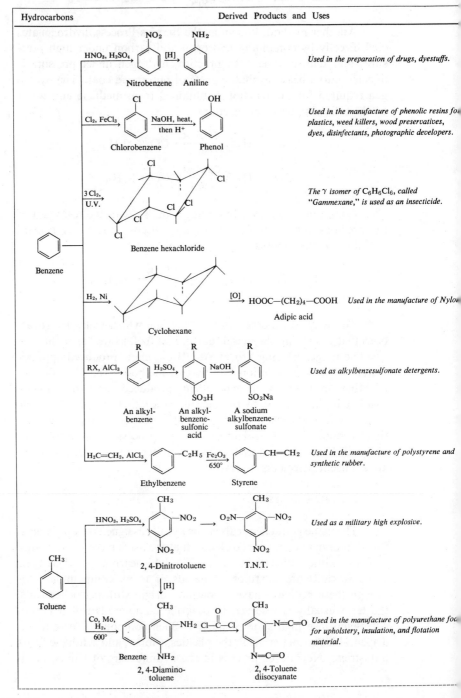

Nitrobenzene   Aniline

Used in the preparation of drugs, dyestuffs.

HNO₃, H₂SO₄ → [H] →

Cl₂, FeCl₃ → NaOH, heat, then H⁺ →

Chlorobenzene   Phenol

Used in the manufacture of phenolic resins for plastics, weed killers, wood preservatives, dyes, disinfectants, photographic developers.

3 Cl₂, U.V. →

Benzene hexachloride

The γ isomer of $C_6H_6Cl_6$, called "Gammexane," is used as an insecticide.

H₂, Ni →

Cyclohexane

[O] → $HOOC-(CH_2)_4-COOH$ *Used in the manufacture of Nylon*

Adipic acid

RX, AlCl₃ →   H₂SO₄ →   NaOH →

An alkyl-benzene   An alkyl-benzene-sulfonic acid   A sodium alkylbenzene-sulfonate

Used as alkylbenzesulfonate detergents.

H₂C=CH₂, AlCl₃ → $-C_2H_5$ Fe₂O₃ 650° → $-CH=CH_2$

Ethylbenzene   Styrene

Used in the manufacture of polystyrene and synthetic rubber.

HNO₃, H₂SO₄ →   2, 4-Dinitrotoluene   →   T.N.T.

Used as a military high explosive.

↓ [H]

Co, Mo, H₂, 600° →   Benzene   2, 4-Diamino-toluene   →   2, 4-Toluene diisocyanate

Used in the manufacture of polyurethane foam for upholstery, insulation, and flotation material.

Toluene

□ ■ TABLE   5.5 — *Continued*

PETROCHEMICALS OBTAINED FROM PETROLEUM

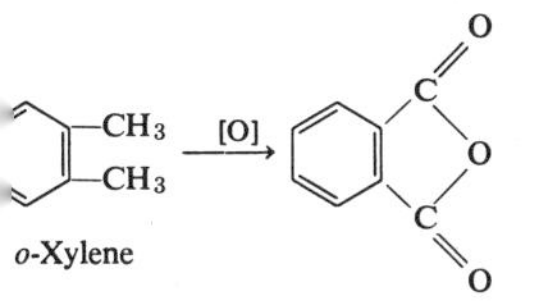

o-Xylene

Phthalic anhydride

Used in the manufacture of glyptal resins for surface coatings and auto finishes.

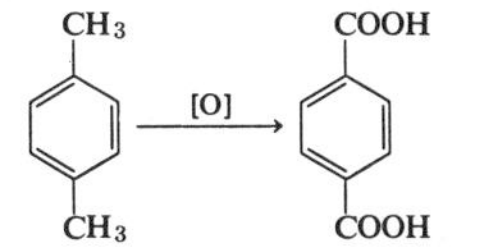

CH₃ / CH₃
p-Xylene

COOH / COOH
Terephthalic acid

Used in the manufacture of polyester fibers — e.g., Dacron.

cides, fertilizers, and detergents are made possible, in a large measure, by the ready availability of chemicals from the petroleum industry. Table 5.5 lists some of the aromatic hydrocarbons obtained from petroleum and the chemicals derived from them. Examples of everyday products made from these derived compounds are included in the table to illustrate the great commercial importance of these raw materials.

□□ *SUMMARY*

[1]   Petroleum is the principal source material from which we obtain fuels (gaseous and liquid), lubricants, and a large number of organic compounds.

[2]   Methane is the principal hydrocarbon constituent of a natural gas used as fuel; liquefied petroleum (L. P.), or "bottled" gas, is largely propane.

[3]   The composition of petroleum varies widely with the geographical location of the producing area.

[4]   The ability of a gasoline to perform well in an internal combustion engine is a measure of its "octane number."

[5]   The octane numbers of hydrocarbons increase with chain branching, unsaturation, and cyclization. Octane numbers of motor fuels may also be increased by the use of "additives."

[6]   High molecular weight hydrocarbons (above C_9) not suitable for use as gasoline are catalytically "cracked" or broken into

smaller molecules. The latter are rearranged (isomerized), cyclized (aromatized), or combined (alkylated) to form compounds of high "octane number."

[7]   The Fischer-Tropsch synthesis and the Bergius process are two German developments for the production of liquid fuel from coal.

[8]   Petrochemicals are organic compounds found in or derived from petroleum and used in the production of commodities other than fuels.

□□ *NEW TERMS*

[1]   aromatization   [4]   motor fuel additives
[2]   catalytic cracking   [5]   octane number
[3]   liquefied petroleum gas (LPG)   [6]   petrochemical

■ □EXERCISES AND PROBLEMS
▼

[1]   Explain why the inclusion of olefinic hydrocarbons in a gasoline blend improves its octane rating, but makes the gasoline less stable to storage.

[2]   Write equations to show how each of the following petrochemicals could be converted to the industrially important products indicated.

(a)   propene $\longrightarrow$ 2-propanol
(b)   ethene $\longrightarrow$ ethylene glycol
(c)   *o*-xylene $\longrightarrow$ phthalic anhydride
(d)   toluene $\longrightarrow$ benzoic acid
(e)   benzene $\longrightarrow$ maleic anhydride

[3]   Cylinders of the type used for L. P. gas storage at cottages and small homes contain, when filled, 100 pounds of fuel. If the liquefied gas is propane, how many liters of the gaseous hydrocarbon at STP must be compressed into each cylinder? (1 lb = 0.4536 kg)

[4]   The following compounds are added as antioxidants to a gasoline to improve its storage characteristics. Draw the structure of each.

(a)   2, 6-di-*tert*-butylphenol

(b) N-phenyl-β-naphthylamine

(c) 2, 4-dimethyl-6-*tert*-butylphenol

[5] Write equations for the preparation of hydrocarbon fuels from coal, water, and hydrogen by (a) the Fischer-Tropsch synthesis; (b) the Bergius process. Use C_nH_{2n+2} as the type formula for your product.

chapter 6

Stereoisomerism

INTRODUCTION

The possibility of isomerism was first discussed in Section 1.9 where we discovered that two different structures could be drawn to represent the molecular formula C_4H_{10}. These two structural variations represented two *different* molecular species — namely, *n*-butane and isobutane. Because these two hydrocarbons are different compounds, each has physical and chemical properties different from those of the other. The substitution reactions of the alkanes and the arenes, as well as the addition reactions of the alkenes, we observed, were reactions that could result in the formation of isomeric products. As we continue our study of organic chemistry we realize that isomerism is an important aspect of it, and that if we understand *why* isomeric products are formed then we also will understand *how* organic molecules react. It is in order, therefore, that we introduce at this time still another form of isomerism. The kind of isomers we shall consider in the following sections are molecular structures in which the same atoms and groups that are joined together in one isomer are similarly joined in the other. The atomic linkages are the same in both isomers but the spatial arrangement of the atoms and groups in each are different. Such isomers are called **stereoisomers** (Gr., *stereos*, solid). Our definition of stereoisomers does not include such spatial variations as those allowed 1, 2-dichloroethane in its staggered and eclipsed forms (Sec. 2.6) nor those for cyclohexane in its boat and chair forms (Sec. 2.12). Such spatial arrangements are interconverted by the expenditure of relatively small amounts of energy and may be accomplished by the simple expedient of rotation about single bonds. Such different arrangements, you will recall, are referred to as conformations. Stereo-isomers, on the other hand, have different **configurations** and can not be interconverted without breaking bonds and rearranging groups.

6.2   GEOMETRIC ISOMERISM

Geometric isomerism is a form of stereoisomerism that results when rotation of one carbon atom with respect to another is restricted by the presence of a double bond or when carbon atoms in a molecule are held more or less rigidly in a ring structure. We encountered our first example of this kind of isomerism in the *cis* and *trans* forms of 2-butene (Sec. 3.3). Geometric isomers, like other isomeric forms reviewed thus far, also have widely different physical properties and often vary greatly in their chemical behavior. Measurable differences in these properties allow us to distinguish between *cis* and *trans* forms rather easily. For example, *cis*-1, 2-dichloroethylene is a polar molecule, while *trans*-1, 2-dichloroethylene is not. Polarity in a molecule is a property that can be measured and expressed in terms of a **dipole moment**[1] and tells us whether or not the molecule is electronically "lop-sided."

(polar)   (nonpolar)

cis-1, 2-Dichloroethylene
B.P. 60°
$\mu = 1.85\ D$

trans-1, 2-Dichloroethylene
B.P. 48°
$\mu = 0$

The chemical behavior of *cis* and *trans* isomers may also vary sufficiently to enable us to distinguish one from the other. For example, the two carboxyl groups of maleic acid are on the same side of the double bond and thus properly oriented in space to permit the easy removal of a water molecule, when heated, to give maleic anhydride. Its *trans* isomer, fumaric acid, cannot form the anhydride.

[1]The dipole moment is calculated by

$$\mu = e \times d$$

where e is the charge (in electrostatic units) and d is the distance in Angstroms (Å). Dipole moments are expressed in Debye units, D.

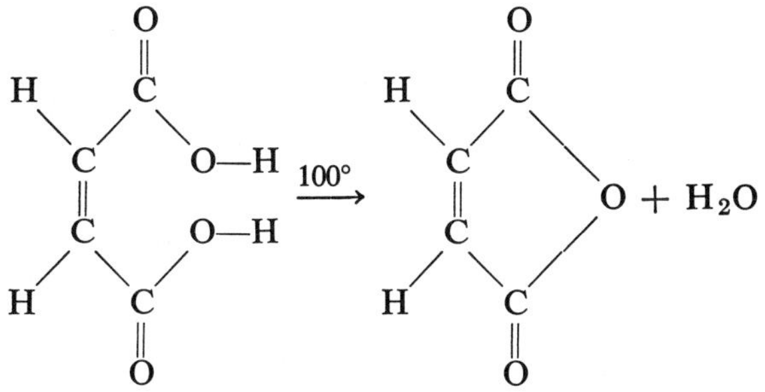

Maleic acid
(*cis*-Butenedioic
acid)
M.P. 130°

Maleic anhydride

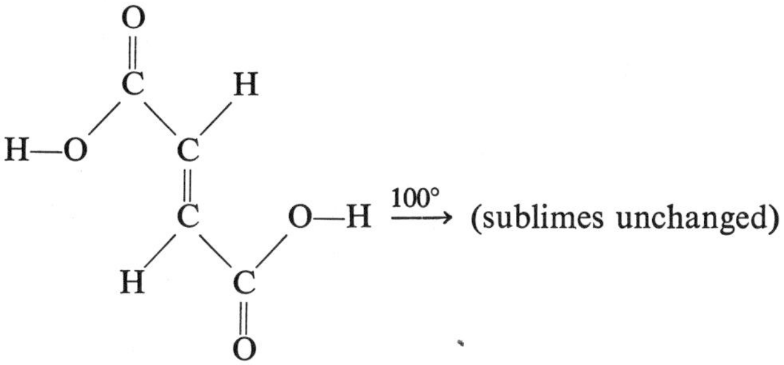

Fumaric acid
(*trans*-Butenedioic acid)
M.P. 270°

Exercise 6.1   Natural rubber and its isomer, gutta-percha, are polymers of isoprene. Natural rubber has a *cis*-configuration; gutta-percha has a *trans*-configuration. Following are partial structures of each natural product. Can you identify them?

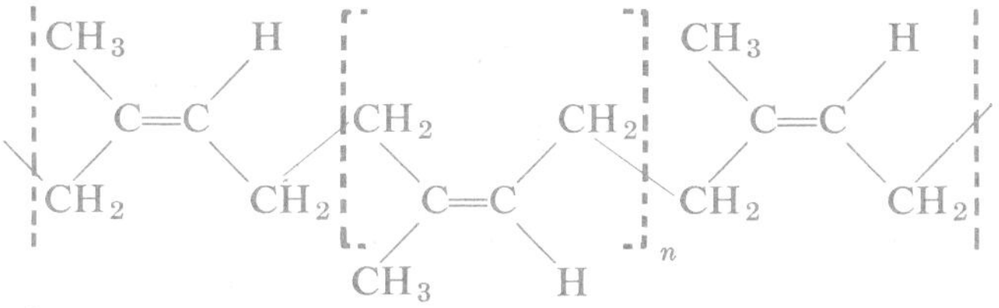

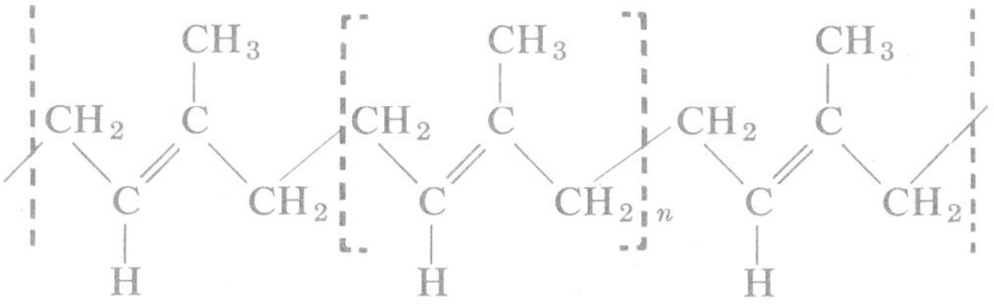

6.3   OPTICAL ISOMERISM. POLARIZED LIGHT

We now come to another kind of stereoisomerism known as **optical isomerism.** Optical isomers have the same chemical properties and the same physical properties with one notable exception. They differ in the direction in which each is able to rotate a beam of *plane-polarized* light.[2] The degree of rotation is the same for each optical isomer, but the direction of rotation is opposite.

In order to understand the phenomenon of "optical activity," it would be helpful to review the nature of plane-polarized light. Ordinary white light exhibits an electromagnetic wave motion in which waves of varying lengths are vibrating in all possible planes at right angles to the path of the ray. Monochromatic light, used in the measurement of optical activity, is light of only one wavelength. It usually is produced in one of two ways: (1) all unwanted wavelengths of ordinary light are removed by means of a colored filter, or (2) light of one wavelength is generated from a special source such as a sodium or a mercury lamp. Monochromatic light, like ordinary light, also consists of waves vibrating in all possible planes at right angles to the path of propagation.

Certain substances such as tourmaline crystals, polaroid, or specially prepared prisms, called Nicol prisms, act as screens when light is passed through them. Waves vibrating in only one plane pass through such special screens and all those vibrating in other planes either are rejected or absorbed. Such specially filtered light is said to be *plane-polarized.*

We can illustrate the action of such a **polarizer** best with the Nicol prism. The Nicol prism is an ingenious device made of calcite, $CaCO_3$. Calcite is a clear crystal with the shape of a rectangular rhombohedron and having an unusual optical property called *birefringence*, or double refraction. A ray of light entering the crystal is refracted or bent in two slightly different directions to produce two rays. To form the Nicol prism, the crystal is cut in a plane diagonally through the obtuse angles and perpendicular to the two end faces. The cut surfaces then are polished and recemented with Canada balsam. After entering the crystal and striking the cemented surface,

---

[2]Optical isomers may vary in their rates of reaction with other optically active substances. This is especially true in biological systems. Thus one optical isomer may be attacked by a bacterium, the other not. Again, one of a pair of optical isomers may have a hormonal activity far greater than that of the other. These differences are due to the spatial requirements of each reactant in combining with or attacking the other.

one of the refracted rays vibrating in one plane is transmitted and others are reflected out of the crystal. Figure 6.1 illustrates graphically how a beam of monochromatic light vibrating in more than one plane might appear before (a) and after (b) it had passed through a Nicol prism polarizer.

■□FIGURE 6.1

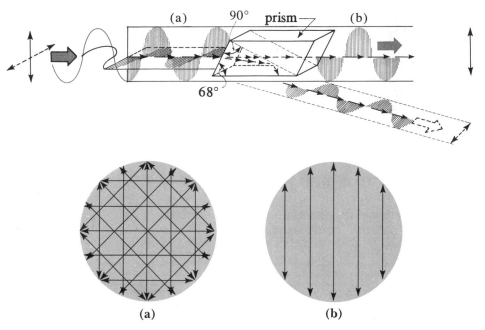

(a) A beam of monochromatic light vibrating in all planes.
(b) A beam of plane-polarized light.

A maximum transmission of plane-polarized light may be observed through a second prism, called the **analyzer** only when the latter is oriented in the same optical plane as the polarizer. On the other hand, when the analyzer is rotated, the intensity of the emergent beam, as seen by the viewer, is gradually diminished. A point of minimum transmission is reached when the second prism has been rotated through an angle of 90° from the point of maximum transmission. The phenomenon can be illustrated graphically by using two polaroid lenses (Fig. 6.2).

An *optically active* compound is one which is capable of rotating the plane of polarized light. The compound is said to be **dextro-**

■□FIGURE 6.2

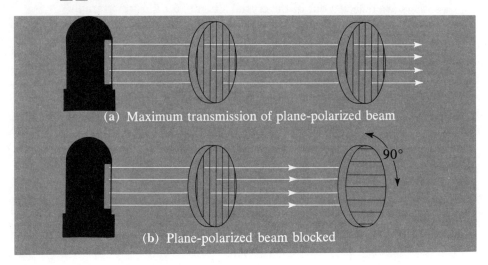

(a) Maximum transmission of plane-polarized beam

(b) Plane-polarized beam blocked

■□FIGURE 6.3

SCHEMATIC DIAGRAM OF THE POLARIMETER
SHOWING COMPONENTS.

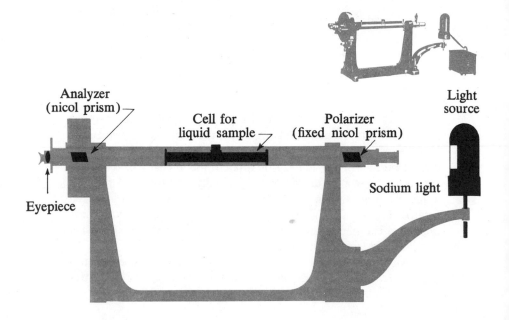

rotatory (L., *dexter*, right) when the plane of polarized light is rotated to the right, or clockwise. A dextrorotatory substance is always indicated by the positive (+) sign. A compound is described as **levorotatory** (L., *laevus*, left) when the direction of rotation is to the left, or counterclockwise. In this case the negative (−) sign is used to describe its rotation. The angle of rotation, α, is measured in degrees.

Optical activity in organic compounds is observed and measured by means of an instrument called a **polarimeter** (Fig. 6.3). The value of the specific rotation, $[\alpha]$, depends upon the length of the tube containing the sample solution, measured in decimeters, and upon the concentration of the solution measured in grams per milliliter. The density must be known if the sample is a pure liquid.

$$[\alpha] = \frac{\text{observed rotation in degrees}}{\text{length of sample tube in dm} \times \text{concentration (g/ml)}}$$

In order to standardize the specific rotation values of optically active substances, both the temperature at which observations are made and the light source employed are indicated. For example, the term $[\alpha]_D^{25°} = +54°$ indicates that the specific rotation of an optically active compound is 54° to the right when the measurement is made at 25°C and the D line of the spectrum (sodium light source, 5893 Å) is used.

6.4   MOLECULAR ASYMMETRY AND OPTICAL ISOMERISM

A carbon atom is described as being **asymmetric**[3] when four *different* atoms or groups are bonded to it. An asymmetric carbon atom in a formula usually is indicated by an asterisk placed near it. For example, in the formula for *sec*-butyl chloride (below) number two carbon atom is indicated as being asymmetric.

$$
\begin{array}{ccccccc}
 & H & & H & & H & & H \\
 & | & & | & & |* & & | \\
H- & C & - & C & - & C & - & C & -H \\
 & | & & | & & | & & | \\
 & H & & H & & Cl & & H
\end{array}
$$

sec-Butyl chloride

---

[3]Molecules can be asymmetrical — not atoms. An asymmetric carbon atom is only the *point* of asymmetry. This is a sufficient condition for optical isomerism, not a necessary one.

■ □ FIGURE 6.4

NONSUPERIMPOSABLE MIRROR IMAGES.

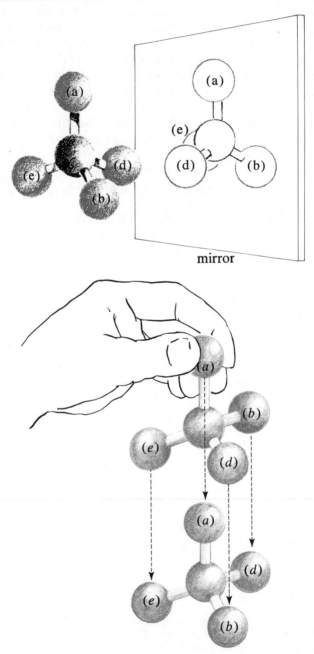

mirror

Optical isomerism is possible whenever an asymmetric carbon atom is part of a molecular structure. Four unlike groups bonded to a carbon atom make possible two structural forms — the *dextro* and *levo* forms of a pair of optical isomers. The relationship that such optical isomers bear to each other corresponds to that which the right hand bears to the left. They are nonidentical mirror images and are nonsuperimposable. In other words, one isomer cannot be positioned above the other with all four of the different substituents of the isomer above coinciding with those of the isomer below (Fig. 6.4). Mirror-image, optical isomers also are called **enantiomorphs** (Gr., *enantios*, opposite; *morph*, form), or **enantiomers.**

Exercise 6.2 Draw stereochemical formulas for three olefins of formula C_5H_9Br that would show optical activity. Do any of them also have *cis* and *trans* forms?

6.5 PROJECTION FORMULAS AND RELATIVE CONFIGURATIONS

Most molecules containing carbon are three-dimensional. The four bonds of a saturated carbon atom, as was pointed out in the first chapter, are directed to the vertices of a tetrahedron. Tetrahedral structures are difficult to draw on a flat surface such as the blackboard or a sheet of paper and therefore are drawn as **projection formulas** with all four groups in the same plane as the carbon atom to which they are bonded (Fig. 6.5(b)). The spatial positions of four groups bonded to a central carbon atom is of little importance if two or more of the groups are identical, for in this case there will be no difference in the relative positions of the four bonded groups, regardless of their arrangement about the carbon atom. However, a random bond assignment must not be made when drawing and naming the structures of optical isomers because two configurations are now possible. The need for relating the configurations of optical isomers to some standard structure soon became apparent to early chemists who were working with optically active compounds, and it was decided to relate their configurations to that of glyceraldehyde, $HOCH_2\overset{*}{C}H(OH)CHO$. The carbon chain of glyceraldehyde was to be written vertically with only the asymmetric carbon atom in the plane of the paper. Both the carbonyl and the hydroxymethyl groups were to be written as if *behind* the plane — the carbonyl at the top and the hydroxymethyl group at the bottom. The hydroxyl group and the hydrogen atom attached to the asymmetric carbon were to be written as if in *front* of the plane of the paper — the hydroxyl to the right and the hydrogen to the left (Fig. 6.5(a)). Flattening out the structure as shown in Fig. 6.5(a) produces the projection formulas shown in Fig. 6.5(b). This configuration was designated the D-configuration of glyceraldehyde and was identified by a small capital D. Any other optically active molecule with a relative configuration thus would be identified as belonging to the D (dee) series. Its mirror-image isomer, with an opposite configuration, was identified as belonging to the L (ell) series.

■□FIGURE 6.5

(a) PERSPECTIVE AND (b) PROJECTION FORMULAS OF D(+) GLYCERALDEHYDE.

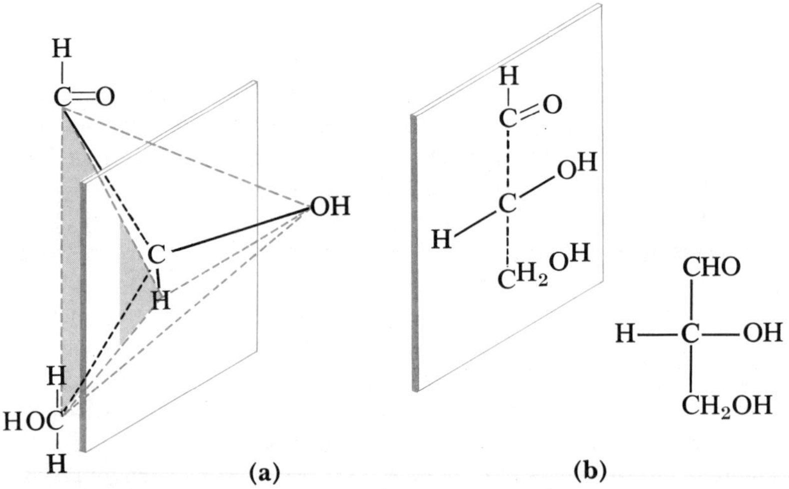

(a)   (b)

The designations "D" and "L" refer to configuration only and are not to be interpreted as "dextro" and "levo." The latter terms refer to the direction of rotation and are symbolized by the plus and minus signs respectively. They sometimes are abbreviated, dextro is *d* and levo is *l*. The D-form of glyceraldehyde was arbitrarily chosen as the dextrorotatory isomer without a knowledge of its absolute or true configuration. The choice was a fortuitous one, for not until 1951, with the use of modern analytical methods, was the dextro isomer definitely established as being the D-form. Had the absolute configuration of the dextro isomer of glyceraldehyde been found to be that of the L-form, much of the chemical literature of the previous seventy-five years would have needed rewriting, because all D and L forms studied during that time would have been related to the wrong compound. It is possible, you see, for an optically active substance to have the L-configuration and yet be dextrorotatory.

We will have an opportunity to practice using the D and L conventions when we study the carbohydrates and amino acids.

6.6   ASYMMETRIC SYNTHESIS

The structure of *sec*-butyl chloride is that of an asymmetric molecule since there are four different groups attached to the number two carbon.

$$CH_3CH_2-\overset{\overset{\displaystyle H}{|}}{\underset{\underset{\displaystyle Cl}{|}}{C}}{}^{*}-CH_3$$

However, the preparation of *sec*-butyl chloride by the direct chlorination of *n*-butane leads to an optically inactive product because an equal number of dextro and levo isomers are produced. Such 50-50 mixtures of equal parts of enantiomorphs are called **racemates,** *d, l*-mixtures, or ($\pm$)-mixtures. The optical activity of one half of the isomers in the mixture is nullified by that of the other half and the mixture is said to be optically inactive by what is called **external compensation.**

It is not difficult to understand why equal amounts of enantiomeric forms of *sec*-butyl chloride result when one considers the planar structure of the hydrocarbon free radical that forms as one of the reaction intermediates (Sec. 2.9). Obviously, there is an equal opportunity for the chlorine molecule to react with the free radical from either side. Although millions or even billions of molecules are involved, the probability of approaching from either side is exactly one half. Employing the same convention for indicating bond positions as that used in Exercise 2.3, page 42, we can show two reaction sequences graphically (see page 150) to illustrate the asymmetric synthesis of racemic *sec*-butyl chloride.

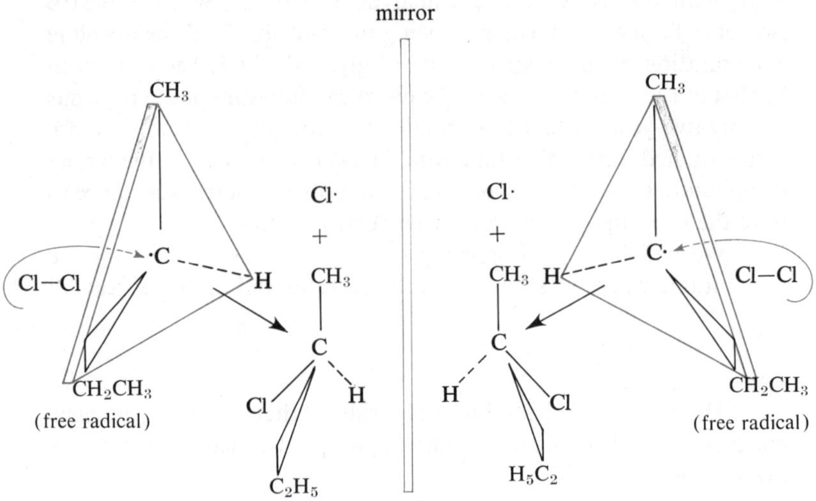

mirror

(±)-*sec*-Butyl chloride (a racemic mixture)

Any laboratory synthesis that leads to the production of an asymmetric molecule nearly always produces a racemic mixture. In nature, however, it appears that a stereospecificity governs both the synthesis and the reactions of optically active substances. For ex-ample the catalytic reduction of pyruvic acid, $CH_3-\overset{\overset{\displaystyle O}{\|}}{C}-COOH$, in the laboratory leads to racemic lactic acid, or a *d, l*-mixture. On the other hand, pyruvic acid is reduced by yeast to *levo*-lactic acid. Lactic acid isolated from muscle tissue is *dextro*-lactic acid.

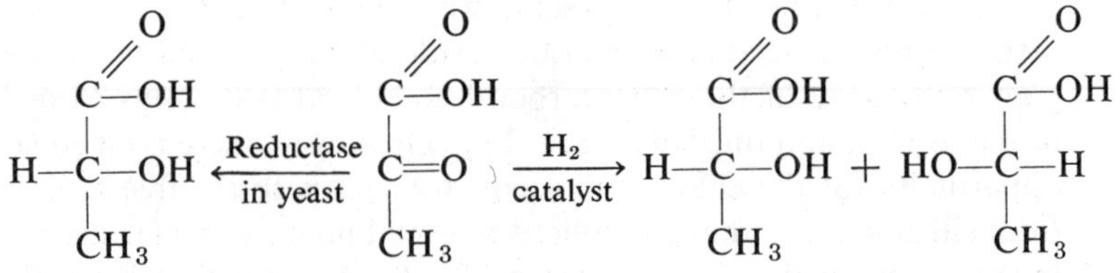

D—(−) Lactic acid   Pyruvic acid   *d, l*-Lactic acid

Most natural products are optically active and usually are stereospecific in their reactions. A study of optical isomerism, therefore, must be a prelude to any study of natural substances.

> **Exercise 6.3** Using solid, dotted, and wedge-shaped bonds draw two stereochemical formulas for 2-pentene. (a) Does the addition of HBr to either structure lead to resolvable optical isomers? (b) Could the addition of HBr to either structure lead to an optically inactive molecule?

6.7   COMPOUNDS CONTAINING TWO ASYMMETRIC CARBON ATOMS.

(Case A) Two Unlike Asymmetric Carbon Atoms. The total number of optical isomers possible when a molecule contains n unlike asymmetric carbon atoms is 2^n. This is a statement of the **van't Hoff rule.**[4] The rule may be illustrated by considering the stereoisomerism possible for a molecule with a configuration like that exhibited by the ball and stick model shown.

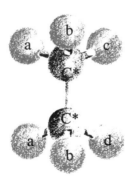

Designating the upper asymmetric carbon α and the lower one β in structures **I** to **IV** (see next page), and arbitrarily assigning $(+)$ or $(-)$ values to the contribution each makes to the total rotatory power of the molecule, it can be shown that two configurations are possible for each asymmetric carbon atom.

Structures **I** and **II** represent a pair of enantiomers as do structures **III** and **IV**. Although structures **II** and **III** (also structures **II** and **IV**, **I** and **III**, and **I** and **IV**) are optically active stereoisomers,

---

[4] J. H. van't Hoff (1852–1911), Dutch physical chemist, was one of the first to recognize asymmetry in a compound in which four different groups were attached to a carbon atom. He postulated that the four different groups in such an asymmetric structure could have two possible spatial arrangements.

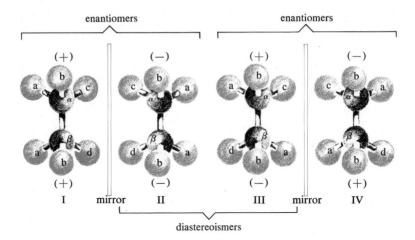

they are not mirror images. Stereoisomers that are not mirror images are called **diastereoisomers.**

(*Case B*) *Two Similar Asymmetric Carbon Atoms.*   The structure of 2, 3-dibromobutane is an example of a compound having two asymmetric carbon atoms that are similar — that is, both carbons hold identical groups. A compound with two similar asymmetric carbon atoms can have three isomeric forms. Two forms will be optically active mirror images and the third optically inactive.

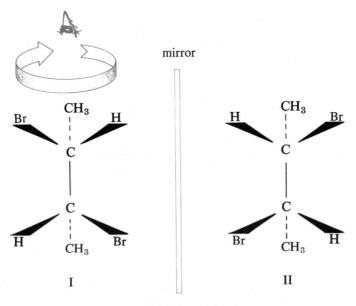

(±)-2,3-Dibromobutane

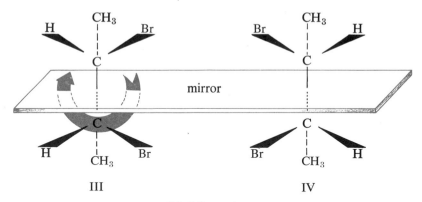

meso-2,3-Dibromobutane

The order of substituents in the upper part of structure **I**, when viewed from above and clockwise, is exactly opposite to that of its lower half. Structure **I** has its mirror image in structure **II**. In each structure the configuration of one half of the molecule, when viewed from above, is exactly opposite to that of the other half. Structures **I** and **II** are nonsuperimposable mirror images. On the other hand, the order of substituents in the upper half of either structure **III** or **IV** is the same as that of each corresponding lower half when viewed from above and clockwise. In fact, structure **IV** is but structure **III** rotated (in the plane of the paper) 180°. Structures **III** and **IV**, therefore, are one and the same. In each, the upper half is a mirror image of the lower half. Such an arrangement of substituents makes for an optically inactive, or a *meso*, form. A meso form is thus optically inactive by internal compensation. Any effect the upper half of such a structure might have upon plane-polarized light is exactly opposite to that produced by the lower half. The meso form of 2,3-dibromobutane, as might be expected, has physical properties unlike those of the optically active (+) and (−)-forms.

Exercise 6.4   In Section 3.7, page 72, we learned that the catalytic hydrogenation of 1,2-dimethylcyclopentene gave *cis*-1,2-dimethylcyclopentane. Are any of the carbon atoms in the disubstituted cycloalkane bonded to four different groups? Is *cis*-1,2-dimethylcyclopentane optically active?

A.   Mechanical Separation.   The separation of a racemic mixture into its optically active D and L forms is called **resolution.** The first resolution of a racemic mixture was the historic accomplishment of Pasteur in 1848. He observed that the crystalline tartaric acid salts (Sec. 12.7), when precipitated from solution, appeared to consist of "right- and left-handed" crystals. He carefully selected a number of each kind by using a pair of tweezers and a magnifying glass. Separate solutions of the same concentration were prepared of each form and their rotations observed. The rotation values of the two solutions were found to be alike *but of opposite direction.* Mechanical resolutions such as the one done by Pasteur are seldom possible. Other methods of resolution are usually necessary.

B.   Preparation and Separation of Diastereoisomers.   Reaction of a racemic mixture with an optically active reagent results in the preparation of diastereoisomers. The physical properties of diastereoisomers are different and they may be separated by crystallization, distillation, or by some other technique. An example of such chemical resolution is the preparation of salts from a racemic acid and a *levo*-base.

Enantiomers   *Diastereoisomers*

$$\left\{\begin{array}{l} dextro\text{-acid} \\ levo\text{-acid} \end{array}\right\} + levo\text{-base} \longrightarrow \left\{\begin{array}{l} dextro\text{-acid} \cdot levo\text{-base salt} \\ levo\text{-acid} \cdot levo\text{-base salt} \end{array}\right\}$$

Each diastereoisomer, having physical properties different from those of the other, may be separated by fractional crystallization. Subsequent treatment with a mineral acid liberates the optically active organic acid.

$$dextro\text{-acid} \cdot levo\text{-base salt} + HCl \longrightarrow dextro\text{-acid} + levo\text{-base} \cdot HCl$$

$$levo\text{-acid} \cdot levo\text{-base salt} + HCl \longrightarrow levo\text{-acid} + levo\text{-base} \cdot HCl$$

C.   Biochemical Resolution.   Certain microorganisms preferentially attack one isomer to the exclusion of the other when allowed to "feed" upon a racemic mixture. One optical form is thus destroyed. An example of this kind of microbiological separation is the resolution of racemic tartaric acid by *Penicillium glaucum.* This mold uses up the *dextro*-tartaric acid and leaves the *levo* form unattacked.   Biochemical resolutions as preparative procedures, however, are limited in their application.

Frequently the resolution of a *d, l*-mixture becomes the most difficult step in a preparation. For example, the natural form of epinephrine (adrenaline) is *levo* rotatory and has a physiological activity about fifteen to twenty times that of the *dextro* rotatory form.

Epinephrine

A laboratory preparation of this hormone leads to a racemic mixture. Isolation of the *levo* isomer in pure form is a procedure more costly than extracting the hormone from the adrenal glands of cattle. Therefore, on the basis of their differences in activity there would appear to be little advantage in resolving the racemic mixture into *dextro* and *levo* forms. However, the racemic mixture of epinephrine, if given a patient, must be administered in twice the dosage that he would receive if he were given the natural extract. The patient then is free to use the isomer he can.

□□ *SUMMARY*

[1]   Isomers that have similar structural formulas but different configurations (spatial arrangements) are called **stereoisomers.**

[2]   Stereoisomers may be either **geometric** (*cis-trans*) or **optical** isomers.

[3]   An **optically active** compound is one capable of rotating the plane of polarized light. Compounds that are asymmetrical are optically active. An asymmetric carbon atom is one with four different atoms or groups bonded to it.

[4]   Plane-polarized light is light in which all rays are vibrating in a single plane.

[5]   Optical isomers that are mirror images, or enantiomers, rotate plane-polarized light to the same degree, but in opposite directions.

[6]   The direction of rotation, if to the right, is designated **dextro** (+); if to the left, **levo** (−). *Dextro* and *levo* forms also may be referred to as *d* and *l* forms.

[7]   The configurations of many optically active compounds may be related to that of glyceraldehyde and designated as D- or L-forms.

[8] Optical activity can be measured by means of an instrument called a **polarimeter.**

[9] A synthesis which produces a compound containing an asymmetric carbon atom usually results in a 50-50 mixture of *dextro* and *levo* forms. Such a mixture is called a **racemic mixture.** Racemic mixtures are optically inactive.

[10] A molecule with *n different* asymmetric carbon atoms can have 2^n optical isomers.

[11] A molecule with *similar* asymmetric carbon atoms can have, in addition to *d* and *l* forms, one or more **meso** forms. *Meso* forms are optically inactive.

[12] **Diastereoisomers** are optical isomers that are not mirror images.

[13] Separation of a mixture of optical isomers into its *d* and *l* components is called **resolution.** Resolution can be accomplished mechanically, chemically, or biologically.

□□ *NEW TERMS*

[1]	configuration	[8]	*d, l*-mixture
[2]	dextrorotatory	[9]	polarimeter
[3]	diastereoisomers	[10]	polarized light
[4]	D-form	[11]	polarizer
[5]	enantiomers	[12]	racemic mixture
[6]	levorotatory	[13]	resolution
[7]	*meso* form		

■ □SUPPLEMENTARY EXERCISES
▼   AND PROBLEMS

[1] Predict the number and kind of stereoisomers possible for each of the following.

(a) Acrylic acid, $H_2C{=}CH{-}COOH$
(b) Phenylalanine, $C_6H_5{-}CH_2CH(NH_2)COOH$
(c) 2, 3-Butanediol, $CH_3CH(OH)CH(OH)CH_3$
(d) 3-Bromocyclohexene
(e) Isoprene, $H_2C{=}C(CH_3)CH{=}CH_2$

[2]   Identify the asymmetric carbon atoms in each of the structures below.   Theoretically, how many stereoisomeric forms are possible for each of these natural substances?

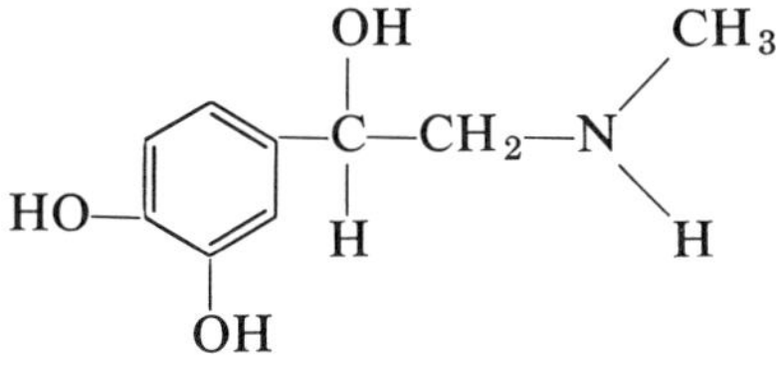

(a) Epinephrine

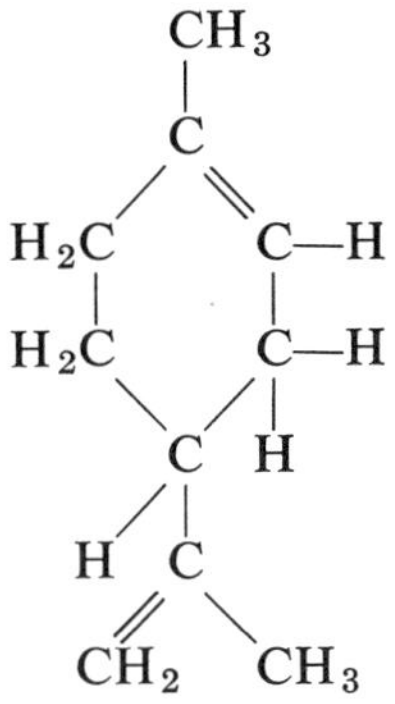

(b) Limonene

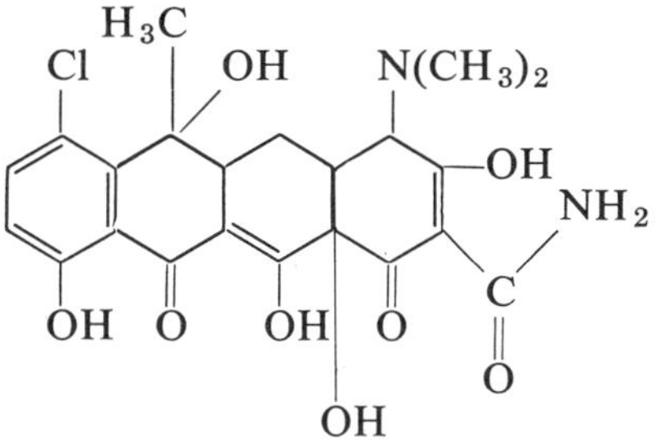

(c) Aureomycin

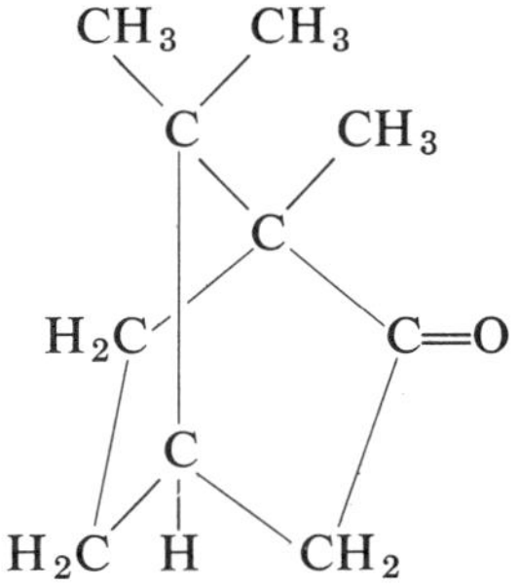

(d) Camphor

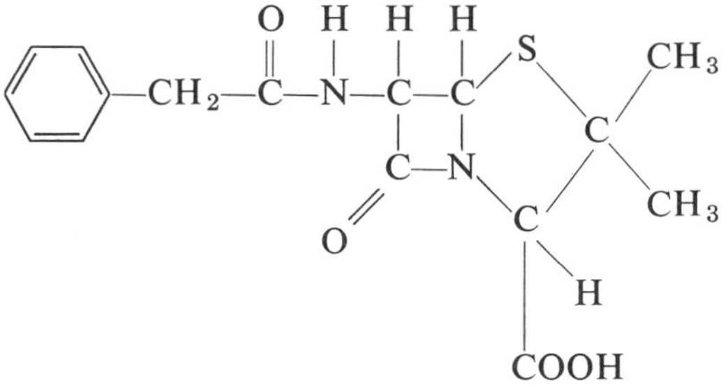

(e) Penicillin G

$$CH_3-(CH_2)_5-CH(OH)-CH_2-CH{=}CH-(CH_2)_7COOH$$

(f) Ricinoleic acid

[3]   Could the following compounds be resolved into (+) and (−) forms?

(a) $CH_3CH_2CH(OH)CH_3$

(b) $CH_3CH(Br)CH_3$

(c)

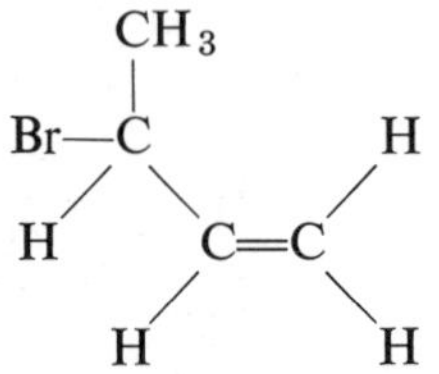

$$CH_3$$

Br—C   H

H   C=C

H   H

(d)

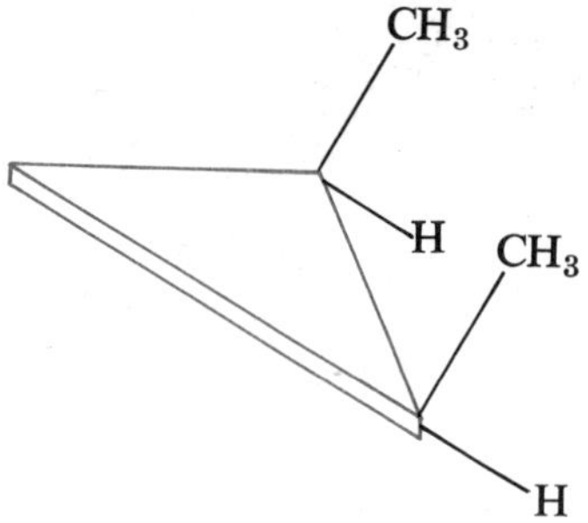

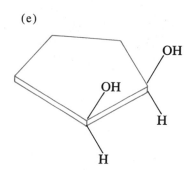

(e)

CH_3

H   CH_3

H

OH

OH

H

H

(f)

$$H$$

—C—CH_3

Cl

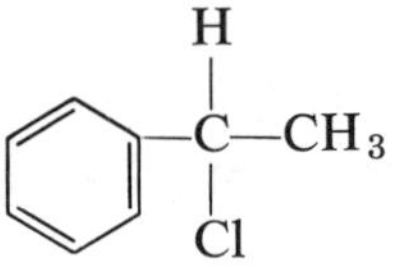

[4]   Complete the following reactions. Are the principal products resolvable into optically active forms?

(a)   1-Butene + HBr ⟶

(b)   2-Butene + HBr ⟶

(c)   Cyclopentene + HBr ⟶

(d)   Cyclopentene + Br_2 ⟶

(e)   2-Butene + HOCl ⟶

(f)   Propylene + HOCl ⟶

(g)   Propylene + cold, dilute $KMnO_4$ ⟶

[5]   If ethyl alcohol had a pyramidal structure such as that shown in (I) below, what kind of isomerism would be possible? What kind of isomerism would be possible if ethyl alcohol had a planar structure such as that shown in (II)?

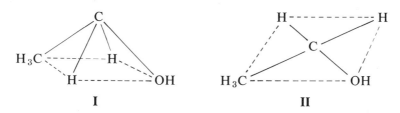

I   II

Why is there but one structure possible for ethyl alcohol?

[6]   What stereoisomers are possible when bromine is added to *trans*-2-butene? What stereoisomers are possible when bromine is added to *cis*-2-butene? (*Hint: See Section 3.8. Also draw three-dimensional structures for reactants and products.*)

[7]   An optically active liquid (A), C_4H_9Cl, when heated with alcoholic KOH lost its optical activity. The product, an optically inactive gas (B), C_4H_8, was bubbled through bromine-carbon tetrachloride solution to give a new substance (C), $C_4H_8Br_2$, that could not be resolved into $(+)$ and $(-)$ forms. Write the reactions that lead to products (B) and (C) and show the stereochemistry involved by drawing three-dimensional formulas.

chapter 7

Organic Halogen Compounds

INTRODUCTION

The earth's crust (including the oceans) contains inorganic halides of every kind in great abundance. In contrast to this, there are relatively few naturally-occurring organic compounds in which halogen atoms are co-valently bonded to carbon. Yet, the importance of this family of sub-stances is so great that many synthetic routes lead to end products only by way of some halogen intermediate. Many organic halogen compounds are synthesized, therefore, simply to be used as chemical reagents. Others are prepared as useful commodities in their own right and are employed as propellants in aerosol[1] sprays, as refrigerants, insecticides, herbicides, fire-extinguishing agents, dry cleaners, and plastics.

We found double and triple bonds in the olefins and acetylenes to be the structural features which bestowed a characteristic reactivity upon these compounds. We shall now study for the first time a functional group composed of a single atomic species — the covalently bound halogen.

CLASSIFICATION AND NOMENCLATURE

All organic halogen compounds may be classified either as aliphatic or aromatic. If aliphatic, they are alkyl halides that may be classified further according to structure — that is, they are either primary, secondary, or tertiary alkyl halides. This classification is based upon the nature of the carbon atom to which the halogen atom is bonded.

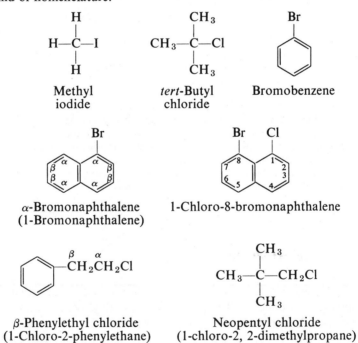

The nomenclature of the halogen compounds is not difficult to learn. Common names frequently are used for the simpler members of this family. In such names the alkyl group to which the halogen is attached is given first, and this is then followed by the name of the halogen. The halogen (as halide) is a separate word. Alkyl halides of five carbons or greater and the aromatic halogen compounds are named more conveniently as substituted hydrocarbons according to IUPAC rules. The following examples illustrate each kind of nomenclature.

Exercise 7.1   Draw all structures possible that have the molecular formula $C_5H_{11}Cl$. Classify each as a primary, secondary, or tertiary chloride. Name each according to the IUPAC system.

PREPARATION OF ORGANIC HALOGEN COMPOUNDS

A.   Preparation by Direct Halogenation of Hydrocarbons.   The aromatic halogen compounds in which the halogen is joined to a ring carbon atom may be prepared by direct halogenation (Sec. 4.8-A). Direct halogenation of the alkanes, by bringing the hydrocarbon into direct contact with the halogen, proceeds uncontrolled to produce isomeric and polysubstituted products. For this reason direct halogenation of alkanes seldom is used. The chlorination of methane, for example, when carried out in sunlight, produces every possible substituted methane (Sec. 2.9-B).

An alkyl side chain on the aromatic nucleus, when halogenated directly, also results in polysubstituted products of varying amounts.

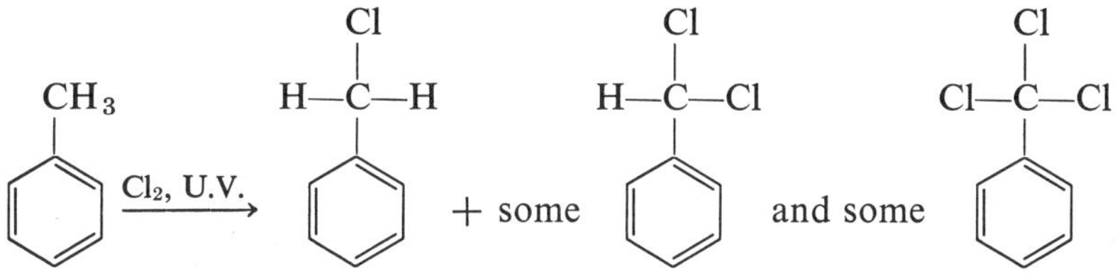

| Toluene | Benzyl chloride | Benzal chloride | Benzotrichloride |

On side chains longer than methyl, however, the halogen atom shows a predilection for the ring-adjacent carbon. The reason for this is that side chain halogenation, like halogenation of an alkane, proceeds via a free radical intermediate (Sec. 2.9). The odd electron, if on the ring-attached carbon, may delocalize and enter into resonance with the π electrons of the ring. This stabilizes the free radical intermediate and favors its formation. We shall see this same phenomenon manifest throughout chemical behavior — namely, the reaction that leads to a stabilized intermediate, or product, is the reaction favored.

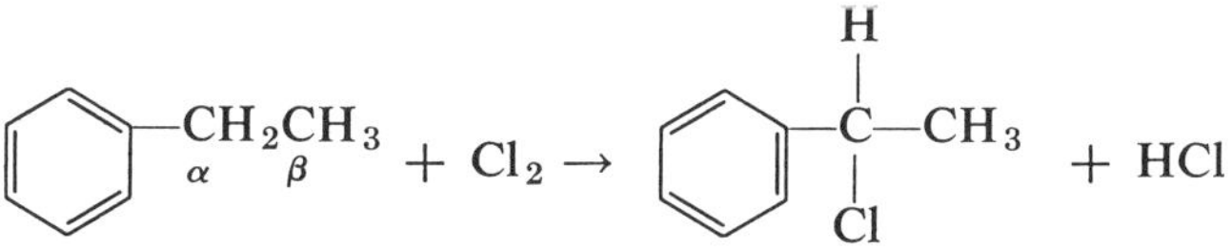

Ethylbenzene α-Phenylethyl chloride
                             (1-Chloro-1-phenylethane)

B.   Preparation from Alcohols.   A laboratory preparation of an alkyl halide usually begins with an alcohol as starting material. Treatment of the appropriate alcohol with any of the following reagents results in replacement of the hydroxyl group, —OH:

   (a) concentrated hydrobromic acid, HBr.
   (b) concentrated hydriodic acid, HI.
   (c) concentrated hydrochloric acid, $HCl + ZnCl_2$.
   (d) phosphorus tribromide, phosphorus triiodide, or phosphorus pentachloride.
   (e) thionyl chloride, $SOCl_2$.

Two examples of the preparation of organic halogen compounds from alcohols by the use of these reagents are given below.

$$3\ CH_3CH_2OH + PBr_3 \rightarrow 3\ CH_3CH_2Br + H_3PO_3$$

Ethyl alcohol   Ethyl bromide

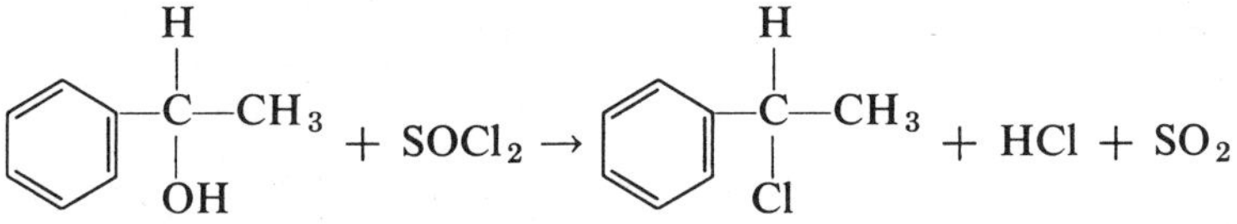

1-Phenylethanol   1-Chloro-1-phenylethane

Thionyl chloride, $SOCl_2$, is a superior chlorinating reagent because the by-products formed in this case are gases and escape from the reaction mixture.

C.   Preparation from Olefins.   Halogen acids (HBr, HCl, HI) will add to olefins to yield alkyl halides (Sec. 3.9-A). The mode of addition follows Markovnikov's Rule.

Propylene   Isopropyl bromide
(Propene)   (2-Bromopropane)

D.   Preparation *via* Halogen Exchange.   Certain halides, in some instances, are best prepared from other halides by an exchange. This method lends itself especially well to the preparation of iodo and fluoro compounds. Sodium iodide, unlike sodium chloride or sodium bromide, is soluble in anhydrous acetone. If an alkyl chloride is dissolved in a solution of sodium iodide in acetone, the halogens exchange. The equilibrium favors formation of the alkyl iodide because the sodium chloride which forms is not soluble in acetone and precipitates.

$$R—Cl + Na^+I^- \xrightarrow{\text{Acetone}} R—I + NaCl$$

Fluorine compounds often are prepared *via* a halogen exchange through the use of inorganic fluorides, rather than by reactions utilizing fluorine or hydrogen fluoride because the latter chemicals are extremely reactive and difficult to handle.

$$2\,CH_3Br + Hg_2F_2 \rightarrow 2\,CH_3F + Hg_2Br_2$$

Methyl	Mercurous	Fluoro-	Mercurous
bromide	fluoride	methane	bromide

Exercise 7.2   If you were given propene and benzene as your only organic starting materials and any other inorganic reagents that you might require, how would you prepare (a) isopropyl chloride, (b) *n*-propyl bromide, (c) *n*-propyl iodide, and (d) 2-chloro-2-phenylpropane?

7.4   POLYHALOGEN COMPOUNDS

Halogenated products prepared from methane become increasingly dense, higher boiling, and nonflammable as halogen successively replaces the four hydrogen atoms. Polychlorinated methanes may be prepared by the direct halogenation of methane (Sec. 7.3-A) or, as in the case of carbon tetrachloride, by using replacement methods.

$$C + 2\,S \longrightarrow CS_2$$
$$CS_2 + 3\,Cl_2 \longrightarrow CCl_4 + S_2Cl_2$$
$$2\,S_2Cl_2 + CS_2 \longrightarrow CCl_4 + 6\,S$$

The chlorine atoms of carbon tetrachloride, in turn, can be exchanged for fluorine in the preparation of the fluorinated methanes. For example,

$$CCl_4 + 2\,SbF_3 \quad \rightarrow \quad CCl_2F_2 \quad + \quad 2\,SbF_2Cl$$

Dichlorodifluoromethane
(Freon-12)

Carbon tetrachloride is an excellent solvent for oils, waxes, fats, and greases and is used as a dry cleaner. While it is nonflammable, it is very volatile and its vapor is toxic. Carbon tetrachloride, as a fire extinguishing agent, has been replaced largely by liquefied carbon dioxide, bromotrifluoromethane ($CBrF_3$), and dibromodifluoromethane (CBr_2F_2). The fluorinated methanes may be used safely in confined spaces such as submarines, aircraft, boats, and automobiles. Carbon tetrachloride, on the other hand, hydrolyzes when heated in the presence of water to give phosgene, an extremely poisonous gas.

$$CCl_4 + H_2O \xrightarrow{\text{Heat}} \overset{\displaystyle O}{\overset{\displaystyle \|}{Cl-C-Cl}} + 2\,HCl$$

Phosgene

The trihalomethanes, chloroform, bromoform, and iodoform, may be prepared by treating acetone or ethyl alcohol with alkaline solutions of the halogens. This reaction is called the **haloform reaction** and is specific for the group $CH_3\!-\!\overset{\displaystyle R}{\overset{\displaystyle |}{C}}\!=\!O$, or for a group which may be oxidized to it — e.g., $CH_3\!-\!\overset{\displaystyle R}{\underset{\displaystyle H}{\overset{\displaystyle |}{\underset{\displaystyle |}{C}}}}\!-\!OH$. The R in each of the general formulas is a hydrogen atom, or an alkyl, or an aryl group. Alkaline solutions of the halogens (essentially hypohalite solutions) are oxidizing agents capable of converting methyl carbinols (Sec. 8.3) to methyl ketones (Sec. 9.2) as represented by the general formulas above. The mechanics of the haloform reaction are discussed in detail in Sec. 9.9, but the following sequence of reactions illustrates how ethyl alcohol may be converted into chloroform.

$$Cl_2 + 2\,NaOH \rightarrow NaCl + NaOCl + H_2O$$

$$
\begin{array}{ccc}
\text{H} & \text{H} & \text{H} \\
| & | & | \\
\text{H—C—C—OH} + NaOCl \rightarrow & CH_3\text{—C}{=}\text{O} & + NaCl + H_2O \\
| & | & \\
\text{H} & \text{H} &
\end{array}
$$

Ethyl alcohol   Sodium   Acetaldehyde
            hypochlorite

$$
\begin{array}{c}
\text{H} \\
| \\
CH_3\text{—C}{=}\text{O}
\end{array}
+ 3\,Cl_2 + 4\,NaOH \rightarrow
$$

$$
HCCl_3 + H\text{—}\overset{\displaystyle O}{\overset{\displaystyle \|}{C}}\text{—O}^-Na^+ + 3\,H_2O + 3\,NaCl
$$

Chloroform   Sodium
                 formate

Chloroform, once prepared commercially from ethyl alcohol by the preceding series of reactions, is a heavy, sweet-tasting, non-flammable, volatile liquid. Medicinally, it found some use at one time as an inhalation anesthetic, but has such a narrow margin of safety that its use as such is limited, Iodoform, CHI_3, a yellow powder with a characteristic, pungent odor, has found some application in medicine as a topical antiseptic.

Exercise 7.3   An alcohol, $C_4H_{10}O$, gave a positive halo-form reaction when treated with a sodium hypohalite solution. What is the structure of the alcohol?

The polyfluorinated hydrocarbons recently have come to occupy the limelight of halogen chemistry. Not only are these compounds extremely inert, but they are nontoxic, noncorrosive, low boiling liquids and gases. They are widely used as refrigerants and as propellants in aerosol sprays of all kinds. These are marketed under the name of **"Freons"** and are used to dispense from pressurized cans shaving creams, hair sprays, perfumes, paints, toothpaste, insecticides, and even foods (whipped cream, cheeses).

Polyfluoro- and polychloroethylenes are used as the structural units in several very useful plastics. One of these, **Teflon,** is a polyfluoroethylene.

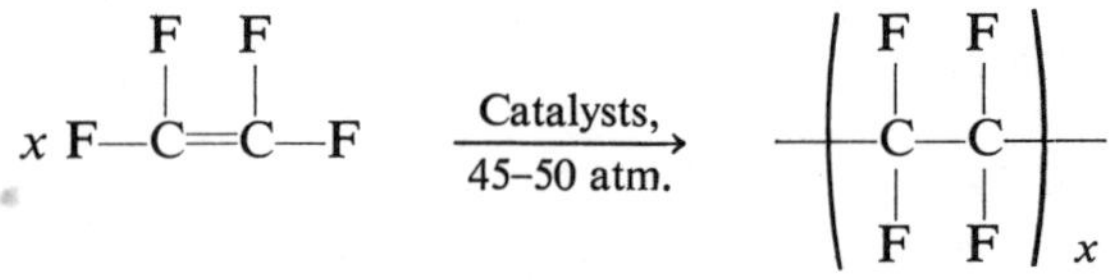

$$x \ F{-}\underset{\underset{F}{|}}{\overset{\overset{F}{|}}{C}}{=}\underset{\underset{F}{|}}{\overset{\overset{F}{|}}{C}}{-}F \quad \xrightarrow[\text{45--50 atm.}]{\text{Catalysts,}} \quad \left(\!\!\begin{array}{c} \overset{F}{|} \ \overset{F}{|} \\ {-}C{-}C{-} \\ \underset{F}{|} \ \underset{F}{|} \end{array}\!\!\right)_{\!x}$$

$(x \ = \ 5{,}000{-}20{,}000)$ "Teflon"

Teflon is a waxy plastic completely inert to nearly all reagents and ideal for gasket materials and valve packings where corrosive chemicals and high temperatures are encountered. Its great resistance to high temperatures suggested its use as nose cone material for missiles and spacecraft. Teflon is widely used as a liner in frying pans, muffin tins, and other utensils to provide nonsticking surfaces.

Vinylidene chloride, or 1, 1-dichloroethylene ($CH_2{=}CCl_2$), can be polymerized to produce a clear, inert plastic exceptionally well adapted to the packaging of foods. The familiar "Saran Wrap" is a popular example of such a polymer. Polyhalogenated hydrocarbons also have been found to be very effective pesticides. Perhaps the best known of these is the insecticide DDT, the structure for which is shown below.

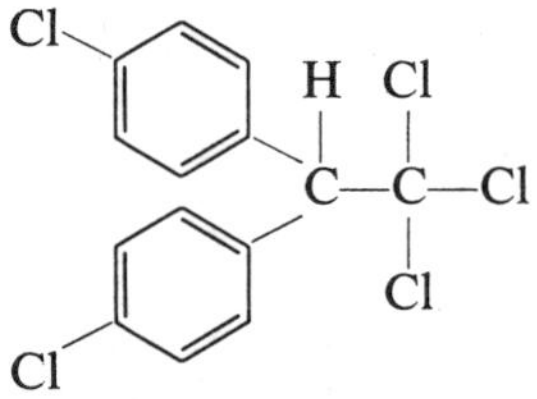

*Di*chlorodiphenyl*tri*chloroethane

Ethylene bromide, 1, 3-dichloropropene, and 1, 2-dibromo-3-chloropropane are used as soil fumigants for the control of nematodes. Another insecticide, benzene hexachloride, abbreviated as BHC or 666 is prepared by the addition of chlorine to benzene. Nine different isomers are possible for this structure, but, strangely enough, only one of the seven forms thus far isolated (designated the gamma, γ, form) shows the insecticidal property. For this reason the insecticide is sometimes referred to as "Gammexane."

γ-Benzene hexachloride (Gammexane)

Nearly every homemaker faced with the problem of storing woolens for the summer is familiar with the larvicide p-dichloro-benzene. p-Dichlorobenzene is widely used in place of naphthalene (the original "moth balls") for protection against moth damage.

p-Dichlorobenzene

The indiscriminate use of polychlorinated insecticides in agri-culture has been severely criticized in recent years by conservationists because of the persistent and damaging effects these substances have on wildlife, especially birds and fish.

7.5   REACTIONS OF THE ALKYL HALIDES

The reactions of the alkyl halides are principally of two types — **substitution** and **elimination.** The halogen atom in a substitution reaction is displaced by another electron-rich *nucleophilic* (nucleus-loving) reagent. Such nucleophilic reagents are Lewis bases and often are negative ions. Substitution reactions may take place by way of two different pathways. These pathways are referred to as **reaction mechanisms.** In one of these, the rate of reaction depends only upon the concentration of *one* reacting species and is called a *substitution nucleophilic, unimolecular,* or simply S_N1. In the other substitution mechanism, the rate of reaction usually depends upon the concentration of *two* reacting species and is called a *substitution nucleophilic, bimolecular,* or S_N2. The rate at which a reaction proceeds is never greater than the slowest step, and this phase of a reaction is called the **rate-determining step.** In S_N1 reactions, the rate-determining step is the formation of a carbonium ion. Any factors such as steric (Sec. 8.5-B), resonance stabilization (Sec. 4.3, Sec. 7.6), and inductive effects (Sec. 10.3) which help to promote the formation of the carbonium ion will, of course, increase the rate of the reaction. The reaction rate may be increased further through the assistance of a polar solvent. Polar solvent molecules help to segregate both cation and anion, when formed, and thus assist in charge formation. An example of a reaction that proceeds largely by way of the S_N1 mechanism is the hydrolysis of *tert*-butyl chloride in an 80% aqueous alcoholic solution.

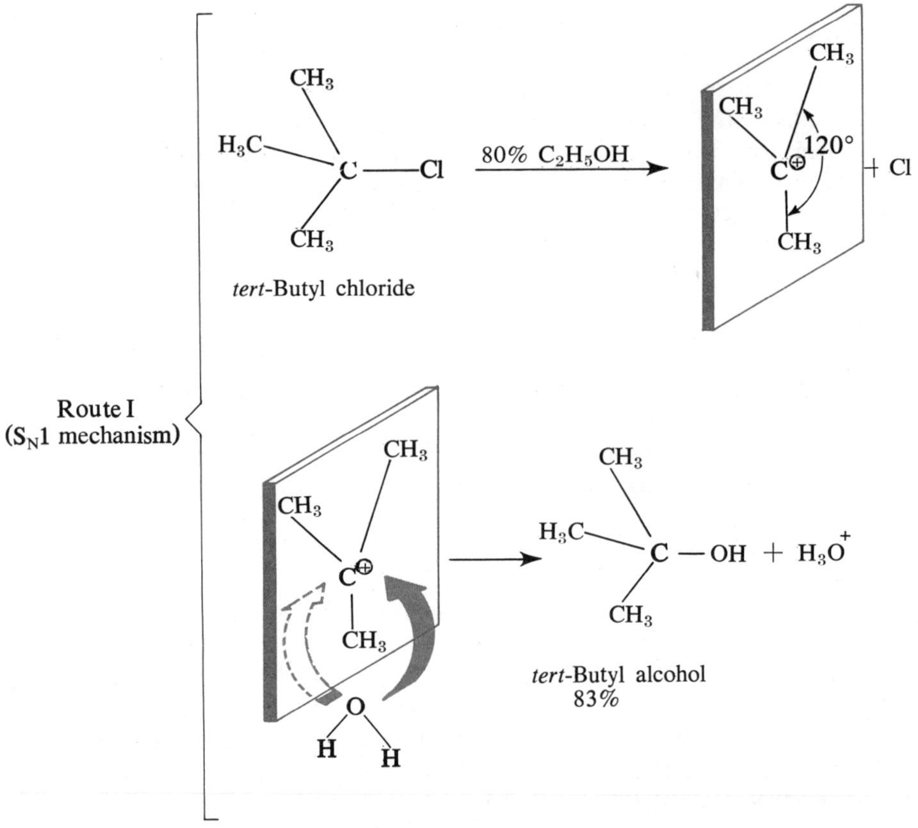

Route I
(S_N1 mechanism)

tert-Butyl chloride

80% C_2H_5OH

tert-Butyl alcohol
83%

Theoretically, the intermediate free carbonium ion is most stable when in a planar configuration. This being the case, you will note that the attacking nucleophile (water) may approach the positive carbon from either front or back. The end result in the hydrolysis of *tert*-butyl chloride is the same, but a choice in the direction of combination may lead to racemization if optically active molecules are hydrolyzed in this manner. Let us illustrate this point using an optically active form of α-phenylethyl chloride.

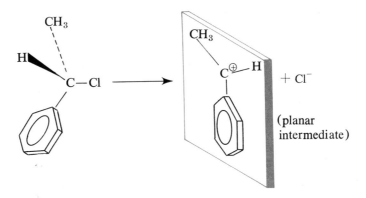

(planar
intermediate)

(+) or (−)−α−Phenylethyl chloride

mirror

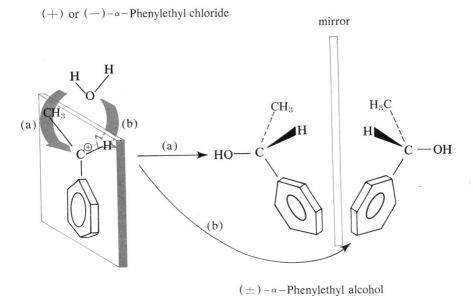

(±)−α−Phenylethyl alcohol

Regardless of which optical isomer of α-phenylethyl chloride is hydrolyzed, the product is always a partially racemized mixture. Racemization is seldom complete to the extent that an equal number of (+) and (−) forms are produced because the departing anion (chloride, in this case) may still be near enough to one face of the carbonium intermediate to interfere with the approach of the nucleophile from that side. The isomeric product resulting from the backside approach thus usually predominates. However, racemization is characteristic of all S_N1 reactions.

Let us now return to the *tert*-butyl chloride hydrolysis reaction and see what has happened to the remainder of our starting material. In order to account for the other 17% we must consider another possible reaction route. If, instead of combining with the nucleophilic reagent, the carbonium ion loses a proton (Route II), then the product of the reaction is an olefin and the reaction mechanism is referred to as E1. As in the S_N1 mechanism, the number in the abbreviation refers to unimolecular. The E, in such cases, indicates elimination. Because of the competition between substitution and elimination, more than one product often results.

Route II
(E1 mechanism)

The S_N2 reaction mechanism may be illustrated by the alkaline hydrolysis of *sec*-butyl chloride to *sec*-butyl alcohol. In this case the rate of reaction depends upon the concentration of both *sec*-butyl chloride and the hydroxide ion. The hydroxide ion displaces the chloride ion, not by a head-on approach to the face of the carbon atom bonded to the chlorine, but by an attack from the rear. In making this backside approach a new bond forms between the carbon atom and the hydroxyl group as the bond between the carbon and the chlorine is broken. Thus, the reaction appears to proceed through an unstable reaction intermediate, called the **transition state,** in which the carbon atom is loosely bonded to both the hydroxyl and chlorine groups. This reaction intermediate often is shown in brackets.

Inasmuch as all the groups bonded to the carbon atom involved in the substitution are different (C_2H_5—, CH_3—, H, and Cl), their spatial arrangement or configuration in the product becomes exactly opposite of that in the starting material. Such a reversal of configuration is referred to as a **Walden inversion,** and invariably occurs in a S_N2 reaction. Thus, if we were to begin with "left-handed" *sec*-butyl chloride, we will obtain as our product "right-handed" *sec*-butyl alcohol. Indeed, it was through such stereochemical studies that the S_N2 mechanism was established.

Route I (S_N2 mechanism)

sec-Butyl chloride   (transition state)   sec-Butyl alcohol

It should be pointed out that there is also an E2 reaction path which may enter into competition with the S_N2 mechanism through the elimination of a β-hydrogen atom. You will remember the dehydrohalogenation reactions used in the preparation of the olefins (Sec. 3.5) as examples of such β-eliminations.

Route II (E2 mechanism)

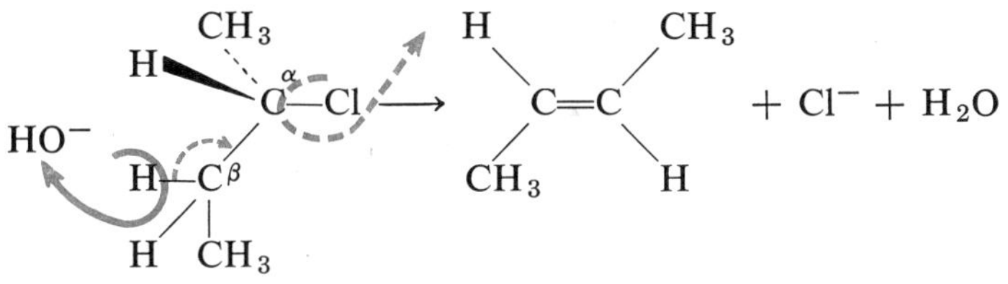

sec-Butyl chloride   2-Butene

Which of the four reaction mechanisms predominates depends upon the concentration of reagents, the structures of the alkyl halides involved, the solvent used, and the nature of the nucleophile. A generalization helpful in predicting the mechanism by which alkyl halides are substituted is that tertiary and secondary alkyl halides usually react by a S_N1 mechanism; straight chain halides usually by the S_N2 pathway. The order of reactivity in elimination reactions of the halides by class is **tertiary > secondary > primary.**

The more important nucleophilic substitutions of alkyl halides are illustrated by the following general equations. The nucleophile in each case is underlined in color.

$$R—X + Na^+OH^- \longrightarrow R—OH + Na^+X^-$$

Hydroxide   An
base   alcohol

$$R—X + Na^+OR^- \longrightarrow R—OR + Na^+X^-$$

Alkoxide   An
base   ether

$$R—X + Na^+SH^- \longrightarrow R—SH + Na^+X^-$$

Sodium   A thio
acid   alcohol

$$R—X + Na^+\underline{CN^-} \longrightarrow R—CN + Na^+X^-$$

Sodium   An alkyl
cyanide   cyanide
(nitrile)

$$R—X + Na^+\underline{NH_2}^- \longrightarrow R—NH_2 + Na^+X^-$$

Sodium   An
amide   amine

$$R—X + Na^+ : \underline{C{\equiv}C—H} \longrightarrow R—C{\equiv}C—H + Na^+X^-$$

Sodium
acetylide

$$R—X + :\underline{NH_3} \longrightarrow R\overset{+}{N}H_3 + X^-$$

Ammonia   An ammonium
ion

A generalization helpful in selecting the proper halogen compound to employ in a reaction is that the iodides are more reactive than the bromides, and the bromides are more reactive than the chlorides. Unfortunately, their cost parallels this same order.

Exercise 7.4   When *cis*-3-methylcyclopentyl chloride is heated with potassium hydroxide only *trans*-3-methylcyclopentanol is formed. Draw both structures. Did this displacement proceed by the S_N1 or the S_N2 reaction pathway?

7.6   REACTIONS OF ARYL, VINYL, AND ALLYL HALIDES

The displacement reactions of the alkyl halides discussed in the previous section are not applicable to the aryl halides unless, of course, halogen is in the side chain. Halogen held to a doubly-bonded carbon such as that found in chlorobenzene is unreactive. The ring halogen is not sufficiently labile to engage in displacement reactions similar to those illustrated for the alkyl halides. Only when the *ortho* and/or the *para* positions of the aromatic ring are occupied by strong electron-attracting groups can the ring halogen be displaced by a nucleophile. Electron-attracting groups in the *ortho* or *para* positions diminish the electron density at the halogen-attached ring carbon and make it susceptible to attack. For example, 2, 4-dinitrochlorobenzene may be hydrolyzed in a potassium hydroxide solution to produce 2, 4-dinitrophenol. Under the same conditions chlorobenzene fails to react.

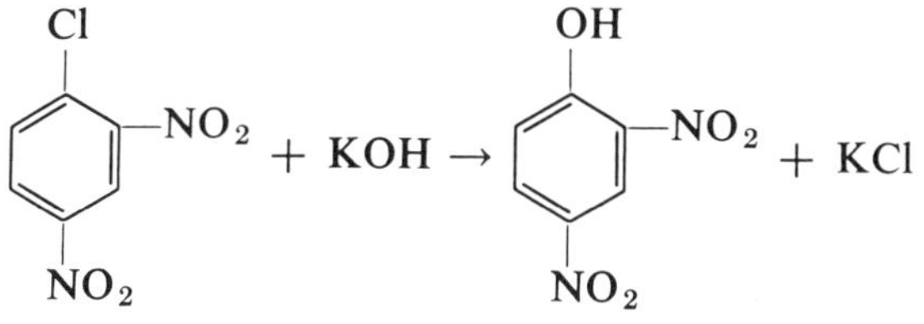

2, 4-Dinitro-   2, 4-Dinitrophenol
chlorobenzene

Halogen bonded to a carbon atom in the side chain of an aromatic ring essentially is part of an alkyl halide (Sec. 7.3).

Vinyl chloride, $CH_2{=}CH{-}Cl$, also has a chlorine joined to an unsaturated carbon atom and, like chlorobenzene, is rather unreactive. The electrons of chlorine, it appears, can interact with the π electrons of the carbon-carbon double bond to shift *away from* the chlorine as shown in the resonance structure below. As a result, the chlorine atom is held somewhat closer to the carbon, the carbon-halogen bond is strengthened, and displacement of chlorine is made more difficult. Chlorine on the benzene ring represents a similar system, except that in this case the electrons of chlorine can interact with the π electrons of the benzene ring.

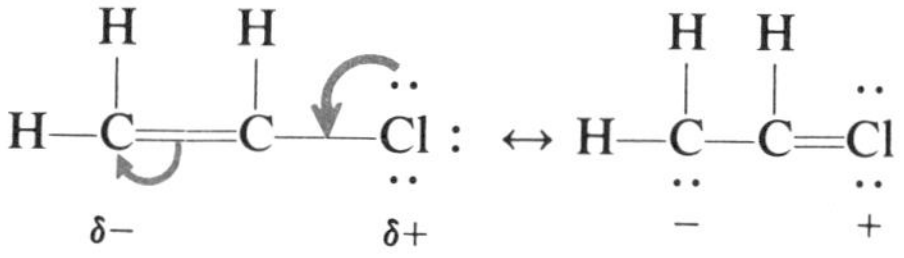

Resonance forms of vinyl chloride

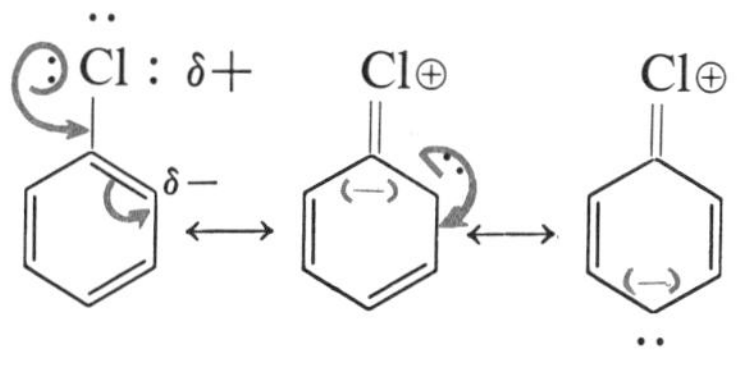

Contributing forms to the chlorobenzene structure

In contrast to vinyl halides, **allyl halides,** $CH_2=CH-CH_2X$, are extremely reactive. The olefinic carbon in allylic halides is second from the one holding the halogen atom. A different factor now comes into play. The allyl carbonium ion which remains, once the halide ion has separated, is stabilized by resonance. The stability thus achieved appears to assist in the formation of the carbonium ion.

$$CH_2=\overset{\overset{\displaystyle H}{|}}{C}-CH_2Cl \rightarrow CH_2=\overset{\overset{\displaystyle H}{|}}{C}-\overset{\oplus}{C}H_2 + Cl^-$$

$$H-\overset{\overset{\displaystyle H}{|}}{C}=\overset{\overset{\displaystyle H}{|}}{C}-\overset{\overset{\displaystyle H}{|}}{\underset{\underset{\displaystyle H}{|}}{\overset{\oplus}{C}}} \leftrightarrow \overset{\oplus}{C}-\overset{\overset{\displaystyle H}{|}}{\underset{\underset{\displaystyle H}{|}}{C}}=\overset{\overset{\displaystyle H}{|}}{C}-H$$

Contributing forms to the allyl carbonium ion hybrid

Benzyl chloride, which has a similar allylic structure, reacts in a manner similar to that of allyl chloride.

Benzyl chloride

Contributing forms to the benzyl carbonium ion hybrid

Halogen compounds that react by way of an ionic intermediate (tertiary, allyl, and benzyl) readily precipitate silver halide when warmed with alcoholic silver nitrate. This is a convenient test for highly reactive alkyl halides. Vinyl and aryl halides do not react under these conditions.

We now can generalize further the order of reactivity of halogen compounds in S_N1 reactions as follows:

allylic > benzylic > tertiary > secondary > primary > vinyl

The order is opposite for S_N2 types of reactions.

Exercise 7.5   Which type of reaction mechanism, S_N1, S_N2, E1, E2, is illustrated by each of the following reactions?

(a) $CH_2{=}CH{-}CH_2Cl + AgNO_3 + C_2H_5OH \longrightarrow$
$AgCl + CH_2{=}CH{-}CH_2OC_2H_5 + HNO_3$

(b) $(CH_3)_3CCl + KOH \xrightarrow{\text{Alcohol}} (CH_3)_2C{=}CH_2$

(c) $CH_3CH_2CH_2CH_2Cl + NaI \xrightarrow{\text{Acetone}}$
$CH_3CH_2CH_2CH_2I + NaCl$

(d) $CH_3{-}CH{=}CHCl + \overset{+}{Na}\overset{-}{NH_2} \longrightarrow$
$CH_3{-}C{\equiv}C{-}H + NH_3 + NaCl$

7.7   REACTIONS OF HALOGEN COMPOUNDS WITH METALS

The reaction of an alkyl halide with magnesium to form the important Grignard reagents already has been discussed (Sec. 2.8-B). The Grignard reagent also may be prepared from aryl halides. An example of a frequently prepared aryl Grignard reagent is phenylmagnesium bromide.

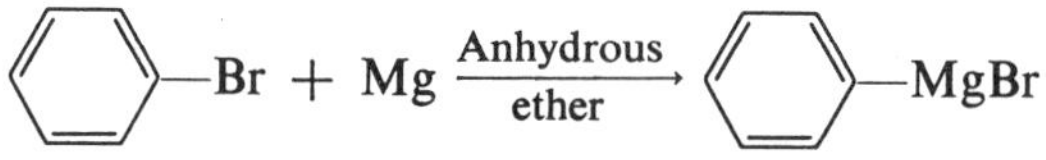

Bromobenzene   Phenylmagnesium
bromide

The Grignard reagent is one of the most useful of all organo-metallic compounds and plays a very important role in numerous synthetic procedures. The various applications of the Grignard reagent are illustrated in later sections.

The Wurtz reaction (Sec. 2.8-A) and the Friedel-Crafts reaction (Sec. 4.8-C) have been illustrated as procedures in syntheses employing alkyl and aryl halides. Another modification of the Wurtz reaction by which two aromatic rings may be coupled, employs copper and iodobenzene. It is called the **Ullman reaction.** For example, iodobenzene, when heated in the presence of finely divided copper, produces biphenyl.

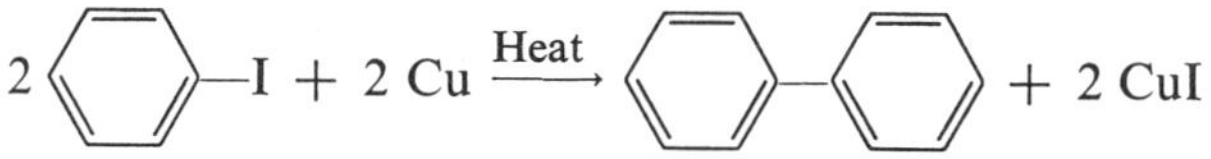

Iodobenzene   Biphenyl

Two reactions especially important to the petroleum industry involve the reaction of alkyl halides and lead. Ethyl and methyl chlorides, when treated with sodium-lead alloy, react to produce the important anti-knock gasoline additives, tetraethyllead **(TEL)**, and tetramethyllead **(TML)**.

$$4\,C_2H_5-Cl + Na_4Pb \longrightarrow (C_2H_5)_4Pb + 4\,NaCl$$

Sodium   Tetraethyl
lead   lead
alloy

☐☐ *SUMMARY*

[1]   Halogen compounds may be classified as:

    a. Aliphatic (R–X) or aromatic (Ar–X).
    b. Primary, secondary, or tertiary halogen compounds.
    c. Iodo, bromo, chloro, or fluoro compounds.

[2]   Halogen compounds can be prepared by

    a. direct halogenation (most useful in the preparation of aromatic halogen compounds).
    b. replacement of the hydroxyl group (—OH) of alcohols.
    c. addition of HX to olefins (Markovnikov's Rule is followed).
    d. exchange for other covalently bound halogens (most useful in the preparation of iodo and fluoro compounds).
    e. the haloform reaction which yields trihalomethanes.

[3]   Reactions of the halogen compounds include

    a. displacement of the halogen atom (as halide) by another negative group — i.e., hydroxy (OH$^-$), alkoxy (OR$^-$), amino (NH$_2$$^-$), mercapto (SH$^-$), cyano (CN$^-$), acetylide (H—C≡C$^-$).
    b. elimination (dehydrohalogenation) to form olefins.
    c. reactions with metals: Wurtz, Friedel-Crafts, Ullmann, preparation of the Grignard reagent, preparation of TEL and TML.

[4]   Important polychloro compounds include chloroform, carbon tetrachloride and polyvinyl chloride.

[5]   The polyfluoromethanes, ethanes, and cyclobutanes known as "Freons" are useful aerosol spray propellants and refrigerants. "Teflon" (polyfluoroethylene) is a very useful inert, heat-resistant plastic.

[6]   The polyhalogenated aromatic compounds DDT, BHC and *p*-dichlorobenzene are useful pesticides.

□□ *NEW TERMS*

[1] E1 reaction
[2] E2 reaction
[3] haloform reaction
[4] nucleophilic reagent
[5] S_N1 reaction
[6] S_N2 reaction
[7] transition state
[8] Walden inversion

■ □ SUPPLEMENTARY EXERCISES
▼ AND PROBLEMS

[1] Name each of the following compounds.

(a) $CH_2\!=\!CH\!-\!CH_2Br$ (b) CH_3MgI (c) 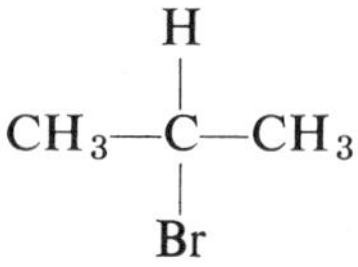 $CH_3\!-\!\overset{\displaystyle H}{\underset{\displaystyle Br}{C}}\!-\!CH_3$

(d) HCl_3

(e)

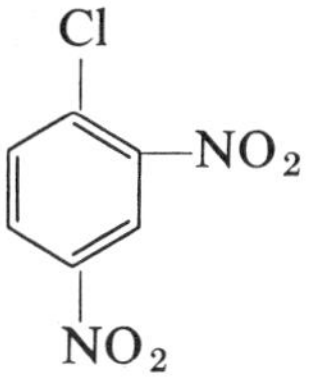

(f)

(g) 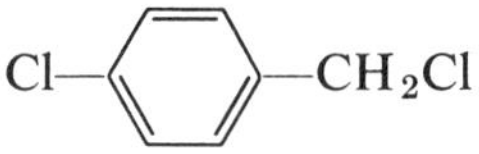 $Cl\!-\!\!\bigcirc\!\!-\!CH_2Cl$

(h)

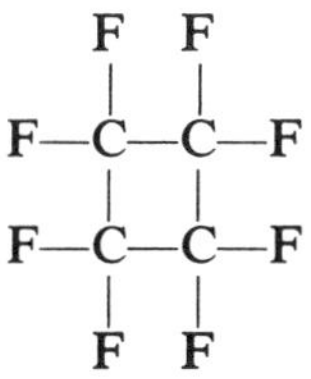

(i)

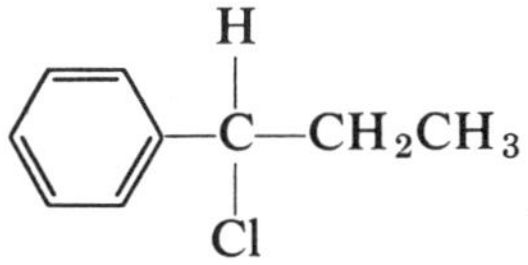

[2]   Write structures for and assign acceptable names to all isomers with the molecular formula (a) C_4H_9Br; (b) $C_8H_8Cl_2$. Are any of the structures you have drawn those of optically active compounds?

[3]   Indicate the principal organic products (if any) given by the following reactions:

(a) $tert$-C_4H_9OH + HCl $\longrightarrow$

(b) $CH_3CH_2CH{=}CH_2$ + HBr $\longrightarrow$

(c)   Bromobenzene + Mg $\xrightarrow{\text{Anhydrous ether}}$

(d)   Product of (a) + alcoholic KOH $\longrightarrow$

(e)   Product of (b) + aqueous KOH $\longrightarrow$

(f)   Product of (e) + I_2 + NaOH $\longrightarrow$

(g)   Chlorobenzene + alcoholic KOH $\longrightarrow$

(h)   Benzoic acid + Br_2 $\xrightarrow{\text{Fe}}$

(i) cis-2-Butene + Br_2 $\longrightarrow$

(j)   2, 4-Dinitrochlorobenzene + NH_3 $\longrightarrow$

(k) n-C_4H_9Cl + NaI $\xrightarrow{\text{Acetone}}$

(l)   Ethylbenzene + Cl_2 $\xrightarrow{\text{Sunlight}}$

(m) n-Butyl chloride + benzene $\xrightarrow{\text{AlCl}_3}$

[4]   Show how the following transformations can be effected.

(a)   isopropyl alcohol $\longrightarrow$ isopropyl bromide $\longrightarrow$ propane
(b)   benzene $\longrightarrow$ ethylbenzene $\longrightarrow$ styrene
(c)   isopropyl bromide $\longrightarrow$ n-propyl bromide
(d)   1, 2-dibromopropane $\longrightarrow$ 2, 2-dibromopropane
(e)   toluene $\longrightarrow$ p-bromotoluene $\longrightarrow$ p-bromobenzoic acid

[5]   Arrange the following halogen compounds in an order of diminishing reactivity towards S_N1 substitution when treated with alcoholic potassium hydroxide.

(a)   chlorobenzene   (f) sec-butyl bromide
(b) $tert$-butyl chloride   (g)   isopropyl iodide
(c)   allyl chloride   (h)   iodobenzene
(d) n-butyl chloride   (i)   2, 4-dinitrochlorobenzene
(e)   vinyl chloride

[6]   What simple chemical test, i.e., test tube reactions, will serve to distinguish between:

(a) cyclohexene and chlorobenzene; (b) α-phenylethyl chloride and β-phenylethyl chloride; (c) chlorobenzene and 2, 4-dinitrochlorobenzene; (d) p-bromotoluene and benzyl bromide.

[7]   A halogen compound contained 58% bromine. When heated with alcoholic potassium hydroxide a combustible gas evolved which absorbed one mole of H_2. On combustion, the gas united with oxygen in a ratio of 1:6 by volume (STP) to give carbon dioxide and water as the only products. When this same gas was subjected to chemical oxidation with hot, concentrated $KMnO_4$, only acetic acid, CH_3COOH, was obtained as the oxidation product. Give the formula for the original compound.

[8]   An analysis of an organic compound established its formula as C_8H_9Cl. What would be its structure and name if it had shown the following behavior:

(a)   It was optically active, precipitated AgCl when warmed with an alcoholic silver nitrate solution, and on oxidation yielded benzoic acid.

(b)   It was optically inactive, precipitated AgCl when warmed with alcoholic silver nitrate, and on oxidation yielded o-phthalic acid, $C_6H_4(COOH)_2$.

(c)   It was optically inactive and on oxidation yielded p-chloro-benzoic acid.

chapter 8

Alcohols, Phenols, and Ethers

> Alcohols, phenols, and ethers represent three classes of oxygen-containing compounds in which the oxygen atom is singly bonded (—O—) to two other atoms. The oxygen atom bridges carbon to hydrogen in both the alcohols and phenols. In ethers, the oxygen is the bridge between two carbon atoms. All three classes of compounds provide us with a great number of useful products. These include germicides, antifreeze agents, pharmaceuticals, explosives, solvents, anesthetics, and plastics.

8 . 2   STRUCTURE OF THE ALCOHOLS AND PHENOLS

Alcohols and phenols may be considered as hydroxyl substituted hydrocarbons of the general formulas R—OH, and Ar—OH respectively. The **hydroxyl group**, (—OH) is the functional group which characterizes both alcohols and phenols. Compounds that have hydroxyl groups joined to carbon atoms of alkyl groups are alcohols. Compounds that have hydroxyl groups joined to carbon atoms like those found in the aromatic ring compounds are phenols. Both types may be illustrated by the following general formulas and specific examples.

$$R—\overset{..}{O}: \qquad CH_3—OH \qquad CH_3CH_2—OH$$
$$\diagdown H$$

An alcohol   Methyl alcohol   Ethyl alcohol

$$Ar—\overset{..}{\underset{|}{O}}:—H$$

A phenol   Phenol β-Naphthol

8.3   CLASSIFICATION AND NOMENCLATURE OF ALCOHOLS AND ETHERS

The alcohols, like the alkyl halides, may be classified as *primary*, *secondary*, or *tertiary* according to the number of hydrocarbon groups attached to the carbon atom bearing the hydroxyl groups. However, the nomenclature of the alcohols is somewhat more extensive than that encountered in other families of substances. **Common,** or **trivial names,** usually are employed for the simpler members having one to four carbon atoms. Such names are formed simply by naming the alkyl group bonded to the hydroxyl function, followed by the word *alcohol*. The following examples are illustrations of common names.

$$CH_3—OH \qquad CH_3—\overset{CH_3}{\underset{H}{\overset{|}{\underset{|}{C}}}}—OH \qquad CH_3—\overset{CH_3}{\underset{CH_3}{\overset{|}{\underset{|}{C}}}}—OH$$

Methyl alcohol   Isopropyl alcohol   *tert*-Butyl alcohol
(A primary alcohol)   (A secondary alcohol)   (A tertiary alcohol)

The IUPAC system of nomenclature is better adapted to naming the more complex members of the alcohol family, for which prefixes such as *secondary* and *tertiary* have little significance. Alcohols are named according to IUPAC rules by selecting and naming the longest carbon chain *including the hydroxyl group*. The terminal e of the parent hydrocarbon (alkane) is replaced by **ol.** As before, the chain is numbered to confer upon the functional group the smallest number. If more than one hydroxyl group appears in the chain, prefixes, such as **di, tri,** etc., are used. Alkyl side chains and other groups are named and their positions indicated. It would be profitable to consider a few examples.

$$C_2H_5—OH \qquad \overset{(3)}{CH_3}—\overset{(2)}{\underset{OH}{\overset{|}{\underset{|}{CH}}}}—\overset{(1)}{CH_3} \qquad \overset{(3)}{CH_3}—\overset{(2)}{\underset{CH_3}{\overset{(1)}{\overset{CH_3}{\overset{|}{\underset{|}{C}}}}}}—OH$$

Ethanol   2-Propanol   2-Methyl-2-propanol
(Ethyl alcohol)   (Isopropyl alcohol)   (*tert*-Butyl alcohol)

$$CH_3-CH_2-\overset{\overset{\displaystyle CH_3}{|}}{CH}-CH_2-OH \qquad\qquad CH_2{=}CH-CH_2-OH$$

2-Methyl-1-butanol   2-Propen-1-ol
                                       (Allyl alcohol)

$$CH_3-\underset{\underset{\displaystyle OH}{|}}{CH}-\underset{\underset{\displaystyle OH}{|}}{CH_2} \qquad CH_2-CH-CH_2$$
$$\qquad\qquad\qquad\quad \underset{OH}{|}\ \ \underset{OH}{|}\ \ \underset{OH}{|}$$

1, 2-Propanediol   1, 2, 3-Propanetriol
(Propylene glycol)   (Glycerol)

The suffix **ol** is generic for compounds that contain hydroxyl groups. Although names such as cres**ol**, glycer**ol**, and cholester**ol** contain no clues to their structures, such names do indicate that each contains one or more hydroxyl groups.

A third system of nomenclature is called a **derived system.** According to this system, alcohols are considered to be derivatives of the simplest one — that is, hydroxy methane, or **carbinol.** Groups attached to the carbon atom bearing the hydroxyl are named as one word with the suffix carbinol.

$$H-\overset{\overset{\displaystyle H}{|}}{\underset{\underset{\displaystyle H}{|}}{C}}-OH \qquad C_2H_5-\overset{\overset{\displaystyle CH_3}{|}}{\underset{\underset{\displaystyle CH_3}{|}}{C}}-OH \qquad CH_3-\overset{\overset{\displaystyle CH_3}{|}}{\underset{\underset{\displaystyle H}{|}}{C}}-\overset{\overset{\displaystyle H}{|}}{\underset{\underset{\displaystyle H}{|}}{C}}-OH$$

Carbinol   Dimethylethylcarbinol   Isopropylcarbinol
(Methyl alcohol)   (*tert*-Amyl alcohol)[1]   (Isobutyl alcohol)

Phenylcarbinol   Diphenylcarbinol
(Benzyl alcohol)

Exercise 8.1   Draw structures for eight alcohols with a molecular formula $C_5H_{12}O$ and name them according to IUPAC rules. Classify each as primary, secondary, and tertiary.

---

[1]Amyl, C_5H_{11}—, is a group name commonly used in alcohol and alkyl halide nomenclature.

Phenols are commonly named as derivatives of the parent substance, and simplest member of the family, **phenol.** Other substituents on the phenol ring are located by number or by *ortho, meta,* or *para* designations. For example,

p-Bromophenol 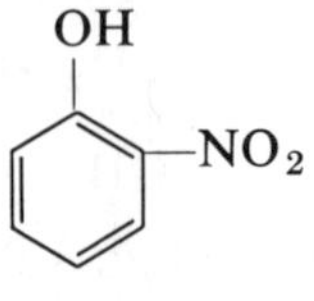   o-Nitrophenol 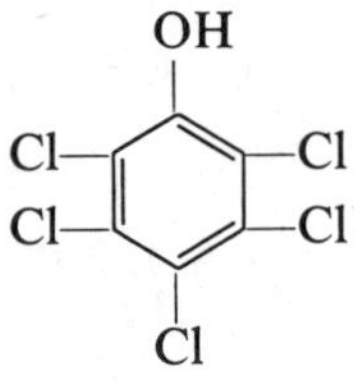   Pentachlorophenol

Sometimes phenols are named as hydroxy compounds or, as in the case of polyhydroxybenzenes, as *di-* or *triols.*

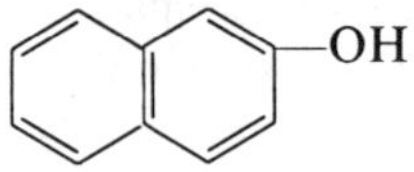

2-Hydroxynaphthalene   3-Hydroxytoluene   1, 3-Benzenediol
(β-Naphthol)   (m-Cresol)   (Resorcinol)

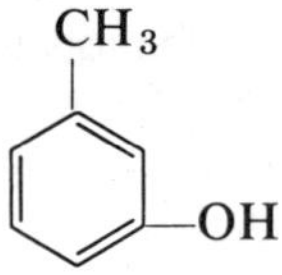

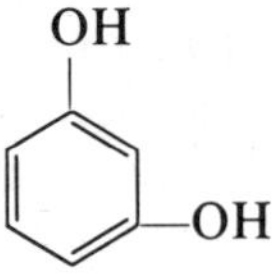

8.4   STRUCTURE AND PROPERTIES OF THE ALCOHOLS AND PHENOLS.
HYDROGEN BONDING

Molecules in which hydrogen is bonded to a highly electronegative element such as fluorine, oxygen, or nitrogen may exhibit a dipole, the positive end of which is a relatively exposed hydrogen nucleus. Because of such exposure a strong attractive force develops between the hydrogen atom of one molecule and the electronegative element of a neighboring molecule. Water in the solid and liquid states exhibits such a dipole, with the hydrogen atoms of one molecule being attracted to the oxygen atoms of another. This type of intermolecular attraction between hydrogen and a donor atom is called **hydrogen bonding,** or **H-bonding,** and is represented between molecules by dotted lines. Liquids in which H-bonding occurs between molecules are called *associated* liquids and have properties unlike those of "normal" liquids.

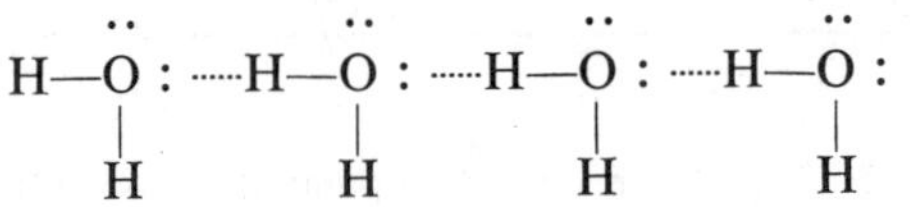

$$H-\overset{..}{O}: \cdots H-\overset{..}{O}: \cdots H-\overset{..}{O}: \cdots H-\overset{..}{O}:$$
$$\quad\ \ \underset{H}{|} \qquad\quad \underset{H}{|} \qquad\quad \underset{H}{|} \qquad\quad \underset{H}{|}$$

The alcohol molecule, like water, also is highly polar and while the alcohol molecule has but one hydrogen attached to oxygen, it also is associated through hydrogen bond formation. Molecules capable of H-bonding thus are attracted to each other much as a series of small magnets aligning themselves with N- and S-seeking poles together.

$$\cdots O-H\cdots O-H\cdots O-H\cdots O-H\cdots O-H\cdots O-H\cdots$$
$$\quad R \quad\quad R \quad\quad R \quad\quad R \quad\quad R \quad\quad R$$

To pass from the liquid into the vapor form, a molecule of alcohol, like one of water, must receive sufficient energy to overcome the attraction of its neighbors. Hydrogen bonding thus explains why the boiling point of water is relatively high for such a simple molecule and also explains why the alcohols have considerably higher boiling points than their nonhydroxylic isomers. For example, the boiling point of ethyl alcohol, C_2H_5OH, is 78°C and that of its isomer, dimethyl ether, CH_3-O-CH_3 (incapable of H-bonding), is -24.9°C. Comparisons made in Table 8.1 illustrate how H-bonding, more than an increase in molecular weight, affects the boiling points of liquids.

□ ■ TABLE 8.1

BOILING POINTS OF SOME SUBSTITUTED ETHANES

Compound	Molecular Wt.	B.P., °C
Ethyl alcohol	46	78.4
Ethyl chloride	64.5	12.2
Ethyl bromide	109	38.0
Ethyl iodide	156	72.4

The lower members of the alcohol family are like water in yet another respect. Inasmuch as the hydroxyl group comprises much of the molecular structure, the lower members of the alcohol family are miscible with water in all proportions. The alcohol molecule becomes more and more oil-like in character as the hydrocarbon segment becomes larger and its solubility in water diminishes markedly. A relationship between solubilities and the size and form of the alkyl groups is given in Table 8.2.

□■ TABLE 8.2

SOLUBILITIES OF C_1—C_6 ALCOHOLS

Name	Formula	Solubility (g/100 g H_2O)
Methanol	CH_3OH	completely miscible
Ethanol	C_2H_5OH	completely miscible
2-Propanol	$(CH_3)_2CHOH$	completely miscible
1-Propanol	$CH_3CH_2CH_2OH$	completely miscible
1-Butanol	$CH_3CH_2CH_2CH_2OH$	9 g
2-Methyl-1-Propanol	$(CH_3)_2CHCH_2OH$	10 g
2-Butanol	$CH_3CH_2CH(OH)CH_3$	12.5 g
2-Methyl-2-Propanol	$(CH_3)_3COH$	completely miscible
1-Pentanol	$CH_3(CH_2)_3CH_2OH$	2.7 g
2-Pentanol	$CH_3CH_2CH_2CH(OH)CH_3$	5.3 g
1-Hexanol	$CH_3(CH_2)_4CH_2OH$	0.6 g

Phenol and other polyhydroxy benzenes are colorless, low melting solids only slightly soluble in water. Perhaps the most distinctive property of phenols, and one which sets them apart from the alcohols, is the acidic character they possess. Phenols thus dissolve readily in hydroxide bases to form salts called phenoxides.

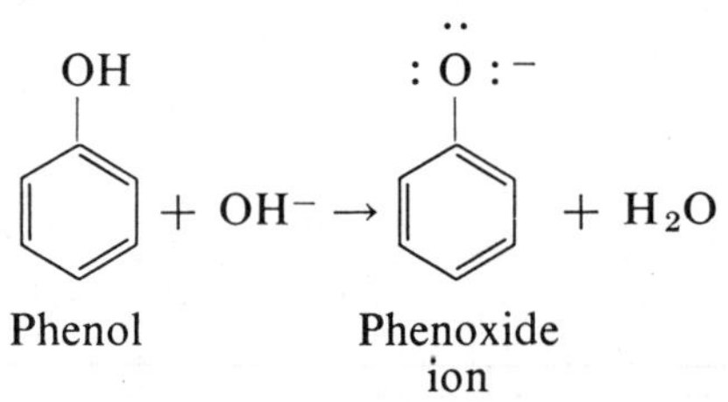

The ease with which phenols form soluble salts may be attributable to resonance in the phenoxide ion. Once the acidic hydrogen of phenol is removed as a proton, an unshared pair of electrons on the oxygen atom may become delocalized and enter into the resonance structure of the ring, as illustrated by the following structures.

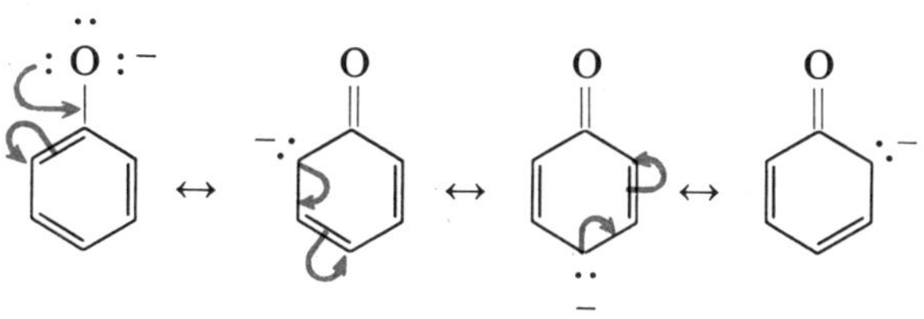

Resonance forms of phenoxide ion

Any reaction that gives as one product an ion stabilized by resonance easily moves in the direction to produce this ion. Such stabilization through resonance not only explains the acidic character of phenol, but also explains why phenol so easily directs substituents to the ortho and para positions.

Exercise 8.2   Which of the following compounds would be most acidic? Least acidic? Why?

(a) Phenol   (b) o-Nitrophenol   (c) o-Cresol

8.5   PREPARATION OF THE ALCOHOLS

Before we consider general methods for the preparation of the alcohols, let us discuss briefly the very important first two alcohols of the aliphatic series.

Methyl alcohol, commonly called **wood alcohol,** was made prior to 1923 by the destructive distillation of hardwoods. Since then, synthetic methyl alcohol has been made much more economically by combining carbon monoxide and hydrogen under high pressure and in the presence of catalysts.

$$CO + 2H_2 \xrightarrow[350°C,\ 200\ atm.]{ZnO\text{-}Cr_2O_3,} CH_3OH$$

Methanol

Methyl alcohol is a very poisonous substance which, if taken internally, causes visual impairment, complete blindness, or death. Death from the ingestion of as little as 30 ml. of methyl alcohol has been reported. At one time methyl alcohol was extensively used as radiator antifreeze but has been replaced largely by ethylene glycol (Sec. 8.6). In order to protect people who recognize no distinction between the alcohols, methyl alcohol antifreeze usually was labelled by its manufacturers by its nonsuggestive IUPAC name, **methanol.**

Ethyl alcohol sometimes is called **grain alcohol** because starch from grain, when hydrolyzed to sugars and fermented by enzymes, produces ethyl alcohol and carbon dioxide. Starch from any source is a suitable starting material. The fermentation of sugar by yeast is a reaction practiced since antiquity and is the basis for the production of alcoholic spirits, and for the leavening action required in the baking process.

$$2\,(C_6H_{10}O_5)_n + n\,H_2O \xrightarrow[\text{in malt}]{\text{Diastase}} n\,C_{12}H_{22}O_{11}$$

Starch   Maltose

$$C_{12}H_{22}O_{11} + H_2O \xrightarrow{\text{Maltase}} 2\,C_6H_{12}O_6$$

Glucose

$$C_6H_{12}O_6 \xrightarrow{\text{Zymase}} 2\,C_2H_5OH + 2\,CO_2$$

Ethanol

Inasmuch as the second step in the preceding sequence produces glucose, ethanol also may be prepared from this simple sugar directly. Grape juice, a rich source of glucose, will ferment to produce a wine with a maximum alcoholic content of approximately 12% by volume. The alcoholic content of liquors usually is designated as **proof spirit,** 100 proof indicating an alcoholic content of 50% by volume. The term "proof spirit" supposedly had its origin in an early and rather crude analytical procedure for determining the alcoholic content of whiskey. Whiskey of high alcoholic content, when poured onto a small mound of gunpowder and ignited, would burn with a flame sufficiently hot to ignite the powder. This was "proof" of spirit content. If the gunpowder failed to ignite, the presence of too much water was indicated and the powder became too wet to burn.

Ethyl alcohol used in the laboratory for solvent purposes seldom is pure alcohol. It usually is a mixture of 95% alcohol and 5% water. Ninety-five per cent represents the maximum purity obtainable when alcohol is distilled because this is the constant-boiling composition. A constant-boiling mixture of liquids, called an **azeotrope,** cannot be separated by fractional distillation. In order to obtain **absolute,** or 100% pure ethyl alcohol, the water must be removed by methods other than fractionation. One method is to distill a ternary mixture composed of alcohol, water, and benzene. These three liquids, in a composition of 18.5%, 7.4%, and 74.1%, respectively, also form an azeotrope with a constant boiling temperature of 64.85°. Therefore, if sufficient benzene is added to 95%

alcohol and the mixture distilled, the water is removed in the distillate along with benzene and some alcohol, but pure alcohol is left in the still pot.

In the laboratory the last traces of water may be removed by chemical combination. Calcium oxide, CaO, for example, reacts with water to produce calcium hydroxide, $Ca(OH)_2$, but does not react with the alcohol. Alcohol "dried" in this manner can be recovered by a simple distillation.

Alcoholic beverages always have been a prime source of tax revenue for most governments. Ethyl alcohol, when used as a solvent or as a reagent, is tax free. In order to prevent the use of tax-free alcohol for purposes other than scientific or industrial, the government requires that it be **denatured.** Denatured alcohol is alcohol rendered unfit for beverages by the addition of substances repugnant and difficult to remove. The reason for the government's vigilance over the manufacture and use of alcohol may be illustrated clearly by the following simple economics. The price of 95% (190-proof) alcohol in bulk lots is approximately $1.29 per gallon when purchased as a tax-free reagent. As 190-proof beverage spirit, the price is approximately $35.00 per gallon!

A. Preparation of Alcohols from Olefins. Large quantities of ethyl alcohol still are made by the fermentation of sugars found in blackstrap molasses, but its synthesis from ethylene has become a very important industrial process and provides most of the alcohol used in the chemical industry. Olefins can be converted to alcohols by hydration which, in this case, is the reverse reaction we employed to produce an olefin from an alcohol (Sec. 3.9-C). In practice, the elements of water are added across the double bond indirectly. Sulfuric acid is added first and the alkyl sulfuric acid thus formed, when diluted with water and heated, undergoes hydrolysis to produce the alcohol according to the following equations which illustrate the preparation of ethanol from ethers.

Ethyl sulfuric acid

Ethanol

Other members of the alcohol family can be prepared from olefins by the same process.

$$R-\overset{\overset{\displaystyle H}{|}}{C}=CH_2 + \overset{+}{H}\ HSO_4^- \rightarrow R-\overset{\overset{\displaystyle H}{|}}{\underset{\underset{\displaystyle OSO_3H}{|}}{C}}-CH_3 \xrightarrow{H_2O} R-\overset{\overset{\displaystyle H}{|}}{\underset{\underset{\displaystyle OH}{|}}{C}}-CH_3$$

A secondary
alcohol

$$R-\overset{\overset{\displaystyle R}{|}}{C}=CH_2 \xrightarrow{H_2SO_4} R-\overset{\overset{\displaystyle R}{|}}{\underset{\underset{\displaystyle OSO_3H}{|}}{C}}-CH_3 \xrightarrow{H_2O} R-\overset{\overset{\displaystyle R}{|}}{\underset{\underset{\displaystyle OH}{|}}{C}}-CH_3$$

A tertiary
alcohol

The only primary alcohol that can be prepared by the hydration of olefins is ethanol from ethylene. Addition to the double bond, you must remember, is in accordance with Markovnikov's rule (Sec. 3.9).

B.   Hydrolysis of Alkyl Halides.   Alcohols may be prepared by the hydrolysis of alkyl halides, but the reaction is of limited usefulness because olefin formation by *elimination* of halogen acid competes with the *substitution* reaction. Alkyl halides are hydrolyzed in a neutral, rather than in an alkaline alcoholic solution in order to minimize the formation of olefins, but some elimination may result even when a neutral hydrolysis is carried out. This is especially true when highly branched tertiary alkyl halides are hydrolyzed. Bulky groups, when attached to the same carbon atom that bears the halogen, not only inhibit a nucleophilic attack from the rear (S_N2), but appear to have a crowding effect upon each other. Strain, due to such crowding, may be relieved by the departure of the halide ion. The intermediate, tertiary carbonium ion now either can be attacked by the solvent at the face of the carbon atom, or at a β hydrogen. You will recognize the first choice as the S_N1, the second as the E1 reaction (Sec. 7.5). The elimination route appears to be favored, especially if an alkaline hydrolysis with a strong base is attempted. Where olefin formation is not possible, the hydrolysis of an alkyl halide results in the formation of an alcohol. A useful application of this method is the synthesis of benzyl alcohol from benzyl chloride.

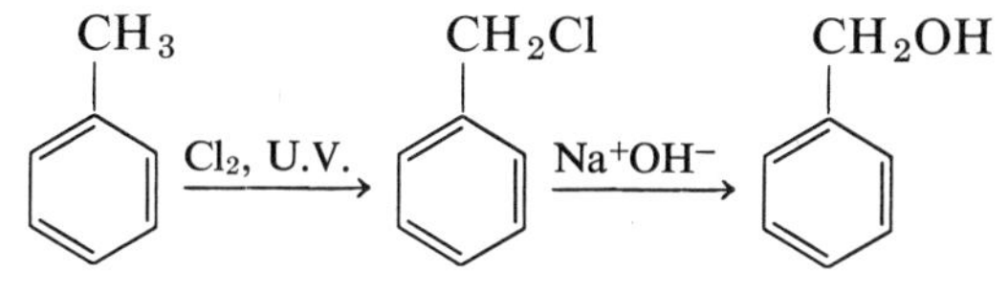

$$CH_3 \quad\quad\quad CH_2Cl \quad\quad\quad CH_2OH$$

Toluene → (Cl₂, U.V.) → Benzyl chloride → (Na⁺OH⁻) → Benzyl alcohol

Toluene   Benzyl chloride   Benzyl alcohol

C. Addition of Grignard Reagents to Aldehydes and Ketones. The addition of Grignard reagents of the form RMgX or ArMgX to aldehydes or to ketones (Chap. 9) provides one of the best routes leading to the preparation of alcohols. An alkyl or aryl magnesium halide adds to the carbonyl group of an aldehyde or a ketone to produce a mixed salt of divalent magnesium. The electropositive magnesium seeks the carbonyl oxygen; the organic group joins the carbonyl carbon. The mode of this addition is illustrated by

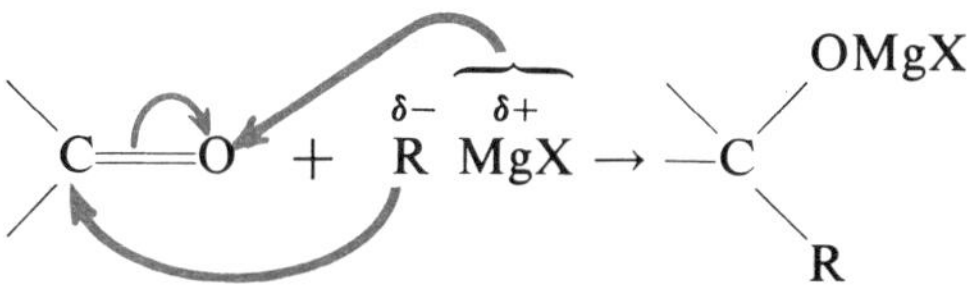

$$C=O \ + \ \overset{\delta-}{R} \ \overset{\delta+}{MgX} \rightarrow -C \overset{OMgX}{\underset{R}{<}}$$

The addition product, when hydrolyzed in dilute hydrochloric acid, is smoothly converted into an alcohol and a magnesium dihalide.

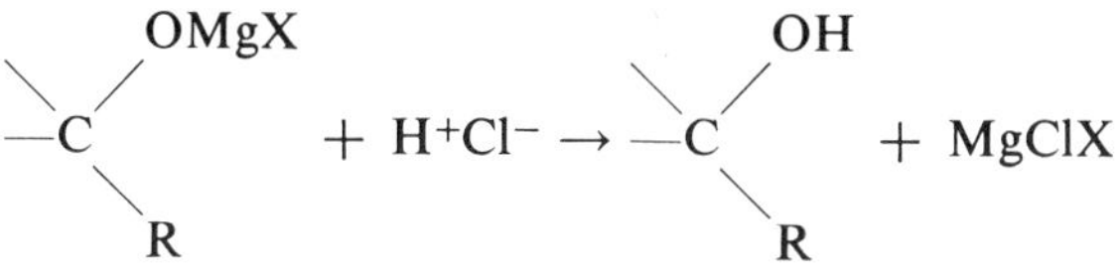

$$-C \overset{OMgX}{\underset{R}{<}} \ + \ H^+Cl^- \rightarrow -C \overset{OH}{\underset{R}{<}} \ + \ MgClX$$

The reaction is a versatile one by which alcohols of any class may be produced. Of the aldehydes, formaldehyde alone yields a primary alcohol when treated with a Grignard reagent. Other aldehydes give secondary alcohols, and ketones yield tertiary alcohols. General equations for the preparation of alcohols of each class from Grignard reagents are illustrated on the next page.

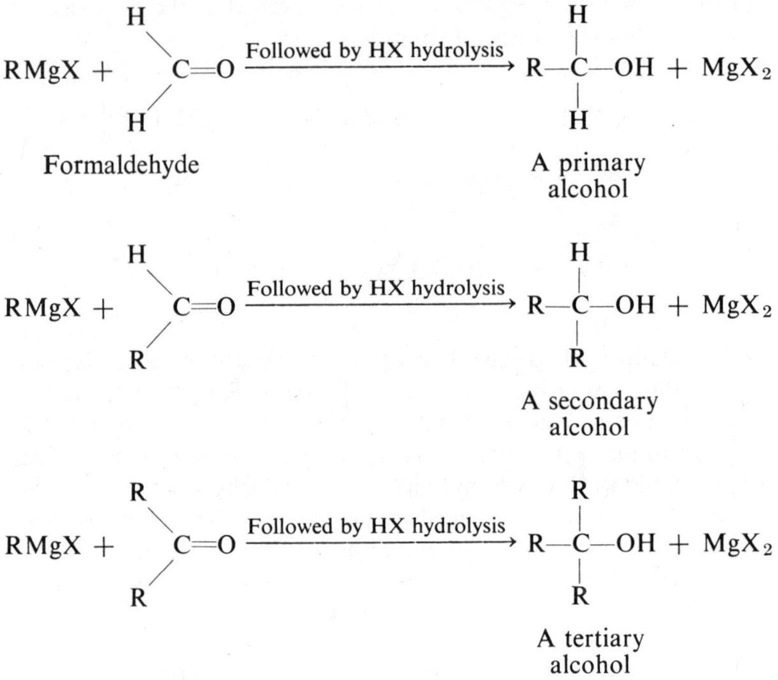

$$RMgX + \begin{array}{c} H \\ \diagdown \\ C{=}O \\ \diagup \\ H \end{array} \xrightarrow{\text{Followed by HX hydrolysis}} \begin{array}{c} H \\ | \\ R{-}C{-}OH \\ | \\ H \end{array} + MgX_2$$

Formaldehyde   A primary
                                                    alcohol

$$RMgX + \begin{array}{c} H \\ \diagdown \\ C{=}O \\ \diagup \\ R \end{array} \xrightarrow{\text{Followed by HX hydrolysis}} \begin{array}{c} H \\ | \\ R{-}C{-}OH \\ | \\ R \end{array} + MgX_2$$

A secondary
alcohol

$$RMgX + \begin{array}{c} R \\ \diagdown \\ C{=}O \\ \diagup \\ R \end{array} \xrightarrow{\text{Followed by HX hydrolysis}} \begin{array}{c} R \\ | \\ R{-}C{-}OH \\ | \\ R \end{array} + MgX_2$$

A tertiary
alcohol

An inspection of the structure of the desired alcohol will always indicate which Grignard reagent and which carbonyl compound may be combined to produce it. For example, the preparation of 3-methyl-2-butanol, a secondary alcohol, suggests an aldehyde for the carbonyl compound. Which aldehyde shall we use, and of what shall we prepare our Grignard reagent? By inspection, it may be seen that the portion of the structure indicated by the broken line can have its origin in acetaldehyde; that indicated by the solid line, in isobutyraldehyde.

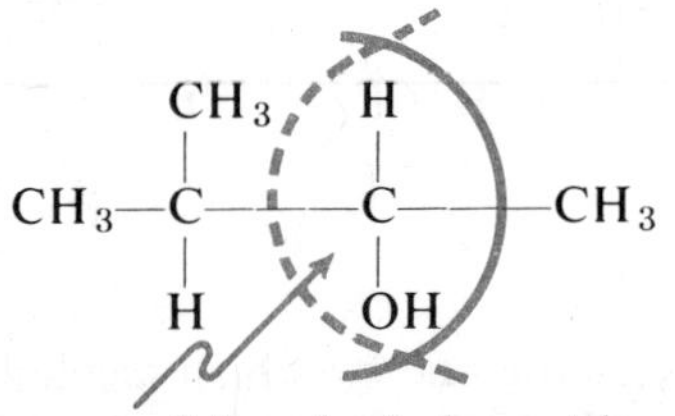

$$CH_3{-}\overset{\displaystyle CH_3}{\underset{\displaystyle H}{C}}{-}\overset{\displaystyle H}{\underset{\displaystyle OH}{C}}{-}CH_3$$

(This part of the alcohol must have its
origin in the carbonyl compound.)

If acetaldehyde is our choice of a carbonyl, it follows that the Grignard used with it must be prepared from an isopropyl halide. On the other hand, if isobutyraldehyde is selected, the Grignard reagent must be prepared from methyl halide. The first set of reagents is more appealing than the second and may be used in the following manner.

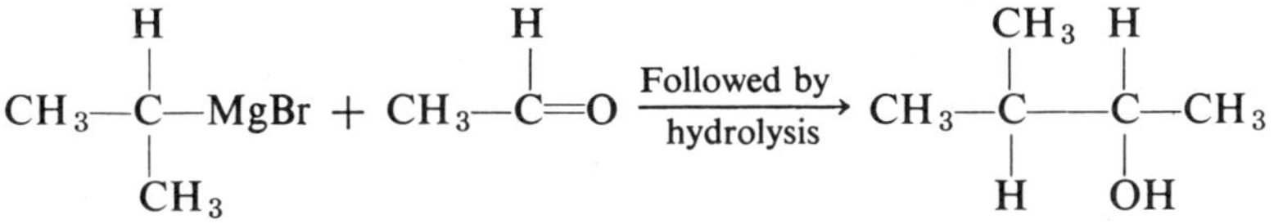

$$\underset{\substack{\text{Isopropyl-}\\\text{magnesium}\\\text{bromide}}}{CH_3-\underset{\underset{CH_3}{|}}{\overset{\overset{H}{|}}{C}}-MgBr} + \underset{\text{Acetaldehyde}}{CH_3-\overset{\overset{H}{|}}{C}=O} \xrightarrow[\text{hydrolysis}]{\text{Followed by}} \underset{\substack{\text{3-Methyl-2-butanol}\\\text{(a secondary alcohol)}}}{CH_3-\underset{\underset{H}{|}}{\overset{\overset{CH_3}{|}}{C}}-\underset{\underset{OH}{|}}{\overset{\overset{H}{|}}{C}}-CH_3}$$

The isomeric, tertiary five-carbon alcohol must, of course, begin with a ketone.

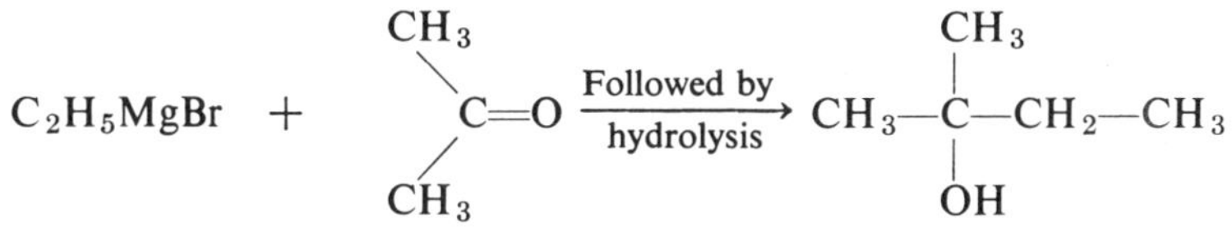

$$\underset{\substack{\text{Ethylmagnesium}\\\text{bromide}}}{C_2H_5MgBr} + \underset{\text{Acetone}}{\underset{CH_3}{\overset{CH_3}{\diagdown\!\!\diagup}}C=O} \xrightarrow[\text{hydrolysis}]{\text{Followed by}} \underset{\substack{\text{2-Methyl-2-butanol}\\\text{(a tertiary alcohol)}}}{CH_3-\underset{\underset{OH}{|}}{\overset{\overset{CH_3}{|}}{C}}-CH_2-CH_3}$$

Another synthetic route leading to a primary alcohol is the reaction of a Grignard reagent with ethylene oxide (Sec. 8.6). As in the carbonyl additions, the magnesium becomes attached to the oxygen atom. The reaction has the added advantage of lengthening the carbon chain by two carbons.

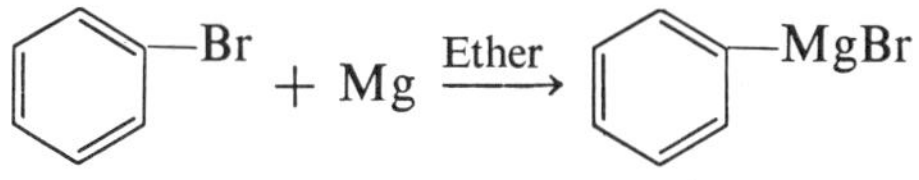

Phenylmagnesium
bromide

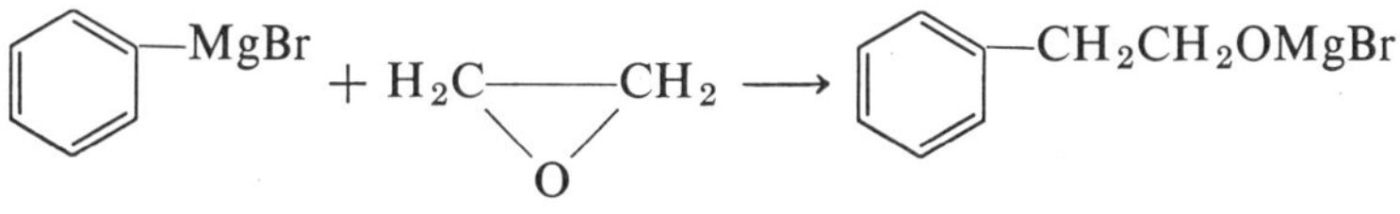

Ethylene
oxide

$$\text{—CH}_2\text{CH}_2\text{OMgBr} \xrightarrow{\text{H}_2\text{O}} \text{—CH}_2\text{CH}_2\text{OH} + \text{HOMgBr}$$

β-Phenylethyl alcohol
(2-Phenylethanol)

Exercise 8.3   Beginning with propylene and any other inorganic reagents that you might require, show how you might prepare (a) isopropyl alcohol, (b) *n*-propyl alcohol, (c) 2, 3-dimethyl-2-butanol.

8.6   POLYHYDRIC ALCOHOLS

Polyhydric alcohols are those which contain more than one hydroxyl group. Compounds that have two hydroxyl groups are called **glycols. Ethylene glycol,** the principal component in permanent types of antifreeze, can be made from ethylene by several different methods. One of these proceeds by way of a chlorohydrin.

$$\text{CH}_2\text{=CH}_2 + \text{HO}^-\text{Cl}^+ \xrightarrow{\text{(Cl}_2\text{+H}_2\text{O)}} \underset{\substack{| \quad | \\ \text{Cl} \quad \text{OH}}}{\text{CH}_2\text{—CH}_2} \xrightarrow{\text{H}_2\text{O, Na}_2\text{CO}_3} \underset{\substack{| \quad | \\ \text{OH} \quad \text{OH}}}{\text{CH}_2\text{—CH}_2}$$

Ethylene   Ethylene   Ethylene
                        chlorohydrin   glycol

Exercise 8.4   The gauche conformation (Sec. 2.6) appears to be preferred for ethylene chlorohydrin. Can you suggest a reason why?

Another industrial method for the preparation of ethylene glycol is a simple hydration of ethylene oxide. Ethylene oxide has its origin in ethylene. Oxygen, in the presence of a silver catalyst, adds to the olefin.

$$2\ \text{CH}_2\text{=CH}_2 + \text{O}_2 \xrightarrow{\text{Ag}} 2\ \underset{\text{O}}{\text{CH}_2\text{—CH}_2}$$

Ethylene   Ethylene oxide

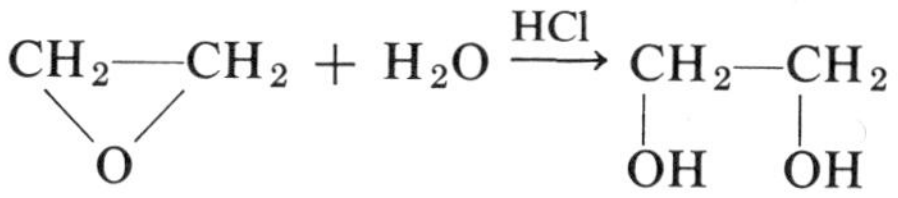

$$CH_2\!-\!CH_2 + H_2O \xrightarrow{\text{HCl}} CH_2\!-\!CH_2$$

Ethylene glycol

Ethylene glycol is miscible with water in all proportions. Its great solubility in water, along with its high boiling point (197.5°C), makes it an excellent antifreeze. Ethylene glycol is not readily lost by evaporation and offers far better winter protection to a water-cooled engine than does methanol (B.P., 64.6°C).

Propylene glycol, $CH_3CH(OH)CH_2OH$, is prepared in a manner similar to that for the preparation of ethylene glycol.

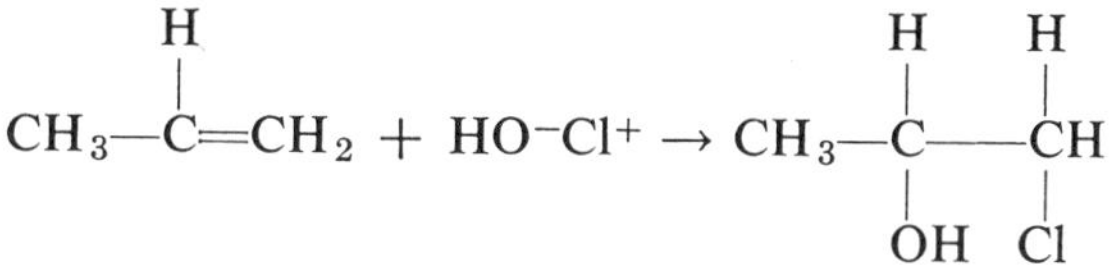

$$CH_3\!-\!C\!=\!CH_2 + HO^-Cl^+ \rightarrow CH_3\!-\!C\!-\!CH$$

Propylene — Propylene chlorohydrin

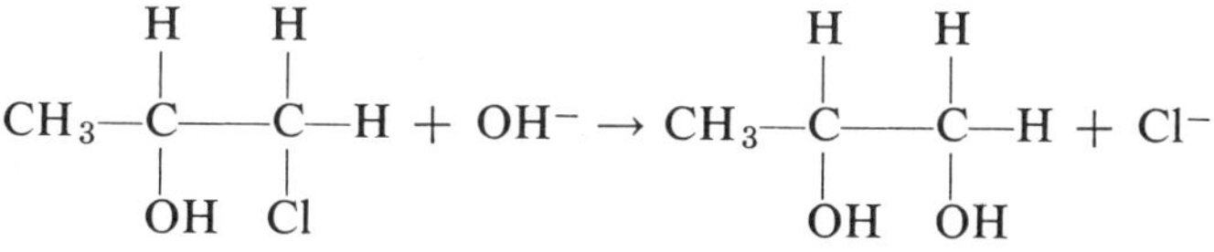

$$CH_3\!-\!C\!-\!C\!-\!H + OH^- \rightarrow CH_3\!-\!C\!-\!C\!-\!H + Cl^-$$

Propylene glycol

Propylene glycol has properties similar to those of ethylene glycol but is much less toxic. The low toxicity of propylene glycol permits its use as an emulsifying solvent and softening agent in cosmetics.

Glycerol ($HOCH_2CH(OH)CH_2OH$), or glycerine, as it is commonly called, is a trihydroxy alcohol, or triol. Like propylene glycol, glycerol also can be made from propylene.

$$CH_3\!-\!CH\!=\!CH_2 + Cl_2 \xrightarrow{600°C} Cl\!-\!CH_2\!-\!CH\!=\!CH_2 + HCl$$

Propylene — Allyl chloride

$$Cl\!-\!CH_2\!-\!CH\!=\!CH_2 + OH^- \rightarrow HO\!-\!CH_2\!-\!CH\!=\!CH_2 + Cl^-$$

Allyl alcohol

$$HO—CH_2—CH{=}CH_2 + HO^-Cl^+ \rightarrow HO—CH_2—\underset{\underset{Cl}{|}}{\overset{\overset{H}{|}}{C}}{-\!-\!-}CH_2$$
$$\phantom{HO—CH_2—CH{=}CH_2 + HO^-Cl^+ \rightarrow HO—CH_2—}\underset{OH}{}$$

Glycerol α-chlorohydrin

$$HO—CH_2—\underset{\underset{OH}{|}}{\overset{\overset{H}{|}}{C}}—CH_2Cl + OH^- \rightarrow HOCH_2—CH(OH)—CH_2OH + Cl^-$$

Glycerol

You might wonder why, in the first step of the previous reaction sequence, chlorine replaces hydrogen of the methyl group and does not add across the double bond. Chlorine substitutes, rather than adds, because at the high temperature under which the reaction is carried out, substitution takes place by way of a free radical mechanism. Addition of halogen, you will recall, takes place by way of a polar mechanism (Sec. 3.8).

Large quantities of glycerol occur as a by-product in the manufacture of soaps from animal and vegetable fats and oils. It is a viscous, sweet-tasting liquid and, as might be expected with three hydroxyl groups present, is miscible with water in all proportions. It is an excellent humectant (moisture-retaining agent) and is used in the tobacco and cosmetic industries. Glycerol also is used for the preparation of "nitroglycerine," the high explosive component of "Dynamite," in the production of plastics, synthetic fibers, and surface coatings.

$$
\begin{array}{c}
H \\
| \\
H—C—OH \\
| \\
H—C—OH \\
| \\
H—C—OH \\
| \\
H
\end{array}
\;+\; 3\,HNO_3 \;\xrightarrow{H_2SO_4}\;
\begin{array}{c}
H \\
| \\
H—C—O—NO_2 \\
| \\
H—C—O—NO_2 \\
| \\
H—C—O—NO_2 \\
| \\
H
\end{array}
\;+\; 3\,H_2O
$$

Glycerol   Glyceryl trinitrate
("Nitroglycerine")

8.7   PREPARATION OF THE PHENOLS

Phenols cannot be prepared from aryl halides by methods similar to those employed for the conversion of alkyl halides into alcohols. Halogen bound to an aromatic ring represents a very stable system and can be displaced only by drastic treatment. In the **Dow process,** for example, phenol is produced from chlorobenzene by alkaline hydrolysis at a very high pressure and temperature. Sodium phenoxide, the initial product formed, is converted to phenol by reaction with hydrochloric acid.

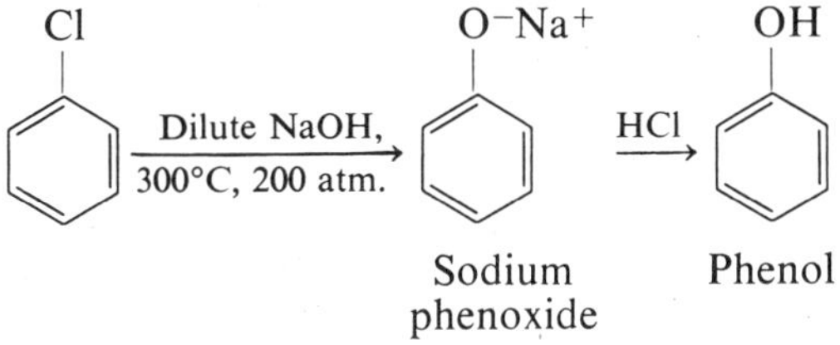

A more recent industrial process produces phenol from isopropylbenzene (cumene). Cumene is obtained from petroleum or may be synthesized from benzene and propene *via* a Friedel-Crafts reaction. Air, when forced through cumene in the presence of a trace of base, produces a hydroperoxide. The latter, on hydrolysis, rearranges and decomposes into phenol and the important by-product acetone.

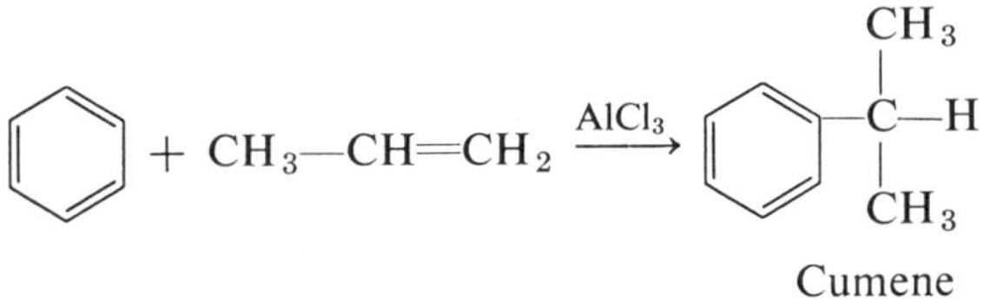

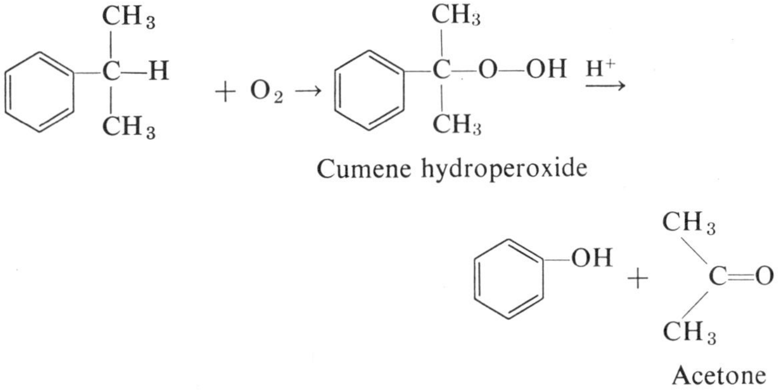

Phenol may be prepared in the laboratory by the fusion of sodium benzenesulfonate (Sec. 4.8-D) with sodium hydroxide. The sodium phenoxide produced by this fusion is converted to free phenol by acid treatment.

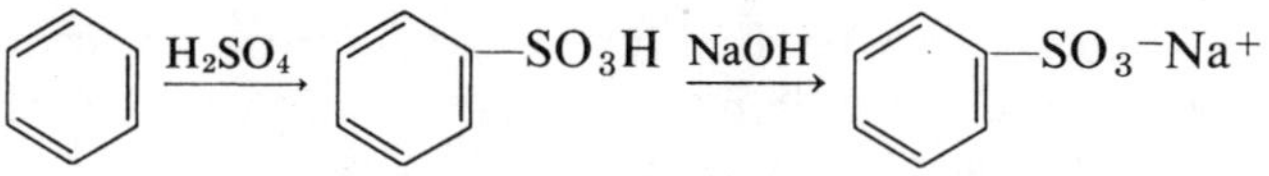

Benzenesulfonic
acid

Sodium
benzenesulfonate

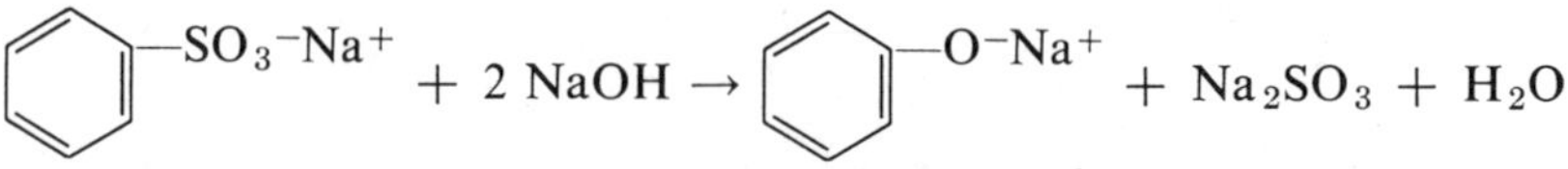

Sodium phenoxide

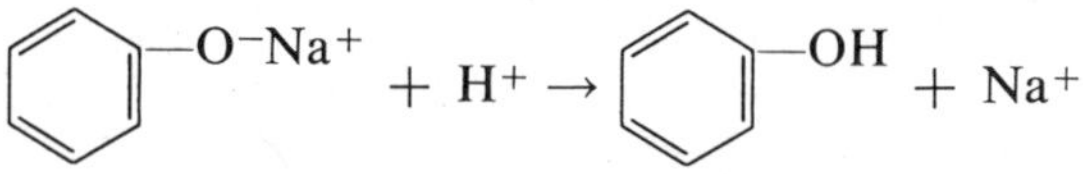

Phenol

8.8   THE GERMICIDAL PROPERTIES OF PHENOLS

Phenol is one of the oldest of disinfectants. All phenolic compounds appear to have a germicidal power which is enhanced by the presence of alkyl groups on the ring. It appears that the optimum size of the side chain for maximum germicidal activity is six carbons, making **n-hexylresorcinol** a very fine antiseptic.

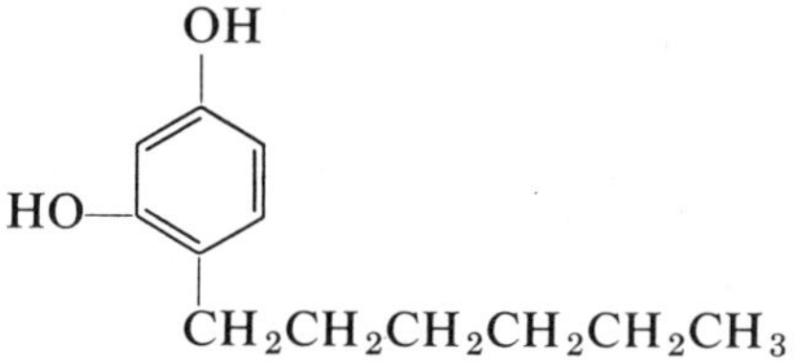

n-Hexylresorcinol

The killing power which an antiseptic has against microorganisms is measured against that of phenol. The germicidal efficiency of an antiseptic is measured in terms of an arbitrary unit called a **phenol coefficient.** For example, a germicide in a 1% solution that kills an organism in the same length of time as that required for a 5% phenol solution, is assigned a phenol coefficient of 5.

Chlorine-substituted phenols are especially active against bacteria and fungi. **Pentachlorophenol,** for example, is an excellent fungicide and wood preservative and is widely used to protect against "dry rot" and termites. The chlorine substituted biphenyl phenolic compound 2, 2'-dihydroxy-3, 3', 5, 5', 6, 6'-hexachlorodiphenyl-methane, popularly known as "Hexachlorophene," has a phenol coefficient of about 125. In dilute form it is extensively used in the manufacture of germicidal soaps, some toothpastes, and many deodorants.

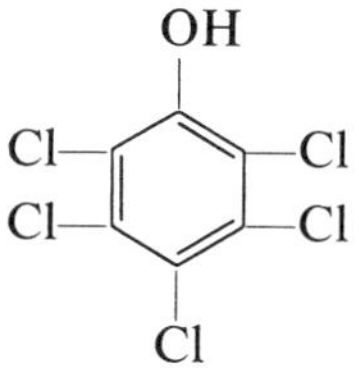

Pentachlorophenol 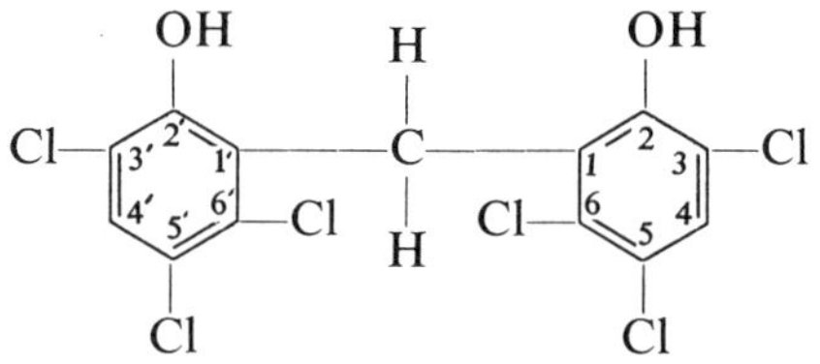   Hexachlorophene

Phenol and its homologs are toxic substances and have a caustic action on animal tissue. Care must be exercised in handling phenols; direct contact or inhalation of their vapors should be avoided.

Exercise 8.5   A germicide in a concentration of one part to 225 parts of water showed the same killing power against *Salmonella typhosa* in ten minutes as did a solution made of one part phenol in 100 parts of water during the same contact time. What is the phenol coefficient of the germicide in question? (*Answer:* 2.25.)

8.9   REACTIONS OF THE ALCOHOLS AND PHENOLS

The reactions of the alcohols and phenols are of the following types:

(A)   Reactions that result in O—H bond cleavage, RO⊣H
(B)   Reactions that result in C—O bond cleavage, R⊢OH
(C)   Reactions that result in oxidation of the carbinol carbon
(D)   Reactions that involve the aromatic ring of phenols.

A-1. Cleavage of the O—H Bond.   Salt Formation.   The aliphatic alcohols are not sufficiently acidic to react with bases such as sodium or potassium hydroxide, but will react with active metals to yield the alcoholates, or alkoxides, of the metal and liberate hydrogen gas.

$$2 \text{ RO} \text{---} \text{H} + 2 \text{ Na} \longrightarrow 2 \text{ RO}^- \text{Na}^+ + \text{H}_2$$

Sodium
alkoxide

Primary alcohols exhibit a greater reactivity on treatment with sodium metal than do secondary alcohols, and the latter show a greater reactivity than tertiary alcohols. Of the alkali metals, potassium is more reactive toward any class of alcohols than is sodium. The liberation of hydrogen gas from an unknown liquid sometimes is used as a test for alcohols. Of course, the liquid to be tested must be free of water.

Phenols are stronger acids than the alcohols and react with aqueous solutions of sodium or potassium hydroxide to yield the phenoxides of these metals. On the other hand, phenols are not

Sodium phenoxide

sufficiently acidic to react with sodium carbonate. This solubility behavior allows phenols to be separated from a mixture which might also include other stronger organic acids which react with sodium carbonate to give water-soluble salts.

A-2. Cleavage of the O—H Bond. Ether Formation.   The alkoxides or phenoxides of the alkali metals are strong bases (nucleophiles) that easily enter into S_N2 displacements of halogen from alkyl halides. This reaction, referred to as the **Williamson Ether Synthesis,** is best used to prepare mixed ethers — that is, ethers in which the two groups bridged by the oxygen atom are not the same.

$$(CH_3)_2CHO^-Na^+ + CH_3I \xrightarrow{S_N2} (CH_3)_2CH-O-CH_3 + NaI$$

Isopropyl methyl ether

If one of the groups in the ether is to be a branched structure, that part of the ether should have its origin in the alkoxide. If the alkyl halide is highly branched elimination, rather than substitution, results.

$$CH_3O^-Na^+ + (CH_3)_2CHI \xrightarrow{E2} CH_3CH=CH_2 + CH_3OH + NaI$$

Propylene

A-3. Ester Formation.   Alcohols, when permitted to react with carboxylic acids (Chapter 10), produce esters. The reaction is catalyzed by strong mineral acids and, as indicated by the double arrow in the equation, is reversible.

$$R-\overset{\overset{\displaystyle O}{\|}}{C}-OH + H-OR \rightleftarrows R-\overset{\overset{\displaystyle O}{\|}}{C}-OR + H_2O$$

| Acid | Alcohol | Ester |

The esterification reaction is discussed in greater detail in Section 10.6-G where the mechanics of the reaction show why it is an O—H bond cleavage with respect to the alcohol.

B-1. Replacement of the Hydroxyl Group by Acid Anions.   The reactions of alcohols with phosphorus halides and thionyl chloride, $SOCl_2$, were reviewed under the preparation of the alkyl halides (Sec. 7.3-B).

Treatment of an aliphatic alcohol with the **Lucas reagent** (a solution of zinc chloride in concentrated hydrochloric acid) produces an alkyl chloride.

$$R-OH + HCl \xrightarrow{ZnCl_2} R-Cl + H_2O$$

The alkyl chloride, when formed in this manner, is insoluble in the reagent and produces either a cloudy appearance or forms two layers. The Lucas reagent is used to distinguish between primary, secondary, and tertiary alcohols because a tertiary alcohol reacts immediately, the secondary after a few minutes, and the primary only when heated for some hours.

An alcohol treated with concentrated sulfuric acid at room temperature produces an alkyl hydrogen sulfate.

$$C_2H_5-OH + H-O-SO_2-OH \longrightarrow C_2H_5-O-SO_2-OH + H_2O$$

Ethyl hydrogen sulfate

The alkyl hydrogen sulfates still have one acidic hydrogen remaining, and are capable of forming salts. The sodium salts of the long chain alkyl hydrogen sulfates are excellent detergents (Sec. 11.8). Among the detergents with familiar trade names are Dreft, Cheer, Vel, and Trend.

$$CH_3-(CH_2)_{11}-O-SO_3H + NaOH \longrightarrow CH_3-(CH_2)_{11}-OSO_3^-Na^+ + H_2O$$

Lauryl hydrogen sulfate   Sodium lauryl sulfate

Alcohols react with nitric acid to yield alkyl nitrates. Perhaps the most widely used alkyl nitrate is glyceryl trinitrate (commonly called "nitroglycerine"), the principal explosive ingredient in dynamite (Sec. 8.6). Glyceryl trinitrate has been employed medicinally as a vasodilator of short duration for the relief of angina pectoris in heart patients.

B-2. Cleavage of the C—O Bond. Dehydration.   Ethanol may, in effect, be dehydrated to an olefin when its hydrogen sulfate ester is heated to 150° or higher.

$$CH_3CH_2—OSO_3H \xrightarrow{150°} H_2C{=}CH_2 + H_2SO_4$$

If the hydrogen sulfate ester is heated with an excess of alcohol at a temperature lower than 150°, the bisulfate ion is displaced by alcohol to produce a simple ether.

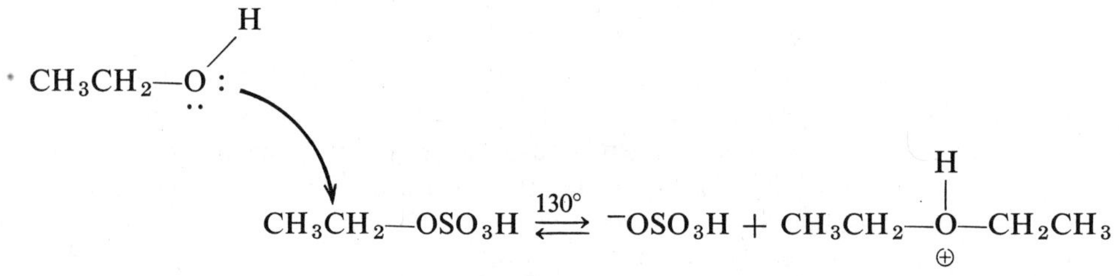

$$CH_3CH_2—OSO_3H \underset{130°}{\rightleftarrows} {}^-OSO_3H + CH_3CH_2—\overset{H}{\underset{\oplus}{O}}—CH_2CH_3$$

$$CH_3CH_2—\overset{H}{\underset{\oplus}{O}}—CH_2CH_3 + {}^-OSO_3H \rightleftarrows CH_3CH_2OCH_2CH_3 + H_2SO_4$$

Diethyl ether

C.   Oxidation.   When oxidized, primary and secondary alcohols give organic products containing the same number of carbon atoms. Primary alcohols can be oxidized to carboxylic acids (Sec. 10.5-A) and secondary alcohols to ketones (Sec. 9.5-A). Tertiary alcohols are not oxidizable without a rupture of carbon-carbon bonds. Reagents usually employed for the oxidation of alcohols are potassium dichromate in combination with concentrated sulfuric acid, or a hot, alkaline solution of potassium permanganate.

$$3\ CH_3CH_2OH + 2\ K_2Cr_2O_7 + 8\ H_2SO_4 \longrightarrow$$

Ethanol

$$3\ CH_3-C\overset{O}{\underset{OH}{\diagup}} + 2\ K_2SO_4 + 2\ Cr_2(SO_4)_3 + 11\ H_2O$$

Acetic acid

$$3\ CH_3-\overset{H}{\underset{OH}{C}}-CH_3 + 2\ KMnO_4 \longrightarrow$$

2-Propanol

$$3\ CH_3-\overset{O}{\overset{\|}{C}}-CH_3 + 2\ MnO_2 + 2\ KOH + 2\ H_2O$$

Acetone

On Balancing Oxidation-Reduction Equations

It would seem in order at this point to illustrate how the equations for the preceding reactions were balanced.

Organic chemists when writing reaction equations frequently indicate to the right of the reaction arrow only the principal organic products obtained. The term "equation," however, implies "balance," and balanced oxidation-reduction equations may be written for organic reactions as well as for inorganic reactions — perhaps not as readily, but certainly with as much sport. Unfortunately, "oxidation number" as applied to carbon atoms in organic compounds does not have the same connotation as when applied to ions in inorganic salts and cannot always be determined by simple inspection. We usually think of an element undergoing oxidation as one losing electrons and one being reduced as gaining electrons. The carbon atom retains four electrons for sharing whether it is oxidized or reduced. The covalently bonded carbon atom *loses part of its normal* "hold" on the electron pair when oxidized — that is, when it is bonded to a more electronegative element. Conversely, it *gains* a greater "hold" on the electron pair when reduced — that is, when it is bonded to a more electropositive element. In other words, the carbon atom becomes *more* or *less* polar in an oxidation-reduction reaction. Therefore, by assigning polar values rather than oxidation numbers to carbon we can balance an oxidation-reduction equation involving carbon quite easily. We need to learn and practice but a few simple rules.

1. The oxidation number of hydrogen is +1 (except in the hydrides of active metals, e.g., $LiAlH_4$, where it is −1).
2. The oxidation number of oxygen is −2 (except in peroxides, e.g., H_2O_2, where it is −1).
3. The oxidation number of an element (or the polar number in the case of carbon) becomes more positive as it is oxidized, less positive when reduced.
4. Two carbon atoms bonded together effect no change in the polar number of either.
5. Oxidation must always be accompanied by an equivalent amount of reduction.

Before any equation can be balanced one must know beforehand the nature of the products obtained when certain reactants are brought together. One also must determine the degree of change in the oxidation or polar number of each element involved in an oxidation number change. For example,

(Polar number of carbinol carbon = −1)

(Polar number of carboxylic carbon = +3)

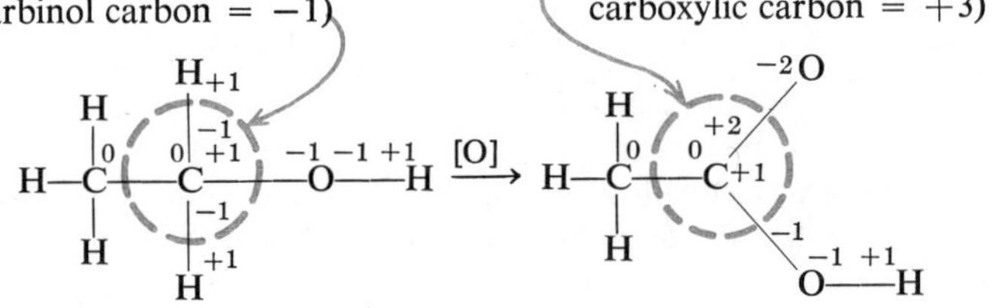

The polar numbers −1 and +3 for the carbon atom in the alcoho and the acid, respectively, were determined according to Rules 1, 2, and 4 by adding algebraically all polar values conferred upon each carbon by the atoms bonded to it. You will note that the number two carbon atom in both alcohol and acid molecule undergoes no change and therefore remains the same throughout the reaction.

Exercise 8.6 Determine the polar number of the carbon atom in each of the following compounds:

(a) CH_4 (b) CH_3OH (c) $H_2C{=}O$, formaldehyde
(d) HCOOH, formic acid, (e) CO_2

We are now ready to balance the equation

(Oxidation)

$$\underset{(-1)}{CH_3CH_2OH} + K_2Cr_2O_7 + H_2SO_4 \longrightarrow \underset{(+3)}{CH_3COOH} + \underset{(+3)}{Cr_2(SO_4)_3}$$

(Reduction)

$$+ K_2SO_4 + H_2O$$

The oxidation step represents a loss of 4 in the polar number of carbon. The reduction step represents a gain of 3 in the oxidation number of each chromium atom for a total electron gain of 6 for both chromium atoms. In accordance with Rule 5, equivalence between oxidation and reduction is established by taking three times the amount of alcohol and its oxidation product, the acid, and twice the amount of oxidizing reagent and its reduction products, $Cr_2(SO_4)_3$ and K_2SO_4.

$$3\ CH_3CH_2OH + 2\ K_2Cr_2O_7 + H_2SO_4 \longrightarrow 3\ CH_3COOH$$

$$+ 2\ Cr_2(SO_4)_3 + 2\ K_2SO_4 + H_2O$$

The oxidation-reduction step is now complete. All that remains to be done is to supply the necessary amount of sulfuric acid on the left side of the equation to provide for the sulfate salts on the other. A simple inspection will tell us that 8 moles of sulfuric acid are required. This amount of sulfuric acid automatically provides enough hydrogen (along with that obtained from the alcohol) to combine with the oxygen provided by the potassium dichromate in excess of that needed for the acetic acid. Excess hydrogen and oxygen then appear together as water on the right side of the equation. Let us now re-write the completed, balanced equation.

$$3\ CH_3CH_2OH + 2\ K_2Cr_2O_7 + 8\ H_2SO_4 \longrightarrow 3\ CH_3COOH$$

$$+ 2\ Cr_2(SO_4)_3 + 2\ K_2SO_4 + 11\ H_2O$$

Exercise 8.7   Balance the equation for the oxidation of 2-propanol to acetone, $(CH_3)_2C{=}O$, using sodium dichromate in sulfuric acid solution as the oxidizing reagent.

D. Ring Substitution in Phenols.   When phenol is nitrated with dilute HNO_3, both the *ortho* and the *para* isomeric nitrophenols are formed.

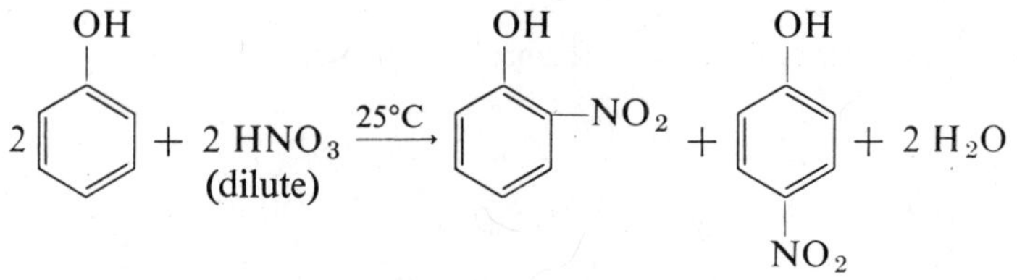

o-Nitrophenol   p-Nitrophenol

The *ortho* form can be separated from its *para* isomer by steam distillation. The *ortho* isomer is able to form a H-bond within itself, or *intra*molecularly, to produce a **chelated ring** (Gr., *chele*, claw). *Para* isomers must hydrogen bond *inter*molecularly to form an associated compound not volatile with steam.

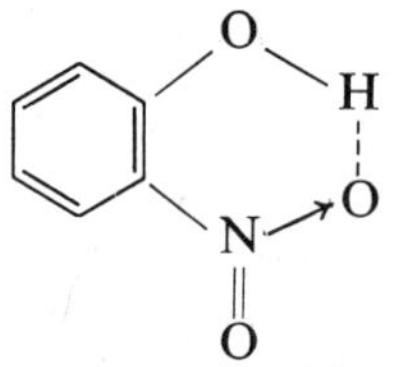

Intramolecular H-Bonding (Chelation)

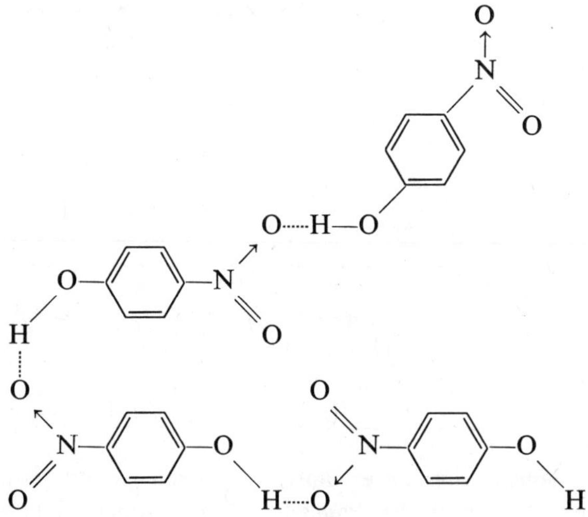

Intermolecular H-Bonding (Association)

Phenol, when nitrated directly with concentrated nitric acid undergoes oxidation. For this reason, the high explosive 2, 4, 6-trinitrophenol, or picric acid, is obtained through a synthesis that begins with chlorobenzene. The first product, 2, 4-dinitrochlorobenzene is then easily hydrolyzed to 2, 4-dinitrophenol (Sec. 7.6) and the nitration continued to give picric acid in good yield.

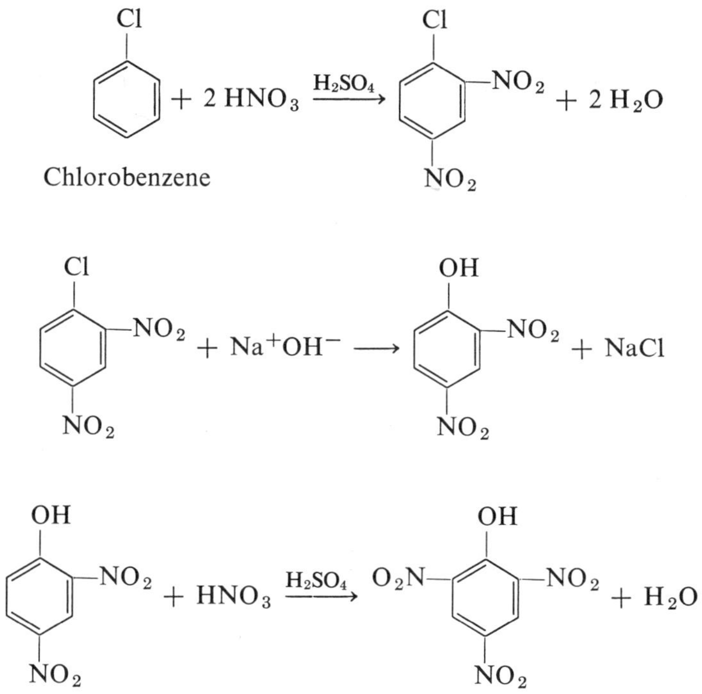

Chlorobenzene

Picric acid
(2, 4, 6-Trinitrophenol)

Many organic substances form crystalline molecular complexes with picric acid. Such derivatives, called **picrates,** have sharp melting points and are very useful in the identification of "unknowns." Butesin picrate, the picrate of *n*-butyl-*p*-aminobenzoate is a useful surface anesthetic for the treatment of burns. Picric acid is a bright yellow compound and also has been used as a direct dye on silk and wool (Sec. 16.4-A).

Phenol, when treated with sulfuric acid, yields both *ortho* and *para* phenolsulfonic acids. The *ortho* isomer predominates at low temperatures, the *para* at high temperatures.

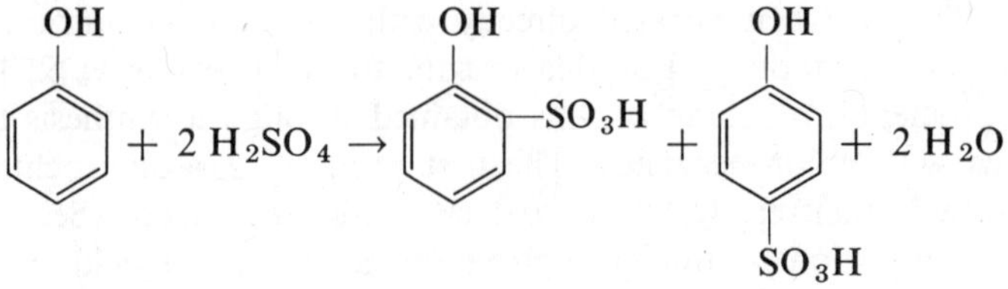

$$\text{OH} + 2\,H_2SO_4 \rightarrow \text{OH}-SO_3H + \text{OH} + 2\,H_2O$$
$$SO_3H$$

o-Phenol-
sulfonic acid

p-Phenol-
sulfonic acid

Phenol is very easily brominated. 2, 4, 6-tribromophenol can be prepared simply by shaking an aqueous phenol solution with a saturated solution of bromine in water.

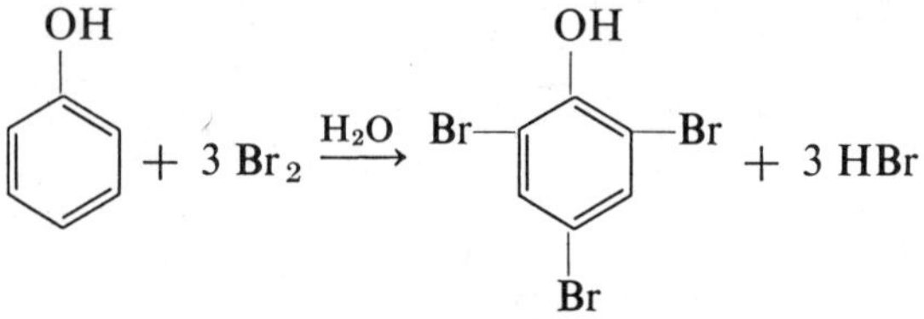

$$\text{OH} + 3\,Br_2 \xrightarrow{H_2O} Br-\text{OH}-Br + 3\,HBr$$
$$Br$$

2, 4, 6-Tribromophenol

The hydroxyl group of phenol is more firmly attached to an unsaturated ring carbon than it is to a singly bonded one and resists the displacement reactions exhibited by the aliphatic alcohols.

The catalytic reduction of phenol produces cyclohexanol.

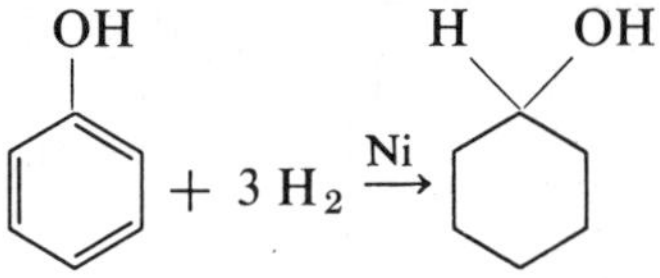

$$\text{OH} + 3\,H_2 \xrightarrow{Ni} \text{H \ OH}$$

Cyclohexanol

Phenol and its related compounds are of great industrial importance. They are starting materials for important pharmaceuticals such as **aspirin** (Sec. 12.7) and **adrenaline** (Sec. 13.7). Certain derivatives of phenol are important photographic developers. The antiseptic power of certain phenolic compounds has already been mentioned. In the plastics industry phenol is used as starting material for **bakelite** (Sec. 9.12) and **nylon.** The important herbicides 2, 4-dichlorophenoxyacetic acid and 2, 4, 5-trichlorophenoxyacetic acid, popularly known as **2, 4-D** and **2, 4, 5-T**, respectively, have their origin in phenol. It is easy to see why a large percentage of the benzene produced each year is converted to phenol.

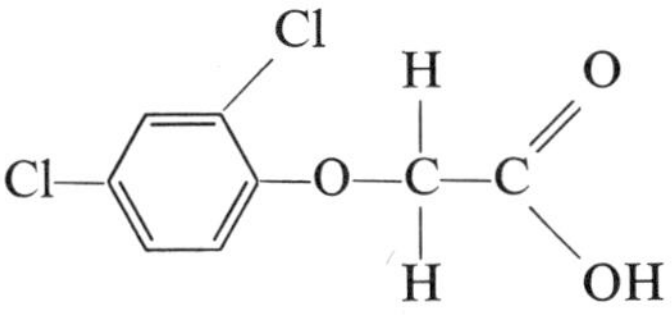

2, 4-Dichloro-
phenoxyacetic acid
(2, 4-D)

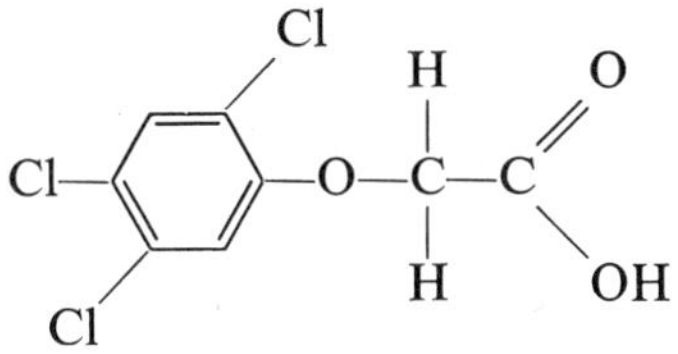

2, 4, 5-Trichloro-
phenoxyacetic acid
(2, 4, 5-T)

Exercise 8.8   What simple test would serve to distinguish a
phenolic compound from cyclohexanol?

8.10   STRUCTURE AND NOMENCLATURE OF ETHERS

Ethers are compounds of the general formula R—O—R,
or R—O—Ar, in which an oxygen bridge joins two hydrocarbon
groups. Although the ethers are isomeric with the alcohols, their
properties are vastly different.

Ethers may be named in one of two ways. According to the
IUPAC system of nomenclature one of the alkyl groups bonded to
the oxygen (the larger group if a mixed ether) is considered to be a
substituted hydrocarbon. The smaller alkyl group with the oxygen is
called an **alkoxy** substituent. In common nomenclature, both groups
bridged by the oxygen are named and followed by the word ether.
Sometimes the prefix "di" is employed if both groups are alike
(symmetrical ethers), but this is not necessary.   The following
examples will illustrate these rules.

$$R—O$$
$$\diagdown R$$

A simple ether

$$CH_3—O—CH_3$$

Methyl ether

$$C_2H_5—O—C_2H_5$$

Ethyl ether

$$R—O$$
$$\diagdown R'$$

A mixed ether

$$CH_3—O—C_2H_5$$

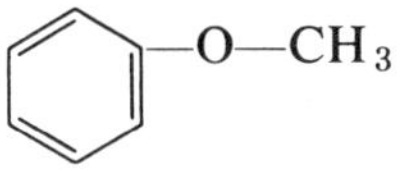

Methyl ethyl ether

—O—CH$_3$

Methyl phenyl ether
(Anisole)

$$-O-C_2H_5$$

$$CH_3CH_2CH_2-O-CH_3$$

Ethoxybenzene	1-Methoxypropane
(Ethyl phenyl ether)	(Methyl *n*-propyl ether)

8.11   PROPERTIES OF ETHERS

Ethers boil at much lower temperatures than do the alcohols from which they are derived because the oxygen atom now is attached only to carbon. Without hydrogen atoms bound to oxygen, H-bonding and association between many molecules no longer is possible. The boiling points of the ethers closely parallel those of the alkanes of the same molecular weight. You will note that the methylene group, $-(CH_2)-$, has almost the same formula weight (14) as an oxygen atom (16). Ethyl ether, with a molecular weight of 74, boils at 35°C; *n*-pentane, with a molecular weight of 72, boils at 36°C. The similarity may be illustrated also with *n*-propyl ether and *n*-heptane.

$$CH_3CH_2CH_2-O-CH_2CH_2CH_3 \qquad CH_3CH_2CH_2CH_2CH_2CH_2CH_3$$

n-Propyl ether	*n*-Heptane
M.W., 102; B.P., 91°C	M.W., 100; B.P., 98°C

The lower members of the aliphatic ethers are highly volatile and very flammable. Ethyl ether, the most important member of the family, is both an excellent organic solvent and a fine general anesthetic. Its high flammability, however, presents a hazard in the laboratory and in the operating room. The vapor of ethyl ether is heavier than air and has an annoying tendency to flow along the top of a laboratory bench and become ignited by a student's burner some distance away.

Chemically, ethers are relatively inert, and in this respect they also are very much like the alkanes. Ethyl ether, while not completely immiscible with water, is an excellent solvent to employ in extraction procedures involving aqueous solutions.[2]

---

[2] At 25°C diethyl ether is soluble in water to the extent of 6%, and water is soluble in ether to the extent of approximately 1.5%. Ether dissolved in water, however, is easily removed by distillation.

8.12   PREPARATION OF ETHERS

A simple ether can be produced by the elimination of a molecule of water from two molecules of alcohol. The mechanism for
this reaction is shown in Section 8.9-B2. In practice, a mixture of the
alcohol and sulfuric acid is heated to a temperature of approximately 140°C. An additional volume of alcohol then is added as the
ether distills.

$$C_2H_5 \overline{(-OH + H)} -O-C_2H_5 \xrightarrow{H_2SO_4} C_2H_5-O-C_2H_5 + H_2O$$

Ethyl alcohol   Ethyl ether

Inasmuch as concentrated sulfuric acid may cause the elimination of a molecule of water intramolecularly, conditions must be
carefully controlled to minimize this competing reaction. The several
courses of reaction open to a mixture of alcohol and sulfuric acid
have already been illustrated (Sec. 8.9-B). The sulfuric acid method
is employed for the preparation of simple ethers. A method applicable to the preparation of mixed ethers involves the reaction of a
metallic alkoxide and an alkyl halide (Williamson's Synthesis). The
choice of reagents to employ in a Williamson ether synthesis, as was
indicated in Section 8.9-A, must be made with some care.

Mixed ethers of the alkyl-aryl type also may be prepared by
the Williamson method. The methyl and ethyl ethers of phenol are
usually prepared by treating sodium phenoxide or phenol with the
appropriate alkyl iodide or dialkyl sulfate in the presence of a base.

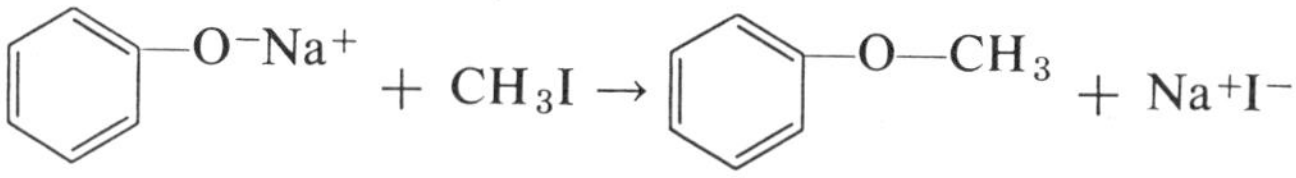

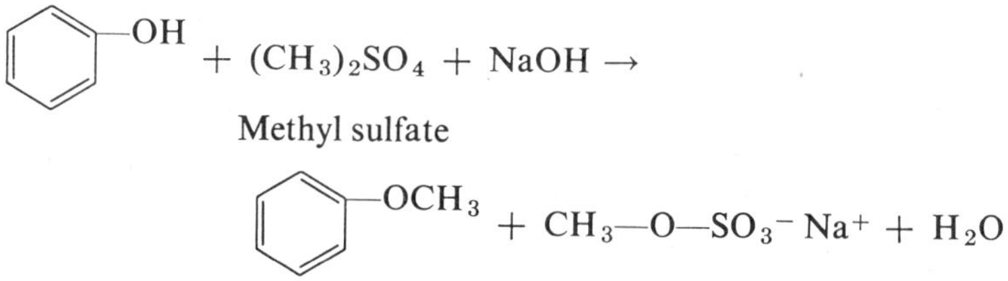

Methyl phenyl ether (Anisole)

Methyl sulfate

Methyl phenyl   Sodium methyl sulfate
     ether
  (Anisole)

Exercise 8.9   A student wants to prepare ethyl *tert*-butyl ether as a laboratory project. What reagents should he chose for this synthesis? Why?

8.13   REACTIONS OF THE ETHERS

The ethers represent an extremely stable group of compounds and their reactions are few. The ethers are soluble in strong mineral acids because of the formation of **oxonium** salts. The ethereal oxygen provides unshared electron pairs for bond formation with an acid. Solubility in sulfuric acid is thus a convenient method for distinguishing ethers from hydrocarbons and alkyl halides.

$$C_2H_5\!-\!\overset{..}{O}: + \;\boxed{H^+}\; A^- \rightarrow C_2H_5\!-\!\overset{\overset{\oplus}{..}}{O}:H + A^-$$
$$\underset{C_2H_5}{\mid} \qquad\qquad\qquad \underset{C_2H_5}{\mid}$$

Oxonium ion

Ethers are resistant to attack by the usual chemical oxidizing agents; yet anhydrous ethyl ether, when exposed repeatedly to air over long periods of time, forms a highly explosive peroxide. Such ether peroxides are extremely dangerous, and anhydrous ether should be tested before it is distilled. In one test a sample of the ether is treated with an acidified solution of potassium iodide. If peroxides are present in the ether they will oxidize the iodide ion, I^-, to molecular iodine, I_2, yielding the characteristic brown color of iodine. Peroxides in ether may be removed by washing the ether with a sodium sulfite solution. The peroxides oxidize sulfites to sulfates and are thus eliminated.

Other reactions of the ethers involve a cleavage of the carbon-oxygen linkage. Concentrated hydriodic acid is an excellent reagent to employ for this cleavage. Each molecule of ether cleaved produces one equivalent of alkyl iodide and one equivalent of alcohol. If hydriodic acid is used in excess, the alcohol initially formed also is converted to an alkyl iodide.

$$R\!-\!O\!-\!R' + HI \rightarrow RI + R'OH$$

$$R\!-\!O\!-\!R' + HI \rightarrow R\!-\!\overset{\overset{\oplus}{..}}{O}:H \;\; I^{\ominus} \xrightarrow[\text{(excess)}]{HI} RI + R'I + H_2O$$
$$\underset{R'}{\diagdown}$$

If one group of an ether is alkyl, such as methyl or ethyl, and the other group is aryl, such as phenyl, then the iodide of one of the alkyl groups usually is one product of the cleavage, the other being a phenol.

$$\text{C}_6\text{H}_5\text{—OCH}_3 + \text{HI} \xrightarrow{100°C} \text{C}_6\text{H}_5\text{—OH} + \text{CH}_3\text{I}$$

Anisole

Cleavage of ethers also may be accomplished by the use of 48% hydrobromic acid.

Exercise 8.10   A student storeroom assistant one morning found that the following labels had come undone from their bottles and were lying on the floor: Ethyl Alcohol, Ethyl Bromide, Ethyl Ether.

What simple test could he have performed on a sample from each of the bottles in order to properly relabel them?

8.14   USES OF ETHERS

Ethyl ether is perhaps most familiar to everyone as a general inhalation anesthetic. Although cyclopropane (Sec. 2.11) has certain advantages, it has not entirely replaced ethyl ether for this purpose. In organic chemistry, ethers are excellent solvents for fats, waxes, oils, plastics, and lacquers. Ethyl ether is the solvent used in the Wurtz reaction (Sec. 2.8-A) and in the preparation of the Grignard reagent (Secs. 2.8-B, 7.7).

Ethylene oxide, as was pointed out earlier, is an important intermediate in the manufacture of ethylene glycol. Ethylene oxide represents a highly strained ring and, unlike the dialkyl ethers, is a very reactive compound. When treated with alcohols, ethylene oxide converts them into monoalkyl ethers of ethylene glycol. These products are called **cellosolves** and combine the excellent solvent properties of both alcohols and ethers. Cellosolves are used as solvents for plastics and lacquers.

$$\underset{\underset{\text{O}}{\diagdown\diagup}}{\text{CH}_2\text{—CH}_2} + \text{C}_2\text{H}_5\text{OH} \rightarrow \text{HOCH}_2\text{—CH}_2\text{—O—C}_2\text{H}_5$$

Ethyl cellosolve

A cellosolve, when combined with a second molecule of ethylene oxide, produces monoalkyl ethers of diethylene glycol. These
products are called **carbitols** and also are fine solvents.

$$HOCH_2-CH_2-O-C_2H_5 + CH_2 \underset{O}{\overset{}{\diagdown\diagup}} CH_2 \rightarrow$$

$$HO-(CH_2)_2-O-(CH_2)_2-O-C_2H_5$$

Ethyl carbitol
(Diethyleneglycol monoethyl ether)

Both the ether linkage and the hydroxyl group are found in
many naturally-occurring substances.

> **Exercise 8.11**   A principle subscribed to by early organic
> chemists to explain solubility behavior of compounds was
> "Like dissolves like." Why can the principle be applied to di-
> ethyleneglycol monoethyl ether to explain its excellent solvent
> properties with complete miscibility in both water and most
> organic solvents?

□□ SUMMARY

[1]   Alcohols may be classified as *primary*, *secondary*, and *tertiary;*
ethers are classified as simple or mixed.

[2]   Alcohols associate through H-bond formation. H-bonding
accounts for their abnormally high boiling points. Ethers are
incapable of H-bonding and are not associated. They are low
boiling, good solvents, and are rather inert chemically.

[3]   Phenols generally do not give the same reactions as do the
aliphatic alcohols. Phenols have an acidic hydrogen. The
hydroxyl group in phenols is a strong *ortho-para* director.
Phenols are used in germicides, herbicides, fungicides, plastics,
dyes, explosives, and many other useful everyday commodities.

[4]   **Nomenclature:**

A. Alcohols (a) (IUPAC) The suffix "ol" replaces terminal
"e" of corresponding alkanes.
(b) (Common) Group attached to —OH is
named and followed by the word alcohol.

(c) (Derived) All groups attached to the hydroxylated carbon; are named as substituents of carbinol, e.g., CH_3OH.

B. Phenols (a) (IUPAC) Are named as hydroxy benzenes.

(b) (Common) Are named as phenol derivatives.

C. Ethers (a) (IUPAC) Are named as alkoxy alkanes.

(b) (Common) Are named simply as ethers. Both hydrocarbon groups are named.

[5] **Preparation:**

A. Alcohols can be prepared by one of the following methods.

(a) Synthetic methanol is prepared from CO and H_2.

(b) Ethanol is prepared by fermentation of sugars.

(c) Alcohols, in general, are prepared by the hydration of olefins (*via* H_2SO_4).

(d) Hydrolysis of alkyl halides.

B. Phenol is prepared from:

(a) Chlorobenzene (Dow process).

(b) Cumene (isopropylbenzene).

(c) Benzenesulfonic acid.

C. Ethers are prepared by one of the following methods.

(a) Simple ethers from alcohols by the sulfuric acid method.

(b) Mixed ethers can be obtained *via* the Williamson synthesis.

[6] **Reactions:** The reactions of alcohols, phenols, and ethers may be summarized as follows.

A. Alcohols (a) Cleavage of the O—H bond to produce alkoxides, ethers, and esters.

(b) Cleavage of the C—O bond to produce alkyl halides, sulfates, and nitrates.

(c) Oxidation of primary alcohols to acids; secondary alcohols to ketones.

B. Phenols (a) Replacement of H by reaction with a strong base.

(b) Reduction of ring by catalytic hydrogenation.

(c) Ring substitution at *o*- and *p*-positions.

C. Ethers (a) Formation of oxonium salts in strong acids.

(b) Formation of peroxides.

(c) Cleavage with HI or HBr.

□□ *NEW TERMS*

[1]   absolute alcohol   [8]   oxonium salt
[2]   associated liquid   [9]   phenol coefficient
[3]   azeotrope   [10] polar number
[4]   chelation   [11] "proof spirit"
[5]   grain alcohol   [12] Williamson synthesis
[6]   H-bonding   [13] wood alcohol
[7]   Lucas reagent

■□SUPPLEMENTARY EXERCISES
▼   AND PROBLEMS

[1]   Assign an acceptable name to each of the following compounds:

(a) $(CH_3)_2CH-O-CH(CH_3)_2$

(b)

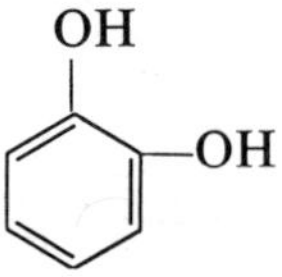

(c) $CH_3CH_2CH(OH)CH_3$

(d)

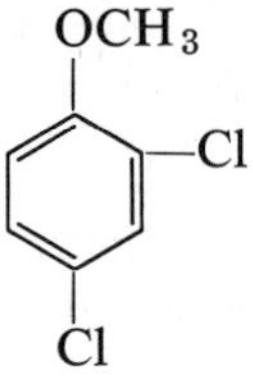

(e) $CH_3CH_2C(CH_3)_2OH$

(f)

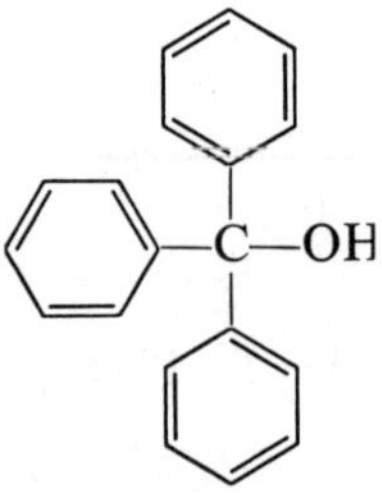

(g) $CH_3CH(OH)CH_2OH$

(h)

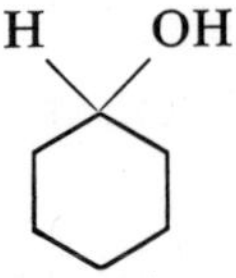

(i) $HOCH_2CH_2OCH_3$

(j) 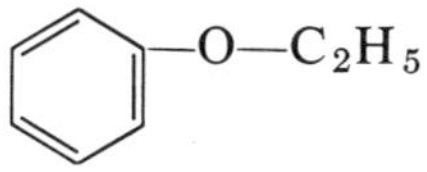 $-O-C_2H_5$

(k) $HOCH_2CH(OH)CH_2OH$

(l) 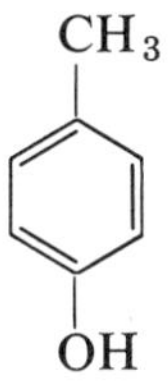
$$CH_3$$
(benzene ring with CH_3 top, OH bottom)

[2]   Write structural formulas for the following.

(a)   α-naphthol   (f)   n-butylcarbinol
(b)   2-propanol   (g)   dibenzyl ether
(c)   benzyl alcohol   (h)   o-nitrophenol
(d)   2, 6-di-*tert*-butylphenol   (i)   sodium benzenesulfonate
(e)   1-phenylethanol   (j)   potassium *tert*-butoxide

[3]   Complete the following reactions.

(a) $CH_3-CH=CH_2 + HOCl \longrightarrow$

(b) $CH_3OCH_2CH_2OH$ + ethylene oxide $\longrightarrow$

(c) $(CH_3)_3COH + HCl \longrightarrow$

(d) $CH_3CH_2OH + H_2SO_4 \xrightarrow[140°C]{\Delta,}$

(e) 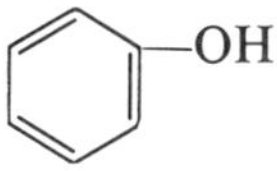   (benzene ring)$-OH + 3 Br_2 \xrightarrow{H_2O}$

(f) 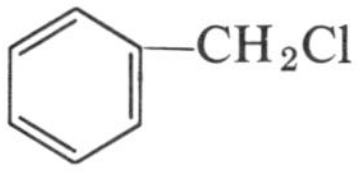   (benzene ring)$-CH_2Cl + Na^+OH^- \xrightarrow{Heat}$

(g)   n-propyl alcohol + $PI_3 \xrightarrow{Heat}$

(h) 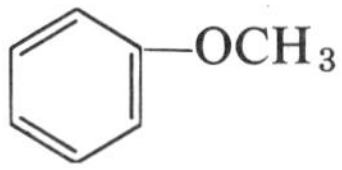   (benzene ring)$-OCH_3 + HI \xrightarrow{Heat}$

(i) C_2H_5OH + sodium metal $\xrightarrow{\text{Room temperature}}$

(j)   n-propyl alcohol + $K_2Cr_2O_7 + H_2SO_4 \longrightarrow$

(k)   Product of (j) + isopropylmagnesium iodide $\xrightarrow[\text{hydrolysis}]{\text{Followed by}}$

(l) 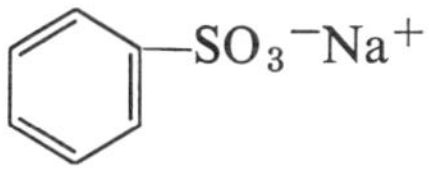   (benzene ring)$-SO_3^-Na^+$ + NaOH $\xrightarrow[\text{acidification}]{\text{Fusion followed by}}$

(m) 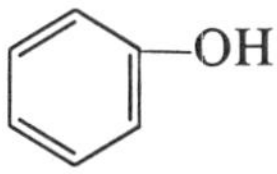   (benzene ring)$-OH + H_2 \xrightarrow[\text{heat}]{Ni,}$

[4]   Using ethyl alcohol as your only organic starting material, write equations showing how you would prepare the following.

(a)   ethylene   (f)   ethylene glycol
(b)   ethyl bromide   (g)   ethylene oxide
(c)   acetylene   (h)   ethyl cellosolve
(d)   1-butyne   (i)   iodoform
(e)   ethylene chlorohydrin   (j)   n-butyl alcohol

[5]   Arrange the compounds in the following series: (A) in an increasing order of solubility in water, (B) in an increasing order of reactivity toward Lucas reagent, and (C) in an increasing order of reactivity with sodium metal.

(a)   1-butanol   (d)   2-methyl-1-propanol
(b)   2-butanol   (e)   ethanol
(c)   2-methyl-2-propanol   (f)   2, 3-dimethyl-2-butanol

[6]   Give a simple chemical test that would distinguish one from the other in each of the following pairs of compounds.

(a)   sec-butyl alcohol and 1-hexyne
(b)   isopropyl alcohol and isopropyl ether
(c)   ethyl ether and n-pentane
(d)   tert-butyl alcohol and n-butyl alcohol
(e)   sec-butyl alcohol and n-butyl alcohol

[7]   Draw the structures of both cis and trans-cyclopentane-1, 2-diol. The trans isomer has a boiling point somewhat higher than that found for the cis isomer. Does this higher boiling point indicate a greater degree of association for the trans isomer? Why would the cis isomer be less inclined to form H-bonds with its neighbors?

[8]   An optically active liquid, $C_5H_{12}O$, reacted readily with the Lucas reagent. When warmed with an alkaline solution of iodine in potassium iodide, the liquid reacted to give iodoform and the sodium salt of isobutyric acid. Write the structure for the original compound.

[9]   A compound containing only carbon, hydrogen, and oxygen was found to give no reaction with metallic sodium, PCl_5, or $SOCl_2$. When heated with an excess of HI only one product was isolated from the reaction mixture. On analysis the reaction product was found to contain 81.5% iodine. What could the original substance have been?

[10]   The capacity of an automobile radiator is 20 quarts. If the density of methanol is 0.796 g/ml, how many quarts of the alcohol must be used to protect the cooling system against freezing at 20°C (−4°F)? (One quart = 960 ml. K_f for water = 1.86°C/mole.)

[11] A student placed a mixture of 95 g of ethanol and 200 g of concentrated sulfuric acid in a flask and heated the mixture at 160–165°C. The gas which evolved was passed through a cooled absorption apparatus containing 47 g of bromine under water. Heating was continued until the color of bromine was discharged. The resulting two layers in the absorption apparatus were separated and the organic layer distilled to yield 28 g of pure product.

(a) Write the equations for the sequence of reactions which took place and identify the final product.

(b) How much of the final product theoretically could the student have prepared?

(c) What was his percentage yield?

chapter 9

The Aldehydes and Ketones

INTRODUCTION

The aldehydes and ketones are compounds that contain the **carbonyl** group — a carbon-oxygen double bond, $-C=O$. The carbonyl is one of the most frequently encountered and, from the standpoint of synthetic organic chemistry, one of the most useful of the functional groups. Compounds which contain one or more carbonyl groups also are widely distributed in nature. For the most part, the aldehydes and ketones are of pleasant odor and are responsible for the active principles in a number of delightful-smelling, natural substances. For this reason, certain aldehydes and ketones are used as perfumes and as flavoring agents.

9.2   THE STRUCTURE OF ALDEHYDES AND KETONES

The aldehydes and ketones often are referred to collectively as carbonyl compounds, but the two families differ in structure and in properties. The carbonyl carbon of an aldehyde is always bonded to *one hydrogen* atom, the remaining bond being shared with an alkyl or an aryl group. An exception is found in the case of formaldehyde (the simplest aldehyde), which has two hydrogens joined to the carbon atom of the carbonyl group. The carbonyl carbon of ketones, on the other hand, is bonded to *two organic* groups. Such groups may be identical or they may be different. Moreover, they may be either alkyl or aryl. The following examples serve to illustrate these structural variations.

$$\underset{\text{(Aliphatic aldehyde)}}{R-\overset{\overset{\displaystyle H}{|}}{C}=O} \qquad \underset{\text{(An aromatic aldehyde)}}{Ar-\overset{\overset{\displaystyle H}{|}}{C}=O}$$

$$\underset{\text{Formaldehyde}}{H-\overset{\overset{\displaystyle H}{|}}{C}=O} \qquad \underset{\text{Acetaldehyde}}{CH_3-\overset{\overset{\displaystyle H}{|}}{C}=O} \qquad \underset{\text{Benzaldehyde}}{C_6H_5-\overset{\overset{\displaystyle H}{|}}{C}=O}$$

$$\underset{\substack{\text{A simple}\\\text{aliphatic ketone}}}{R-\overset{\overset{\displaystyle O}{||}}{C}-R} \qquad \underset{\substack{\text{A mixed}\\\text{aliphatic ketone}}}{R-\overset{\overset{\displaystyle O}{||}}{C}-R'} \qquad \underset{\substack{\text{An aromatic}\\\text{ketone}}}{Ar-\overset{\overset{\displaystyle O}{||}}{C}-Ar}$$

$$\underset{\substack{\text{Dimethyl ketone}\\\text{(Propanone)}}}{CH_3-\overset{\overset{\displaystyle O}{||}}{C}-CH_3} \qquad \underset{\substack{\text{Methyl ethyl ketone}\\\text{(2-Butanone)}}}{CH_3-\overset{\overset{\displaystyle O}{||}}{C}-CH_2CH_3} \qquad \underset{\substack{\text{Diphenyl ketone}\\\text{(Benzophenone)}}}{C_6H_5-\overset{\overset{\displaystyle O}{||}}{C}-C_6H_5}$$

$$\underset{\text{An aliphatic-aromatic ketone}}{Ar-\overset{\overset{\displaystyle O}{||}}{C}-R}$$

Methyl phenyl ketone (Acetophenone)

9.3   NOMENCLATURE

Aldehydes are assigned common names derived from those of the carboxylic acids into which they are convertible by oxidation.

$$\underset{\text{Formaldehyde}}{H-\overset{\overset{\displaystyle O}{||}}{C}-H} \xrightarrow{\text{[O]}} \underset{\text{Formic acid}}{H-\overset{\overset{\displaystyle O}{||}}{C}-OH}$$

$$CH_3\overset{\overset{\displaystyle O}{\|}}{-}C-H \xrightarrow{[O]} CH_3\overset{\overset{\displaystyle O}{\|}}{-}C-OH$$

Acetaldehyde   Acetic acid

Common names for the simple ketones are formed by naming both groups attached to the carbonyl carbon atom, then adding the word *ketone*. Trivial names, long in use, also are commonly employed. The IUPAC system of nomenclature follows established rules. The longest carbon chain (including the carbonyl carbon) is named after the parent hydrocarbon with *al* added as a suffix to designate an *al*dehyde. The carbonyl carbon atom of an aldehyde is always number one in the carbon chain and takes precedence over other functional groups that may be present. The carbonyl carbon atom of ketones, on the other hand, may appear at any point in the chain and must be located by number. The suffix *one* is used to designate a ket*one*. The examples illustrate these rules.

$$CH_3\overset{\overset{\displaystyle H}{|}}{-}C=O$$

Ethanal
(Acetaldehyde)

$$CH_3\overset{\overset{\displaystyle H}{|}}{-}\underset{\underset{\displaystyle CH_3}{|}}{C}\overset{\overset{\displaystyle H}{|}}{-}C=O$$

2-Methylpropanal
(Isobutyraldehyde)

$$CH_3\overset{\overset{\displaystyle H}{|}}{-}C=\overset{\overset{\displaystyle H}{|}}{C}-\overset{\overset{\displaystyle H}{|}}{C}=O$$
(4)   (3) (2) (1)

2-Butenal
(Crotonaldehyde)

$$CH_3\overset{\overset{\displaystyle O}{\|}}{-}C-CH_3$$

Propanone
(Acetone)

$$CH_3\overset{\overset{\displaystyle O}{\|}}{-}C-CH_2CH_2CH_3$$
(1)   (2) (3) (4)   (5)

2-Pentanone
(Methyl *n*-propyl ketone)

$$CH_3-CH_2\overset{\overset{\displaystyle O}{\|}}{-}C-CH_2-CH_3$$

3-Pentanone
(Diethyl ketone)

In many naturally occurring substances both *al* and *one* suffixes frequently are employed in nonsystematic names to indicate the presence of aldehyde or ketone functions. The stem of the name frequently indicates the source of the substance. For example, *civetone*, a ketone found in a glandular secretion of the civet *cat*, has a cyclic structure. Civetone in a very dilute solution has a pleasant odor and is used in perfumery. *Citral*, an aldehyde found in oil of citrus fruits, is an unsaturated aldehyde used as a flavoring agent. The structures of both natural carbonyl compounds are shown on the next page.

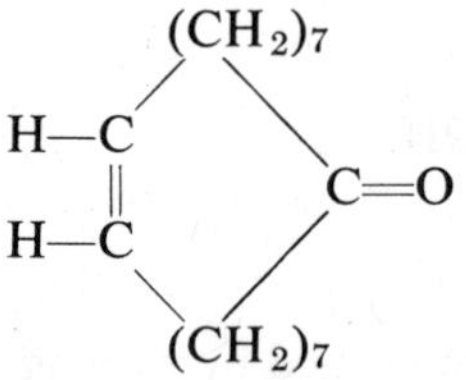

Civetone
(secretion of civet cat)
(9-Cycloheptadecene-1-one)

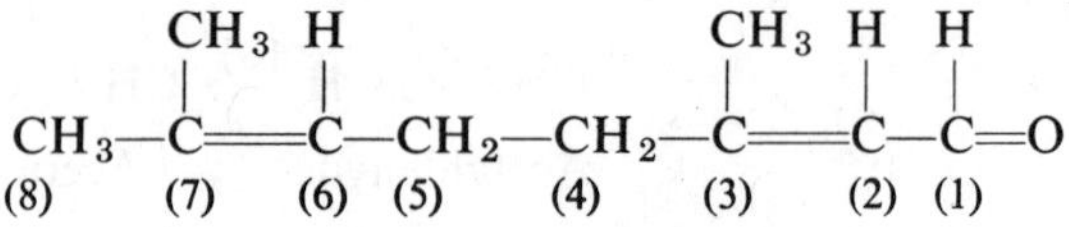

Citral (oil of lemon)
(3, 7-Dimethyl-2, 6-octadienal)

Exercise 9.1   The open chain aldehydes and ketones are isomeric. Draw structures for seven carbonyl compounds with the molecular formula $C_5H_{10}O$. Assign IUPAC names to each.

PROPERTIES

With the exception of formaldehyde, a gas, the lower molecular-weight aldehydes and ketones are liquids that have lower boiling points than alcohols of the same carbon content. The carbonyl compounds, lacking hydroxyl groups, do not hydrogen bond as do the alcohols, and therefore, are unassociated liquids. Table 9.1 compares the boiling points of some aldehydes and ketones with those of alcohols of the same carbon content.

□■ TABLE 9.1

BOILING POINTS OF ALDEHYDES AND KETONES COMPARED TO THOSE OF ALCOHOLS WITH THE SAME CARBON CHAIN

Name of Compound	Formula	B.P.(°C)
Formaldehyde		−21
Methyl alcohol		64.6

■ TABLE 9.1 — *Continued*

Acetaldehyde	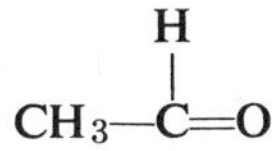 $\underset{\displaystyle CH_3-\overset{\displaystyle \overset{\displaystyle H}{\mid}}{C}=O}{}$	20.2
Ethyl alcohol	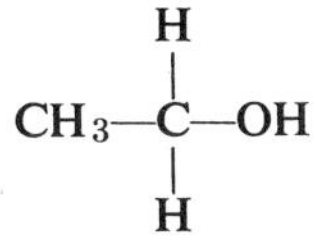 $CH_3-\overset{\displaystyle \overset{H}{\mid}}{\underset{\displaystyle \underset{H}{\mid}}{C}}-OH$	78.3
Propionaldehyde	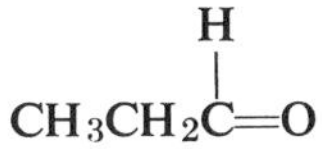 $CH_3CH_2\overset{\displaystyle \overset{H}{\mid}}{C}=O$	48.8
n-Propylalcohol	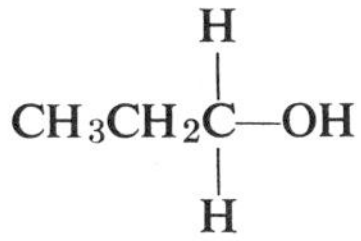 $CH_3CH_2\overset{\displaystyle \overset{H}{\mid}}{\underset{\displaystyle \underset{H}{\mid}}{C}}-OH$	97.8
Acetone	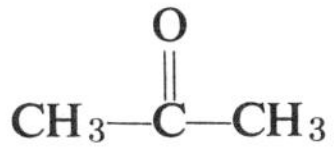 $CH_3-\overset{\displaystyle \overset{O}{\parallel}}{C}-CH_3$	56.1
Isopropyl alcohol	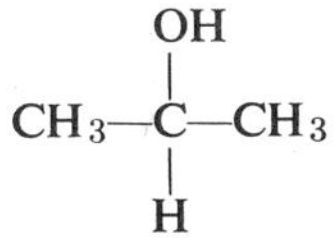 $CH_3-\overset{\displaystyle \overset{OH}{\mid}}{\underset{\displaystyle \underset{H}{\mid}}{C}}-CH_3$	82.5
n-Butyraldehyde	 $CH_3-CH_2CH_2-\overset{\displaystyle \overset{H}{\mid}}{C}=O$	75.7
n-Butyl alcohol	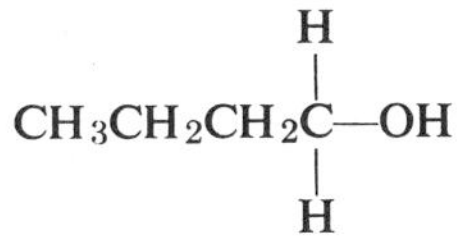 $CH_3CH_2CH_2\overset{\displaystyle \overset{H}{\mid}}{\underset{\displaystyle \underset{H}{\mid}}{C}}-OH$	117.7
Methyl ethyl ketone	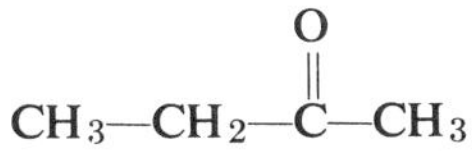 $CH_3-CH_2-\overset{\displaystyle \overset{O}{\parallel}}{C}-CH_3$	79.6
sec-Butyl alcohol	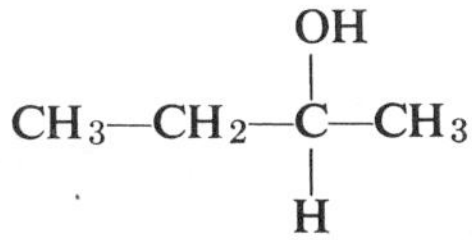 $CH_3-CH_2-\overset{\displaystyle \overset{OH}{\mid}}{\underset{\displaystyle \underset{H}{\mid}}{C}}-CH_3$	99.5

The aldehydes and ketones, except the lower members which contain up to four carbon atoms, are practically insoluble in water. The lower members of the aldehyde family have sharp, irritating odors, but the higher molecular weight members, and nearly all members of the ketone family are fragrant. As was pointed out in the introductory section, certain of these are used in perfumery and as flavoring agents.

9.5   PREPARATION OF ALDEHYDES AND KETONES

A-1. Oxidation of Alcohols (Dehydrogenation).   The word *aldehyde* is a composite name originally given to this family of compounds to describe them as products of *al*cohol *dehy*drogenation. The oxidation of primary and secondary alcohols through dehydrogenation is a method for the preparation of aldehydes and ketones, respectively.   Dehydrogenation is accomplished by passing the alcohol vapors over a heated copper or silver catalyst.

$$\begin{array}{c} H \\ | \\ R-C-O \\ | \\ \boxed{H\ \ H} \end{array} \xrightarrow[250°C]{Cu,} H_2 + R-\overset{\displaystyle H}{\underset{}{C}}=O$$

$$\begin{array}{c} R \\ | \\ R-C-O \\ | \\ \boxed{H\ \ H} \end{array} \xrightarrow[250°C]{Cu,} H_2 + R-\overset{\displaystyle R}{\underset{}{C}}=O$$

Chemical oxidation of a primary alcohol is one of the most direct methods for the preparation of the simple aldehydes. Formaldehyde and acetaldehyde, perhaps the most important members of the aliphatic series of aldehydes, may be produced by oxidation of methyl and ethyl alcohols, respectively. The oxidation is generally done in air with the help of a catalyst.

$$2\ H-\overset{\displaystyle H}{\underset{\displaystyle H}{C}}-OH + O_2\ (air) \xrightarrow[250°C]{Cu,} 2\ H-\overset{\displaystyle H}{\underset{}{C}}=O + 2\ H_2O$$

Formaldehyde

It should be pointed out that a partially oxidized carbon atom such as is present in aldehydes is especially susceptible to further oxidation. An aldehyde formed by the oxidation of an alcohol, therefore, will be converted directly into an acid unless some provision is made for its removal from the reaction mixture.

$$R-\underset{\underset{H}{|}}{\overset{\overset{H}{|}}{C}}-OH \xrightarrow{[O]} \left[R-\underset{\underset{H}{|}}{\overset{\overset{OH}{|}}{C}}-OH \right] \xrightarrow{-H_2O} R-\overset{\overset{H}{|}}{C}=O \xrightarrow{[O]} R-\overset{\overset{O}{||}}{C}-OH$$

Primary   Aldehyde   Acid
alcohol

$$3\ CH_3CH_2OH + Cr_2O_7{}^{2-} + 8\ H^+ \xrightarrow{50°C} 3\ CH_3\overset{\overset{H}{|}}{C}=O + 2\ Cr^{3+} + 7\ H_2O$$

Ethyl alcohol   Acetaldehyde
(B.P. 78.3°C)   (B.P. 20.8°C)

$$3\ CH_3-\overset{\overset{H}{|}}{C}=O + Cr_2O_7{}^{2-} + 8\ H^+ \longrightarrow 3\ CH_3-\overset{\overset{O}{||}}{C}-OH + 2\ Cr^{3+} + 4\ H_2O$$

Acetic acid
(B.P. 118.1°C)

The boiling points of the aldehydes not only are much lower than those of the alcohols from which they may be obtained (Table 9.1), but also are considerably lower than the boiling points of the corresponding acids they would yield on further oxidation. This difference in physical properties is fortunate for it makes possible the removal of the aldehyde as it is formed but the alcohol in which the aldehyde had its origin is returned to the reaction mixture to be converted into more product.

Ketones also may be prepared by oxidation methods using secondary alcohols as starting material. Ketones, unlike the aldehydes, are not easily oxidized (carbon-carbon bonds must be broken), and can be made in high yield by this method.

$$CH_3-\underset{\underset{OH}{|}}{\overset{\overset{H}{|}}{C}}-CH_3 \xrightarrow{[O]} CH_3-\underset{\underset{O}{||}}{C}-CH_3$$

2-Propanol   2-Propanone
(Isoproply alcohol)   (Acetone)

A-2. Oxidation of Alkenes (Ozonization).   The oxidation of alkenes as a possible route to carbonyl compounds is discussed in some detail in Section 3.10-C.

B.   Hydrolysis of Gem-Dihalides.   Two halogen atoms, when positioned on the same carbon atom (*gem*-dihalides), may be hydrolyzed to the carbonyl group.

The hydrolysis of *gem*-dihalides, as a preparative method, is employed most advantageously for the preparation of aromatic aldehydes. Beginning with toluene (readily available from petroleum), the side chain on the benzene ring can easily be chlorinated to benzal chloride. The latter is then hydrolyzed to benzaldehyde.

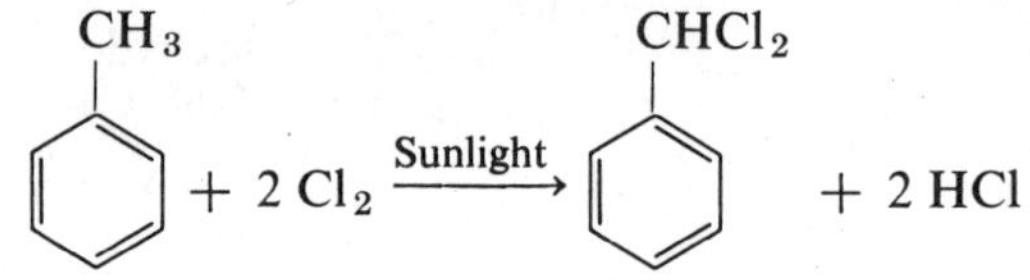

Toluene   Benzal
                           chloride

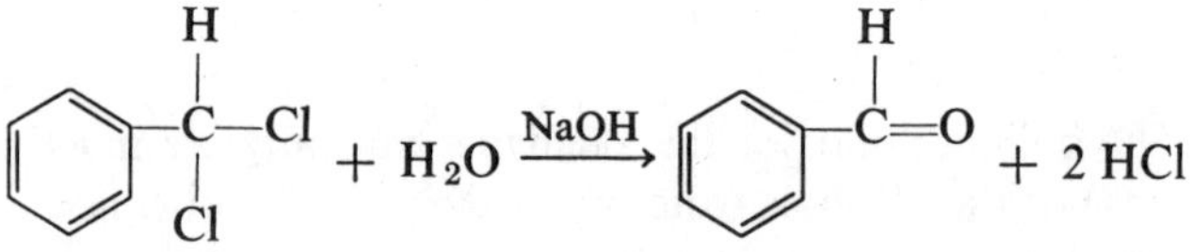

Benzaldehyde

C.   Hydration of Alkynes.   Acetaldehyde may be made by hydration of acetylene. This reaction is discussed in Section 3.18-B.

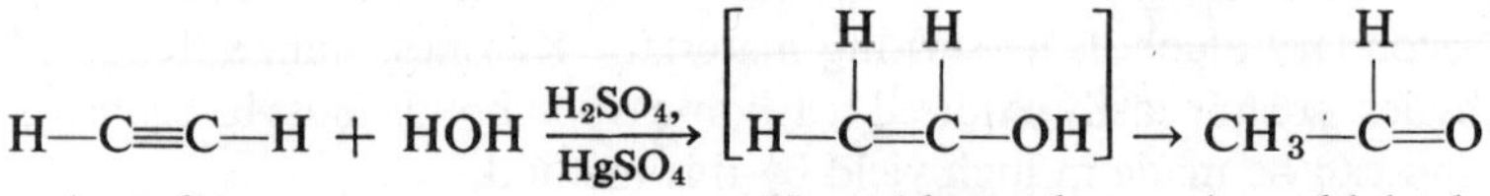

$$H\text{---}C\equiv C\text{---}H + HOH \xrightarrow[\text{HgSO}_4]{\text{H}_2\text{SO}_4,} \left[H\text{---}\underset{|}{\overset{|}{C}}\text{=}\underset{|}{\overset{|}{C}}\text{---OH} \right] \rightarrow CH_3\text{---}\underset{|}{\overset{|}{C}}\text{=}O$$

Acetylene   Unstable enol   Acetaldehyde
                                   intermediate

Large quantities of acetaldehyde prepared commercially by this method are used in the production of acetic acid. An alkyl-substituted acetylene, when hydrated, yields a methyl ketone. Note that the mode of addition is in accordance with Markovnikov's Rule (Sec. 3.9).

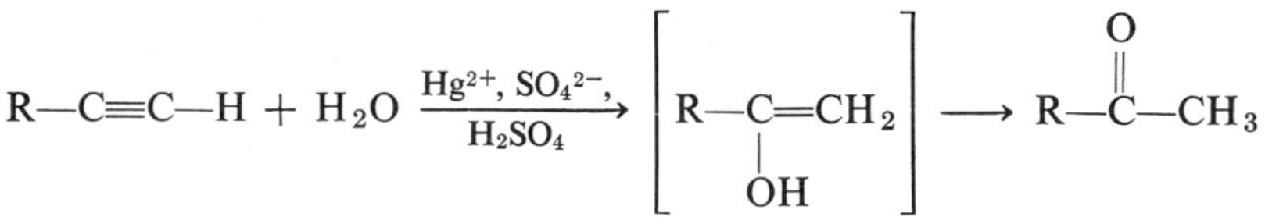

$$R-C\equiv C-H + H_2O \xrightarrow[\text{H}_2\text{SO}_4]{\text{Hg}^{2+}, \text{SO}_4^{2-},} \left[\begin{array}{c} R-C=CH_2 \\ | \\ OH \end{array} \right] \longrightarrow R-\overset{\overset{\displaystyle O}{\|}}{C}-CH_3$$

D. Pyrolysis of Metal Salts of Acids.   Acetic acid vapor, when passed through a heated tube packed with one of the oxides of calcium, manganese, or thorium, produces acetone. The metallic salt of acetic acid, the first product, immediately decomposes into acetone and a metallic carbonate.

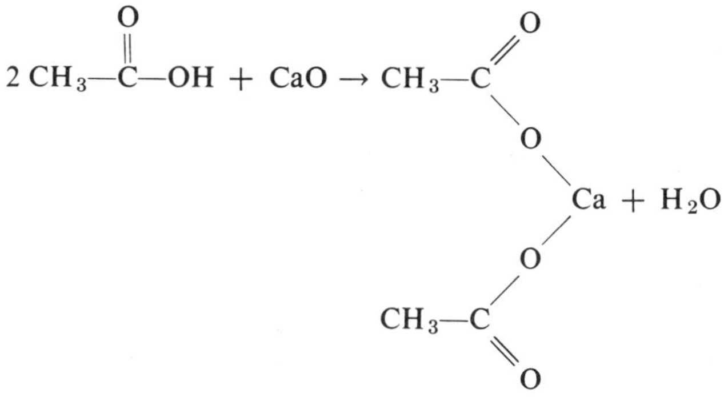

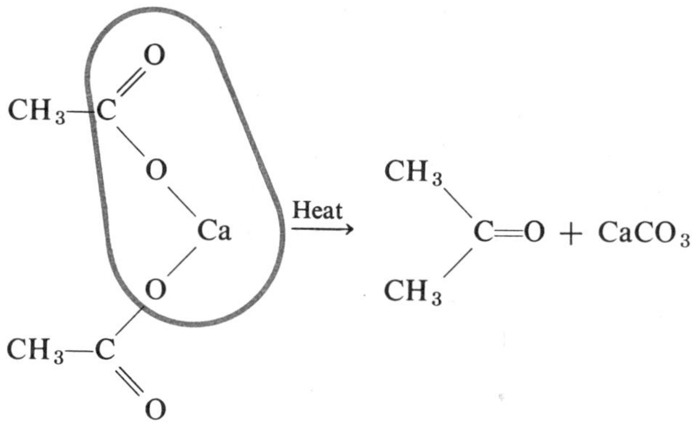

Calcium acetate   Acetone   Calcium
                                                                    carbonate

The reaction just described is a general laboratory method for the preparation of symmetrical ketones from acids. A similar reaction, when used with dicarboxylic acids, results in a ring closure to yield cyclic ketones. The preparation of cyclopentanone from adipic acid is illustrated on the next page.

$$\underset{\text{Adipic acid}}{\begin{array}{c} \text{CH}_2 \\ \diagup \quad \diagdown \quad \text{O} \\ \text{CH}_2 \qquad \overset{\|}{\text{C}}\text{—OH} \\ | \qquad\qquad \\ \text{CH}_2 \qquad \text{C—OH} \\ \diagdown \quad \diagup \overset{\|}{} \\ \text{CH}_2 \quad \text{O} \end{array}} \quad \xrightarrow[285-295°C]{\text{Ba(OH)}_2,} \quad \underset{\text{Cyclopentanone}}{\begin{array}{c} \text{CH}_2\text{—CH}_2 \\ | \qquad\qquad \diagup \\ \qquad\qquad \text{C}=\text{O} + \text{CO}_2 + \text{H}_2\text{O} \\ \text{CH}_2\text{—CH}_2 \end{array}}$$

Industrially, acetone is prepared by the dehydrogenation of iso-propyl alcohol and, to a lesser degree, as a by-product in the Weiz-mann fermentation of carbohydrates. The Weizmann fermentation, a process discovered by Chaim Weizmann[1] during World War I, is a bacterial fermentation. Sugar from either corn mash or blackstrap molasses is inoculated with the bacterium, *Clostridium acetobutyli-cum.* Under anaerobic ("without air") conditions the fermentation produces *n*-butyl alcohol, acetone, and ethyl alcohol in approximate yields of 60%, 30%, and 10%, respectively.

Acetone is used principally as a solvent and as an intermediate in organic synthesis. Ketene, $CH_2=C=O$, a very reactive unsatu-rated ketone, is prepared from acetone by pyrolysis.

$$(CH_3)_2C=O \xrightarrow{700°C} CH_2=C=O + CH_4$$
$$\text{Ketene}$$

E.   Friedel-Crafts Acylation.   The preparation of benzaldehyde from toluene already has been illustrated (Sec. 9.5-B).   Certain aromatic aldehydes may be prepared by the direct introduction of the aldehyde group into the benzene nucleus through a modified Friedel-Crafts reaction known as **formylation.**   Formyl chloride,

$$\overset{\displaystyle O}{\underset{\displaystyle H—C—Cl,}{\|}}$$ is an unstable compound and decomposes to carbon monoxide and hydrogen chloride.   A combination of these two gases in the presence of anhydrous aluminum chloride accomplishes the same result as if the acid chloride were used.   The reaction is known as the Gatterman-Koch reaction.

[1]Chaim Weizmann, 1874–1952. University of Manchester. First president of newly founded Israel.

$$ HCl + CO \rightarrow \left[Cl-C\begin{smallmatrix}H\\ \diagup\\ \diagdown\\ O \end{smallmatrix} \right] $$

$$ \underset{\text{Toluene}}{\overset{CH_3}{\bigcirc}} + \left[Cl-C\begin{smallmatrix}H\\ \diagup\\ \diagdown\\ O \end{smallmatrix} \right] \xrightarrow{AlCl_3} \underset{\underset{CHO}{}}{\overset{CH_3}{\bigcirc}} + HCl $$

Toluene   *p*-Tolualdehyde

Aromatic ketones also may be prepared by the Friedel-Crafts acylation reaction using either acid chlorides or acid anhydrides. In either case, an acyl group, $R-\overset{O}{\overset{\|}{C}}-$, is attached directly to the aromatic ring. The method is illustrated in the preparation of acetophenone using acetyl chloride, the acid chloride of acetic acid.

$$ \underset{\text{Acetyl chloride}}{CH_3-C\begin{smallmatrix}O\\ \diagup\\ \diagdown\\ Cl \end{smallmatrix}} + AlCl_3 \longrightarrow CH_3-\overset{O}{\overset{\|}{\underset{\oplus}{C}}} \cdots \overset{(-)}{ClAlCl_3} $$

Acetyl chloride

$$ \bigcirc \overset{CH_3}{\underset{\underset{ClAlCl_3}{(-)}}{\overset{\oplus}{C}}}_{O} \longrightarrow \bigcirc \overset{O}{\overset{\|}{C}}-CH_3 + HCl + AlCl_3 $$

Acetophenone

Furfuraldehyde, $C_5H_4O_2$, usually called **furfural,** is a very important industrial aldehyde obtained from agricultural wastes such as corn cobs and oat hulls (Sec. 17.3). It is a colorless liquid when freshly distilled, but on exposure to air becomes oxidized to a deep brown or black liquid. Treatment of furfural (a cyclic ether as well as a carbonyl compound) with a mineral acid results in a ring cleavage. In neutral or basic solutions furfural gives all the reactions of benzaldehyde. Furfural is used in the petroleum industry for the refining of lubricants, as starting material in the manufacture of some nylon, and in synthetic resins. The structure of furfural is shown.

$$\begin{array}{ccc} H{-}C & {-\!\!-\!\!-} & C{-}H \\ \| & & \| \\ H{-}C & & C{-}CHO \\ & \diagdown \quad \diagup & \\ & O & \end{array}$$

Furfuraldehyde
(Furfural)

9.6   THE CARBONYL GROUP

It would be profitable to discuss briefly the nature of the carbonyl group before we consider the reactions of the aldehydes and ketones.   The unsaturated carbonyl carbon atom, like the doubly bonded carbon atoms of olefins, is joined by three σ bonds to three other atoms. All lie in the same plane and form angles of 120° with each other. The planarity of the carbonyl group is illustrated below, using formaldehyde as an example.

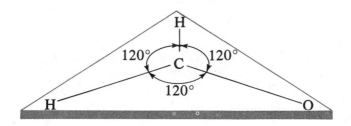

The fourth bond, a π bond, is made up of a pair of shared p electrons, one each from the carbonyl carbon and the oxygen atom. These π electrons, analogous to the π electrons of the carbon-carbon double bond, confer upon the carbonyl group a special reactivity. The oxygen atom, you will remember, is far more electronegative (electron-attracting) than is the carbon atom. This attraction for electrons on the part of the oxygen atom produces an unequal distribution of electrons between the nuclei of the carbon and the oxygen atoms. The carbon-oxygen bond is thus a highly polarized one — the oxygen electron-rich and the carbon electron-deficient.

$$\diagup C{=}\ddot{O}: \quad \leftrightarrow \quad \overset{\delta+}{\diagup} C{=}\overset{\delta-}{O} \quad \leftrightarrow \quad \overset{+}{\diagup} C{-}\ddot{O}:^{-}$$

The addition reactions illustrated in the following sections show the course of the reaction in each instance to be the same. The carbonyl carbon atom is attacked by a nucleophilic group (an electron-pair donor, a base); the carbonyl oxygen accepts the positive part of the reactant.

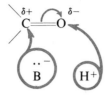

Exercise 9.2   Of the two structures shown, which carbonyl carbon atom will be more readily attacked by the hydroxide ion? Why?

$$CH_3-\overset{\overset{\displaystyle O}{\|}}{C}-CH_3 \qquad CH_3-\overset{\overset{\displaystyle O}{\|}}{C}-CCl_3$$

The carbonyl group, when attached to the benzene nucleus, deactivates the ring through its electron-attracting power.   This effect not only makes the ring more resistant to further attack by electrophilic groups, but helps direct entering groups to the *meta* position when substitution does take place.

9.7   ADDITION REACTIONS

A.   Addition of Hydrogen Cyanide.   The elements of hydrogen cyanide, HCN, add to aldehydes and ketones to yield **cyanohydrins** when the reaction is carried out with a basic catalyst.

$$HCN + \overset{(-)}{OH} \longrightarrow H_2O + \overset{(-)}{CN}$$

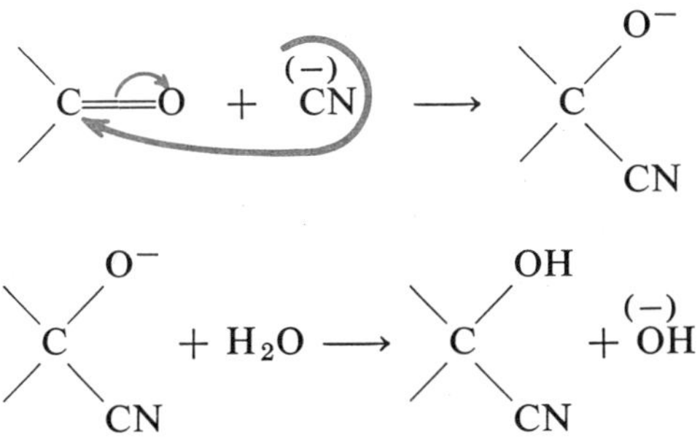

$$\underset{/}{\overset{\backslash}{C}}=O + \overset{(-)}{CN} \longrightarrow \overset{\backslash}{\underset{/}{C}}\overset{\displaystyle O^-}{\underset{\displaystyle CN}{}}$$

$$\overset{\backslash}{\underset{/}{C}}\overset{\displaystyle O^-}{\underset{\displaystyle CN}{}} + H_2O \longrightarrow \overset{\backslash}{\underset{/}{C}}\overset{\displaystyle OH}{\underset{\displaystyle CN}{}} + \overset{(-)}{OH}$$

Hydrogen cyanide, a highly toxic gas, is never handled directly, but is produced at the site of a reaction by treating sodium or potassium cyanide with a mineral acid. However, the amount of acid used must never be enough to react with all the cyanide ion, otherwise the basic conditions favorable to the reaction will be lacking.

$$CH_3 \atop \diagdown \atop CH_3 \diagup \!\!\!\! C{=}O + NaCN + H_2SO_4 \xrightarrow{\text{10–20°C}} {CH_3 \atop \diagdown} \!\!\! C \!\!\! {\diagup OH \atop \diagdown CN} \atop {CH_3 \diagup} + NaHSO_4$$

Acetone   Acetone
                                  cyanohydrin

Aldehydes, aliphatic methyl ketones, and cyclic ketones form cyanohydrins. Inasmuch as these addition compounds can be hydrolyzed to acids (Sec. 10.5-B) the cyanohydrins are valuable intermediates in organic synthesis. The conversion of acetaldehyde to lactic acid is an example.

$$CH_3{-}\overset{\displaystyle H}{\underset{}{C}}{=}O + HCN \rightarrow CH_3{-}\overset{\displaystyle H}{\underset{\displaystyle OH}{C}}{-}CN$$

Acetaldehyde   Acetaldehyde
                                cyanohydrin

$$CH_3{-}\overset{\displaystyle H}{\underset{\displaystyle OH}{C}}{-}CN + HCl + 2\,H_2O \rightarrow CH_3{-}\overset{\displaystyle H}{\underset{\displaystyle OH}{C}}{-}\overset{\displaystyle O}{\overset{\displaystyle \|}{C}}{-}OH + NH_4Cl$$

Lactic acid
(a hydroxy acid)

B.   Addition of Sodium Bisulfite.   A saturated solution of sodium bisulfite, when mixed with aldehydes, cyclic ketones, and with some methyl ketones, forms addition products. These are crystalline solids which may be separated from the mixture by filtration. Treatment of the addition product with a mineral acid regenerates the original carbonyl compound.

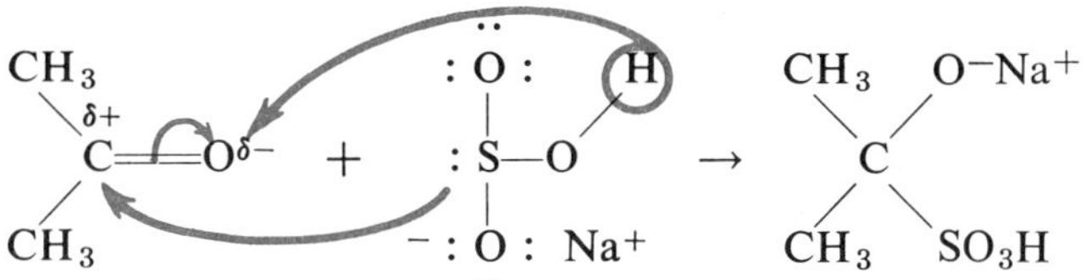

Bisulfite addition
compound of acetone

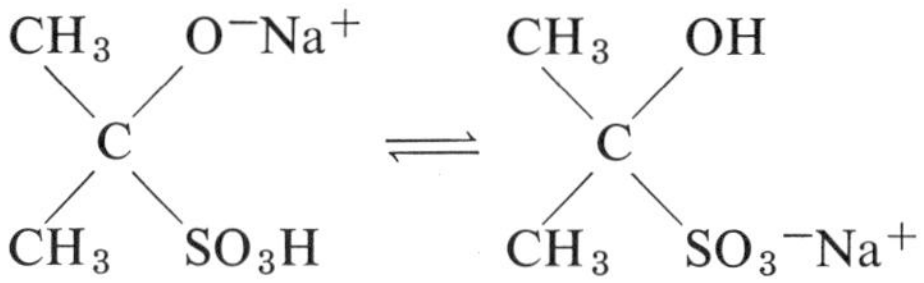

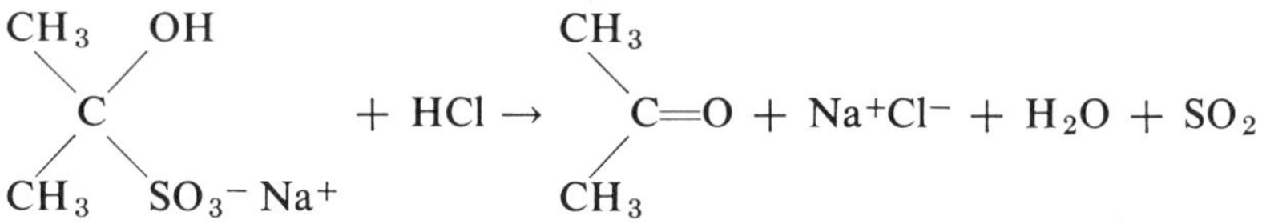

The reaction provides a useful method for the separation of aldehydes and certain ketones from mixtures. Aromatic ketones and aliphatic ketones having both alkyl groups larger than methyl show little or no tendency to form bisulfite addition compounds.

Exercise 9.3   Suggest a reason why cyclopentanone forms a sodium bisulfite addition compound but diethyl ketone does not.

C. Addition of Water and Alcohols.   The aldehydes and ketones show little tendency to form stable hydrates. In a few compounds, in which the carbonyl group is attached to other strong electron-attracting groups, a hydrate sufficiently stable to be isolated is formed. One of the best examples of such a compound is trichloroacetaldehyde, or **chloral,** which forms a stable hydrate used medicinally as a soporific.

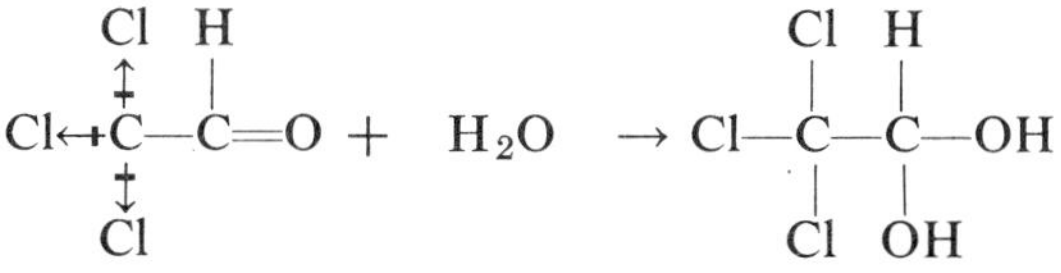

Chloral   Chloral hydrate

On the other hand, alcohols will add to aldehydes in the presence of acid catalysts. An unstable addition product called a **hemiacetal,** formed in the first stage of the reaction, reacts with a second molecule of alcohol to yield a stable compound called an **acetal.**

$$CH_3-\overset{\overset{\displaystyle H}{|}}{C}{=}O + C_2H_5OH \underset{}{\overset{H^+A^-}{\rightleftharpoons}} CH_3-\overset{\overset{\displaystyle H}{|}}{\underset{\displaystyle OC_2H_5}{C}}{\diagup}^{OH}$$

A hemiacetal
(unstable)

$$CH_3-\overset{\overset{\displaystyle H}{\diagup}}{\underset{\displaystyle OC_2H_5}{C}}-OH \quad + C_2H_5OH \underset{}{\overset{H^+A^-}{\rightleftharpoons}} CH_3-\overset{\overset{\displaystyle H}{\diagup}}{\underset{\displaystyle OC_2H_5}{C}}-OC_2H_5 + H_2O$$

Acetaldehyde diethyl acetal
(stable)

The reaction is reversible and the acetal, when hydrolyzed in an acid solution, readily regenerates the original alcohol and aldehyde.

Ketals do not form as readily as do acetals and usually are not formed directly by the addition of alcohols to ketones.

D.   Addition of Grignard Reagents.   The addition of Grignard reagents (Sec. 7.7) of the form RMgX or ArMgX to aldehydes or to ketones as a route to the alcohols has already been presented in detail in Section 8.5-C.

Exercise 9.4   Using propene and any inorganic reagents that you might need, show how you could obtain the necessary Grignard reagent and carbonyl compound needed to prepare 2, 3-dimethyl-2-butanol.

9.8   ADDITION REACTIONS WITH LOSS OF WATER

A.   Condensation with Ammonia Derivatives.   Certain derivatives of ammonia that contain the primary amino group, —NH$_2$, add to aldehydes and ketones to form unstable intermediates. The initial addition product loses the elements of water (condensation) to form a carbon-nitrogen double bond.

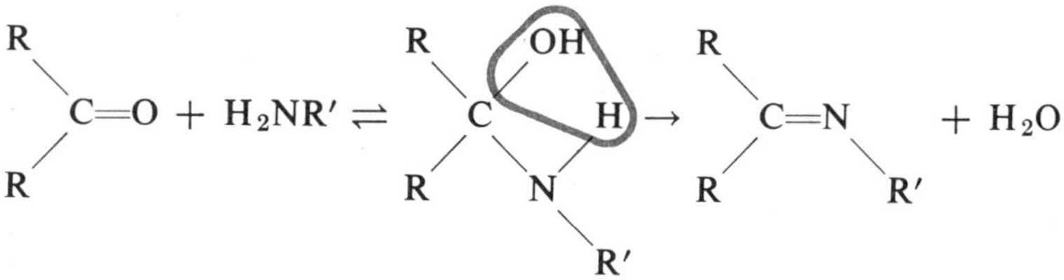

$$\underset{R}{\overset{R}{>}}C=O + H_2NR' \rightleftharpoons \underset{R}{\overset{R}{>}}C\underset{N}{\overset{OH}{<}}H \rightarrow \underset{R}{\overset{R}{>}}C=N\overset{R'}{} + H_2O$$

Many of these condensation products are crystalline solids with sharp melting points. For this reason they frequently are employed for the preparation of aldehyde and ketone derivatives needed in identification work. Ammonia derivatives commonly used and their condensation products are the following.

Carbonyl Compound	Ammonia Derivative		Condensation Product	
$R-\overset{R}{\underset{\|}{C}}=O$	$\overset{H}{\underset{H}{>}}N-OH$	$\xrightarrow{H^+}$	$R-\overset{R}{\underset{\|}{C}}=N-OH$	$+\ H_2O$
A ketone*	Hydroxylamine		An oxime	
$R-\overset{R}{\underset{\|}{C}}=O$	$\overset{H}{\underset{H}{>}}N-\overset{H}{\underset{\|}{N}}-C_6H_5$	$\xrightarrow{H^+}$	$R-\overset{R}{\underset{\|}{C}}=N-\overset{H}{\underset{\|}{N}}-C_6H_5$	$+\ H_2O$
A ketone*	Phenylhydrazine		A phenylhydrazone	
$R-\overset{R}{\underset{\|}{C}}=O$	$\overset{H}{\underset{H}{>}}N-\overset{H}{\underset{\|}{N}}-\overset{O}{\overset{\|\|}{C}}-NH_2$	$\xrightarrow{H^+}$	$R-\overset{R}{\underset{\|}{C}}=N-\overset{H}{\underset{\|}{N}}-\overset{O}{\overset{\|\|}{C}}-NH_2$	$+\ H_2O$
A ketone*	Semicarbazide		A semicarbazone	

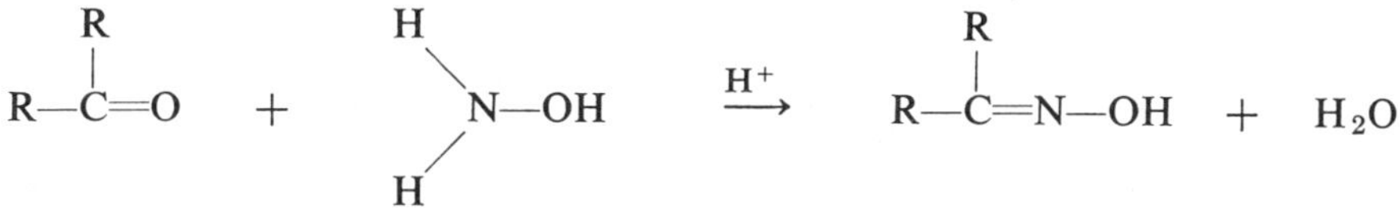

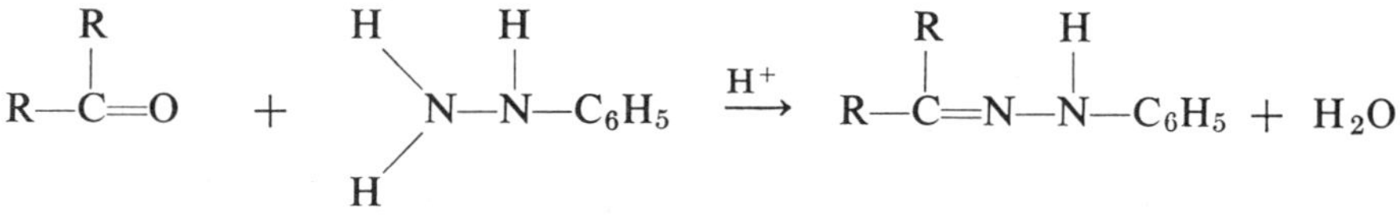

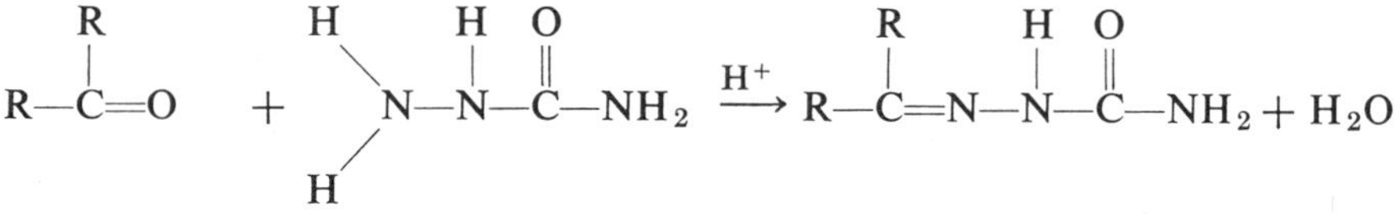

*If an R were H, the compound would be an aldehyde.

The carbonyl derivative formed in each case simply is designated as the **aldoxime**, the **ketoxime**, the **phenylhydrazone**, or the **semicarbazone** of the carbonyl compound from which it was prepared.

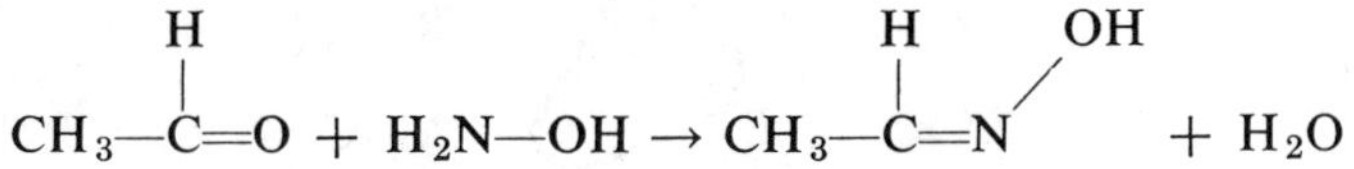

$$\underset{\substack{\text{Acetaldoxime}\\(\text{M.P. }47°\text{C})}}{CH_3-\overset{\overset{\displaystyle H}{|}}{C}=O + H_2N-OH \rightarrow CH_3-\overset{\overset{\displaystyle H}{|}}{C}=N\overset{\diagup OH}{} + H_2O}$$

$$\underset{CH_3CH_2}{\overset{CH_3CH_2}{\diagdown}}C=O + H_2NOH \longrightarrow \underset{CH_3CH_2}{\overset{CH_3CH_2}{\diagdown}}C=N\overset{\diagup OH}{} + H_2O$$

Diethylketoxime (M.P. 69°C)

Exercise 9.5   Draw two possible structures for the oxime obtainable from 2-butanone. To what type of stereoisomers are these related?

The semicarbazones usually are higher melting solids than are the oximes or phenylhydrazones. Should the oxime or the phenylhydrazone of an unknown carbonyl compound be a low melting solid or an oil, as is sometimes the case, the semicarbazone usually will serve to identify it. Frequently, the higher the molecular weight of a carbonyl derivative the higher its melting point. Thus, 2, 4-*dinitrophenylhydrazine* often is used in place of phenylhydrazine for the preparation of carbonyl derivatives.

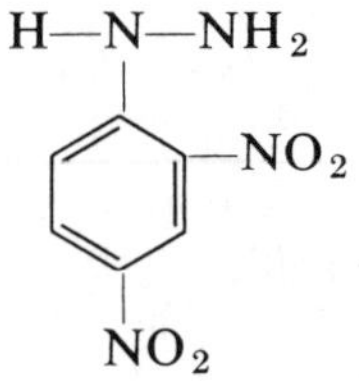

$$H-N-NH_2$$

2, 4-Dinitrophenylhydrazine

Table 9.2 illustrates the wide divergence in melting points of oximes, phenylhydrazones, and semicarbazones of some common carbonyl compounds.

□■ TABLE 9.2

DERIVATIVES USEFUL FOR THE IDENTIFICATION OF ALDEHYDES
AND KETONES

Compound	Formula	B.P., °C	Oxime M.P. °C	Phenylhy- drazone M.P., °C	Semi- carbazide M.P., °C	2, 4-Dini- trophenyl- hydrazone M.P., °C
Acetone	$CH_3-\overset{\displaystyle O}{\overset{\|}{C}}-CH_3$	56	59	42	187	126
Acetaldehyde	$CH_3-\overset{\displaystyle H}{\underset{\|}{C}}=O$	20	47	63	162	147
α-Methyl-n- butyraldehyde	$CH_3CH_2CH(CH_3)\overset{\displaystyle H}{\underset{\|}{C}}=O$	93	oil	oil	103	120
Benzaldehyde	$\text{C}_6\text{H}_5-\overset{\displaystyle H}{\underset{\|}{C}}=O$	179	35	158	222	237
Methyl ethyl ketone	$C_2H_5-\overset{\displaystyle CH_3}{\underset{\|}{C}}=O$	80	oil	oil	146	117
Diethyl ketone	$(C_2H_5)_2C=O$	102	69	oil	139	156
Di-n-propyl ketone	$(C_3H_7)_2C=O$	145	oil	oil	133	75
Isopropyl methyl ketone	$(CH_3)_2CH\overset{\displaystyle CH_3}{\underset{\|}{C}}=O$	94	oil	oil	113	117
Cyclopentanone	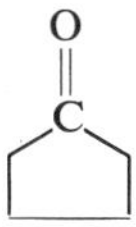 (cyclopentanone structure)	131	56	50	205	142

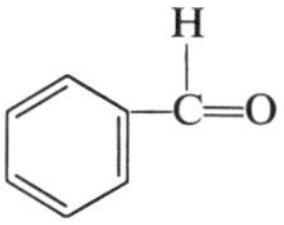

B.   Self-Addition (α-Hydrogen and the Aldol Condensation.)
The attraction which the oxygen atom of the carbonyl group holds
for electrons is relayed not only to the carbonyl carbon atom, but
also to the adjacent carbon, or α-carbon atom. This attraction,
called an inductive effect, weakens the bonds between the α-carbon
atom and its attached hydrogen atoms. As a result the latter (called

α-hydrogens) are held more loosely and may be removed by strongly basic reagents. Because they are removable, these hydrogens are referred to as active, or "acidic," hydrogens.

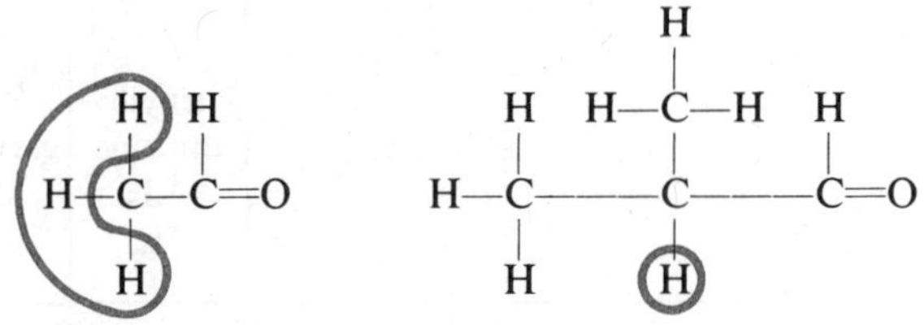

Acetaldehyde
(three α-hydrogens)

Isobutyraldehyde
(one α-hydrogen)

The carbon anion (carbanion) which remains after an α-hydrogen atom is removed as a proton may act as a nucleophilic reagent against the carbonyl carbon atom of another molecule. A condensation of this type between two molecules of an aldehyde or a ketone is called the aldol[2] condensation. An aldol condensation involving two molecules of acetaldehyde is illustrated.

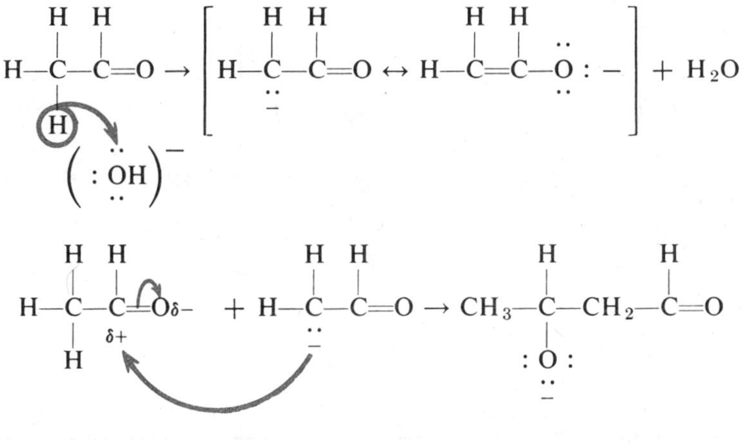

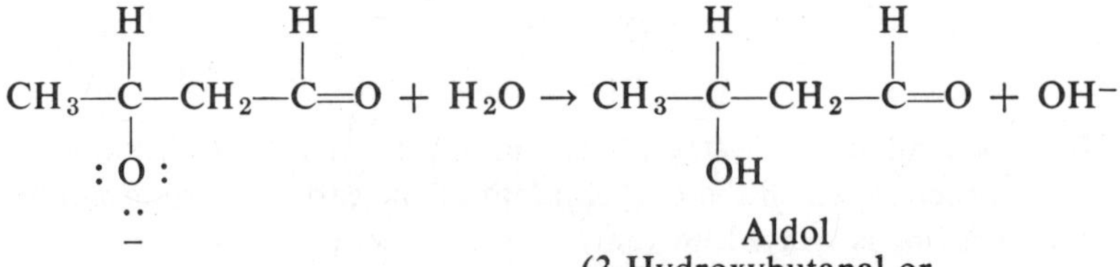

Aldol
(3-Hydroxybutanal or
β-Hydroxybutyraldehyde)

[2]Aldol, a composite word for aldehyde + alcohol.

Aldols readily lose water when heated to give α, β-unsaturated carbonyl compounds.

$$CH_3\underset{\underset{OH}{|}}{\overset{\overset{H}{|}}{C}}\text{---}\underset{\underset{H}{|}}{\overset{\overset{H}{|}}{C}}\text{-}\overset{\overset{H}{|}}{C}\text{=}O \xrightarrow{\text{Heat}} H_2O + CH_3\overset{\overset{H}{|}}{C}\text{=}\overset{\overset{H}{|}}{C}\text{-}\overset{\overset{H}{|}}{C}\text{=}O$$

2-Butenal
(Crotonaldehyde)

Ketones also are capable of an aldol type condensation.

$$CH_3\text{-}\underset{\underset{CH_3}{|}}{C}\text{=}O + OH^- \rightarrow H_2O + \left[:\bar{C}H_2\text{-}\underset{\underset{CH_3}{|}}{C}\text{=}O \right]$$

$$CH_3\text{-}\overset{\overset{CH_3}{|}}{C}\text{=}O + :\bar{C}H_2\text{-}\underset{\underset{CH_3}{|}}{C}\text{=}O \rightarrow CH_3\text{-}\underset{\underset{:\overset{..}{O}:}{|}}{\overset{\overset{CH_3}{|}}{C}}\text{-}CH_2\text{-}\overset{\overset{CH_3}{|}}{C}\text{=}O$$

$$CH_3\text{-}\underset{\underset{:\bar{\overset{..}{O}}:}{|}}{\overset{\overset{CH_3}{|}}{C}}\text{-}CH_2\text{-}\overset{\overset{CH_3}{|}}{C}\text{=}O + H_2O \rightarrow CH_3\text{-}\underset{\underset{OH}{|}}{\overset{\overset{CH_3}{|}}{C}}\text{-}CH_2\text{-}\overset{\overset{O}{\parallel}}{C}\text{-}CH_3 + OH^-$$

4-Hydroxy-4-methyl-2-pentanone
(Diacetone alcohol)

$$CH_3\text{-}\underset{\underset{OH}{|}}{\overset{\overset{CH_3}{|}}{C}}\text{---}\underset{\underset{H}{|}}{\overset{\overset{H}{|}}{C}}\text{-}\overset{\overset{O}{\parallel}}{C}\text{-}CH_3 \xrightarrow{\text{Heat}} CH_3\text{-}\overset{\overset{CH_3}{|}}{C}\text{=}\overset{\overset{H}{|}}{C}\text{-}\overset{\overset{O}{\parallel}}{C}\text{-}CH_3$$

4-Methyl-3-pentene-2-one
(Mesityl oxide)

Exercise 9.6   Write the structures for the four condensation products possible when a mixture of acetaldehyde and n-butyraldehyde is warmed with dilute sodium hydroxide.

An aldehyde that lacks an α-hydrogen can enter into an aldol condensation with another aldehyde only by supplying the carbanion acceptor. An excellent illustration of this kind of situation is found in the preparation of pentaerythritol, $(HOCH_2)_4C$, a polyhydric alcohol used in the preparation of explosives. The first step in the preparation of pentaerythritol is the condensation of formaldehyde with acetaldehyde to produce trimethylolacetaldehyde.

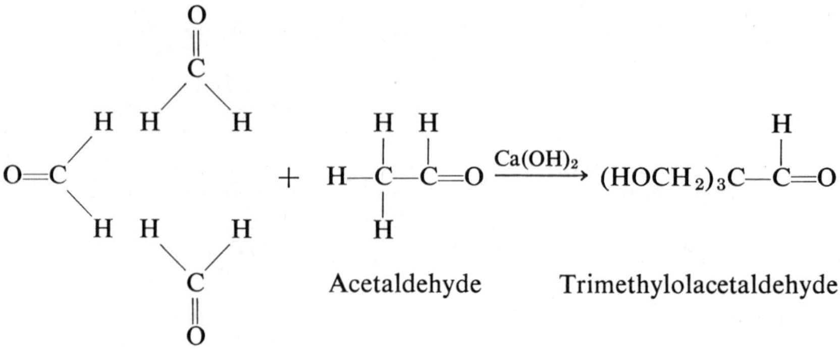

Formaldehyde + Acetaldehyde $\xrightarrow{\text{Ca(OH)}_2}$ Trimethylolacetaldehyde

The second step is a "crossed" Cannizzaro reaction (Sec. 9.10-B) between two aldehydes neither of which has α-hydrogen.

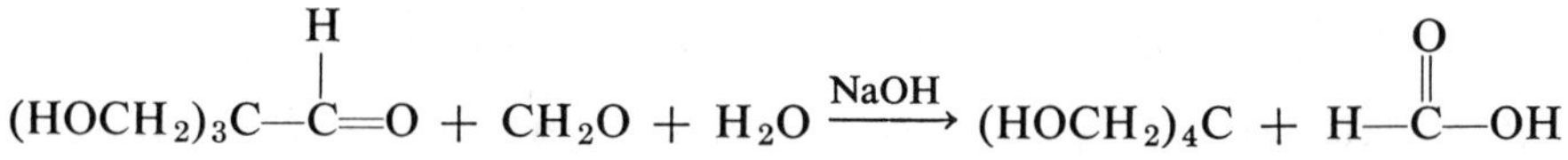

$$(HOCH_2)_3C-\overset{H}{\underset{}{C}}=O + CH_2O + H_2O \xrightarrow{\text{NaOH}} (HOCH_2)_4C + H-\overset{O}{\underset{}{C}}-OH$$

Pentaerythritol   Formic acid
(as sodium salt)

Benzaldehyde reacts with acetaldehyde to produce cinnamaldehyde, an α, β-unsaturated aromatic aldehyde used as a flavoring agent.

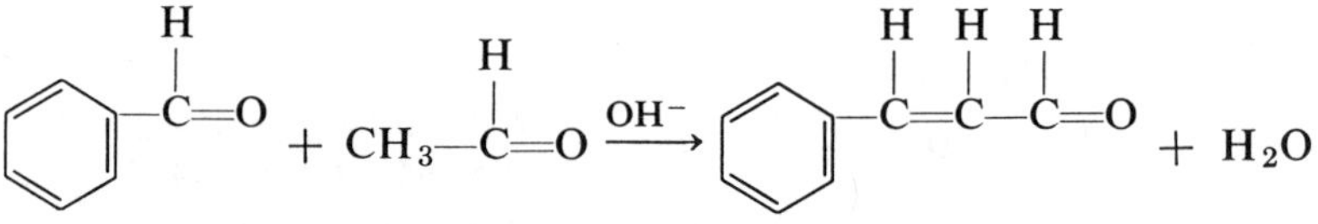

Benzaldehyde + $CH_3-\overset{H}{\underset{}{C}}=O \xrightarrow{\text{OH}^-}$ Cinnamaldehyde + H_2O

9.9   REPLACEMENT OF α-HYDROGEN BY HALOGEN
(HALOFORM REACTION)

Acetaldehyde or a methyl ketone, when warmed with an alkaline solution of either chlorine, bromine, or iodine, produces as one reaction product chloroform, bromoform, or iodoform, respectively. This reaction, called the **haloform reaction,** when involving either of the above carbonyls appears to take place in two stages. In the first stage, the three hydrogen atoms on the α-carbon are successively replaced by halogen, each hydrogen more easily than the one before because of the strong inductive effect of the halogen atom already bonded.

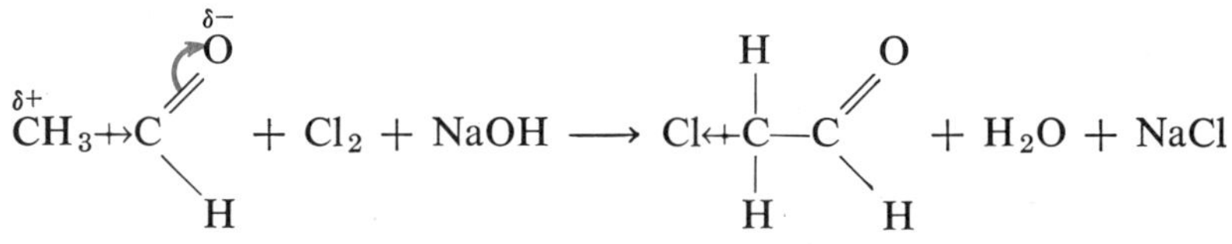

$$CH_3 \rightarrow C\overset{\delta-}{\underset{H}{\overset{O}{\Big\backslash\!\!\!\!/}}} + Cl_2 + NaOH \longrightarrow Cl\!\leftrightarrow\!\overset{H}{\underset{H}{C}}\!-\!\overset{O}{\underset{H}{C}}\overset{\Big\backslash\!\!\!\!/}{} + H_2O + NaCl$$

Acetaldehyde

$$Cl\!\leftrightarrow\!\overset{H}{\underset{H}{C}}\!-\!\overset{O}{\underset{H}{C}}\overset{\Big\backslash\!\!\!\!/}{} + 2\,Cl_2 + 2\,NaOH \longrightarrow Cl_3C\!\leftrightarrow\!\overset{O}{\underset{H}{C}}\overset{\Big\backslash\!\!\!\!/}{} + 2\,H_2O + 2\,NaCl$$

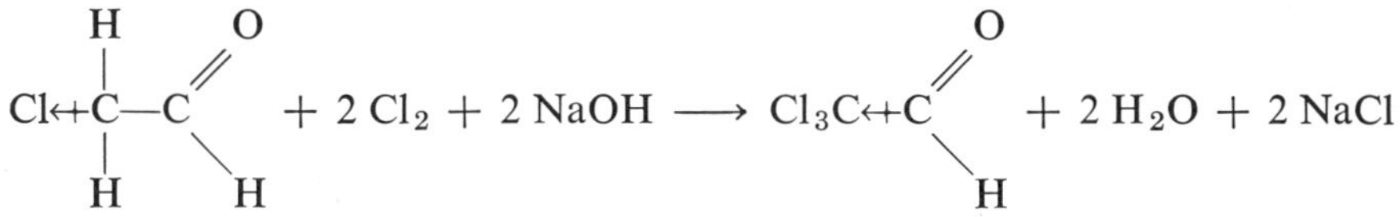

In the second stage of the reaction the molecule is cleaved by basic (nucleophilic) attack against the carbonyl carbon.

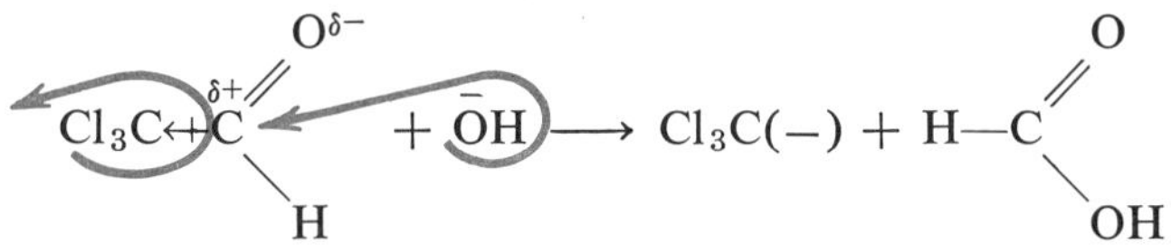

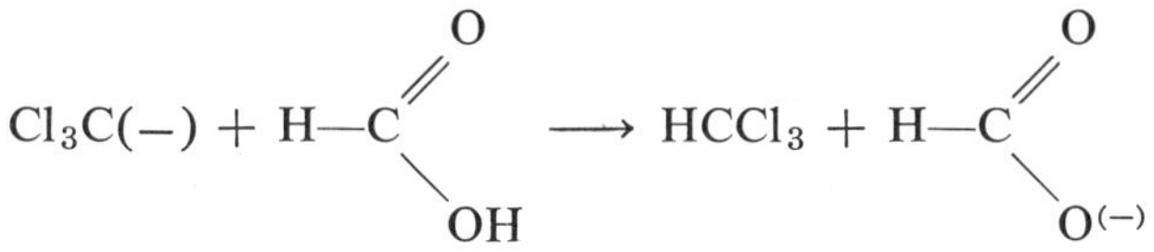

$$Cl_3C\!\leftrightarrow\!\overset{O^{\delta-}}{\underset{H}{\overset{\delta+}{C}}} + \overline{OH} \longrightarrow Cl_3C(-) + H\!-\!C\overset{O}{\underset{OH}{\Big\backslash\!\!\!\!/}}$$

$$Cl_3C(-) + H\!-\!C\overset{O}{\underset{OH}{\Big\backslash\!\!\!\!/}} \longrightarrow HCCl_3 + H\!-\!C\overset{O}{\underset{O^{(-)}}{\Big\backslash\!\!\!\!/}}$$

Chloroform

$$H\!-\!C\overset{O}{\underset{O^{(-)}}{\Big\backslash\!\!\!\!/}} + NaOH \longrightarrow H\!-\!C\overset{O}{\underset{O^{(-)}Na^+}{\Big\backslash\!\!\!\!/}} + OH^-$$

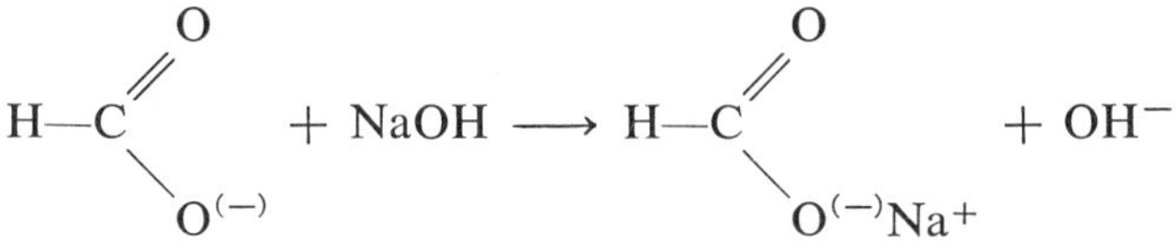

Sodium formate

A structural requirement for any compound that gives a positive haloform reaction is that it contain an **acetyl group,** $CH_3\!-\!\overset{O}{\overset{\|}{C}}\!-$ or one oxidizable to an acetyl group. The first requirement is met by acetaldehyde and all methyl ketones. The second requirement, of

$$CH_3-\overset{\displaystyle H}{\underset{\displaystyle |}{\overset{\displaystyle |}{C}}}-OH.$$

course, is met by all methyl carbinols of the structure, $CH_3-\overset{H}{\underset{|}{\overset{|}{C}}}-OH$.

Of the primary alcohols, ethanol alone gives the haloform reaction because it is oxidizable to acetaldehyde. The haloform reaction is useful not only as a preparative method for the haloforms (Sec. 7.4), but also as a diagnostic test for the presence of the groupings indicated. In practice, a solution of iodine is added to an unknown compound in an aqueous alkaline solution. A positive reaction will yield iodoform, CHI_3, a bright yellow solid (chloroform and bromoform are liquids) which may be identified by its sharp pungent odor and its melting point.

9.10   OXIDATION REACTIONS

A.   Oxidation by Tollens' Reagent, Fehling's, and Benedict's Solutions.   Aldehydes are so easily oxidized that even the mildest of oxidizing reagents will serve to bring about their conversion to acids. Ketones, on the other hand, are fairly resistant to oxidation. The oxidation of ketones, when forced by the use of strong oxidizing reagents and heat, results in a rupture of carbon–carbon bonds to produce acids.

$$CH_3-\overset{O}{\overset{\|}{C}}-CH_2CH_3 \xrightarrow[\text{heat}]{KMnO_4, H^+,} CH_3-\overset{O}{\overset{\|}{C}}\diagdown OH \quad \text{and/or} \quad CH_3-CH_2-\overset{O}{\overset{\|}{C}}\diagdown OH$$

An exception to this general rule may be found in the oxidation of ketones by selenium dioxide, SeO_2. A methylene group adjacent to the carbonyl becomes oxidized by the use of this reagent to another carbonyl group. Methyl ethyl ketone, for example, can be oxidized to diacetyl.

$$CH_3-CH_2-\overset{O}{\overset{\|}{C}}-CH_3 + SeO_2 \rightarrow CH_3-\overset{O}{\overset{\|}{C}}-\overset{O}{\overset{\|}{C}}-CH_3 + H_2O + Se$$

2-Butanone   Butanedione
(Methyl ethyl ketone)   (Diacetyl)

The ease with which an oxidation takes place provides a simple method for distinguishing between aldehydes and ketones. Mild oxidizing agents may be used for this purpose. **Tollens' reagent,** an ammoniacal solution of silver oxide, $Ag(NH_3)_2OH$, and **Fehling's solution,** an alkaline solution of cupric ion complexed with sodium potassium tartrate (Rochelle salt), are two reagents commonly used to detect the presence of an aldehyde group. When Tollens' reagent is used to oxidize an aldehyde, the silver ion is reduced to the metallic form and, if the reaction is carried out in a clean test tube, deposits as a mirror.

$$R{-}\overset{\overset{\displaystyle H}{|}}{C}{=}O + 2\,Ag(NH_3)_2OH \rightarrow R{-}\overset{\overset{\displaystyle O}{\|}}{C}{-}O^-NH_4{}^+ + 2\,Ag + H_2O + 3\,NH_3$$

When Fehling's solution is used to oxidize an aldehyde, the complexed cupric ion (deep blue) is reduced to cuprous oxide (red).

$$R{-}\overset{\overset{\displaystyle H}{|}}{C}{=}O + 2\,Cu(OH)_2 + NaOH \rightarrow R{-}\overset{\overset{\displaystyle O}{\|}}{C}{-}O^-Na^+ + Cu_2O + 3\,H_2O$$

Aromatic aldehydes react with Tollens' reagent but not with Fehling's solution. A means of distinguishing between aliphatic and aromatic aldehydes is thus provided by this difference in reactivity with the two reagents.

B.   Autooxidation and Reduction (Cannizzaro Reaction).   Aldehydes which lack an α-hydrogen, when heated with a concentrated sodium or potassium hydroxide solution, undergo an intermolecular oxidation-reduction. One molecule of such an aldehyde is reduced to an alcohol at the expense of another molecule. The second molecule is oxidized to an acid. The mechanism for this interesting disproportionation, known as the **Cannizzaro reaction,** is illustrated using formaldehyde.

$$\underset{\text{Formaldehyde}}{\overset{\displaystyle H}{\underset{\displaystyle H}{>}}C{=}O + Na\overset{+}{O}\overset{-}{H}} \rightleftharpoons \overset{\displaystyle H}{\underset{\displaystyle H}{>}}C\overset{\displaystyle O^-}{\underset{\displaystyle OH}{<}} + Na^+$$

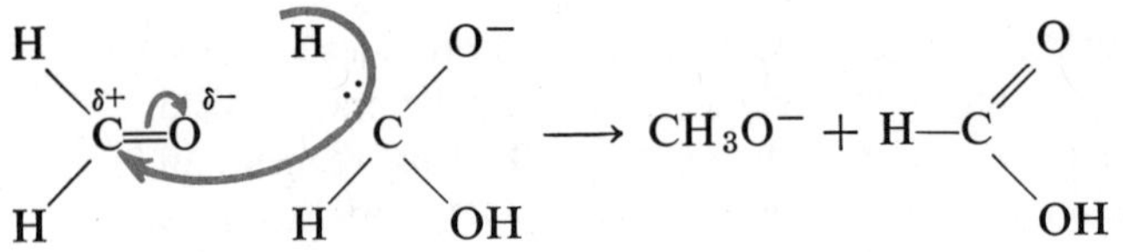

$$H-C\overset{O}{\underset{OH}{\big\backslash}} \longrightarrow CH_3O^- + H-C\overset{O}{\underset{OH}{\big\backslash}}$$

Hydride ion transfer (slow)

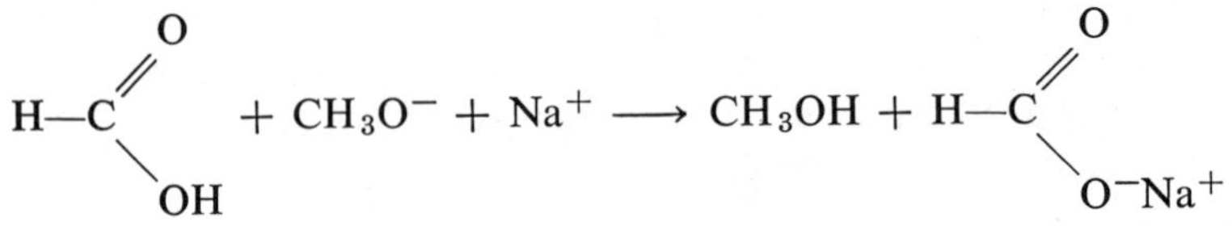

$$H-C\overset{O}{\underset{OH}{\big\backslash}} + CH_3O^- + Na^+ \longrightarrow CH_3OH + H-C\overset{O}{\underset{O^-Na^+}{\big\backslash}}$$

Acid-base reaction (fast)

Methyl alcohol	Sodium formate

Two different aldehydes, each lacking α-hydrogen, engage in a **crossed Cannizzaro reaction** when heated in an alkaline solution. This type of Cannizzaro reaction was illustrated in the preparation of pentaerythritol (Sec. 9.8-B).

9.11   REDUCTION

The carbonyl group of aldehydes and ketones may be reduced to primary and secondary alcohols respectively. This transformation can be accomplished either catalytically with hydrogen (hydrogenation) or by means of a chemical reducing agent such as lithium aluminum hydride, $LiAlH_4$.

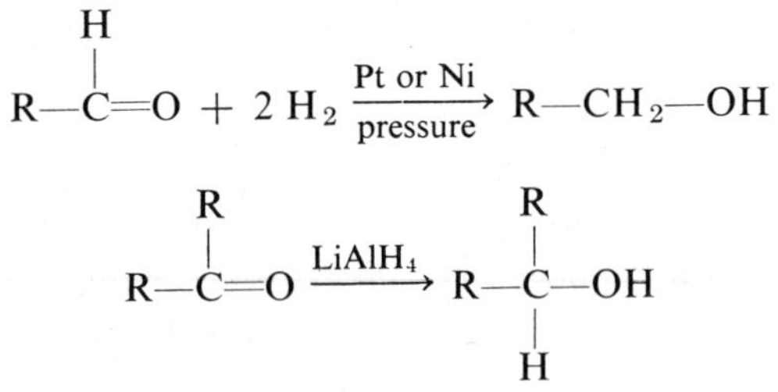

$$R-\overset{H}{\underset{}{C}}=O + 2 H_2 \xrightarrow[\text{pressure}]{\text{Pt or Ni}} R-CH_2-OH$$

$$R-\overset{R}{\underset{}{C}}=O \xrightarrow{LiAlH_4} R-\overset{R}{\underset{H}{C}}-OH$$

Another reducing agent specific for the reduction of carbonyl groups is sodium borohydride, $NaBH_4$. This reagent is less reactive than $LiAlH_4$ and may be used in water or alcoholic solutions. Lithium aluminum hydride, on the other hand, reacts violently with such hydroxylic solvents.

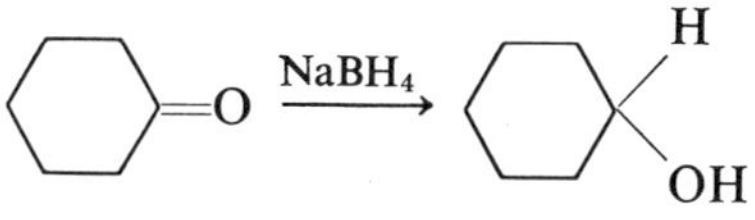

Cyclohexanone   Cyclohexanol

Exercise 9.7   Cyclohexanone (b.p. 156°) may be prepared by the oxidation of cyclohexanol (b.p. 161°). If you had prepared cyclohexanone by this method, how could you isolate it uncontaminated by traces of unreacted cyclohexanol?

The carbonyl group of a ketone can be reduced to a methylene group when refluxed with concentrated hydrochloric acid in the presence of amalgamated zinc. The reaction, known as the **Clemmensen reduction,** provides a method for converting carbonyls to hydrocarbons, and often is used as a sequel to the Friedel-Crafts acylation of the aromatic ring. The net result, in this case, is the monosubstitution of the ring by an unbranched alkyl group — an objective not always possible in the Friedel-Crafts alkylation.

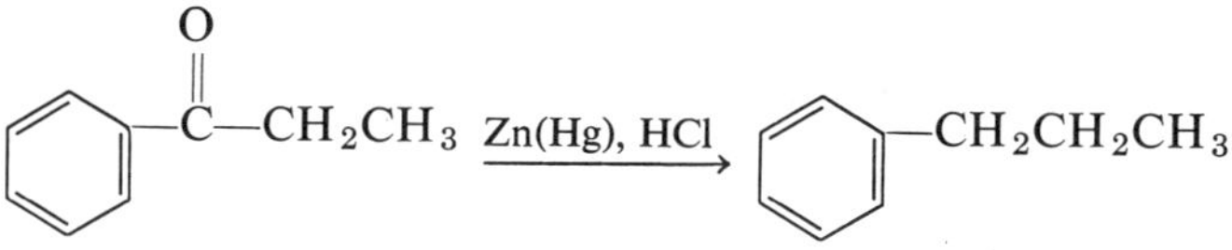

Propiophenone   *n*-Propylbenzene
(Ethyl phenyl ketone)

9.12   POLYMERIZATION OF ALDEHYDES

Acetaldehyde, as you have noted, is rather unstable toward oxidation. This inherent instability, along with a boiling point of only 20°C, makes acetaldehyde a difficult compound to store and use. Fortunately, when treated with acid at a low temperature, acetaldehyde undergoes self-addition to give the cyclic trimer,[3] **paraldehyde** (b.p. 125°C).

---

[3]Monomer: Gr., *mono*, one; *meros*, part. The simplest structural unit in a polymer. A trimer is composed of three molecules of monomer.

$$\underset{\text{Acetaldehyde}}{\begin{array}{c} CH_3 \quad H \\ \diagdown \quad \diagup \\ C \\ \diagdown\diagdown \\ O \qquad O \\ \| \\ CH_3{-}C \qquad C{-}CH_3 \\ \diagup \qquad \diagup\diagup \\ H \qquad O \qquad H \end{array}} \quad \xrightarrow{H^+} \quad \underset{\text{Paraldehyde}}{\begin{array}{c} CH_3 \quad H \\ \diagdown \quad \diagup \\ C \\ \diagup \quad \diagdown \\ CH_3 \; O \qquad O \; CH_3 \\ \diagdown \quad \diagup \\ C \qquad C \\ \diagup \quad \diagdown \\ H \qquad O \qquad H \end{array}}$$

In this form the aldehyde is not only stable to oxidation but no longer is easily lost by evaporation. Paraldehyde, when warmed, depolymerizes to regenerate acetaldehyde. Acetaldehyde, when warmed in concentrated alkaline solution, appears to undergo repeated aldol condensation accompanied by dehydration and polymerization to yield viscous, resinous products of undetermined structure. Acetaldehyde (as paraldehyde) has been used medicinally, as a soporific, but its most important use is as a starting material in many organic syntheses.

Formaldehyde is not marketed in its gaseous form, but either as **formalin**, a 37–40% aqueous solution, or as the polymer, **paraformaldehyde**, $HO(CH_2O)_nH$, with n having an average value of 30. Paraformaldehyde is an amorphous white solid prepared by slowly evaporating formalin under reduced pressure. The polymerization involves the self-addition of many molecules of formaldehyde.

$$\begin{array}{c} H \\ \diagdown \\ C{=}O + H_2O \rightleftarrows [HOCH_2OH] \\ \diagup \\ H \end{array}$$

$$[HOCH_2OH] + n\ HCHO \rightarrow HO\left(\begin{array}{c} H \\ | \\ {-}C{-}O{-} \\ | \\ H \end{array}\right)_{n+1} H$$

Paraformaldehyde

Depolymerization of paraformaldehyde, as in the case of paraldehyde, is brought about by heating. This ready change of state from solid to gaseous allows formaldehyde to be easily stored and used.

A high molecular weight linear polymer named "Delrin" has been prepared from formaldehyde. It is a remarkable plastic and shows promise of becoming a very useful one for structural materials where strength and resiliency are important.

Formaldehyde is perhaps the most important member of the aldehyde family. Its industrial importance lies principally in its ability to **copolymerize**[4] with phenol, with urea [$(H_2N)_2C{=}O$], and with melamine ($C_3H_6N_6$, a cyclic triamino compound) to produce hard, electrical nonconducting, infusible resins of the "Bakelite" and "Melmac" type. Structural units of these useful plastics are shown.

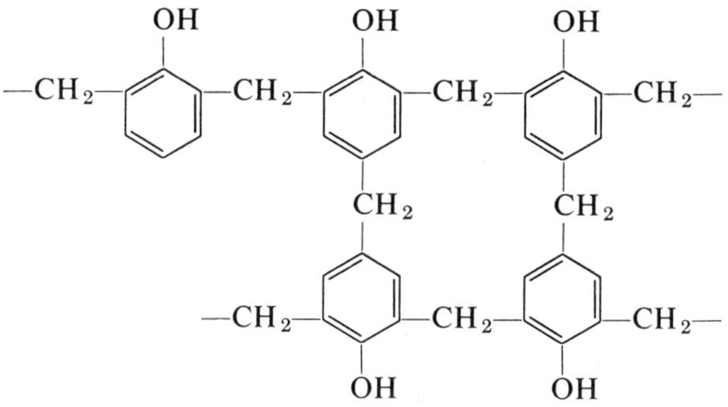

(a)

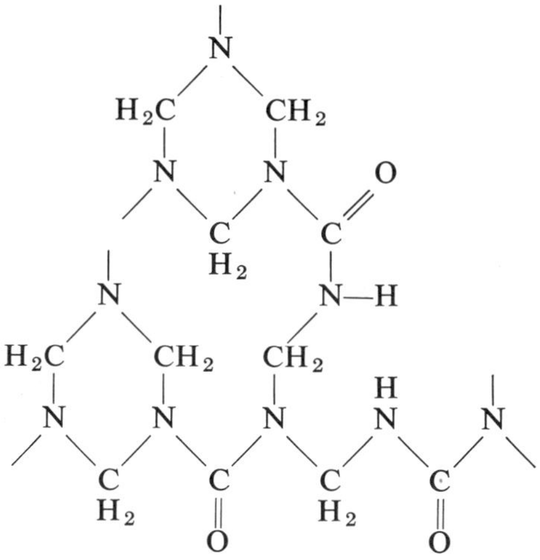

(b)

Structural units in (a) Bakelite and (b) urea-formaldehyde resins.

[4]Copolymerization: a reaction in which two or more unlike monomers polymerize with each other.

Formaldehyde reacts with proteins to harden them and makes them less susceptible to putrefaction. For this reason it is used in the preservation of biological specimens and in embalming agents. Formaldehyde is toxic to insects and many microorganisms, and in the form of paraformaldehyde "candles" is conveniently used as a fumigant.

□□ *SUMMARY*

[1]   **Structure**

The functional group of both the aldehydes and ketones is the

carbonyl group, $C{=}O$. The general formula for the alde-

hydes is $R{-}\overset{\overset{\text{H}}{|}}{C}{=}O$; for the ketones, $R{-}\overset{\overset{\text{R}}{|}}{C}{=}O$.

[2]   **Nomenclature**

IUPAC nomenclature uses the suffix **al** to name an aldehyde; **one** to designate a ketone. Systematic nomenclature is governed by IUPAC rules previously outlined.

[3]   **Properties**

(A) The simple aldehydes and ketones are nonassociated, low boiling liquids.

(B) Only aldehydes and ketones of low molecular weight are soluble in water.

(C) The simple aldehydes have sharp, irritating odors.

(D) The aromatic aldehydes and nearly all the ketones are fragrant.

(E) The electron-withdrawing effect of the carbonyl oxygen is transmitted to the α-carbon atom and bestows acidic properties upon the hydrogen atoms bonded to it.

[4]   **Preparation**

(A) General methods for the preparation of the aldehydes are
(a) The catalytic dehydrogenation (oxidation) of primary alcohols.
(b) The hydrolysis of geminal dihalides (must be 1, 1-dihalides).

(B) Special methods of preparation of aldehydes are
(a) The Gatterman-Koch reaction for aromatic aldehydes.
(b) The hydration of acetylene for preparing acetaldehyde.

(C) General methods for the preparation of the ketones are
(a) The oxidation of secondary alcohols.

(b) Hydrolysis of geminal dihalides (other than 1, 1-dihalogen substituted alkanes).

(c) The pyrolysis of calcium salts of acids to give symmetrical ketones.

(D) Special methods for the preparation of ketones are

(a) The Friedel-Crafts acylation reaction for aromatic ketones.

(b) The Weizmann fermentation for acetone.

[5] Reactions of Carbonyl Compounds

(A) Oxidation.

Aldehydes are easily oxidized to acids even by mild oxidizing reagents; ketones generally cannot be oxidized without a rupture of the carbon chain.

(B) Addition of nucleophilic reagents — i.e., bases, electron-pair donors.

(a) The following reagents give "straight" addition products.

(i) HCN adds to aldehydes and ketones to form cyanohydrins.

(ii) $NaHSO_3$ adds to aldehydes, methyl ketones, and cyclic ketones to give sodium bisulfite salts.

(iii) Hydrogen adds to the carbonyl group of aldehydes and ketones to produce primary and secondary alcohols respectively.

(iv) Grignard reagents, when treated with aldehydes, lead to the preparation of *secondary* alcohols; when treated with ketones, Grignard reagents lead to the preparation of *tertiary* alcohols. The only aldehyde capable of forming a primary alcohol with a Grignard reagent is formaldehyde.

(b) Certain nitrogen-containing nucleophilic reagents add to aldehydes and ketones to produce unstable addition products. Subsequent loss of water (condensation) produces a carbon-nitrogen double bond. *Hydroxylamine* reacts with aldehydes and ketones to yield *oximes;* hydrazine and its derivatives give the corresponding *hydrazones.* *Semicarbazide* reacts to produce *semicarbazones.* All three types of derivatives are useful in the identification of "unknowns."

(C) Reactions of α-Hydrogen.

(a) An aldol condensation results when an aldehyde or a ketone with α-hydrogen is treated with a dilute base. The product (an aldol) readily loses water to yield an α, β-unsaturated carbonyl.

(b) Acetaldehyde and methyl ketones undergo replacement of all three α-hydrogen atoms when warmed with an alkaline solution of the halogens to yield *haloforms* and salts of acids.

(D) Disproportionation.

Aldehydes lacking α-hydrogen atoms undergo the Cannizzaro reaction when treated with concentrated sodium or potassium hydroxide. Ketones do not give the Cannizzaro reaction.

(E) Polymerization.

Formaldehyde is capable of self-addition to yield polymers of varying molecular weights. Acetaldehyde trimerizes to paraldehyde. Formaldehyde copolymerizes with phenol (Bakelite), and with urea, and melamine (Melmac). These are useful plastics with desirable thermal and electrical properties.

□□ *NEW TERMS*

[1]   acetal
[2]   acyl group
[3]   aldol condensation
[4]   carbonyl group
[5]   cyanohydrin
[6]   Fehling's solution

[7]   hemiacetal
[8]   oxime
[9]   phenylhydrazone
[10] semicarbazone
[11] Tollens' reagent

■ □ SUPPLEMENTARY EXERCISES
▼   AND PROBLEMS

[1]   Assign an acceptable name to each of the following compounds.

(a) 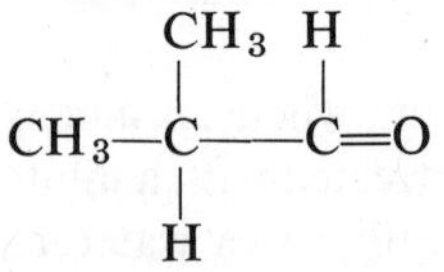   CH₃—C—C=O   (b) 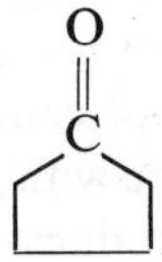   (cyclopentanone structure)

(c) 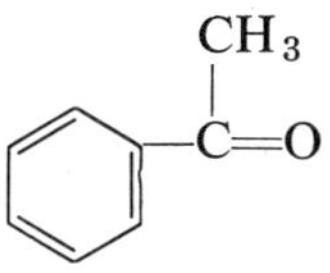 [structure: benzene ring with $-C(CH_3)=O$ substituent]

(d) 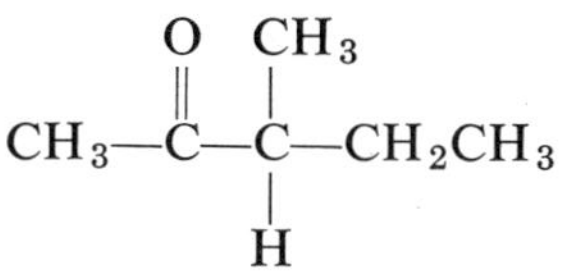 $CH_3-\overset{\overset{\displaystyle O}{||}}{C}-\overset{\overset{\displaystyle CH_3}{|}}{\underset{\underset{\displaystyle H}{|}}{C}}-CH_2CH_3$

(e) 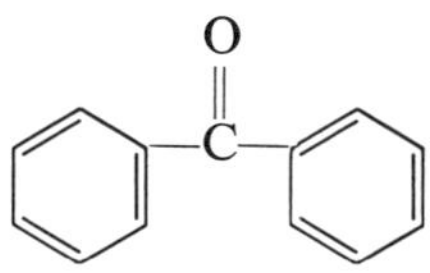 [structure: two benzene rings joined by a $\overset{\overset{\displaystyle O}{||}}{C}$ carbonyl group]

(f) 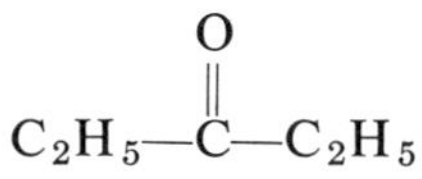 $C_2H_5-\overset{\overset{\displaystyle O}{||}}{C}-C_2H_5$

[2] Write structures for the following.
(a) propionaldehyde   (e) α-bromoacetophenone
(b) diisopropyl ketone   (f) cinnamaldehyde
(c) 2-methylpropanal   (g) furfural
(d) 2-octanone

[3] Complete the following reactions, naming the principal organic products formed.
(a) isopropyl alcohol + I_2 in aqueous KI + NaOH $\longrightarrow$
(b) acetone + NaCN + HCl $\longrightarrow$
(c) acetaldehyde + C_2H_5OH $\xrightarrow{H^+}$
(d) methyl ethyl ketone + C_2H_5MgBr $\xrightarrow[\text{hydrolysis}]{\text{Followed by}}$
(e) acetophenone + H_2NOH $\xrightarrow{H^+}$
(f) n-butyraldehyde + $NaHSO_3$ $\longrightarrow$
(g) acetaldehyde $\xrightarrow{10\% \text{ NaOH}}$
(h) benzaldehyde + KOH $\longrightarrow$
(i) methanol $\xrightarrow{\text{CuO, heat}}$
(j) acetaldehyde + $Ag(NH_3)_2OH$ $\longrightarrow$

[4] Write structures for the products formed when each of the following is treated with ethylmagnesium bromide, followed by acid hydrolysis.

(a) 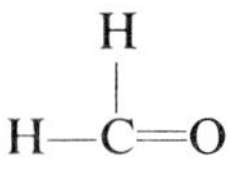 $H-\overset{\overset{\displaystyle H}{|}}{C}=O$

(b) $CH_3-\overset{\overset{\displaystyle H}{|}}{C}=O$

(c) $CH_3-\overset{\overset{\displaystyle CH_3}{|}}{C}=O$

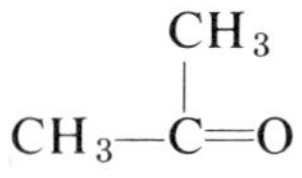

(d) 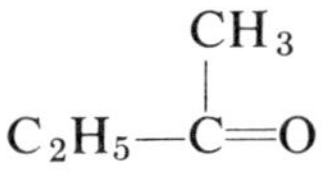 $C_2H_5-\overset{\overset{\displaystyle CH_3}{|}}{C}=O$

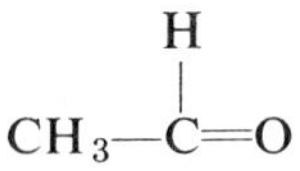

(e) 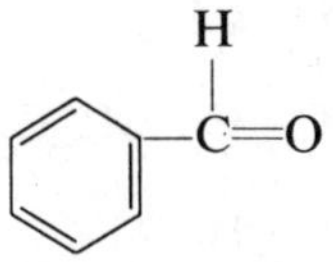 [benzene ring]$-\underset{\overset{|}{H}}{C}{=}O$

(f) 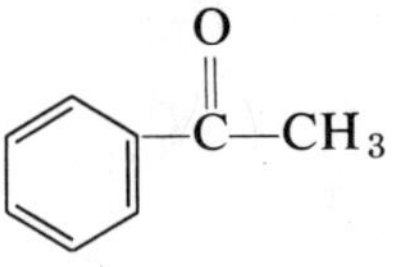 [benzene ring]$-\overset{\overset{O}{\|}}{C}-CH_3$

[5]   Which of the following compounds will give a positive iodo-form reaction?

(a) $(CH_3)_2CHOH$

(b) $C_2H_5-\underset{\overset{|}{}}{\overset{\overset{CH_3}{|}}{C}}{=}O$

(c) $CH_3-\underset{\overset{|}{CH_3}}{\overset{\overset{CH_3}{|}}{C}}-OH$

(d) 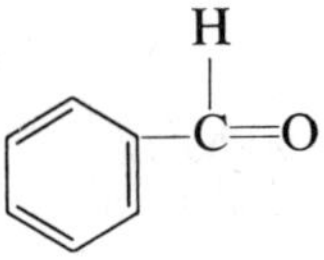   [benzene ring]$-\underset{\overset{|}{H}}{C}{=}O$

(e) CH_3CH_2OH

(f) 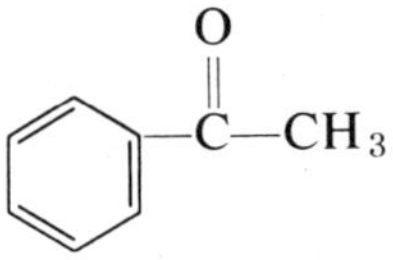   [benzene ring]$-\overset{\overset{O}{\|}}{C}-CH_3$

(g) $CH_3CH_2-\underset{\overset{|}{H}}{\overset{\overset{OH}{|}}{C}}-CH_3$

(h) $CH_3CH_2-\underset{\overset{|}{H}}{C}{=}O$

[6]   Using acetylene as your only organic starting material show how you would synthesize each of the following compounds. You may use whatever inorganic reagents you consider necessary.

(a)   acetaldehyde
(b)   ethyl bromide
(c)   iodoform
(d)   acetic acid

(e)   2-butanol
(f)   methyl ethyl ketone
(g)   diacetyl
(h)   propionic acid, CH_3CH_2COOH

[7]   Identify the aldehyde or ketone that will react with ethylmagnesium bromide to produce

(a)   2-butanol
(b)   3-methyl-3-pentanol
(c)   n-propyl alcohol

(d)   2-methyl-2-butanol
(e)   3-methyl-3-octanol

[8]   Indicate simple test tube reactions which would serve to distinguish between the following pairs of carbonyl compounds without the need for taking boiling points, melting points, or preparing solid derivatives.

(a) $CH_3-\overset{\overset{H}{|}}{C}=O$, $(CH_3)_2C=O$

(b) $CH_3(CH_2)_5-\overset{\overset{CH_3}{|}}{C}=O$, [benzaldehyde structure: $C_6H_5-\overset{\overset{H}{|}}{C}=O$]

(c) $CH_3-\overset{\overset{CH_3}{|}}{\underset{\underset{CH_3}{|}}{C}}-\overset{\overset{H}{|}}{C}=O$, $CH_3CH_2-\overset{\overset{O}{||}}{C}-CH_3$

(d) $C_2H_5-\overset{\overset{O}{||}}{C}-C_2H_5$, [cyclopentanone]=O

(e) [acetophenone: $C_6H_5-\overset{\overset{O}{||}}{C}-CH_3$], [benzaldehyde: $C_6H_5-\overset{\overset{H}{|}}{C}=O$]

[9] A student was given an "unknown" carbonyl compound from among those listed in Table 9.2. He obtained a boiling point of 90–92°. Consulting Table 9.2 he noted that his unknown could possibly be one of two different compounds. He proceeded to prepare a 2, 4-dinitrophenylhydrazone of his compound but realized too late that this derivative would still leave the identity of his "unknown" in question. Without preparing a second derivative, what simple test tube reaction would help him to establish the identity of his unknown? What derivative should he then prepare?

[10] Compound (A), $C_5H_{12}O$, when refluxed with potassium dichromate and sulfuric acid was converted to (B), $C_5H_{10}O$. Compound (B) formed a derivative with 2, 4-dinitrophenylhydrazine but gave neither a positive haloform reaction nor would it form an addition product with sodium bisulfite. Give the structure and name of the original compound.

[11] An olefin, C_6H_{12}, after ozonization and followed by hydrolysis, yielded two products. One of these gave a positive iodoform reaction but a negative Tollens' test. The other product gave a positive Tollens' test, but a negative iodoform reaction. What is the structure and name of the olefin?

chapter 10

The Carboxylic Acids
and Their Derivatives

INTRODUCTION

Substances which contain a **carboxyl group,** $-C\overset{\displaystyle O}{\underset{\displaystyle OH}{\diagup\!\!\diagdown}}$ (also written simply as $-COOH$, or as $-CO_2H$), make up a large family of compounds known as **carboxylic acids.** The carboxyl group represents the highest oxidation state of a carbon atom when bonded to another carbon and is a group found as a part of the structure of many natural products. It is not surprising to learn that acids occur naturally when one considers the fact that we live in an oxidizing atmosphere. Many carboxylic acids have been known for a long time. Acetic acid, CH_3COOH, for example (the sour principle of vinegar from which it takes its name), is a substance known since antiquity and frequently is referred to in the Bible. A number of acids play vital roles in body functions and are important intermediates in the metabolic processes. A large number of acids, or their derivatives, are useful everyday commodities.

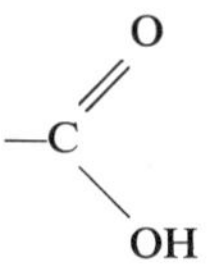

10.2   FORMULAS AND NOMENCLATURE

Carboxylic acids of the aliphatic series frequently are referred to as "fatty" acids because those containing an even number of carbon atoms (four or greater) exist in a combined form with glycerol as fats and oils. Acids which contain but one carboxyl group (monocarboxylic) have the general formula $R-COOH$ (R = alkyl) or $Ar-COOH$ (Ar = aryl).

$$H-C{\overset{\displaystyle O}{\underset{\textstyle OH}{\big\langle}}} \qquad CH_3-C{\overset{\displaystyle O}{\underset{\textstyle OH}{\big\langle}}} \qquad CH_3CH_2CH_2-C{\overset{\displaystyle O}{\underset{\textstyle OH}{\big\langle}}}$$

Formic acid   Acetic acid   *n*-Butyric acid

The carboxyl group in aromatic acids is attached directly to the benzene ring. However, the phenyl group, C_6H_5—, may appear as a substituent on any carbon atom of an aliphatic acid. Such acids should be classified as aryl-substituted aliphatic acids, because their reactions essentially are those given by acids of the aliphatic series.

COOH

—COOH   —CH₂—COOH

Br

Benzoic acid   *p*-Bromobenzoic acid   Phenylacetic acid

Many of the carboxylic acids have been known before rules for systematic nomenclature were devised. As a result, they usually are called by their common names. Many of these have their origin in Greek and Latin and their names often indicate the original source of the acid. There are no easy rules for remembering common names and they simply must be learned. IUPAC nomenclature follows general rules. The final **e** of the hydrocarbon stem is replaced by **oic,** followed by the word **acid.** The names, formulas, and derivations of some of the more common carboxylic acids are given in Table 10.1.

The carbon atom of the carboxyl group is always carbon 1 in systematic nomenclature, other numbers locating the position of substituents. Greek letters, α-, β-, γ-, δ-, etc., are used to locate substituents in common names. The α-carbon in an acid is always the carbon atom adjacent, or joined, to the carboxyl group.

$$\overset{\delta}{C}-\overset{\gamma}{C}-\overset{\beta}{C}-\overset{\alpha}{C}-C{\overset{\displaystyle O}{\underset{\textstyle OH}{\big\langle}}}$$
(5) (4) (3) (2) (1)

In a few cases, certain acids are more conveniently named as derivatives of acetic acid. The following examples will illustrate all three methods for naming substituted fatty acids.

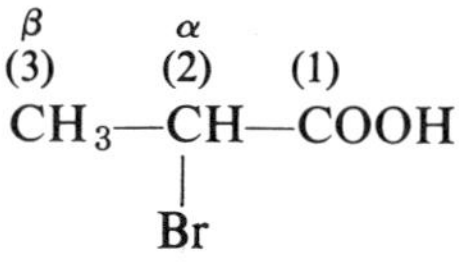

$$\underset{Br}{\overset{\overset{\beta}{(3)}\quad\overset{\alpha}{(2)}\quad(1)}{CH_3-CH-COOH}}$$

α-Bromopropionic acid
(2-Bromopropanoic acid)

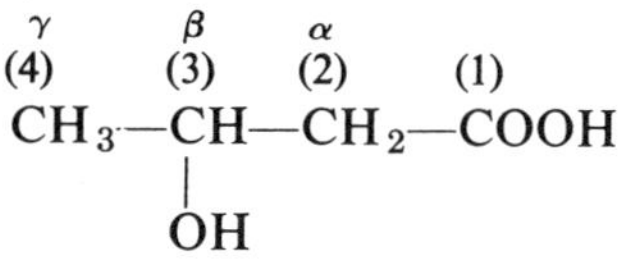

$$\underset{OH}{\overset{\overset{\gamma}{(4)}\quad\overset{\beta}{(3)}\quad\overset{\alpha}{(2)}\quad(1)}{CH_3-CH-CH_2-COOH}}$$

β-Hydroxybutyric acid
(3-Hydroxybutanoic acid)

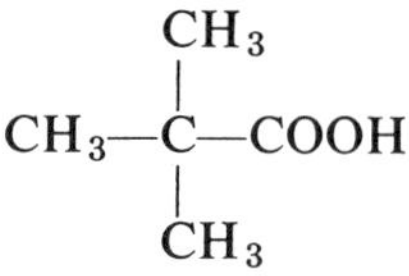

$$\underset{CH_3}{\overset{CH_3}{CH_3-C-COOH}}$$

Trimethylacetic acid
(2, 2-Dimethylpropanoic acid)

$$CH_2{=}CH-CH_2COOH$$

Vinylacetic acid
(3-Butenoic acid)

□■ TABLE 10.1

SOME COMMON CARBOXYLIC ACIDS

Name		Formula	Derivation
(Common)	(IUPAC)		
Formic	Methanoic	H—COOH	L. *formica*, ant
Acetic	Ethanoic	CH_3COOH	L. *acetum*, vinegar
Propionic	Propanoic	CH_3CH_2COOH	Gr. *protos* first; *pion* fat
n-Butyric	Butanoic	$CH_3CH_2CH_2COOH$	L. *butyrum*, butter
n-Valeric	Pentanoic	$CH_3(CH_2)_3COOH$	L. *valere*, powerful
Caproic	Hexanoic	$CH_3(CH_2)_4COOH$	L. *caper*, goat
Caprylic	Octanoic	$CH_3(CH_2)_6COOH$	L. *caper*, goat
Capric	Decanoic	$CH_3(CH_2)_8COOH$	L. *caper*, goat
Lauric	Dodecanoic	$CH_3(CH_2)_{10}COOH$	Laurel
Palmitic	Hexadecanoic	$CH_3(CH_2)_{14}COOH$	Palm oil
Stearic	Octadecanoic	$CH_3(CH_2)_{16}COOH$	Gr., *stear*, tallow
Benzoic	Benzenecar-boxylic acid	 ⬡—COOH	(gum benzoin)

Aromatic acids usually are designated by common names, or named as derivatives of the parent acid — benzoic, C_6H_5COOH.

Substituents, when joined to the benzene ring, are designated either by number, or by the prefixes ortho-(o-), meta-(m-), or para-(p-). The ring carbon atom that bears the carboxyl group is always number 1 when an aromatic acid is named as a substituted benzoic acid.

OH   COOH

—COOH   H₃C—   —CH₃

Salicylic acid   2, 6-Dimethylbenzoic acid
(o-Hydroxybenzoic acid)

—CH—COOH
        |
        OH

Mandelic acid
(α-Hydroxyphenylacetic acid)

10.3   ACIDITY AND STRUCTURE

The carboxylic acids are much weaker acids than the mineral acids (HCl, H_2SO_4, HNO_3), but they are more acidic than the phenols. The carboxylic acids do not show a strong tendency to dissociate into protons and their corresponding acid anions. Indeed, the equilibrium between the ionized and unionized forms of a carboxylic acid lies far to the left. The reaction of acetic acid with water may be used as an illustration.

$$CH_3-C \overset{O}{\underset{OH}{\diagdown}} \quad + H_2O \rightleftharpoons CH_3-C \overset{O}{\underset{O^-}{\diagdown}} \quad + H_3\overset{+}{O}$$

Acetic acid   Acetate ion   Hydronium
                                                            ion

Acetic acid in a 0.1 M aqueous solution has been found to dissociate only to the extent of 1.34% at room temperature. Statistically, this means that less than two molecules of acetic acid out of every hundred undergo ionization at any one time. The hydronium ion concentration may be related to that of other components in the acid solution by means of an equilibrium constant (in this case an ionization constant, K_i). A small numerical value for K_i

indicates a weak acid in which the bulk of the acid molecules remain in the undissociated form.

$$K_i = \frac{\text{concentration of hydronium ion} \times \text{concentration of acetate ion}}{\text{concentration of undissociated acetic acid}^1}$$

$$= \frac{[H_3O^+][CH_3COO^-]}{[CH_3COOH]}$$

$$= \frac{(0.1 \times 0.0134)^2}{0.1 \times (1 - 0.0134)} = 1.8 \times 10^{-5}$$

The value of the numerator in an equilibrium expression such as this increases only with an increase in the hydronium ion concentration. The value of the denominator, in this event, becomes correspondingly smaller. The ionization constant thus is a ready index to the strength of a weak acid.

Exercise 10.1 On the basis of their ionization constants (Table 10.2), which is the stronger acid — α-chloropropionic acid or β-chloropropionic acid?

Although the tendency of carboxylic acids to dissociate is but slight, two factors play a part in the process. The first factor, **resonance stabilization,** helps to explain why the carboxylic acids are acids at all. The gain in stability afforded through resonance of the acid anion serves as the driving force which helps to promote the ionization process.

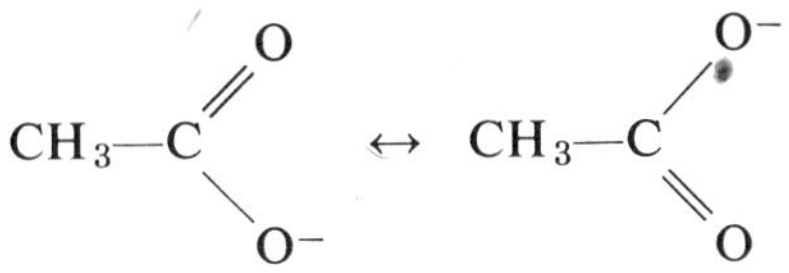

(a)   (b)

---

[1]The concentration of water has been omitted from the above expression for K_i because the number of water molecules involved in the formation of hydronium ions is negligible with respect to the total number of water molecules present. It may be assumed that the concentration of water remains nearly constant.

The resonance forms of the acetate ion actually appear to be that of a hybrid intermediate to (a) and (b) and is more correctly represented by the structure below.

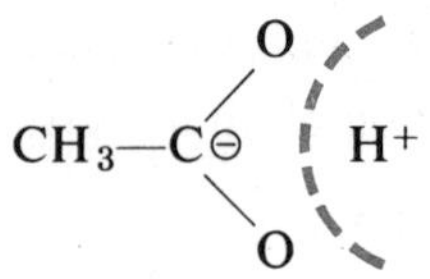

$$CH_3-C\ominus \quad | \quad H^+$$

The second factor is due to an **inductive effect.**[2] Electrophilic groups, when substituted into the hydrocarbon portion of an acid, have the effect of promoting ionization.   Such groups withdraw electrons from the carboxyl group, promote the departure of the positive proton, and help stabilize the anion. For example, chloroacetic acid, Cl↔CH$_2$COOH, is far more acidic than acetic acid due to the inductive effect of the chlorine atom.

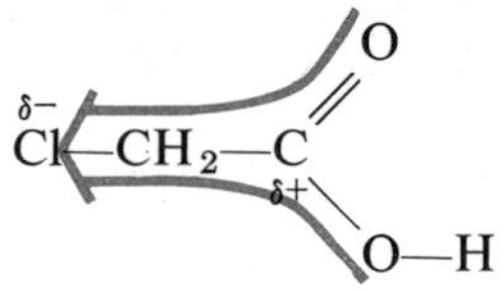

$$Cl\!-\!CH_2-C\!\!\overset{O}{\underset{O-H}{}}$$

A second chlorine atom increases the acidity still further, and three chlorine atoms on the α-carbon produces an acid strength almost equivalent to that of hydrochloric acid. The inductive effects diminish when electron-withdrawing groups are farther removed from the carboxyl group, and are strongest when such substituents are positioned on the α-carbon.   Inductive effects also vary with the electronegativities of elements bonded to the α-carbon atom. Reference to Table 10.2 will show that K_i for fluoroacetic acid is nearly three times that of iodoacetic acid. The inductive effects of electron-releasing groups, when bonded to the α-carbon, intensify the negative charge at the carboxyl, make proton departure more difficult, and serve to make the acid weaker.

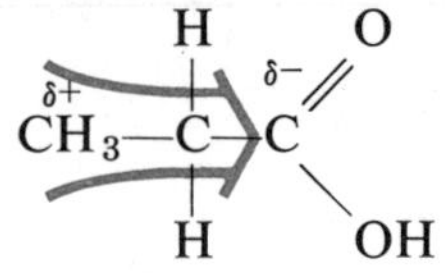

$$CH_3-C\overset{H}{\underset{H}{}}C\overset{O}{\underset{OH}{}}$$

---

[2]Inductive effect — An electrostatic effect in which electrons are attracted or repelled. The effect is referred to as a minus I ($-$I) effect if electrons are withdrawn to enhance acidity; a plus I ($+$I) effect if electrons are supplied to weaken acidity.

Ring-deactivating groups (Sec. 4.10), when substituted in the *ortho* or *para* positions of benzoic acid make the substituted acid stronger than benzoic. On the other hand, ring-activating groups, only when substituted in the *para* position, have an acid-weakening effect. Table 10.2 compares the strengths of a number of carboxylic acids and illustrates the effects of substituents and their positions upon acid strength.

□■ TABLE 10.2

RELATIVE STRENGTHS OF SOME ORGANIC ACIDS (25°C)

Name of Acid	Structure	K_i
Water*	H—OH	1.8×10^{-16}
Formic	H—COOH	2×10^{-4}
Acetic	CH_3COOH	1.8×10^{-5}
Monochloroacetic	$ClCH_2COOH$	1.55×10^{-3}
Dichloroacetic	$Cl_2CHCOOH$	5×10^{-2}
Trichloroacetic	Cl_3CCOOH	3×10^{-1}
Bromoacetic	$BrCH_2COOH$	1.4×10^{-3}
Iodoacetic	ICH_2COOH	7.5×10^{-4}
Fluoroacetic	FCH_2COOH	2.2×10^{-3}
Trimethylacetic	$(CH_3)_3CCOOH$	8.9×10^{-6}
Propionic	CH_3CH_2COOH	1.34×10^{-5}
α-Chloropropionic	$CH_3CHCOOH$ Cl	1.6×10^{-3}
β-Chloropropionic	$ClCH_2CH_2COOH$	8×10^{-5}
Benzoic	C_6H_5COOH	6.35×10^{-5}
Phenylacetic	⬡—CH_2COOH	5.6×10^{-5}
p-Chlorobenzoic	Cl—⬡—COOH	1×10^{-4}
p-Nitrobenzoic	O_2N—⬡—COOH	3.75×10^{-4}
p-Methoxybenzoic	CH_3O—⬡—COOH	3.38×10^{-5}

*While water does not belong in the above category, it is included for reference value. The value of K is given for the equation: $K = [H^+][OH^-]/[H_2O]$, where $[H_2O]$ is 55.5 moles per liter.

Exercise 10.2   Arrange the acids in the following set in an order of diminishing acidity: (a) acetic acid, (b) propionic acid, (c) trimethylacetic acid, (d) α-chloropropionic acid, (e) β-chloropropionic acid.

10.4   PROPERTIES

The lower molecular weight members of the aliphatic series of carboxylic acids are liquids with sharp or disagreeable odors. Those with four to ten carbon atoms are particularly obnoxious. The odor of rancid butter, limburger cheese, and stale sweat vividly exemplify this unpleasant property. The higher members are wax-like solids and almost odorless. The boiling points of fatty acids increase regularly by an approximate 20°C increment per methylene unit. The abnormally high boiling points of the fatty acids are ac-counted for by hydrogen bond formation between acid molecules. Hydrogen bonding also accounts for the fact that molecular weight measurements reveal the fatty acids to be largely "dimeric," or double, molecules.

$$ R-C \begin{matrix} O \cdots H-O \\ \\ O-H \cdots O \end{matrix} C-R $$

Carboxylic acids, with the exception of the first five members of the aliphatic series, are not very soluble in water. The aromatic acids usually are crystalline solids, also sparingly soluble in cold water.

10.5   PREPARATION OF ACIDS

A number of straight-chain aliphatic acids and some aromatic acids are available as natural products. Others can be prepared by one of the following methods.

A.   Oxidation Methods.   Direct oxidation of primary alcohols provides one of the most direct routes to the corresponding aliphatic acids. Potassium or sodium dichromate in combination with con-centrated sulfuric acid is frequently used to bring about this change.

$$3 \text{ R}-\text{CH}_2\text{OH} + 2 \text{ Cr}_2\text{O}_7{}^{2-} + 16 \text{ H}^+ \longrightarrow 3 \text{ R}-\overset{\displaystyle O}{\underset{\displaystyle OH}{C}} + 4 \text{ Cr}^{3+} + 11 \text{ H}_2\text{O}$$

The benzene carboxylic acids are obtained by the oxidation of alkyl derivatives of benzene. The benzene ring itself appears to be rather resistant to oxidation but facilitates the oxidation of the carbon atom attached to it. Should more than one alkyl group be attached to the ring, all become oxidized to carboxyl groups. Thus, toluene and other monoalkylated benzenes yield benzoic acid and the three isomeric xylenes, $C_6H_4(CH_3)_2$, yield the corresponding phthalic acids.

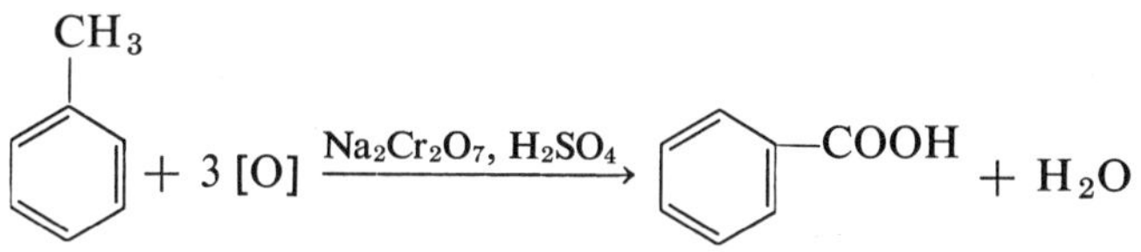

Toluene   Benzoic acid

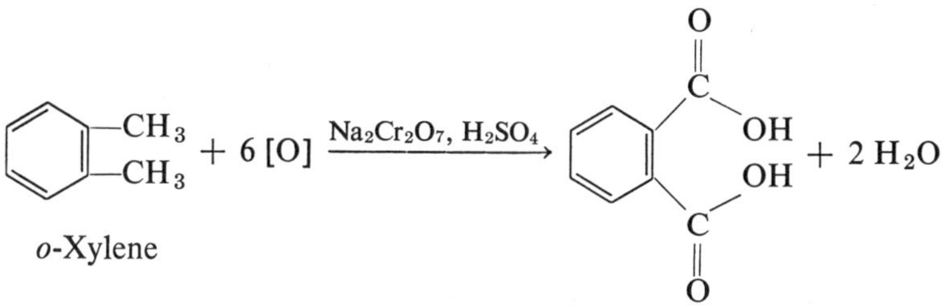

o-Xylene

1, 2-Benzenecarboxylic acid
(o-Phthalic acid)

Although the length of the side chain on the benzene nucleus may vary, it is degraded to the last or ring-attached carbon atom. All other carbon atoms in the side chain are oxidized to carbon dioxide.

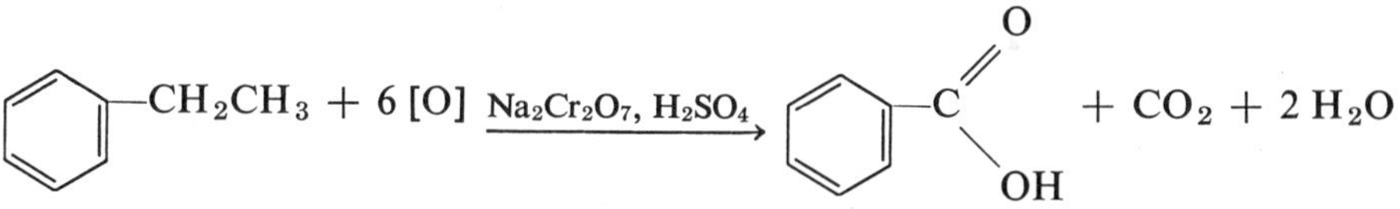

Ethylbenzene   Benzoic acid

Exercise 10.3   Complete and balance the equation for the oxidation of ethylbenzene. (*Hint: See Section 8.9-C.*)

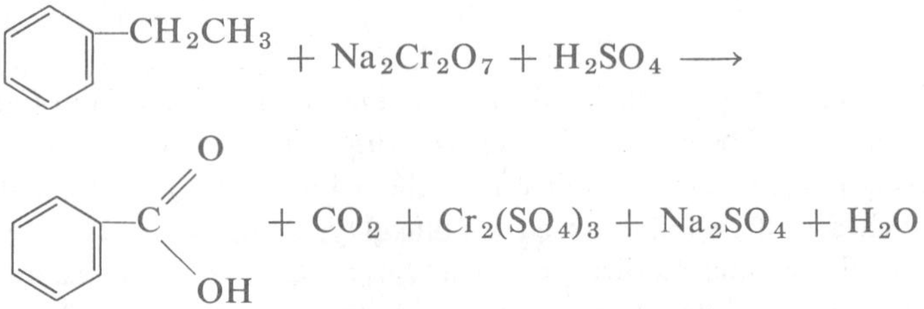

$$\text{(benzene ring)}-CH_2CH_3 + Na_2Cr_2O_7 + H_2SO_4 \longrightarrow$$

$$\text{(benzene ring)}-C\!\!\stackrel{O}{\diagdown}\!\!OH + CO_2 + Cr_2(SO_4)_3 + Na_2SO_4 + H_2O$$

Naphthalene, obtainable from coal tar, is another source of *o*-phthalic acid. Phthalic anhydride, formed when *o*-phthalic acid is heated in excess of 200°C, is an important industrial material used in the manufacture of glyptal resins for surface coatings (Sec. 12.5).

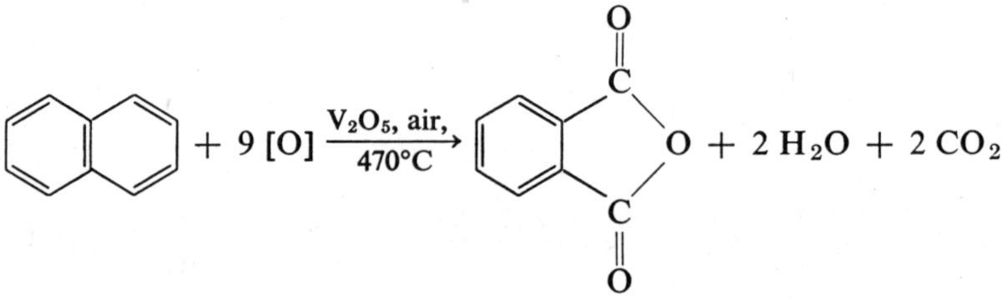

$$\text{Naphthalene} + 9 \, [O] \xrightarrow[470°C]{V_2O_5, \text{ air,}} \text{Phthalic anhydride} + 2 \, H_2O + 2 \, CO_2$$

Naphthalene   Phthalic anhydride

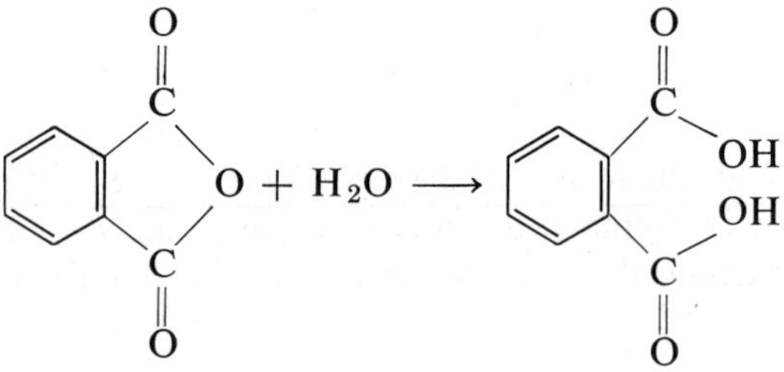

$$\text{(phthalic anhydride)} \; O + H_2O \longrightarrow \text{(phthalic acid)}$$

o-Phthalic acid

B.   Hydrolysis Methods.   The nitriles (prepared from alkyl halides and potassium cyanide) may be hydrolyzed to carboxylic acids by refluxing with aqueous acid or alkali.

$$C_2H_5Br + KCN \longrightarrow C_2H_5{-}CN$$

Ethyl cyanide
(Propionitrile)

Acid hydrolysis

$$C_2H_5{-}CN + 2\,H_2O + HCl \longrightarrow C_2H_5{-}C\begin{array}{l} {/\!\!/}O \\ \diagdown OH \end{array} + NH_4{}^{+}Cl^{-}$$

Propionic acid

Alkaline hydrolysis

$$C_2H_5{-}CN + 2\,H_2O + NaOH \longrightarrow C_2H_5{-}C\begin{array}{l} {/\!\!/}O \\ \diagdown O^{-}Na^{+} \end{array} + NH_3 + H_2O$$

Sodium propionate

The nitriles are named according to the acids they yield when hydrolyzed. Thus, methyl cyanide, CH_3CN, is named *acetonitrile;* phenyl cyanide, C_6H_5CN, *benzonitrile*, etc. The formation of nitriles from alkyl halides, when followed by hydrolysis, provides a method for increasing the length of the carbon chain. The same result can be achieved by the addition of hydrogen cyanide to an appropriate organic compound. For example, aldehydes add hydrogen cyanide to yield cyanohydrins and thus provide a route to the α-hydroxy acids.

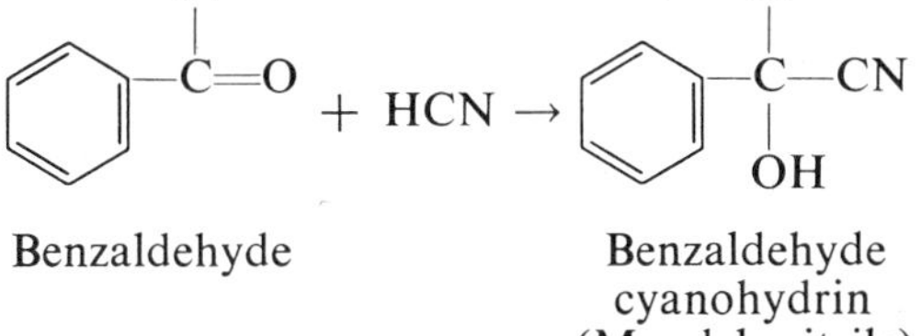

Benzaldehyde

Benzaldehyde
cyanohydrin
(Mandelonitrile)

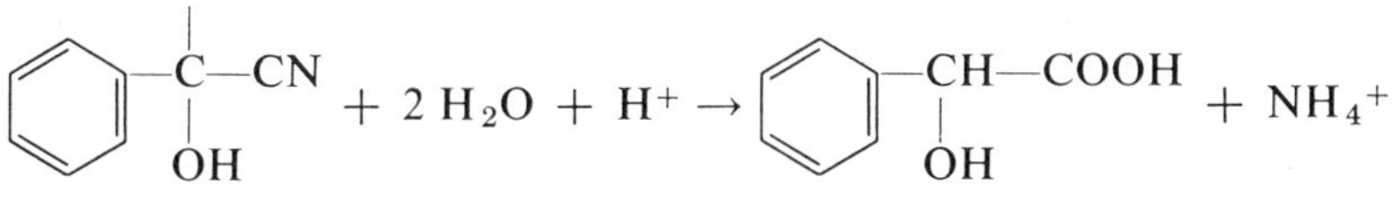

Mandelic acid

Benzotrichloride, produced by the chlorination of toluene in sunlight, can be converted by hydrolysis to benzoic acid as shown in the following reaction.

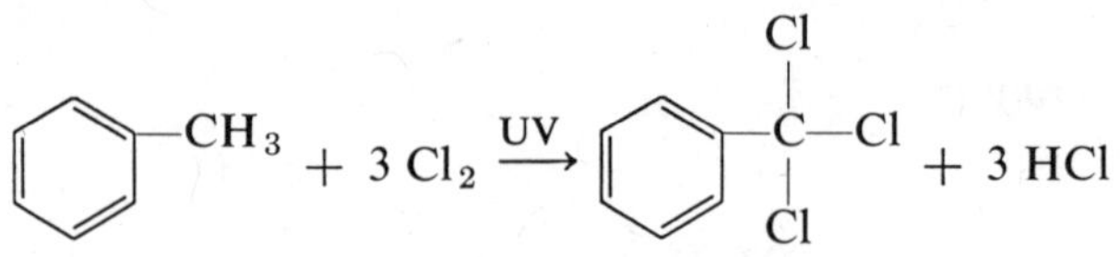

Toluene   Benzotrichloride

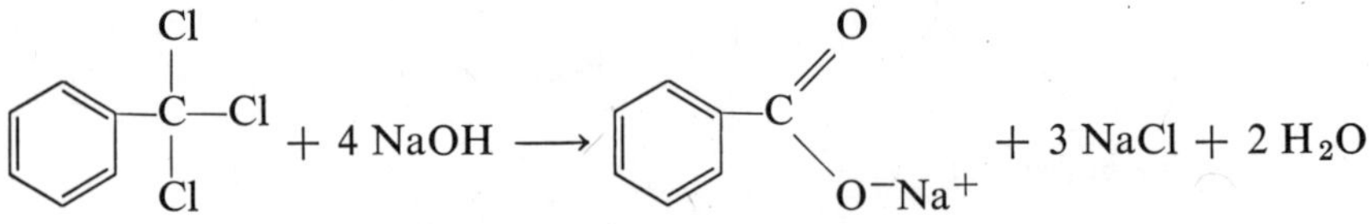

Sodium benzoate

The free organic acid can be precipitated from the salt solution by acidification with hydrochloric acid.

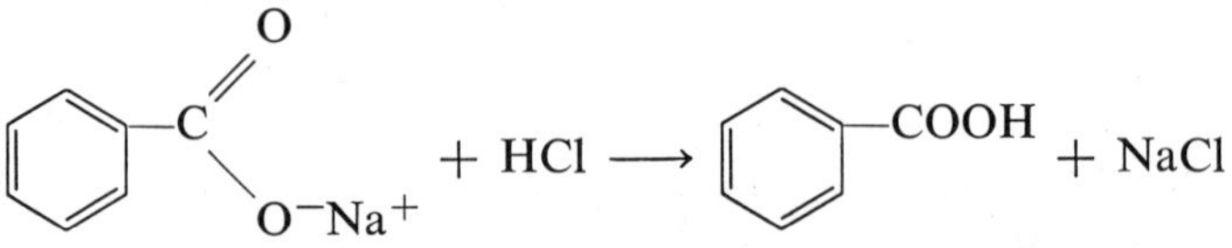

Benzoic acid

C. The Carbonation of Grignard Reagents. Grignard reagents are especially useful for the preparation of acids, either aliphatic or aromatic. One of the best general methods for the preparation of carboxylic acids is to treat the appropriate Grignard reagent with anhydrous carbon dioxide.

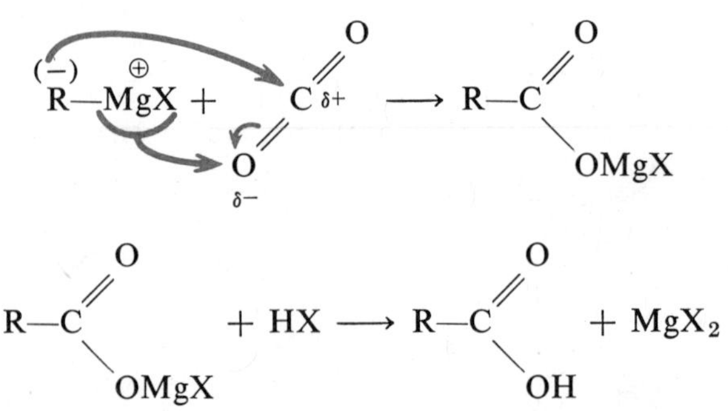

You will note that the carbonation of a Grignard reagent, like the hydrolysis of a nitrile, is a reaction that also increases by one the length of the carbon chain.

10.6   REACTIONS OF THE CARBOXYLIC ACIDS AND THEIR DERIVATIVES

All types of reactions engaged in by carboxylic acids give products which correctly can be said to have been derived from acids. The term "acid derivatives," however, usually is reserved to describe those in which some other structure has replaced the hydroxyl group and from which the original acid can be regained by hydrolysis. In the following sections are outlined a number of the more general reactions of the acids. Following these are the specific reactions of the derivative. It soon will become apparent that in a number of instances a reaction involving one acid derivative is a route leading to the preparation of another.

A.   Preparation of Salts.   The carboxylic acids, although feebly acidic when compared to mineral acids, are relatively strong when compared to water (Table 10.2). They may be neutralized quantitatively by carbonates, bicarbonates, and hydroxide bases to produce salts and water.

$$2\ R-\!\!\!\overset{\displaystyle O}{\underset{\displaystyle OH}{C}} + Na_2CO_3 \longrightarrow 2\ R-\!\!\!\overset{\displaystyle O}{\underset{\displaystyle O^-Na^+}{C}} + CO_2 + H_2O$$

$$R-\!\!\!\overset{\displaystyle O}{\underset{\displaystyle OH}{C}} + NaHCO_3 \longrightarrow R-\!\!\!\overset{\displaystyle O}{\underset{\displaystyle O^-Na^+}{C}} + CO_2 + H_2O$$

$$R-\!\!\!\overset{\displaystyle O}{\underset{\displaystyle O\bar{H}}{C}} + NaOH \longrightarrow R-\!\!\!\overset{\displaystyle O}{\underset{\displaystyle O^-Na^+}{C}} + H_2O$$

Salts of organic acids are named as one would name salts of inorganic acids — that is, the cation is named first followed by the name of the acid anion. The latter is derived by dropping the *ic* of the acid and adding *ate*. For example,

$$CH_3-\!\!\!\overset{\displaystyle O}{\underset{\displaystyle O^-Na^+}{C}} \qquad\qquad CH_3-(CH_2)_{16}-\!\!\!\overset{\displaystyle O}{\underset{\displaystyle O^-Li^+}{C}}$$

Sodium acetate   Lithium stearate

The equivalent weight of an acid can be determined by titrating it with a standardized base. The **neutralization equivalent** of an acid, abbreviated as **N.E.**, gives a measure of its molecular weight and often is useful in helping to establish the acid's identity. The neutralization equivalent may be defined as the weight of acid in grams that is required to neutralize one gram equivalent of standardized base. If an unknown acid is monoprotic — that is, has but one proton to lose — its neutralization equivalent and its molecular weight is one and the same. A dicarboxylic acid, of course, has a neutralization equivalent one-half its molecular weight, a tricarboxylic acid, one-third, etc. You will want to ascertain for yourself the correctness of the N.E. values for the examples below.

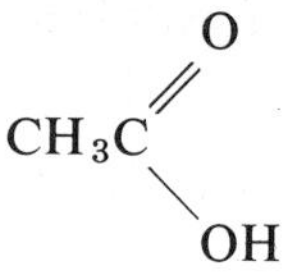

Acetic acid
N.E. = 60

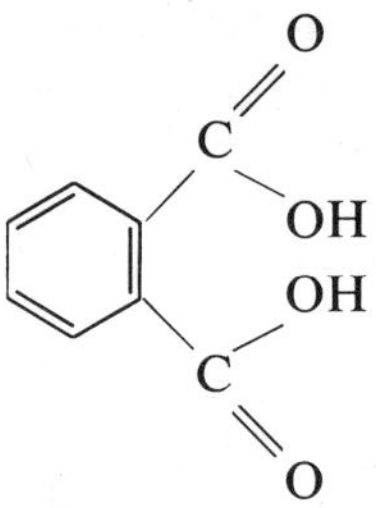

Phthalic acid
N.E. = 83

Exercise 10.4   The proper identity of an acid was in doubt. It could be either *d, l*-mandelic acid or *d, l*-tropic acid.

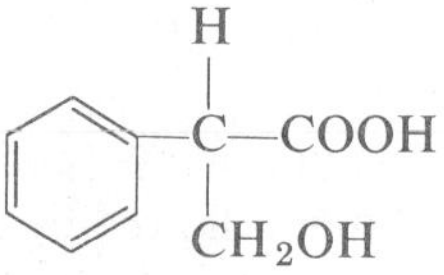

d, l-Tropic acid
(M.P. 117°)

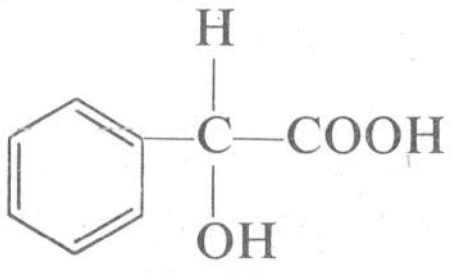

d, l-Mandelic acid
(M.P. 118°)

A 0.228-g sample of the acid required 15 ml of 0.1 N sodium hydroxide when titrated to the phenolphthalein end point. Which acid was it?

B.   Reactions of Salts.   The partial or complete pyrolytic de-carboxylation of metal salts of acids has already been reviewed as a method for the preparation of ketones (Sec. 9.5-D).   The ammonium salts of carboxylic acids, when heated strongly, lose the elements of water to form acid amides.

$$CH_3-C \begin{matrix} O \\ \diagup \\ \diagdown \\ O\overset{-}{N}H_4^{+} \end{matrix} \quad \overset{Heat}{\longrightarrow} \quad CH_3-C \begin{matrix} O \\ \diagup \\ \diagdown \\ NH_2 \end{matrix} \quad + H_2O$$

Ammonium acetate   Acetamide

Alkali metal salts of the long chain fatty acids are called **soaps** (Chapter 11).   Lithium stearate, Sec. 10.6-A, and other heavy metal salts, when blended with oils, form lubricating greases.   Calcium propionate, $(CH_3-CH_2-\overset{O}{\overset{||}{C}}-O-)_2Ca$, is a commonly used additive in bread to retard spoilage (molding).   Certain of the zinc salts of the higher fatty acids also are excellent fungicides and are used in the treatment of skin diseases such as athletes foot.   One of these, zinc undecylenate (from 10-undecenoic acid), is particularly effective. Its structure is shown.

$$\left(CH_2=\overset{H}{\overset{|}{C}}-(CH_2)_8-\overset{O}{\overset{||}{C}}-O \right)_2 Zn$$

Zinc undecylenate

The cupric salts of naphthenic acids (cyclic, nonaromatic acids derived from petroleum) are used as wood preservatives.

C.   Preparation of Acid Halides.   The acid halides also are referred to as the **acyl halides.** The name of an acyl group, $R-C\begin{smallmatrix} O \\ \diagup \\ \diagdown \end{smallmatrix}$, is derived from an aliphatic acid by dropping the *ic* ending of the acid and adding *yl*.   The aromatic acid halides (aroyl halides) are formed and named in the same manner.   The following examples will illustrate the usage of the term as a group name.

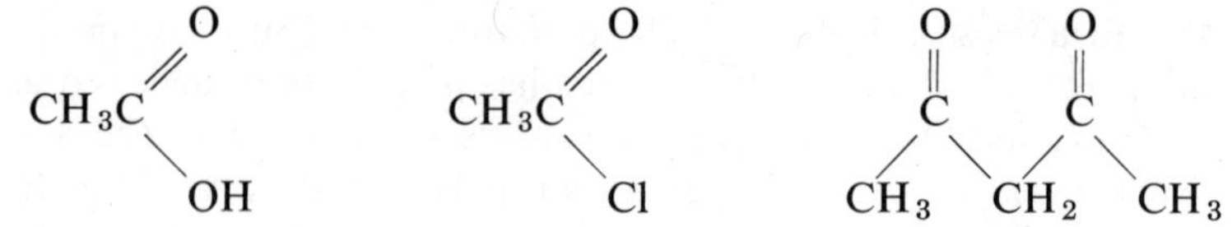

Acetic acid   Acetyl chloride   Acetylacetone
(Ethanoic acid)   (Ethanoyl chloride)   (2, 4-Pentanedione)

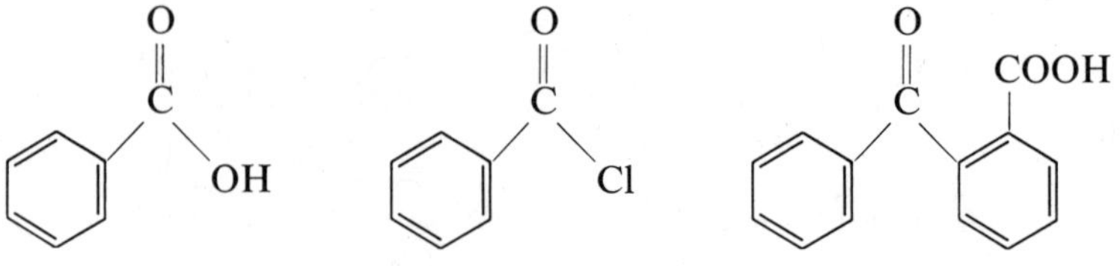

Benzoic acid   Benzoyl chloride   o-Benzoylbenzoic acid
                                                              (Benzophenone-
                                                              o-carboxylic acid)

Acid halides other than the chlorides can be made, but the chlorides are more easily and economically prepared. The acyl chlorides are very reactive compounds and usually are employed where acyl halides are required. They are easily prepared by the reaction of the appropriate acid with either phosphorus trichloride or phosphorus pentachloride.

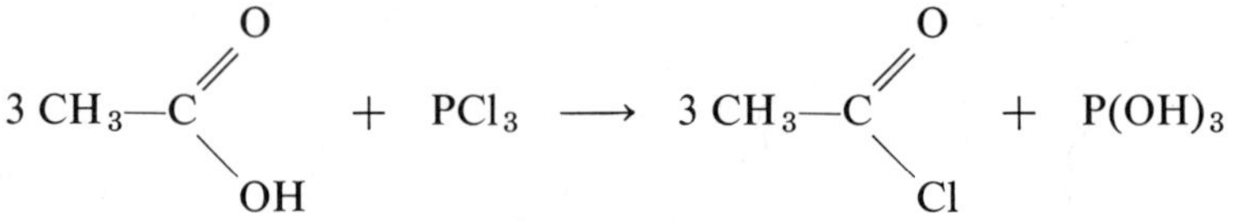

Acetic acid   Phosphorus   Acetyl chloride
                          trichloride

Thionyl chloride, often used in the preparation of acid chlorides, is a superior reagent to the phosphorus halides for two reasons: (1) the by-products of the reaction are gases and are easily removed, (2) the reagent is a low boiling liquid. The second advantage permits any excess reagent to be easily removed by distillation.

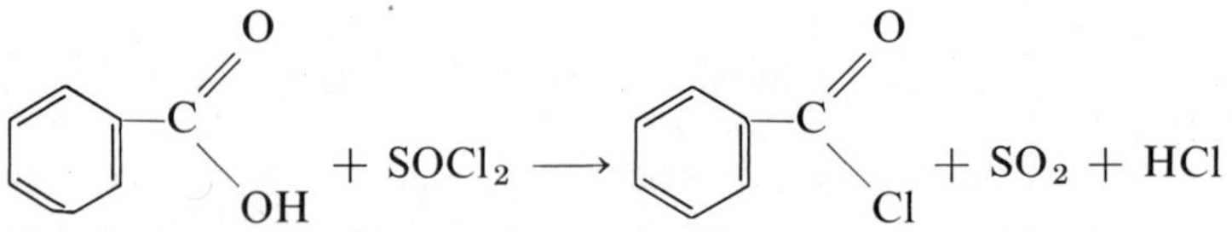

Benzoic acid   Thionyl   Benzoyl
                          chloride   chloride

D.   Reactions of the Acid Halides.   The acid halides are low boiling liquids of irritating odor. They are extremely reactive compounds because the inductive effect of the halogen atom further diminishes the electron density on the carbonyl carbon atom. Attack on the carbonyl carbon by nucleophilic groups (electron-pair donors or bases) is enhanced.

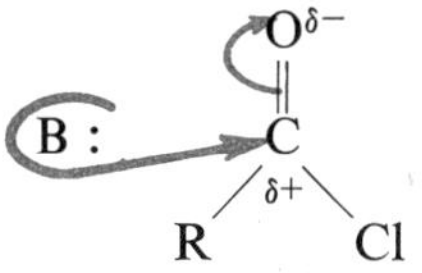

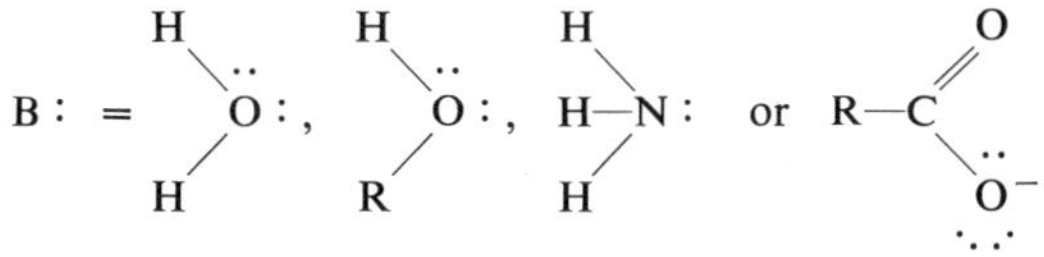

The reaction of an acyl halide with water is called **hydrolysis** and results in the displacement of halogen by hydroxyl to reform the original organic acid.

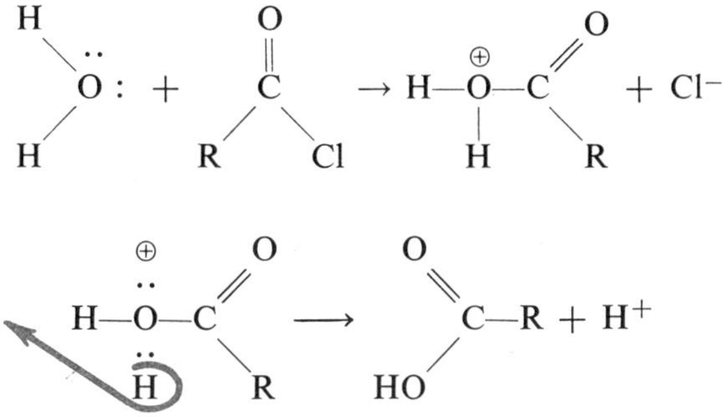

The net equation may be shown as

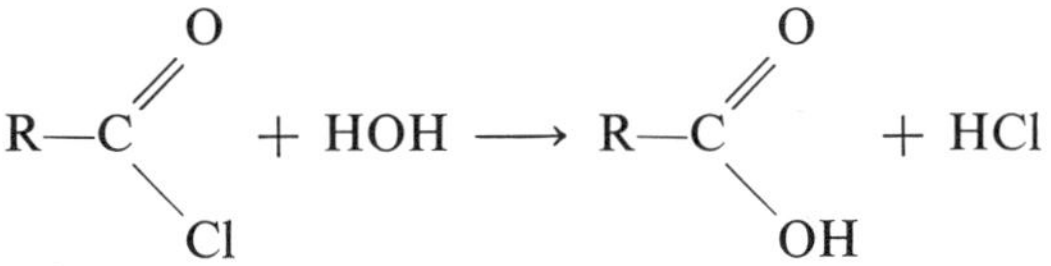

The reaction of an acyl halide with an alcohol is called **alcoholysis** and results in the displacement of halogen by an alkoxy group, —OR, to produce an **ester** (Sec. 10.6-G).

$$R-\overset{\displaystyle O}{\underset{\displaystyle Cl}{C}} + HOR' \longrightarrow R-\overset{\displaystyle O}{\underset{\displaystyle OR'}{C}} + HCl$$

An ester

The reaction of an acyl halide with ammonia is called **ammonolysis,** and results in the displacement of halogen by an amino group, $-NH_2$, to produce an **amide** (Sec. 10.6-I).

$$R-\overset{\displaystyle O}{\underset{\displaystyle Cl}{C}} + 2\,NH_3 \longrightarrow R-\overset{\displaystyle O}{\underset{\displaystyle NH_2}{C}} + NH_4Cl$$

An amide

Acyl halides react with salts of acids to yield acid **anhydrides.**

$$CH_3-\overset{\displaystyle O}{\underset{\displaystyle O^-Na^+}{C}} + CH_3-\overset{\displaystyle O}{\underset{\displaystyle Cl}{C}} \longrightarrow \underset{\displaystyle O}{\overset{\displaystyle CH_3}{C}} \underset{\displaystyle O}{\overset{\displaystyle O}{}} \underset{\displaystyle O}{\overset{\displaystyle CH_3}{C}} + Na^+\,Cl^-$$

Sodium acetate   Acetyl chloride   Acetic anhydride

Acyl halides undergo halogenation in the α-position more readily than do acids and thus provide an easy route to α-halogenated acids. In practice, α-bromoacids usually are prepared. The appropriate acid is treated with red phosphorus and bromine to produce the acyl bromide as the initial product.

$$6\,CH_3C\overset{\displaystyle O}{\underset{\displaystyle OH}{}} + 2\,P + 3\,Br_2 \longrightarrow 6\,H-\overset{\displaystyle H}{\underset{\displaystyle H}{C}}-C\overset{\displaystyle O}{\underset{\displaystyle Br}{}} + 2\,P(OH)_3$$

Acetyl bromide

$$CH_3-\overset{\displaystyle O}{\underset{\displaystyle Br}{C}} + Br_2 \longrightarrow BrCH_2-\overset{\displaystyle O}{\underset{\displaystyle Br}{C}} + HBr$$

α-Bromoacetyl
bromide

Subsequent reaction of the α-bromoacetyl bromide with unreacted acid results in a transfer of the more reactive acetyl bromine, not the α-bromine. The reaction thus continues until all the original acid is converted into the α-bromo derivative. This method for preparing the α-halogen acids is called the **Hell-Volhard-Zelinsky reaction.**

$$Br-\underset{\underset{H}{|}}{\overset{\overset{H}{|}}{C}}-C\overset{O}{\underset{Br}{\diagup}} \; + \; CH_3-C\overset{O}{\underset{OH}{\diagup}} \; \rightleftarrows \; Br-\underset{\underset{H}{|}}{\overset{\overset{H}{|}}{C}}-C\overset{O}{\underset{OH}{\diagup}} \; + \; CH_3-C\overset{O}{\underset{Br}{\diagup}}$$

α-Bromoacetic acid

Exercise 10.5   What simple test tube reaction would serve to distinguish between bromoacetic acid and acetyl bromide?

E.   Preparation of Acid Anhydrides.   The preparation of an acid anhydride is a reaction that has the net effect of removing a molecule of water from between two molecules of the acid.

$$CH_3-C\overset{O}{\underset{OH \quad HO}{\diagup}} \quad C-CH_3 \longrightarrow \begin{array}{c} CH_3-C\overset{O}{\diagdown} \\ O + H_2O \\ CH_3-C\diagdown_O \end{array}$$

Acetic anhydride

Direct dehydration, however, is seldom practiced. Dehydration usually is accomplished indirectly by reaction between the sodium salt of the acid with its acid chloride (Sec. 10.6-D). Two acyl groups are thus bridged by an oxygen atom by a method much like that employed in the Williamson ether synthesis (Sec. 8.9A-2). Acetic anhydride is by far the most important acid anhydride. Industrially it is prepared from the very reactive unsaturated ketone, ketene. Acetic acid adds to ketene to produce acetic anhydride.

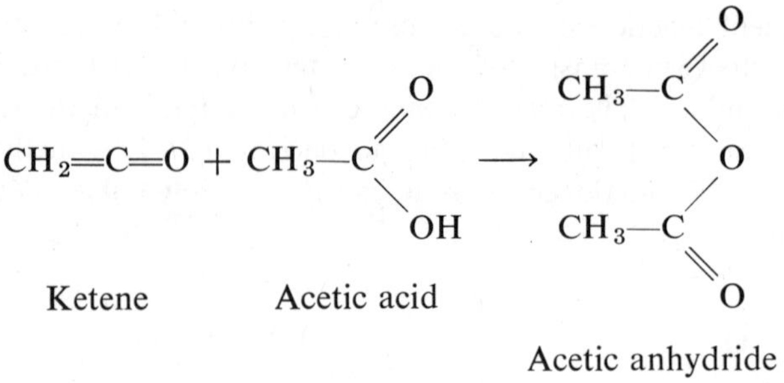

$$CH_2{=}C{=}O + CH_3{-}\overset{\displaystyle O}{\underset{\displaystyle OH}{C}} \longrightarrow \quad CH_3{-}\overset{\displaystyle O}{C}\diagdown O \diagup \overset{}{C}{-}CH_3$$

Ketene   Acetic acid

Acetic anhydride

F.   Reactions of the Acid Anhydrides.   The reactions of the acid anhydrides with water, alcohol, and ammonia parallel those already shown for the acyl halides.   As shown by the following reactions, at least one molecule of the organic acid is a product of each reaction.

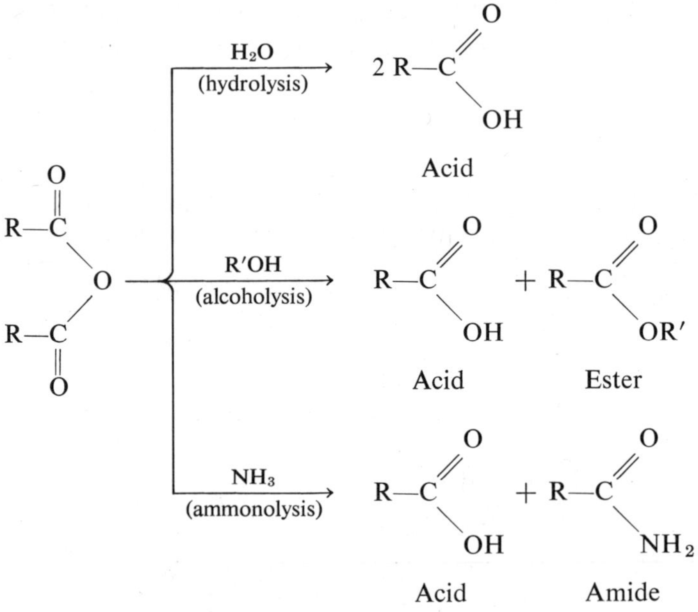

$$\underset{\displaystyle\substack{\\ R-C}}{\overset{\displaystyle O}{\parallel}}\diagdown O \diagup \underset{\displaystyle\underset{\displaystyle O}{\parallel}}{R-C}$$

$\xrightarrow[\text{(hydrolysis)}]{H_2O}$ $2\ R{-}\overset{\displaystyle O}{C}{-}OH$

Acid

$\xrightarrow[\text{(alcoholysis)}]{R'OH}$ $R{-}\overset{\displaystyle O}{C}{-}OH$ $+\ R{-}\overset{\displaystyle O}{C}{-}OR'$

Acid   Ester

$\xrightarrow[\text{(ammonolysis)}]{NH_3}$ $R{-}\overset{\displaystyle O}{C}{-}OH$ $+\ R{-}\overset{\displaystyle O}{C}{-}NH_2$

Acid   Amide

Acid anhydrides may be used in place of acyl halides as acylating reagents in the Friedel-Crafts reaction (Sec. 9.5-E).

G.   Preparation of Esters.   An acid, when heated with an alcohol in the presence of a mineral acid, produces an ester. A direct esterification of alcohols and acids in this manner is known as the **Fischer esterification.**

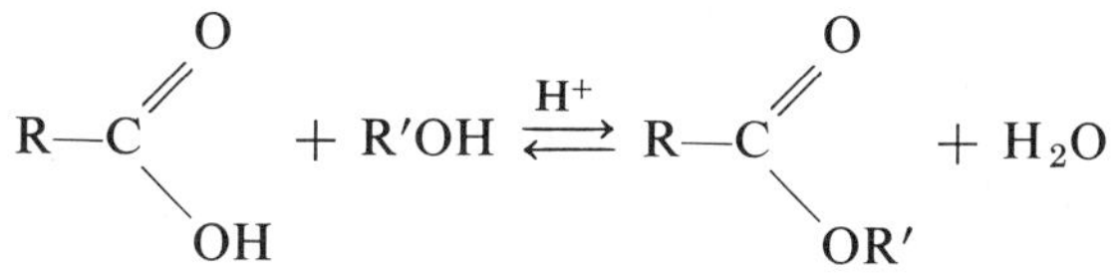

$$R-C{\overset{O}{\underset{OH}{}}} + R'OH \xrightleftharpoons{H^+} R-C{\overset{O}{\underset{OR'}{}}} + H_2O$$

The esterification reaction, when carried out directly as shown above, is reversible, and reaches equilibrium when appreciable amounts of reactants still remain. In the case of ethyl acetate, equilibrium is reached when approximately two-thirds of the alcohol and acid have reacted, starting with equimolar quantities of these reagents.

$$K_e = \frac{\text{ethyl acetate} \times \text{water}}{\text{acetic acid} \times \text{ethyl alcohol}} = \frac{(2/3)^2}{(1/3)^2} = 4$$

The principle of LeChatelier may be applied to shift the equilibrium to the right (promote esterification) either by increasing the concentration of the alcohol or the acid, or by removing the ester or the water as it is formed. The reverse reaction (hydrolysis), on the other hand, can be made complete only when carried out in an alkaline solution (Sec. 10.6-H).

Esters are named in a manner similar to that used in naming the salts of the carboxylic acids, in that the group attached to the carboxyl is named first.

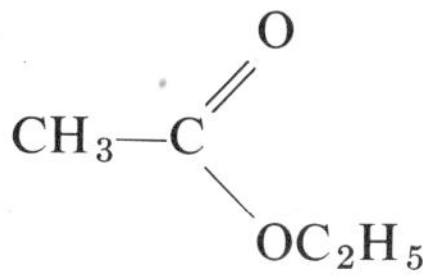

$$CH_3-C{\overset{O}{\underset{OC_2H_5}{}}}$$

Ethyl acetate

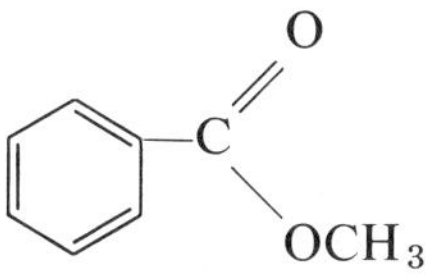

Methyl benzoate

A casual inspection of the esterification reaction might suggest a neutralization between an acid and a base. Actually, the oxygen atom in the water that results as one product of the esterification reaction has its origin in the acid. When alcohols containing the O^{18} isotope are used in the esterification reaction, the labeled oxygen is found exclusively in the ester and not found in the water. The following reaction mechanism has been proposed for the esterification reaction.

$$CH_3-C{\overset{O}{\underset{OH}{}}} + H^+ \rightleftharpoons CH_3-C{\overset{OH}{\underset{OH}{}}}{}^{\oplus} \rightleftharpoons CH_3-C{\overset{O}{\underset{O^{\oplus}}{}}}$$

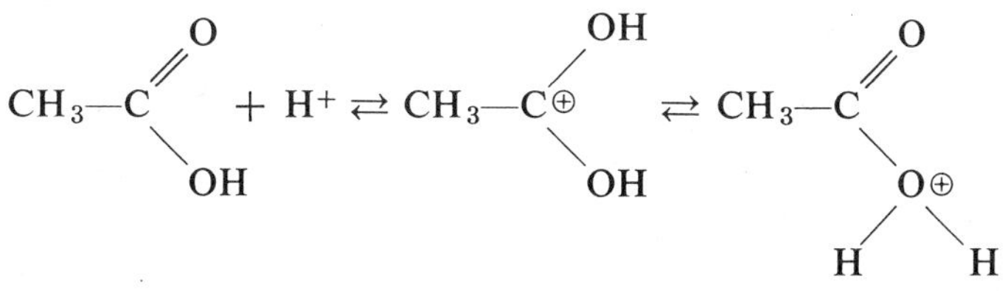

$$CH_3-\overset{OH}{\underset{OH}{\overset{|}{C}}}{}^{\oplus} \;+\; \overset{18}{O}-C_2H_5 \;\rightleftarrows\; CH_3-\overset{OH}{\underset{OH}{\overset{|}{C}}}-\overset{18\oplus}{O}-C_2H_5$$
$$\text{(with H on O)}\qquad\qquad\qquad\text{(with H on O)}$$

$$CH_3-\overset{OH}{\underset{OH}{\overset{|}{C}}}-\overset{18\oplus}{O}-C_2H_5 \;\rightleftarrows\; CH_3-\overset{OH}{\underset{\overset{18}{O}\overset{\oplus}{}}{\overset{|}{C}}}-\overset{18}{O}-C_2H_5$$
$$\text{(with H on O)}\qquad\qquad\qquad \overset{\oplus}{O}\!\!\diagdown\!\!\underset{H\quad H}{}$$

$$CH_3-\overset{OH}{\underset{\overset{\oplus}{O}\diagup\diagdown}{\overset{|}{C}}}-\overset{18}{O}-C_2H_5 \;\rightleftarrows\; H_2O \;+\; CH_3-\overset{OH}{\underset{\oplus}{\overset{|}{C}}}-\overset{18}{O}-C_2H_5$$
$$\qquad H\quad H$$

$$CH_3-\overset{OH}{\underset{\oplus}{\overset{|}{C}}}-\overset{18}{O}-C_2H_5 \;\rightleftarrows\; H^+ \;+\; CH_3-C\!\!\diagup\!\!\overset{O}{\diagdown}\!\!\underset{\overset{18}{OC_2H_5}}{}$$

Esters also may be prepared by heating the salt of an acid with an alkyl halide. This reaction is not reversible.

$$R-C\!\!\diagup\!\!\overset{O}{\diagdown}\!\!\underset{O^-Ag^+}{} \;+\; R'I \;\longrightarrow\; AgI\!\!\downarrow \;+\; R-C\!\!\diagup\!\!\overset{O}{\diagdown}\!\!\underset{OR'}{}$$

The esters are liquids of rather pleasant odor. A number are responsible (at least in part) for the odors of certain fruits and other plant parts, and are used in artificial flavorings and in perfumes. The esters are excellent solvents for lacquers and plastics.

H. Reactions of the Esters. The acid hydrolysis of esters has been shown to be a reaction in equilibrium with the esterification reaction. In order to hydrolyze an ester irreversibly — that is, to have it quantitatively reform the acid (as a salt) and the alcohol, hydrolysis must be carried out in an alkaline solution. Alkaline hydrolysis of an ester is called **saponification** because soaps are prepared by the alkaline hydrolysis of fats and oils, esters of glycerol (Sec. 11.4). The acid component of an ester, when the latter is saponified, always forms a salt of the organic acid. Subsequent treatment of the salt with mineral acid regenerates the organic acid.

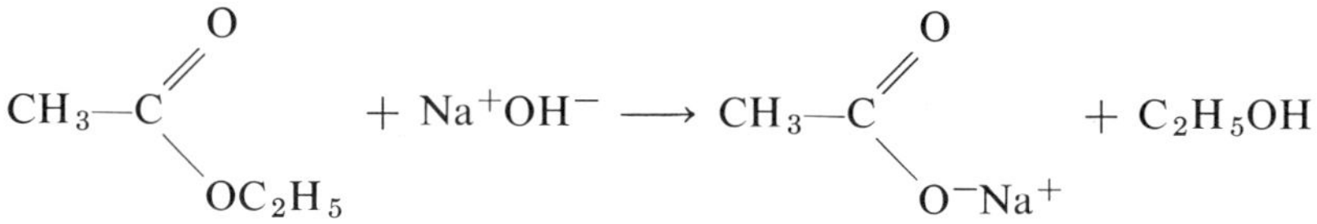

$$CH_3-C\overset{O}{\underset{OC_2H_5}{\diagup}} \quad + Na^+OH^- \longrightarrow CH_3-C\overset{O}{\underset{O^-Na^+}{\diagup}} \quad + C_2H_5OH$$

Ethyl acetate   Sodium acetate

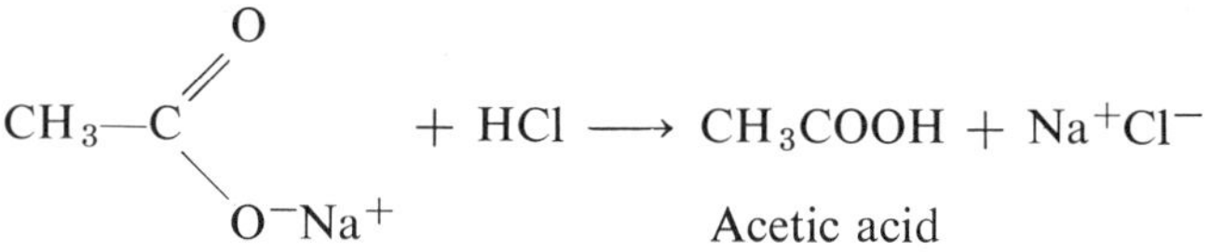

$$CH_3-C\overset{O}{\underset{O^-Na^+}{\diagup}} \quad + HCl \longrightarrow CH_3COOH + Na^+Cl^-$$

Acetic acid

Ammonolysis of an ester forms an alcohol and an **amide.**

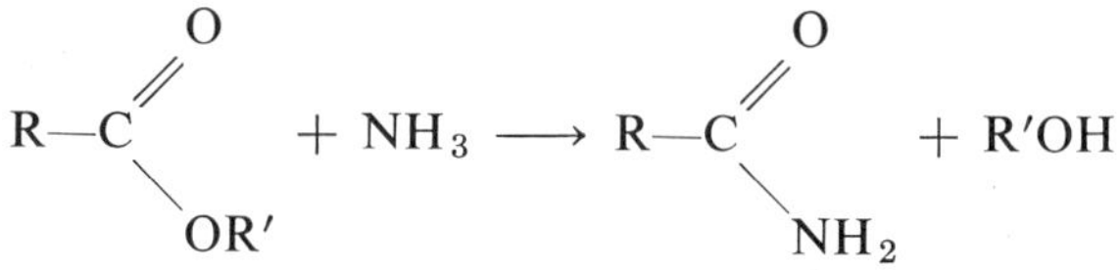

$$R-C\overset{O}{\underset{OR'}{\diagup}} \quad + NH_3 \longrightarrow R-C\overset{O}{\underset{NH_2}{\diagup}} \quad + R'OH$$

An amide

Esters may be reduced to alcohols. The reduction can be accomplished chemically by using either sodium metal and an alcohol or by the use of lithium aluminum hydride, $LiAlH_4$.

$$2\,Na + 2\,ROH \longrightarrow 2\,RO^-Na^+ + H_2$$

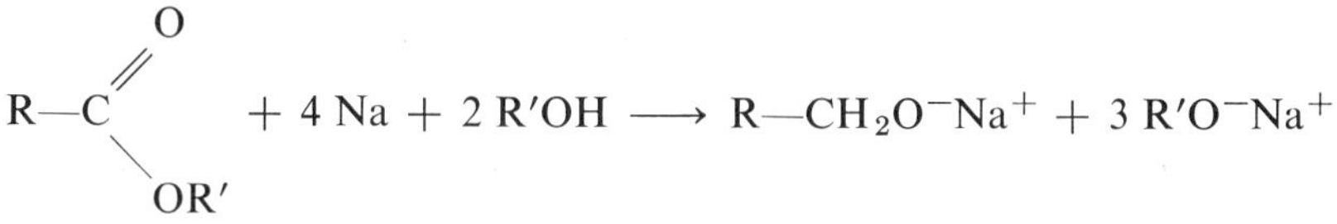

$$R-C\overset{O}{\underset{OR'}{\diagup}} \quad + 4\,Na + 2\,R'OH \longrightarrow R-CH_2O^-Na^+ + 3\,R'O^-Na^+$$

$$R-CH_2O^-Na^+ + H_2O \longrightarrow R-CH_2-OH + Na^+OH^-$$

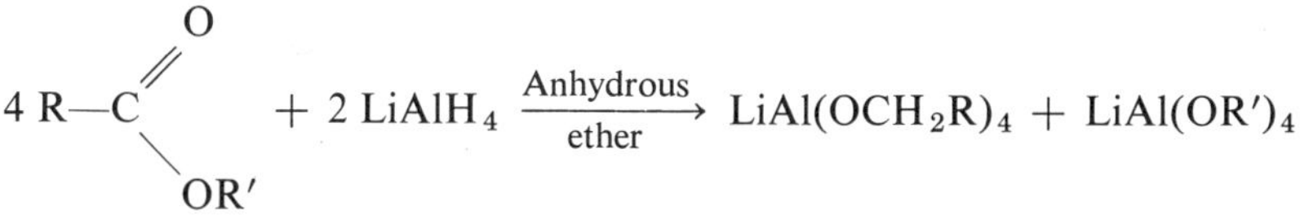

$$4\,R-C\overset{O}{\underset{OR'}{\diagup}} \quad + 2\,LiAlH_4 \xrightarrow[\text{ether}]{\text{Anhydrous}} LiAl(OCH_2R)_4 + LiAl(OR')_4$$

$$LiAl(OCH_2R)_4 + 4\,HCl \longrightarrow LiCl + AlCl_3 + 4\,RCH_2OH$$

Esters, when allowed to react with a Grignard reagent, form tertiary alcohols. Two of the three alkyl groups of a tertiary alcohol when made by this synthesis have their origin in the Grignard reagent. Tertiary alcohols made by the reaction of a ketone and a Grignard reagent, you will recall, received one group from the Grignard reagent, the other two from the ketone (Sec. 8.5-C).

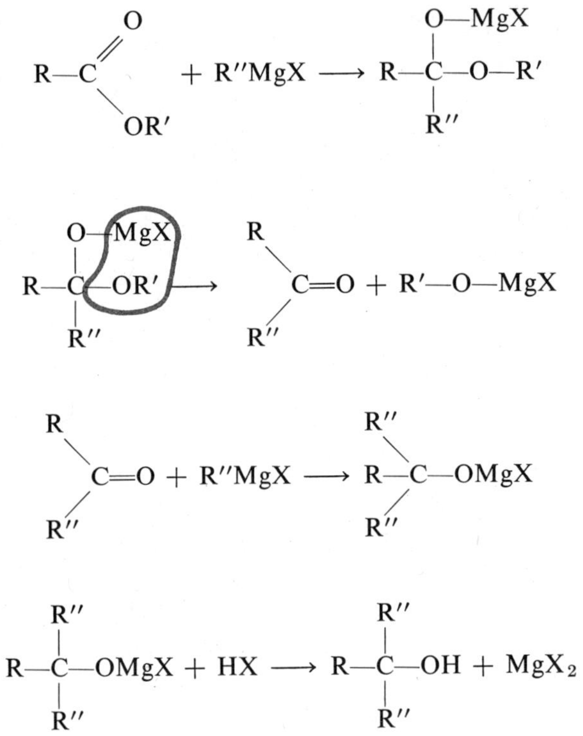

$$
R-\overset{O}{\underset{}{\overset{\|}{C}}}\diagdown_{OR'} + R''MgX \longrightarrow R-\underset{\underset{R''}{|}}{\overset{\overset{O-MgX}{|}}{C}}-O-R'
$$

$$
R-\underset{\underset{R''}{|}}{\overset{\overset{O-MgX}{|}}{C}}-OR' \longrightarrow \underset{R''}{\overset{R}{\diagdown}}C{=}O + R'-O-MgX
$$

$$
\underset{R''}{\overset{R}{\diagdown}}C{=}O + R''MgX \longrightarrow \underset{R''}{\overset{R''}{\diagdown}}R-C-OMgX
$$

$$
R-\underset{\underset{R''}{|}}{\overset{\overset{R''}{|}}{C}}-OMgX + HX \longrightarrow R-\underset{\underset{R''}{|}}{\overset{\overset{R''}{|}}{C}}-OH + MgX_2
$$

Exercise 10.6   What simple test tube reaction would serve to distinguish between acetic anhydride and ethyl acetate?

The α-hydrogen atoms of an ester such as ethyl acetate are weakly acidic and in the presence of a strong base such as sodium ethoxide react to produce the ester anion. The ester anion is a strong nucleophile which then may attack the carbonyl carbon of a second ester molecule. Elimination of an ethoxide ion results in the formation of the β-keto ester, ethyl acetoacetate in this case. The reaction, illustrated by the following sequence, is called the **Claisen condensation**[3] and bears a resemblance to the aldol condensation (Sec. 9.8-B) except that it is a substitution, rather than an addition reaction.

$$C_2H_5O^- + H{-}\overset{\overset{\displaystyle H}{|}}{\underset{\underset{\displaystyle H}{|}}{C}}{-}\overset{\displaystyle O}{C}{\diagdown}{OC_2H_5} \rightleftarrows C_2H_5OH + \ :CH_2{-}\overset{\displaystyle O}{C}{\diagdown}{OC_2H_5}$$

Ethoxide ion   Ester anion

$$CH_3{-}\overset{\displaystyle O}{C}{\diagdown}{OC_2H_5} + \ :CH_2{-}\overset{\displaystyle O}{C}{\diagdown}{OC_2H_5} \rightleftarrows CH_3{-}\overset{\overset{\displaystyle O^-}{|}}{\underset{\underset{\displaystyle OC_2H_5}{|}}{C}}{-}CH_2{-}\overset{\displaystyle O}{C}{\diagdown}{OC_2H_5}$$

$$CH_3{-}\overset{\overset{\displaystyle :\ddot{O}:^-}{|}}{\underset{\underset{\displaystyle OC_2H_5}{|}}{C}}{-}CH_2{-}\overset{\displaystyle O}{C}{\diagdown}{OC_2H_5} \rightleftarrows C_2H_5O^- + \ \underset{CH_3}{}\overset{\displaystyle O}{C}\underset{\underset{\displaystyle H_2}{}}{C}\overset{\displaystyle O}{C}{\diagdown}{OC_2H_5}$$

Ethyl acetoacetate

The β-keto esters are compounds useful in a number of organic syntheses that lead to ketones and carboxylic acids difficult or impossible to obtain by other methods. These reactions are possible because ethyl acetoacetate also can form an ester anion and enter into a variety of nucleophilic displacements. To describe these in detail is beyond the scope of this text. However, it should be pointed out that ethyl acetoacetate is an unusual compound in that it exhibits properties not only those of an ester and those of a ketone, but also properties usually associated with phenolic compounds. This unusual behavior is due to a type of isomerism called **tautomerism**. Tautomers are equilibrium isomers which in this case are the *keto* and *enol* forms of ethyl acetoacetate.

[3]Ludwig Claisen (1851–1930) was professor of chemistry at the University of Kiel.

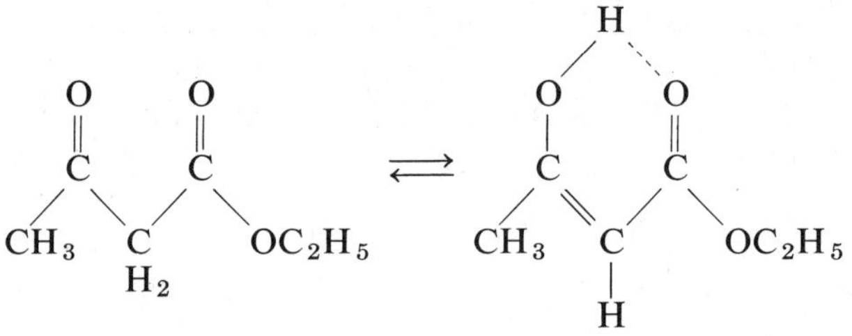

Keto form 92.5%

Reacts with $C_6H_5NHNH_2$

Enol form 7.5%

Reacts with bromine and gives a red color with $FeCl_3$ *(a test reaction for phenolic compounds)*

I.   Preparation of Amides.   Amides are conveniently prepared in the laboratory by the ammonolysis of acyl halides (Sec. 10.6-D) or acid anhydrides.

Amides are named after their parent acids by replacing *ic* or *oic* with *amide*. Examples of both common and systematic names are shown.

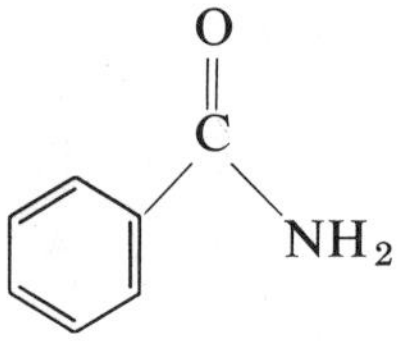

Benzamide

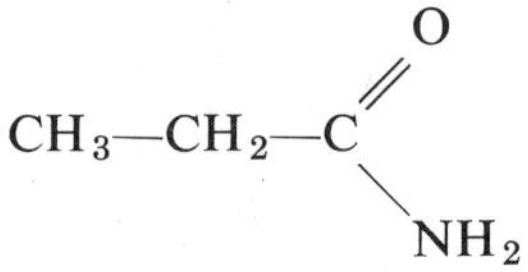

Propionamide
(Propanamide)

With the exception of formamide, $H—\overset{\displaystyle O}{\overset{\|}{C}}—NH_2$, the amides are solids, with sharp melting points. This property makes them very useful derivatives for the identification of acids.

J.   Reactions of the Amides.   The amides can be hydrolyzed in acid or in alkaline solution. Hydrolysis carried out in an acid solution produces the free organic acid and an ammonium salt. Hydrolysis carried out in a basic solution produces the free base (NH_3), and the salt of the organic acid. Both types of procedures are illustrated by the following reaction equations.

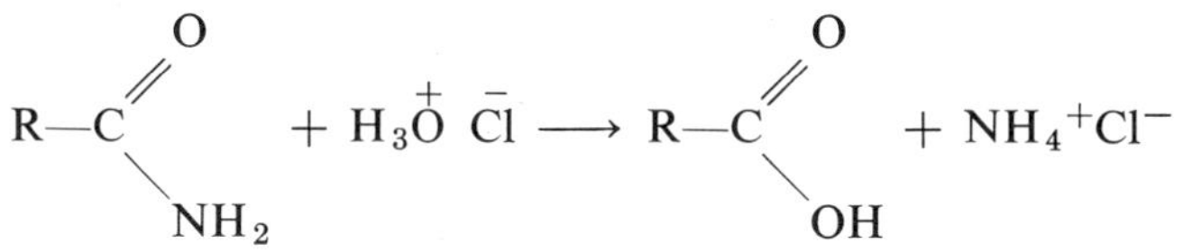

$$R-C{\overset{O}{\underset{NH_2}{}}} + H_3\overset{+}{O}\ \overset{-}{Cl} \longrightarrow R-C{\overset{O}{\underset{OH}{}}} + NH_4^+Cl^-$$

Acid hydrolysis

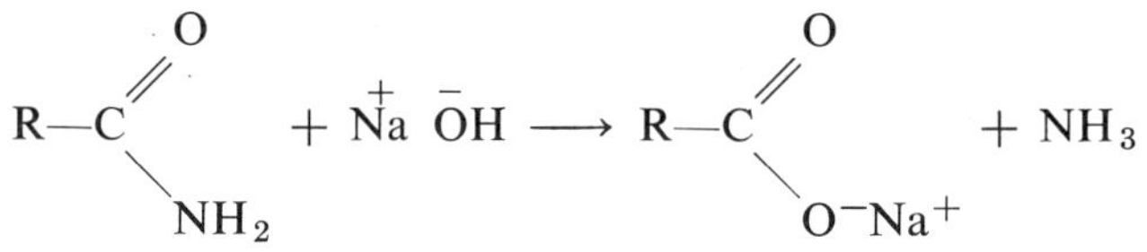

$$R-C{\overset{O}{\underset{NH_2}{}}} + Na\ \overset{+}{O}\overset{-}{H} \longrightarrow R-C{\overset{O}{\underset{O^-Na^+}{}}} + NH_3$$

Alkaline hydrolysis

The amides form nitriles when heated in the presence of a strong dehydrating agent such as phosphorus pentoxide.

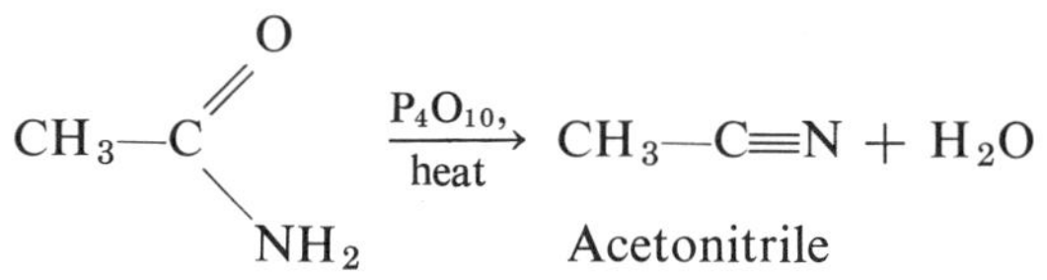

$$CH_3-C{\overset{O}{\underset{NH_2}{}}} \xrightarrow[\text{heat}]{P_4O_{10},} CH_3-C{\equiv}N + H_2O$$

Acetonitrile

Exercise 10.7   What simple test will serve to distinguish benzamide (M.P., 128°) from benzoic acid (M.P., 122°)?

10.7   PROPERTIES OF THE AROMATIC ACIDS

The reactions of the aromatic carboxylic acids, in general, are very similar to those of the aliphatic acids. The benzene ring, when attached directly to the carboxyl group, increases the acidic properties of the latter. Electron-withdrawing substituents *ortho* or *para* to the carboxyl group further increase the acidity of benzoic acid (Table 10.2). Ring substituents *ortho* to the carboxyl group can inhibit or completely prevent the direct esterification of an aromatic acid by an alcohol. Conversely, an ester of benzoic acid with substituents in the *ortho* positions, is not easily hydrolyzed. This type of interference, attributable to the spatial requirements of groups, is called **steric hindrance.** Such steric effects, when caused by substituents on positions ortho to the reactive group, sometimes are specifically referred to as *ortho* effects.   The carboxyl group, you will recall, is a *meta-director* and prevents other substituents from entering *ortho* positions.   *Ortho, para*-substituted benzoic acids, therefore, must be prepared indirectly. For example, *p*-nitrobenzoic acid is not prepared from benzoic acid but is obtained by the oxidation of *p*-nitrotoluene.

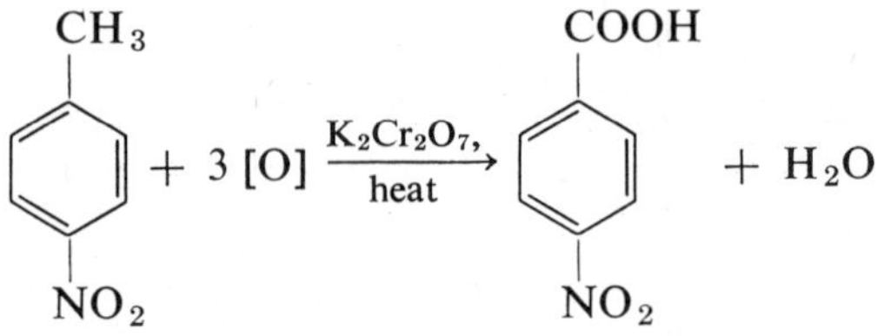

p-Nitrotoluene   p-Nitrobenzoic acid

The synthesis of an organic compound often requires following a correct reaction sequence. Sometimes such routes are lengthy and circuitous, but the only ones leading to the desired product. Other orientation problems are relatively simple.

10.8   FORMIC ACID

The structure and properties of formic acid are somewhat different from those of other members of the acid series and deserve special mention. In the first place, the structure of formic acid is that of both an aldehyde and an acid. As such it is easily oxidized by mild oxidizing agents. Tollens' reagent (Sec. 9.10), for example, oxidizes it to carbon dioxide and water.

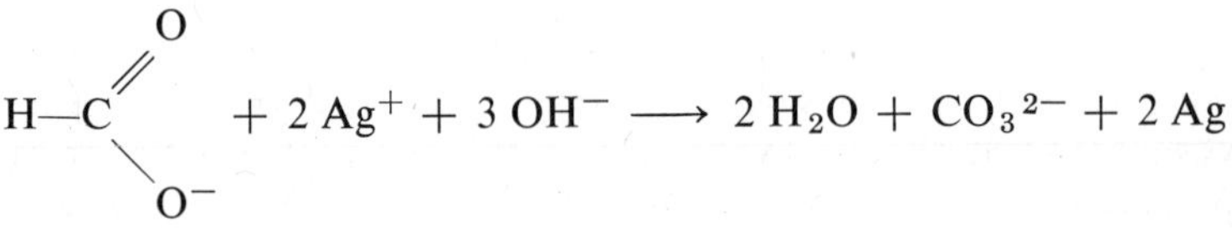

Formate ion

The acid chloride of formic acid, unlike those of its homologs, is not stable at ordinary temperatures. All attempts to prepare formyl chloride yield only carbon monoxide and hydrogen chloride. However, in combination these two gases sometimes enter into a Friedel-Crafts reaction as formyl chloride (Sec. 9.5-E).

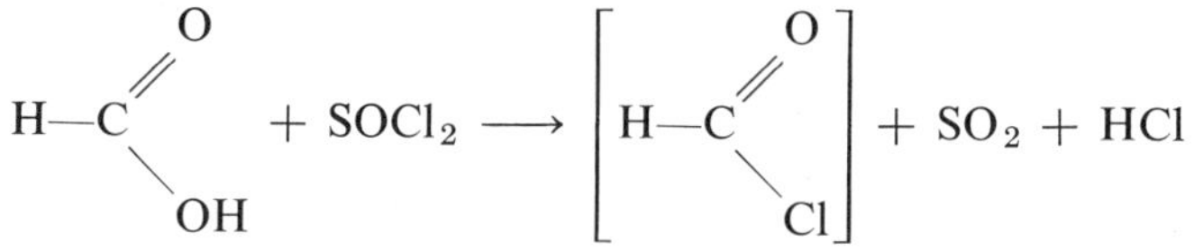

$$H-C\overset{O}{\underset{OH}{<}} + SOCl_2 \longrightarrow \left[H-C\overset{O}{\underset{Cl}{<}}\right] + SO_2 + HCl$$

Formyl chloride
(expected product)

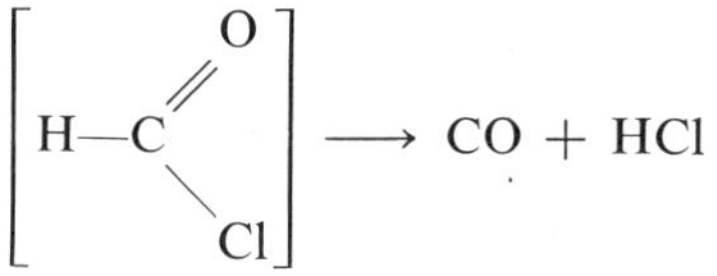

$$\left[H-C\overset{O}{\underset{Cl}{<}}\right] \longrightarrow CO + HCl$$

Formic acid is prepared industrially by heating carbon monoxide and sodium hydroxide.

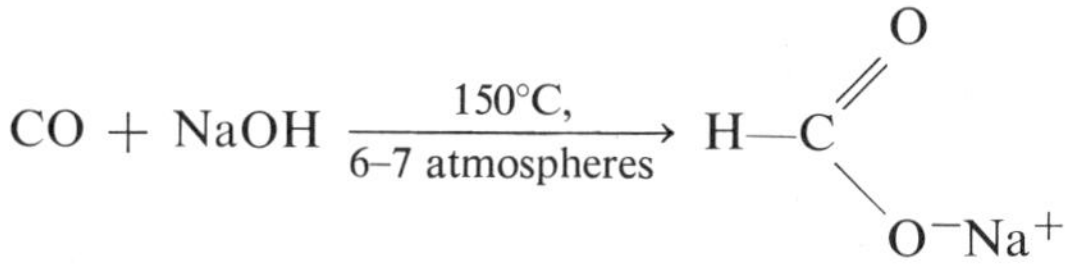

$$CO + NaOH \xrightarrow[\text{6-7 atmospheres}]{150°C,} H-C\overset{O}{\underset{O^-Na^+}{<}}$$

Sodium formate

The free acid is liberated from its sodium salt by reaction with sulfuric acid.

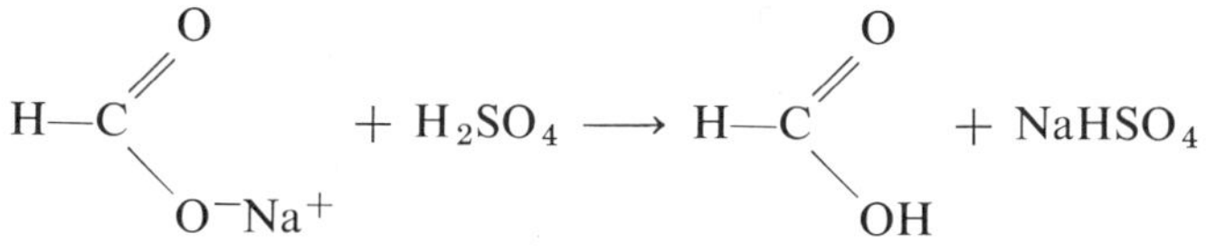

$$H-C\overset{O}{\underset{O^-Na^+}{<}} + H_2SO_4 \longrightarrow H-C\overset{O}{\underset{OH}{<}} + NaHSO_4$$

Formic acid

Formic acid also is obtained as a by-product in the production of pentaerythritol (Sec. 9.8-B).

Exercise 10.8   At 25°C formic acid ionizes to the extent of 4.3% in a 0.10 M solution. (a) What is the hydrogen ion concentration of this solution, $[H^+]$? (b) How much greater is the $[H^+]$ of a 0.1 M formic acid solution than that of a 0.1 M acetic acid solution?

Answer: (a) 0.0043 M, (b) 3.2 times greater.

10.9   ACETIC ACID

Acetic acid, although classified as one of the fatty acids, is not a component acid of fats and oils. It is the sour principle of vinegar — a 5% solution of acetic acid. Synthetic acetic acid brought to this dilution is "white" vinegar whereas "brown" vinegar is the natural product of apple juice fermentation. Vinegars also may be made from other fruit juices. The fermentation process produces ethyl alcohol as the first product. Certain enzymes, if present, then catalyze the further oxidation of ethyl alcohol to acetic acid.

$$C_6H_{12}O_6 \xrightarrow[\text{of yeast}]{\text{Enzymes}} 2\,C_2H_5OH + 2\,CO_2$$

Fruit sugar

$$C_2H_5OH + O_2\ \text{(air)} \xrightarrow[\text{acetobacter}]{\text{Enzymes of}} CH_3\!-\!\!\overset{\displaystyle O}{\underset{\displaystyle OH}{C}} + H_2O$$

Pure acetic acid, m.p. 16.7°C, is referred to as "glacial" acetic acid because it appears as an icelike solid at lower than room temperature. Acetic acid is by far the most important of the monocarboxylic acids.

Exercise 10.9   Vinegar has a density of 1.0055 g/ml. If this represents a 5% (by weight) acetic acid solution, what is the concentration of vinegar in terms of molarity?

Answer: 0.8378 M.

□□ *SUMMARY*

[1]   **Structure**

The carboxyl group, —COOH, is the functional group of the carboxylic acids. The aliphatic acids are referred to as *fatty acids* because many appear in a combined form with glycerol as fats.

[2]   **Nomenclature of Acids**

The carboxylic acids usually are assigned common names. Systematic nomenclature follows general rules already learned. The suffix *oic* is added to the alkane stem followed by the word *acid.* Substituents in the hydrocarbon segment of an acid may be located by Greek letters, by numbers, or (in the case of aromatic acids) by *ortho, para,* and *meta* prefixes.

Removal of the hydroxyl group of an acid forms the *acyl*

$$\left(\begin{array}{c} O \\ \nearrow \\ R-C \\ \searrow \end{array} \right) \text{ or the } aroyl \left(\begin{array}{c} O \\ \nearrow \\ Ar-C \\ \searrow \end{array} \right) \text{ group.}$$

[3] **Properties of the Acids**

The carboxylic acids are weak acids. They are capable of associating (H-bonding) and are high boiling liquids or crystalline solids sparingly soluble in water. H-bonding also makes possible the formation of double molecules or dimers.

[4] **Preparation of the Acids**

The carboxylic acids may be prepared by any of the following methods.

a. Oxidation of primary alcohols, methyl ketones (haloform reaction, Sec. 9.9) or side chains on the aromatic nucleus.
b. Hydrolysis of nitriles.
c. Carbonation of Grignard reagents.

[5] **Reactions**

Aliphatic and aromatic acids give reactions that are almost identical. Any differences are of degree rather than of kind. These reactions include:

a. Replacement of the ionizable hydrogen by another cation (salt formation).
b. Replacement of the hydroxyl by halide to yield **acyl** or

$$\text{aroyl halides, } R-C \begin{array}{c} O \\ \nearrow \\ \\ \searrow \\ X \end{array} \text{ or } Ar-C \begin{array}{c} O \\ \nearrow \\ \\ \searrow \\ X \end{array}$$

c. Replacement of the hydroxyl by an alkoxyl, —OR, to yield

$$\text{esters, } R-C \begin{array}{c} O \\ \nearrow \\ \\ \searrow \\ OR \end{array}$$

d. Replacement of the hydroxyl by an amino group to yield

$$\text{amides, } R-C \begin{array}{c} O \\ \nearrow \\ \\ \searrow \\ NH_2 \end{array}$$

e. Replacement of the hydroxyl by carboxylate,

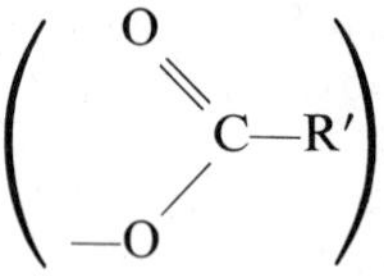

, to yield **anhydrides**,

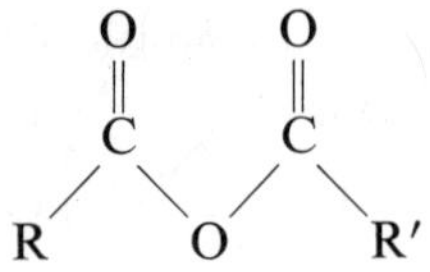

f. Reduction to alcohols. Reduction of an acid may be accomplished directly by the use of LiAlH$_4$. Reduction of an acid may be accomplished *indirectly* via its ester — that is, the ester of an acid is reduced to produce two alcohols.

g. The carboxyl group attached directly to the benzene ring orients incoming substituents to the *meta* position.

h. The acids (with the exception of the first member) are stable to oxidation.

☐☐ *NEW TERMS*

[1] acid dimers

[2] acyl group

[3] aroyl group

[4] alcoholysis

[5] ammonolysis

[6] esterification

[7] glacial acetic acid

[8] hydrolysis

[9] inductive effect

[10] keto-enol isomerism

[11] saponification

[12] steric hindrance

[13] tautomerism

■ ☐SUPPLEMENTARY EXERCISES
▼   AND PROBLEMS

[1] Draw structural formulas for each of the following compounds.

(a) isobutyric acid

(b) β-hydroxy-*n*-butyric acid

(c) 3-butenoic acid

(d) ethyl bromoacetate

(e) 3, 5-dimethylbenzoic acid

(f) propanoyl chloride

(g) sodium trifluoroacetate

(h) phthalic anhydride

(i) butyramide

(j) phenylacetic acid

(k) methyl salicylate

(l) calcium propionate

[2]   Identify each lettered product in the following reaction sequences.

(a) CH_3—COOH $\xrightarrow{SOCl_2}$ (A) $\xrightarrow{NH_3}$ (B) $\xrightarrow{P_2O_5}$ (C)

(b) CH_3CN $\xrightarrow[\text{reflux}]{Na^+OH^-,}$ (A) + (B);

   A + HCl $\longrightarrow$ CH_3COOH + NaCl

(c) $(CH_3)_2C{=}O$ $\xrightarrow{700°C}$ (A) $\xrightarrow{CH_3COOH}$ (B) $\xrightarrow{C_2H_5OH}$ (C) + (D);

   C + NaOH $\longrightarrow$ $CH_3COO^-Na^+$

(d) C_2H_5Br $\xrightarrow[\text{ether}]{\text{Mg, anhydrous}}$ (A) $\xrightarrow[\text{(2) hydrolysis}]{\text{(1) }CO_2}$ (B) $\xrightarrow{PCl_3}$

   (C) $\xrightarrow{C_2H_5OH}$ (D) $\xrightarrow[\text{heat}]{Na, \, C_2H_5OH,}$ (E) + (F);

   (F) + I_2 + NaOH $\longrightarrow$ HCl_3

[3]   Without referring to a table of acidity constants arrange the acids in the following set in an order of diminishing acidity.

   (a) benzoic acid, (b) p-nitrobenzoic acid, (c) phenylacetic acid, (d) p-methoxybenzoic acid.

[4]   Complete the following reaction equations naming the organic product(s) obtained.

(a) 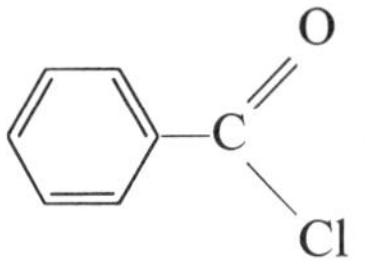   ⟨benzene ring⟩—$\overset{\displaystyle O}{\underset{\displaystyle Cl}{C}}$ + NH_3 $\longrightarrow$

(b) C_2H_5I + KCN $\longrightarrow$

(c) $CH_3\overset{\displaystyle O}{\underset{\displaystyle Cl}{C}}$ + C_2H_5OH $\longrightarrow$

(d) $CH_3\overset{\displaystyle O}{\underset{\displaystyle NH_2}{C}}$ $\xrightarrow{P_4O_{10}}$

(e) CH_3—CH_2—$\overset{\displaystyle CH_3}{\underset{}{C}}{=}O$ + Br_2 + NaOH $\longrightarrow$

(f) $CH_3-C\overset{O}{\underset{NH_2}{\Big\backslash}}$ + NaOH $\xrightarrow{\text{Reflux}}$

(g) $CH_3-C\overset{O}{\underset{OH}{\Big\backslash}}$ + $SOCl_2$ $\longrightarrow$

(h)   Product of (b) + H_2O + NaOH $\xrightarrow{\text{Reflux}}$

(i) C_6H_5Br + Mg $\xrightarrow{\text{Anhydrous ether}}$

(j)   Product of (i) + CO_2 $\xrightarrow[\text{hydrolysis}]{\text{Followed by}}$

[5]   Using limestone ($CaCO_3$) and coke (C) as your only carbon-containing starting material and any other inorganic reagents you may need, show how you might synthesize the following compounds. (*Note:* The product of one reaction may be used as starting material for the preparation of another.)

(a)   acetylene
(b)   acetaldehyde
(c)   ethyl bromide
(d)   2-butanol
(e)   iodoform
(f)   propionic acid
(g)   acetone
(h)   isopropyl alcohol
(i)   2-bromopropane
(j)   n-propyl bromide
(k)   acetic acid
(l)   acetic anhydride
(m)   isopropyl acetate
(n)   isobutyric acid

[6]   Outline a procedure for the removal of acetic acid (b.p., 118°) from a mixture which also contains n-butyl alcohol (b.p., 117°) and n-butyl acetate (b.p., 126°).

[7]   Beginning with toluene as your only organic starting material, outline a reaction or a reaction sequence that would lead to the preparation of the following compounds.

(a)   p-bromotoluene
(b)   4-methylbenzoic acid
(c)   p-bromobenzamide
(d)   p-bromophenylacetic acid
(e)   terephthalic acid,
         $p-C_6H_4(CO_2H)_2$

[8]   A neutral compound which contained only carbon, hydrogen, and oxygen was hydrolyzed to yield two new products (A) and (B). Compound (A) was found to be an acid with a neutralization equivalent of 60 ± 1. Compound (B) gave a positive iodoform test reaction, reacted readily with the Lucas reagent, and on treatment with

concentrated H_2SO_4 gave propylene. Give the name and structure of the original compound.

[9]   A liquid, $C_7H_{14}O_2$, on hydrolysis gave compounds (A) and (B). Compound (A) was found to be an acid with a neutralization equivalent of 88 ± 1. Compound (B) gave a positive iodoform reaction and when treated with PBr_3 formed an alkyl bromide. A Grignard reagent, when prepared from the alkyl bromide and caused to react with carbon dioxide, produced an acid identical to compound (A). Give the structure and name of the original compound.

chapter 11

Fats, Oils, Waxes;
Soap and Detergents

Natural products which are soluble in ether, chloroform, carbon tetrachloride, and other water-immiscible organic solvents, but insoluble in water, are known as **lipids.** The lipids are important constituents of all plant and animal tissue. Of these, the fats and oils are most abundant and it is upon them that our attention will be focused. Fats, oils,[1] and waxes are esters which occur naturally. In addition to the fats and oils (simple lipids), this classification includes other fatlike substances. Not only do the edible fats and oils make up approximately forty per cent of the American diet, but they provide the raw material for the preparation of numerous and important commodities.

11.1   WAXES

Waxes are esters of long-chain, unbranched fatty acids and long-chain alcohols. Both the acid and the alcohol that combine to form a wax may be sixteen to thirty carbons in length. The general formula of a wax is essentially that of a simple ester, $R\!-\!\overset{\displaystyle O}{\overset{\displaystyle \|}{C}}\!-\!O\!-\!R'$.

Both plants and animals produce natural waxes. Waxes usually are mixtures of esters and contain, in addition, small amounts of free acids, alcohols, and even hydrocarbons. The waxes melt over a wide range of temperature (35°–100°C), have a satiny "waxy" feel, and are very insoluble in water. On the other hand, they are

---

[1]Oils, as used in the present chapter, refers to glycerides (see Sec. 11.2) which are liquid at room temperature and *not* to mineral oils or petroleum products.

quite soluble in many organic solvents and may be compounded
into a number of useful everyday commodities. Such wax solutions
generally are used as protective coatings. They are often protective
coatings in nature, too.

Beeswax is largely ceryl myristate, $C_{13}H_{27}\overset{\displaystyle O}{\overset{\|}{C}}-O-C_{26}H_{53}$,
along with some esters of cerotic acid, $C_{25}H_{51}COOH$, and a few
per cent of hydrocarbons. It melts between 62–65°C and is used
in the preparation of shoe polishes, candles, and paper coatings.

Carnauba wax, a plant wax found as a coating on the leaf of the
Brazilian palm, is largely myricyl cerotate, $C_{25}H_{51}\overset{\displaystyle O}{\overset{\|}{C}}-O-C_{31}H_{63}$.
Carnauba wax melts between 80–87°C and is used in polishes and
as a coating on mimeograph stencils.

Spermaceti wax consists mainly of cetyl palmitate,

$$C_{15}H_{31}\overset{\displaystyle O}{\overset{\|}{C}}-O-C_{16}H_{33},$$

along with some free cetyl alcohol, $C_{16}H_{33}OH$. It is obtained from
the head cavity of the sperm whale. Spermaceti wax has a melting
range of 42–50°C and is used primarily as an emollient in ointments
and in cosmetics. It is also used in the manufacture of candles.

Fats and Oils

11.2   STRUCTURE AND COMPOSITION OF FATS AND OILS

Fats and oils differ from waxes in that they are glycerides, or
esters of glycerol, a trihydroxy alcohol (Sec. 8.6).

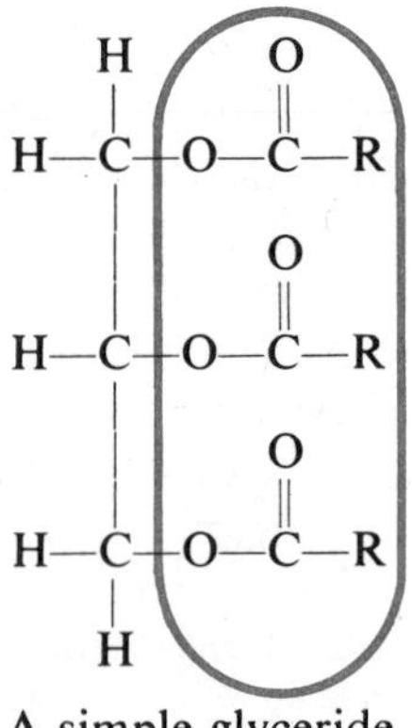

A simple glyceride

A simple glyceride is one in which all R groups in the previous general formula are identical. If R in the general formula represents an aliphatic group, C_nH_{2n+1}, then the number of carbons in the group usually is an odd number from 3 to 17. Such chains are saturated. If R is an unsaturated alkyl group, of the form C_nH_{2n-1}, C_nH_{2n-3}, or C_nH_{2n-5}, then n usually is 17.

$$
\begin{array}{c}
\overset{\displaystyle H}{\underset{\displaystyle |}{}} \quad \overset{\displaystyle O}{\underset{\displaystyle \|}{}} \\
H-\overset{|}{\underset{|}{C}}-O-C-(CH_2)_{14}-CH_3 \\
\\
\overset{\displaystyle O}{\underset{\displaystyle \|}{}} \\
H-\overset{|}{\underset{|}{C}}-O-C-(CH_2)_{14}-CH_3 \\
\\
\overset{\displaystyle O}{\underset{\displaystyle \|}{}} \\
H-\overset{|}{\underset{|}{C}}-O-C-(CH_2)_{14}-CH_3 \\
\overset{\displaystyle |}{\underset{\displaystyle H}{}}
\end{array}
$$

Glyceryl tripalmitate (a simple glyceride)

The natural fats and oils usually are not simple glycerides. The three acid residues produced when fats and oils are hydrolyzed usually vary not only in length but also in the degree of unsaturation. The principal structural difference between oils and fats lies in the degree of saturation of the acid residues, and this accounts for the differences in both the physical and chemical properties of these two classes of glycerides.

The fats are glyceryl esters in which long-chain *saturated* acid components predominate. They are solids or semi-solids and are principally animal products. **Lauric,** $CH_3(CH_2)_{10}COOH$; **palmitic,** $CH_3(CH_2)_{14}COOH$; and **stearic,** $CH_3(CH_2)_{16}COOH$ are the most important acids obtained by the hydrolysis of fats. Such long-chain carboxylic acids usually are called *fatty acids* because they are obtained from fats. They are, for the most part, insoluble in water but soluble in organic solvents. It is entirely possible that all three of the fatty acids named above could be present in a mixed glyceride such as that shown on page 298.

$$
\begin{array}{c}
\overset{\displaystyle H}{\underset{\displaystyle |}{H-C-O-}}\overset{\displaystyle O}{\underset{\displaystyle \|}{C}}-(CH_2)_{10}-CH_3 \\[2ex]
\underset{\displaystyle |}{} \\
H-C-O-\overset{\displaystyle O}{\underset{\displaystyle \|}{C}}-(CH_2)_{14}-CH_3 \\[2ex]
\underset{\displaystyle |}{} \\
H-C-O-\overset{\displaystyle O}{\underset{\displaystyle \|}{C}}-(CH_2)_{16}-CH_3 \\[1ex]
\underset{\displaystyle H}{|}
\end{array}
$$

Glyceryl lauropalmitostearate
(a mixed glyceride)

Oils, on the other hand, are glyceryl esters in which long-chain *unsaturated* acid components predominate. They are liquids and are largely of vegetable origin.

$$
\begin{array}{c}
\overset{\displaystyle H}{\underset{\displaystyle |}{H-C-O-}}\overset{\displaystyle O}{\underset{\displaystyle \|}{C}}-(CH_2)_7-CH{=}CH-(CH_2)_7CH_3 \\[2ex]
\underset{\displaystyle |}{} \\
H-C-O-\overset{\displaystyle O}{\underset{\displaystyle \|}{C}}-(CH_2)_7-CH{=}CH-(CH_2)_7CH_3 \\[2ex]
\underset{\displaystyle |}{} \\
H-C-O-\overset{\displaystyle O}{\underset{\displaystyle \|}{C}}-(CH_2)_7-CH{=}CH-(CH_2)_7CH_3 \\[1ex]
\underset{\displaystyle H}{|}
\end{array}
$$

Glyceryl trioleate (Triolein)[2]
(an oil)

The presence of unsaturation in the acid component of a fat tends to lower its melting point. The most important unsaturated acids obtainable by the hydrolysis of oils are the C_{18} acids — **oleic, linoleic,** and **linolenic,** of which the structures are given below.

$$
\underset{(18)}{CH_3}-(CH_2)_7-\underset{(10)}{CH}{=}\underset{(9)}{CH}-(CH_2)_7-\underset{(1)}{C}\overset{\displaystyle O}{\diagdown}_{OH}
$$

Oleic acid

---

[2]If all fatty acid residues of a glyceride are the same, the name is shortened by dropping "glyceryl" and changing "tri . . . ate" to "tri . . . in."

$$CH_3-(CH_2)_4-CH=CH-CH_2-CH=CH-(CH_2)_7-C\underset{OH}{\overset{O}{<}}$$
$$\text{(18)} \qquad\qquad \text{(13) (12)} \qquad \text{(10) (9)} \qquad\qquad \text{(1)}$$

Linoleic acid

$$CH_3-CH_2-CH=CH-CH_2-CH=CH-CH_2-CH=CH-(CH_2)_7-C\underset{OH}{\overset{O}{<}}$$
$$\text{(18) (17) (16) (15) (14) (13) (12) (11) (10) (9)} \qquad\qquad \text{(1)}$$

Linolenic acid

You will note that the first double bond in each of the above structures is found in the middle of the carbon chain and that other double bonds are farther removed from the carboxyl group. Methylene ($-CH_2-$) units separate one double bond from another, and the unsaturated hydrocarbon portion of these three acids does not represent a conjugated system (Sec. 3.12). Some natural oils do contain acids with systems of alternating single and double bonds. One of these is **tung oil,** which on hydrolysis yields **eleostearic** as the principal acid.

$$\begin{array}{cccccc} \text{(14)} & \text{(13)} & \text{(12)} & \text{(11)} & \text{(10)} & \text{(9)} \end{array}$$
$$CH_3-CH_2CH_2CH_2CH=CH-CH=CH-CH=CH-(CH_2)_7-C\underset{OH}{\overset{O}{<}}$$

Eleostearic acid (conjugated isomer of linolenic acid)

Unsaturation in a fatty acid also makes possible geometric isomerism depending on the configuration of the hydrogen atoms attached to the doubly-bonded carbon atoms. Oleic acid has the *cis* configuration whereas its isomer, elaidic acid has the *trans* configuration. When more than one double bond is present in the fatty acid molecule, of course more than two geometric isomers are possible. Generally speaking, the *cis* isomers are the forms found naturally occurring in the unsaturated acid component of food fats and oils. As may be seen from Table 11.1 the most abundant of all saturated acids found in fats is palmitic; the most abundant of the unsaturated acids found in edible oils is oleic. See page 302 for Table 11.1.

Exercise 11.1   How many geometric isomers are possible for linoleic acid?

11.3   SAPONIFICATION AND IODINE VALUES

The composition of fats and oils is variable and depends not only upon the plant or animal species involved in their production, but also upon climatic and dietetic factors as well. The approximate molecular weights of the acid components in fats and oils may be obtained from **saponification values.** Saponification is a term specifically applied to the hydrolysis of an ester when the action is carried out in alkaline solution. The saponification value of a fat or an oil is an arbitrary unit, defined as the **number of milligrams of potassium hydroxide required to saponify one gram of the fat or oil.** Because there are three ester linkages in a glyceride to hydrolyze, three equivalents of potassium hydroxide are required to saponify one molecular weight of any fat or oil. The following equation and sample calculation illustrate how a saponification value is determined.

$$H_2C-O-\overset{\displaystyle O}{\overset{\|}{C}}-(CH_2)_{14}-CH_3$$

$$HC-O-\overset{\displaystyle O}{\overset{\|}{C}}-(CH_2)_{14}-CH_3 \; + \; 3\;KOH \rightarrow 3\;CH_3(CH_2)_{14}COO^-K^+ \; + \; \begin{array}{c}CH_2OH\\|\\CHOH\\|\\CH_2OH\end{array}$$

$$H_2C-O-\overset{\displaystyle O}{\overset{\|}{C}}-(CH_2)_{14}-CH_3$$

| Glyceryl tripalmitate (tripalmitin) | (3 × gram formula weight) | Potassium palmitate (a soap) | Glycerol |

M.W. = 806

$$\text{Saponification value of tripalmitin} = \frac{168,000 \text{ mg KOH/mole fat}}{806 \text{ g fat/mole fat}}$$

$$= 208 \text{ mg KOH/g fat}$$

A small saponification value for a fat or an oil indicates a high molecular weight.

The extent of unsaturation in a fat or oil is expressed in terms of its **iodine value.** The iodine value is defined as the **number of grams of iodine which will add to 100 grams of fat or oil.** The iodine value of tripalmitin (above) with no unsaturation would, of course, be zero. The determination of an iodine value may be illustrated by using triolein as an example.

$$\underset{\substack{\text{Glyceryl trioleate} \\ \text{(triolein)} \\ \text{M. W.} = 884}}{\begin{array}{l} \text{H}_2\text{C}-\text{O}-\overset{\overset{\displaystyle \text{O}}{\|}}{\text{C}}(\text{CH}_2)_7\text{CH}{=}\text{CH}(\text{CH}_2)_7\text{CH}_3 \\[2mm] \text{HC}-\text{O}-\overset{\overset{\displaystyle \text{O}}{\|}}{\text{C}}(\text{CH}_2)_7\text{CH}{=}\text{CH}(\text{CH}_2)_7\text{CH}_3 \\[2mm] \text{H}_2\text{C}-\text{O}-\overset{\overset{\displaystyle \text{O}}{\|}}{\text{C}}(\text{CH}_2)_7\text{CH}{=}\text{CH}(\text{CH}_2)_7\text{CH}_3 \end{array}} \xrightarrow{\ 3\text{I}_2\ }$$

$$\begin{array}{l} \text{H}_2\text{C}-\text{O}-\overset{\overset{\displaystyle \text{O}}{\|}}{\text{C}}(\text{CH}_2)_7\overset{\overset{\displaystyle \text{I}}{|}}{\text{CH}}\overset{\overset{\displaystyle \text{I}}{|}}{\text{CH}}(\text{CH}_2)_7\text{CH}_3 \\[2mm] \text{HC}-\text{O}-\overset{\overset{\displaystyle \text{O}}{\|}}{\text{C}}(\text{CH}_2)_7\overset{\overset{\displaystyle \text{I}}{|}}{\text{CH}}\overset{\overset{\displaystyle \text{I}}{|}}{\text{CH}}(\text{CH}_2)_7\text{CH}_3 \\[2mm] \text{H}_2\text{C}-\text{O}-\overset{\overset{\displaystyle \text{O}}{\|}}{\text{C}}(\text{CH}_2)_7\overset{\overset{\displaystyle \text{I}}{|}}{\text{CH}}\overset{\overset{\displaystyle \text{I}}{|}}{\text{CH}}(\text{CH}_2)_7\text{CH}_3 \end{array}$$

The above equation reveals that 761.4 g (3 moles) of iodine will add to 884 g of the oil. The number of grams of iodine that will add to 100 g of oil will be $100/884 \times 761.4$ g of iodine, or 86 g of iodine. (Atomic weight of iodine = 126.9)

$$\text{Iodine value} = \frac{6 \times 126.9 \times 100}{884} = 86$$

A high iodine value indicates a high degree of unsaturation. While the above equation shows the addition of molecular iodine, in practice iodine monobromide (IBr) is the reagent actually used.

Table 11.1 indicates the composition of some of the more important fats and oils along with their saponification and iodine values.

TABLE 11.1

FATTY ACID COMPONENTS OF SOME COMMON FATS AND OILS

Component Acids (percent)*

FATS	Myristic C_{14}	Palmitic C_{16}	Stearic C_{18}	Oleic	Linoleic	Linolenic	Eleostearic	Saponification Values	Iodine Values
Butter	7–10	24–26	10–13	28–31	1.0–2.5	0.2–0.5		210–230	30–40
Lard	1–2	28–30	12–18	40–50	7–13	0–1		195–203	46–70
Tallow	3–6	24–32	20–25	37–43	2–3			190–200	30–48
EDIBLE OILS									
Olive oil		9–10	2–3	73–84	10–12	trace		187–196	79–90
Corn oil	1–2	8–12	2–5	19–49	34–62	trace		187–196	109–133
Soybean oil		6–10	2–5	20–30	50–60	5–11		189–195	127–138
Cottonseed oil	0–2	20–25	1–2	23–35	40–50	trace		190–198	105–114
Peanut oil		8–9	2–3	50–65	20–30			188–195	84–102
Safflower oil		6–7	2–3	12–14	75–80	0.5–0.15		188–194	140–156
NONEDIBLE OILS									
Linseed oil		4–7	2–4	25–40	35–40	25–60		187–195	170–185
Tung oil		3–4	0–1	4–15			75–90	190–197	163–171

*Totals less than 100% indicate the presence of lower or higher acids in small amounts.

> **Exercise 11.2**   If 90% or more of the fatty acid components
> of castor oil is ricinoleic acid (see Exercise 2-f, Chapter 6), what
> are the saponification and iodine values for castor oil?
>
> *Answer:* Sap. value = 176–187; Iodine value = 81–90.

Reactions of the Fats and Oils

11.4   SAPONIFICATION. (SOAP PREPARATION)

The glycerides, like other esters, may be hydrolyzed by heating
with a solution of sodium or potassium hydroxide. The hydrolysis
products are glycerol and the alkali metal salts of long-chain fatty
acids (Sec. 10.6-H) The latter are called **soaps,** and alkaline hydrolysis is called **saponification,** whether the term is applied to fats, oils,
or simple esters.

The best soaps are those in which the hydrocarbon segment is
saturated and is from twelve to eighteen carbon atoms in length.
Sodium soaps are hard soaps and commonly are used as cake soaps.
Potassium soaps are soft soaps, produce a finer lather, and usually
are employed in shaving creams. Natural or "hardened" fats
(Sec. 11.5) are saponified by heating them in open kettles with a
solution of sodium hydroxide. The kettles are quite large and can
accommodate over fifty tons of fat per batch. When the reaction is
complete, the thick curds of soap are precipitated by the addition
of sodium chloride (common ion effect). The water layer is drawn
off and the glycerol it contains is recovered by concentration and
distillation. The crude soap, which contains salt, alkali, and some
residual glycerol, is heated with water to dissolve these impurities.
The soap is again reprecipitated by the addition of salt. The washing and precipitation procedure is repeated several times, Finally,
the soap is heated with sufficient water to give a smooth mixture,
which on standing, separates into a homogeneous upper layer of
kettle soap. Kettle soap may be used without further treatment or
it may be blended with other ingredients to produce soaps for special
purposes. Pumice is incorporated for scouring soaps, perfumes for
toilet soaps, and antiseptics (phenol, hexachlorophene) for medi-
cated or deodorizing soaps. When air is blown into molten soap,
the specific gravity of the solidified product is lowered to 0.8–0.9.
This treatment produces a floating soap.

Sodium and potassium soaps are soluble in water and are the
common household soaps. The long-chain fatty acid salts of heavier
metals are not water soluble and may be blended with mineral oils to
form lubricating greases.

11.5   HYDROGENATION. ("HARDENING" OF OILS)

Unsaturation in a fat or an oil may be diminished by catalytic hydrogenation.

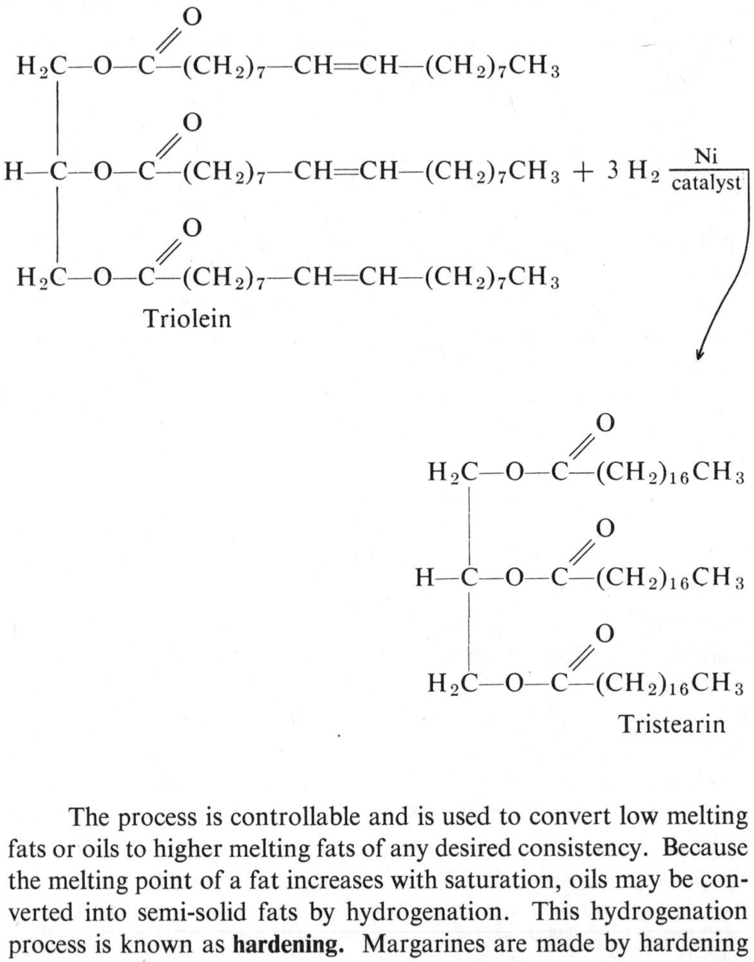

$$H_2C-O-\overset{\displaystyle O}{\overset{\|}{C}}-(CH_2)_7-CH=CH-(CH_2)_7CH_3$$

$$H-\overset{|}{C}-O-\overset{\displaystyle O}{\overset{\|}{C}}-(CH_2)_7-CH=CH-(CH_2)_7CH_3 + 3\,H_2 \xrightarrow[\text{catalyst}]{\text{Ni}}$$

$$H_2\overset{|}{C}-O-\overset{\displaystyle O}{\overset{\|}{C}}-(CH_2)_7-CH=CH-(CH_2)_7CH_3$$

Triolein

$$H_2C-O-\overset{\displaystyle O}{\overset{\|}{C}}-(CH_2)_{16}CH_3$$

$$H-\overset{|}{C}-O-\overset{\displaystyle O}{\overset{\|}{C}}-(CH_2)_{16}CH_3$$

$$H_2\overset{|}{C}-O-\overset{\displaystyle O}{\overset{\|}{C}}-(CH_2)_{16}CH_3$$

Tristearin

The process is controllable and is used to convert low melting fats or oils to higher melting fats of any desired consistency. Because the melting point of a fat increases with saturation, oils may be converted into semi-solid fats by hydrogenation. This hydrogenation process is known as **hardening.** Margarines are made by hardening oils to the consistency of butter. When churned with skim milk, fortified with vitamin A, and artificially colored, these butter substitutes have not only the flavor and color of butter, but its nutritional advantages as well. Butter is approximately 80% fat, and margarine, by federal regulation must also contain not less than 80% fat.

Many of the cooking fats now available have their origin in vegetable oils. When hydrogenation is carried to completion, glycerol and long-chain alcohols are produced. The latter are used in the manufacture of synthetic detergents (Sec. 11.8).

$$H_2C-O-\overset{\overset{\displaystyle O}{\|}}{C}-(CH_2)_{16}CH_3$$

$$H-\underset{|}{\overset{|}{C}}-O-\overset{\overset{\displaystyle O}{\|}}{C}-(CH_2)_{16}CH_3 \ + \ 6\,H_2 \ \xrightarrow{\text{Catalyst}} \ \underset{|}{\overset{\displaystyle CH_2OH}{\underset{\displaystyle CH_2OH}{CHOH}}} \ + \ 3\,CH_3(CH_2)_{16}CH_2OH$$

$$H_2C-O-\overset{\overset{\displaystyle O}{\|}}{C}-(CH_2)_{16}CH_3$$

Glyceryl tristearate   Glycerol   1-Octadecanol

11.6   OXIDATION. (RANCIDITY)

Edible unsaturated fats and oils, when exposed to air and light for long periods of time, not only are subject to slow hydrolysis but the acid components produced also are subject to oxidative cleavage at the site of unsaturation.

$$CH_3-(CH_2)_7-CH\overset{\zeta}{\underset{\varsigma}{=}}CH-(CH_2)_7COOH \ \xrightarrow{O_2\text{(air)}}$$

Oleic acid

$$CH_3(CH_2)_7COOH \ + \ HO-\overset{\overset{\displaystyle O}{\|}}{C}-(CH_2)_7-\overset{\overset{\displaystyle O}{\|}}{C}-OH$$

Pelargonic acid   Azelaic acid

The lower molecular weight and more volatile acids that are produced by this exposure impart an offensive odor to fats. This condition is known as **rancidity.** If the volatile acids are produced by hydrolysis, the resultant rancidity is known as hydrolytic rancidity. Butter, especially, when left uncovered and out of the refrigerator, easily becomes rancid through hydrolytic rancidity. A substantial portion of the fatty acid components of butterfat is made up of butyric, caproic, caprylic, and capric acids. These are liberated when butter is hydrolyzed and are responsible for the unpleasant odor of rancid butter. Oxidation leading to rancidity (oxidative rancidity) in fats and oils is catalyzed by the presence of certain metallic salts. Proper packaging of foods, therefore, is of the utmost importance. The addition of **antioxidants** will stabilize edible fats for long periods of storage. These inhibitors, or interceptors as they sometimes are called, are themselves easily oxidizable substances. Some are natural products such as δ-tocopherol (Sec. 17.12-c) and the lecithins. The lecithins, as evident in the formula (next page), are themselves glycerides.

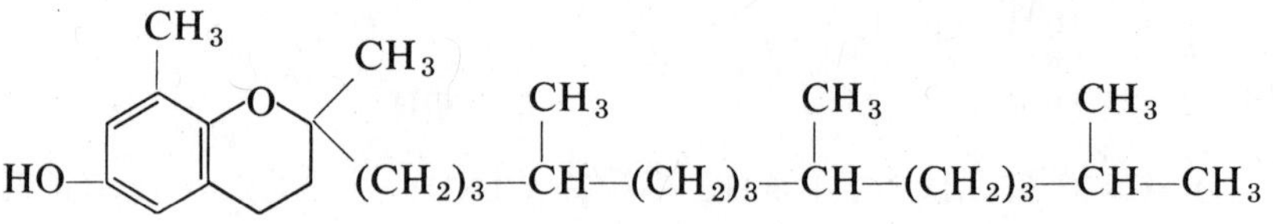

δ-Tocopherol

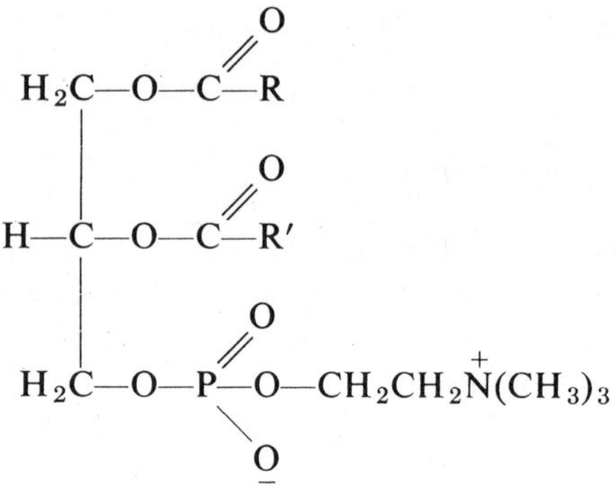

A lecithin

Other antioxidants employed to stabilize fats contain a modified phenolic structure, as does δ-tocopherol (above). One of these
is 3-*tert*-butyl-4-hydroxyanisole, used to stabilize cooking oils at
the high temperatures required for the preparation of potato and
corn chips.

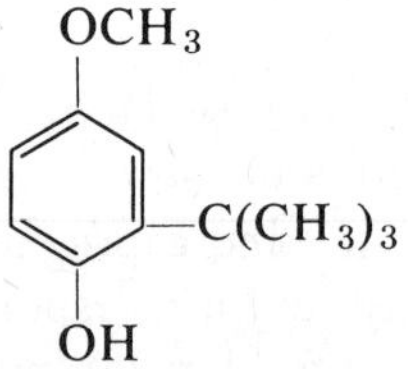

3-*tert*-Butyl-4-hydroxyanisole

Antioxidants effectively suppress rancidity when used in only
minute amounts (0.01–0.001%).

Table 11.2 shows a recent annual U.S. consumption of the
edible fats and oils in the processing of food products.

□■ TABLE 11.2*

FOOD FATS AND OILS CONSUMPTION — YEAR 1967[1]
MILLION POUNDS

	Amount Processed as[2]					
	Shorten-ing	Marga-rine	Salad and Cooking Oils for		Miscl. and Direct Use[6]	Total Edible Usage
			Salad Dressing and Mayon-naise[4]	All Others[5]		
Vegetable Oils[3]						
Soybean	1,708	1,234	718	736	51	4,447
Cottonseed	267	77	109	486	25	964
Corn	12	167	16	215	5	415
Peanut	24	5	—	132	9	170
Safflower	8	35	—	30	10	83
Olive	—	—	—	50	—	50
Coconut	40	16	—	—	305	361
Palm Kernel	2	2	—	—	82	86
Palm	61	—	—	—	8	69
Other	3	2	—	—	—	5
Animal Fats						
Lard	568	125	—	—	1,078	1,771
Tallow	497	10	—	—	10	517
Butter (Prod.)[7]	—	—	—	—	1,102	1,102
TOTAL	3,190	1,673	843	1,649	2,685	10,040

[1]Excludes fats and oils used in manufacture of products for export and overseas donation.

[2]Includes retail trade, food manufacturing usage, caterers, USDA Welfare Programs, etc.

[3]Use of refined and further processed oil in manufacture of edible products.

[4]Commercial usage.

[5]Includes retail trade, use of oil in commercial frying, roasting and other products.

[6]Vegetable oil usage consists mainly of confectionery fats, toppings, milk fillings, and other specialty fats; lard and butter is mainly direct distribution and used as such.

[7]Contains approximately 80 per cent fat.

Source: Based on Dept. of Commerce (Bureau of the Census) data for processing less exports and on USDA data for butter supplies.

*Courtesy Institute of Shortening and Edible Oils, Inc.

11.7 OXIDATION. (DRYING)

The highly unsaturated linseed and tung oils (Table 11.1) are especially reactive. The hydrogen atoms of the methylene group, flanked by doubly-bonded carbon atoms in both linoleic and linolenic acids, appear reactive enough to form peroxides, which then undergo polymerization.

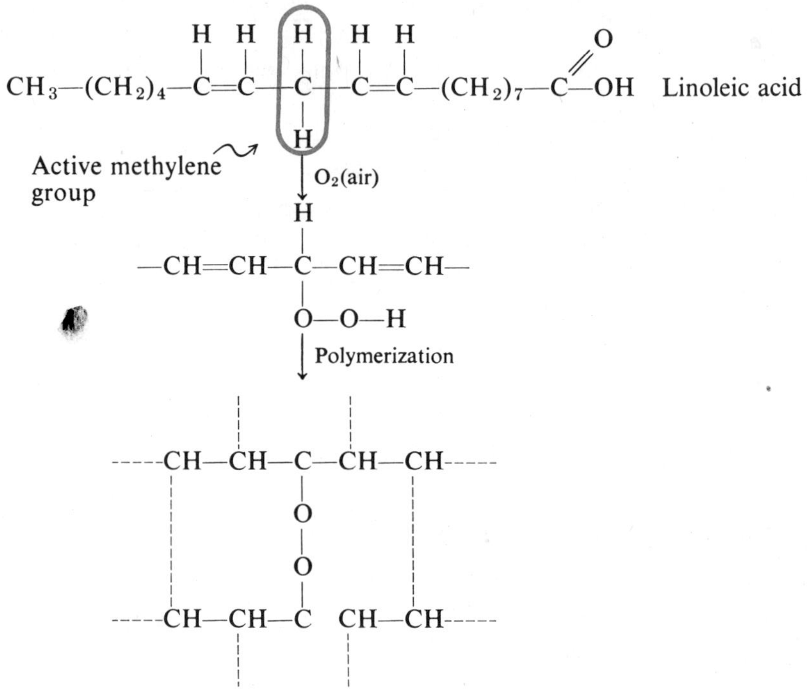

$$CH_3-(CH_2)_4-\overset{\overset{H}{|}}{C}=\overset{\overset{H}{|}}{C}-\overset{\overset{H}{|}}{\underset{\underset{H}{|}}{C}}-\overset{\overset{H}{|}}{C}=\overset{\overset{H}{|}}{C}-(CH_2)_7-\overset{\overset{O}{\parallel}}{C}-OH \quad \text{Linoleic acid}$$

Active methylene group

$\downarrow O_2(\text{air})$

$$-CH=CH-\overset{\overset{H}{|}}{\underset{\underset{O-O-H}{|}}{C}}-CH=CH-$$

$\downarrow$ Polymerization

$$----CH-CH-\overset{|}{\underset{\underset{\underset{\underset{CH}{|}}{O}}{\underset{|}{O}}}{C}}-CH-CH----$$
$$----CH-CH-\overset{|}{C} \quad CH-CH----$$

A cross-linked unit in a polymerized drying oil

Hydroperoxide formation, when accompanied by polymerization, converts highly unsaturated oils into a vast network of interlinked units. Such units form a hard, dry, tough film when exposed to air. Unsaturated oils are for this reason used in the vehicle — i.e., the liquid medium, of paints and varnishes as **drying oils.** A paint usually contains catalysts (lead and cobalt salts) to hasten the drying process. Other ingredients are finely ground pigments and volatile thinners such as turpentine.

Linoleum and **oilcloth** are made by applying a viscous mixture of drying oils, pigments, and fillers as a thick coating onto heavy fabric or cloth. When "dried" these products make very durable surface coverings. Because the oxidation of unsaturated vegetable oils is an exothermic reaction, oily rags used in painting are subject to spontaneous combustion. Such oily waste should be destroyed after use by burning or should be denied oxygen by keeping it in a closed container. This type of autoignition cannot occur if oily rags are spread out so that the heat generated by oxidation cannot build up to a kindling temperature.

11.8   DETERGENTS. (SOAPS AND SYNDETS)

Detergents (L., *detergere*, to wipe off) are cleansing agents and include both soaps and syndets (*syn*thetic *deter*gents). The molecular structures of synthetic detergents and soaps are similar. Both types of cleansing agents are characterized by the presence of a long, nonpolar, hydrophobic (water-hating) hydrocarbon tail and a polar, hydrophilic (water-loving) head.

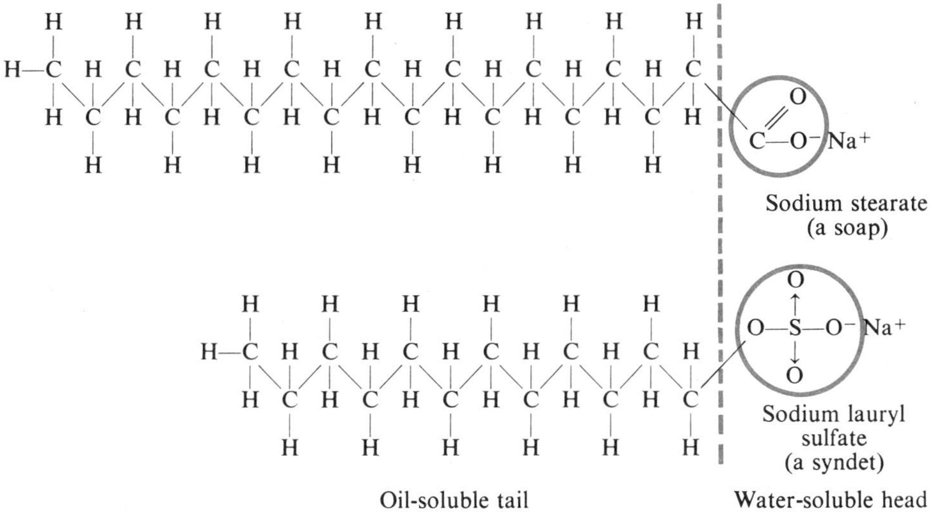

Sodium stearate
(a soap)

Sodium lauryl
sulfate
(a syndet)

Oil-soluble tail   Water-soluble head

Soaps, when used in hard water, precipitate as insoluble calcium, magnesium, and iron salts of the long-chain fatty acids, but synthetic detergents are not precipitated in the presence of these ions. Solubility in hard water is one of the principal advantages which a synthetic detergent has over a soap. On the other hand, the large scale use of syndets in this country within the past decade has presented a serious disposal problem. Many of these detergents have an aromatic ring in the hydrocarbon segment of the molecule. This type is generally classified as alkyl benzene sulfonate (ABS) detergents.

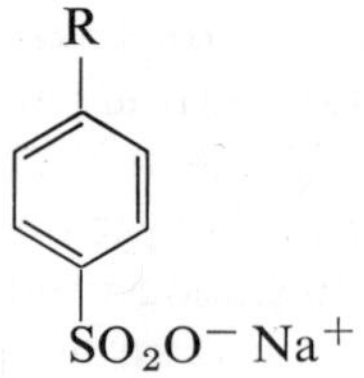

R

(R = long chain alkyl)

$SO_2O^- Na^+$

An alkyl benzene sulfonate

The benzene ring, you will recall, is very resistant to oxidation (Sec. 4.8-E). The straight-chain fatty acid salts with an even number of carbon atoms are biodegradable — that is, easily degraded by microorganisms. Unfortunately some of the early ABS types of detergents resisted degradation (breakdown) and reappeared in some fresh water sources quite active and sudsy. The long-chain hydrocarbon segments of both soap and synthetic detergent molecules shown above are embodied in the acid anion portion of sodium salts. This does not mean that a detergent, like a soap, must be a sodium or a potassium salt. On the contrary, the oil-soluble tail or "business end" of some detergents is cationic. Solubilizing power, not sudsing action, is the principal criterion for a good detergent. For this reason certain detergents have been developed, especially for use in automatic clothes and dish washers, that are neither anionic or cationic but are simply long-chain polar molecules not unlike the carbitols (Sec. 8.14). Examples of all three types of detergents are shown.

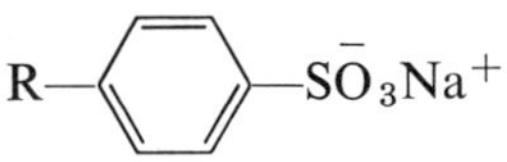

R—⟨ ⟩—$\bar{S}O_3Na^+$ R—$\overset{+}{N}(CH_3)_3Cl^-$

Anionic   Cationic
R = C_{12}—C_{18} R = C_{16}

R—⟨ ⟩—O—$(CH_2CH_2O)_x CH_2CH_2OH$

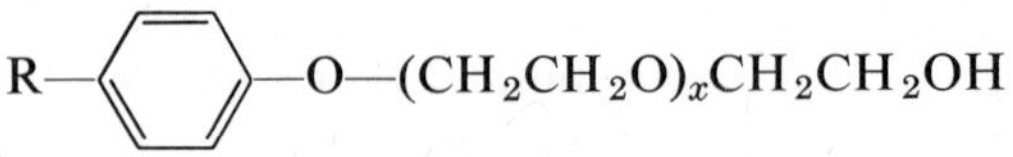

Nonionic
R = C_8—C_{10}; x = 8 — 12

The mechanics of detergent action seem to be the same for both soaps and syndets. In the removal of soil from clothing and grease from dishes, the hydrocarbon segment of the detergent molecule dissolves in the oily or greasy layer (like dissolves like). The oily layer then is dislodged as small globules by the mechanical action of rubbing, tumbling, or stirring. Once loosened, each globule becomes emulsified, or suspended in water, because the polar end of the detergent molecule is attracted to the polar water molecule. Such tiny droplets of "oil-in-water" emulsion do not coagulate, or condense, into huge globules because the electrical nature of the outer film surrounding each droplet is the same. A particle that has adjacent to its surface a double layer of charges of opposite sign is called a **micelle.** One micelle thus tends to repel the other. The role that a detergent or a soap molecule plays in the removal of oil is illustrated (in part) by Figure 11.1.

■ □ FIGURE 11.1

THE SOLVATING ACTION OF SOAP ON A DROPLET OF OIL

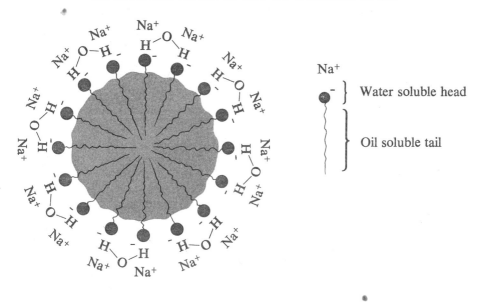

Water soluble head

Oil soluble tail

Exercise 11.3   Could a satisfactory soap be made from butter? Why?

11.9   DIGESTION AND METABOLISM OF FATS

Enzymes called *lipases*[3] are active in the hydrolysis of fats. Gastric lipase, found in the stomach, catalyzes the hydrolysis of fats but to a small extent.   Fats are hydrolyzed mainly in the small intestine where the environment is slightly alkaline.   In this part of the digestive tract the fat first is emulsified by the bile and then hydrolyzed by the action of pancreatic lipase (steapsin), an enzyme made in the pancreas.   The hydrolysis products, glycerol and fatty acids, are absorbed through the wall of the intestinal tract where recombination to form glycerides (fats) occurs.   Fats are transported from the intestinal wall to various parts of the body to be stored as depot fat, used in the formation of protoplasm, or oxidized to supply energy.

The body can make both saturated and monounsaturated fatty acids by modifying dietary fats or synthesizing them from carbohydrates or proteins.   However, certain polyunsaturated fatty acids, referred to as "essential" fatty acids, cannot be made and must be supplied in the diet.

Fats produce approximately 9.5 kcal of heat per gram when oxidized in the body to carbon dioxide and water.   This number of calories is more than twice the energy obtained from the oxidation of an equivalent weight of either protein or carbohydrate.

Fats, once deposited at a storage site, do not remain there for long.   The catabolism (degradation) and anabolism (synthesis) of fats represents a dynamic state.   Most recent evidence indicates that the essential unit in the synthesis or in the degradation of a fat is

$$CH_3-\overset{\overset{\displaystyle O}{\displaystyle \|}}{C}-$$

the acetyl group, CH_3-C-.   The discovery of coenzyme A (A = acetylation) by Lipmann[4] (1947) showed that this substance plays a principal role in metabolism *via* 2-carbon units related to acetic acid.   Coenzyme A is a complex molecule composed of four separately identifiable groups.

---

[3]Enzymes usually are named by appending **ase** to their functions.   Thus an **oxidase** catalyzes chemical combination with oxygen; **dehydrogenase,** the removal of hydrogen.   The fats and oils belong to a general classification of natural substances known as *lipids*.   Thus a **lipase** is an enzyme whose function is specific for a lipid, in this case a fat.

[4]Fritz Lipmann (1899–   ) Member and Professor of the Rockefeller Institute, New York.   Shared the Nobel prize (1953) in medicine and physiology with H. A. Krebs.

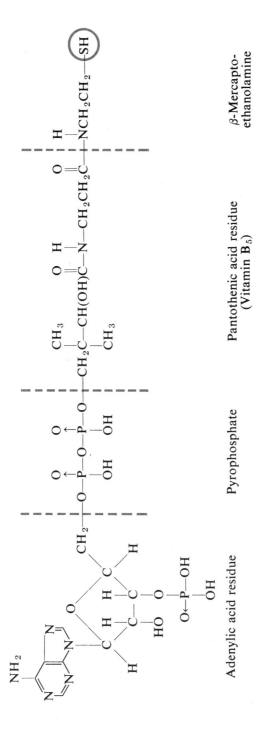

Coenzyme A

The terminal sulfhydryl (—SH) group is a very important part of the coenzyme A structure inasmuch as it is involved in transferring (donating or accepting) the acetyl group. The following equilibrium illustrates how coenzyme A might function.

$$
\underset{\text{CoA}}{\text{CoAS H}} \; + \; \underset{\text{Acetoacetyl CoA}}{\text{CH}_3-\overset{\overset{\displaystyle O}{\|}}{\text{C}}-\text{CH}_2-\overset{\overset{\displaystyle O}{\|}}{\text{C}}-\text{SCoA}} \; \rightleftharpoons \; \underset{\text{Acetyl CoA}}{2\,\text{CH}_3-\overset{\overset{\displaystyle O}{\|}}{\text{C}}-\text{SCoA}}
$$

The following proposed scheme shows one step in the 2-carbon degradation (or synthesis) of a fatty acid through combination with coenzyme A.

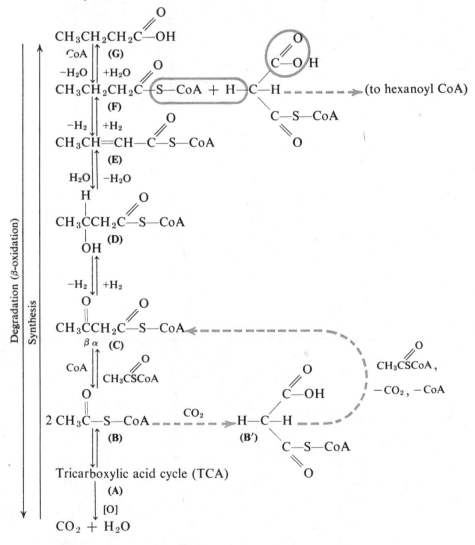

More recent findings indicate that the role of coenzyme A is not quite as simple as that shown in the illustration. After the formation of acetyl coenzyme A (B in sequence) it appears that an essential step (broken line route) in the synthesis of a fat is the reaction of a molecule of acetyl CoA with carbon dioxide to produce a reactive malonyl intermediate, (B′). The malonyl derivative then reacts with a second molecule of acetyl CoA. The loss of carbon dioxide and CoA from this intermediate forms (C). Reduction and subsequent loss of water, and a second reduction, produces butyryl CoA, (F). Butyryl CoA, like acetyl CoA, then condenses with another malonyl CoA intermediate to repeat the cycle, thus increasing the length of the chain by another two-carbon unit. All the reactions are essentially reversible and in normal metabolism of fats the 2-carbon degradation sequence (or synthesis) appears to be repeated each time via a β-keto ester (C).

The discovery of CoA and the mechanism postulated for fatty acid synthesis partly answers the question why the fatty acids predominantly are even-numbered.

□□ SUMMARY

Structure and Classification

[1] Fats, oils and waxes belong to a general classification of natural esters known as lipids.

[2] Waxes are simple esters in which both the acid and alcohol components are long-chain structures.

[3] Fats and oils are long-chain fatty acid esters of glycerol called glycerides. Glycerides may be simple (all fatty acids alike) or mixed (fatty acids different).

[4] Fatty acids may be predominantly saturated (as in fats) or unsaturated (as in oils).

[5] Saponification numbers provide an index to the molecular weight of a fat or oil.

[6] Iodine numbers reveal the degree of unsaturation of a fat or oil.

[7] The reactions of fats and oils may be summarized as follows.

    a. Alkaline hydrolysis (saponification) of a glyceride yields glycerol and soaps.

    b. Hardening (hydrogenation) converts oils to fats. Hydrogenation, if complete, converts a fat to glycerol and long-chain alcohols.

c. Hydrolysis and oxidation of *edible* oils and fats results in rancidity. Rancidity in fat and oil food products can be retarded by the addition of antioxidants.

d. Oxidation of unsaturated *inedible* oils with air forms peroxides and polymers. Such oils are used in paints and lacquers as drying oils.

[8] Fats and oils have more than twice the caloric value of carbohydrates and proteins.

[9] Detergents are cleansing agents and include both soaps and synthetic detergents. Synthetic detergents are called syndets.

[10] Soluble soaps are sodium or potassium salts of long-chain fatty acids; heavy metal salts are water insoluble.

[11] A syndet may be anionic — i.e., a sodium salt of a long-chain alcohol sulfate or an alkyl substituted aryl sulfonate; cationic — i.e., a long-chain substituted ammonium salt, or a long-chain nonionic structure.

[12] The mechanics of cleansing with soaps or with syndets are the same.

[13] Soaps precipitate in hard water; syndets do not.

[14] The catabolism (degradation) and anabolism (synthesis) of fats in the animal system appear to involve a sequence of 2-carbon units related to acetic acid. These degradations or syntheses take place via coenzyme A.

□□ *NEW TERMS*

[1]	anionic detergent	[9]	iodine value
[2]	antioxidant	[10]	lipase
[3]	cationic detergent	[11]	lipid
[4]	coenzyme-A	[12]	margarine
[5]	drying oil	[13]	nonionic detergent
[6]	emulsion	[14]	rancidity
[7]	glyceride	[15]	saponification value
[8]	hardening of oils	[16]	syndet

■ □ SUPPLEMENTARY EXERCISES
▼ AND PROBLEMS

[1]   Name the following compounds.

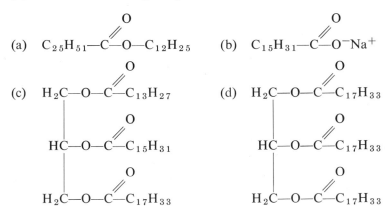

[2]   Draw structures for the following.

(a)   oleic acid
(b)   glyceryl butyropalmitostearate
(c)   a soap

(d)   a sulfate detergent
(e)   a sulfonate detergent
(f)   a cationic detergent

[3]   Draw structures of glycerides which might possibly be those of individual molecules found in

(a)   butter
(b)   tallow
(c)   linseed oil

(d)   tung oil
(e)   safflower oil.

(*Note: Consult Table 11.1*).

[4]   Calculate the saponification number and the iodine value for Compound (c), Exercise [1]. Check your values to see if they come within the ranges given in Table 11.1.

[5]   By means of equations illustrate chemical reactions which, when carried out with a fat or an oil, result in:

(a)   formation of soap
(b)   "hardening" of vegetable oil

(c)   drying of paint
(d)   rancidity in butter

[6]   A grease spot made by hot butter on a linen napkin may be removed by laundering. If the spot had been made on a woolen

flannel skirt or trousers it should be removed by "dry" cleaning. Explain the mechanics involved in each case.

[7]   Why does not soap lather easily in most deep well water?

[8]   Explain the difference between each of the following.

(a)   hydrolysis and saponification
(b)   a drying and a nondrying oil
(c)   a fat and an oil
(d)   a soap and a syndet
(e)   hydrolytic and oxidative rancidity
(f)   a fat and a wax

[9]   Why do most of the long-chain fatty acids contain an even number of carbon atoms?

[10]   The saponification number of a fat is 200 and its iodine value is 30.   Which of the saturated and unsaturated fatty acids probably predominate in this glyceride?   What general conclusions may be made concerning this fat?

chapter 12

Bifunctional Acids

INTRODUCTION

> Compounds discussed in previous chapters usually had but one functional group. Occasionally, as in the case of the diols and the dihalides, more than one functional group was encountered, but in these instances the groups were of the same kind. In the present chapter the compounds considered are primarily acids but have, in addition to the carboxyl, another functional group. The chemical behavior of a bifunctional acid, for the most part, is the behavior characteristic of each group separately. However, the dual nature of bifunctional acids confers special properties upon these compounds. Such changes in properties are particularly significant when the functional groups are in close proximity to each other.

Dicarboxylic Acids

12.2 NOMENCLATURE AND PROPERTIES

The aliphatic dicarboxylic acids are naturally occurring, colorless, crystalline solids often referred to by common names usually of Latin or Greek derivation. Such names frequently indicate a natural source of the acid. IUPAC nomenclature follows established rules. One simply adds the suffix *dioic* to the parent hydrocarbon of the same number of carbon atoms. For example, oxalic acid (HOOC—COOH), the simplest member of the dicarboxylic acid series, is named **ethanedioic acid.** Malonic acid (HOOC—CH_2— —COOH), the next member of the family, is named **propanedioic acid,** etc. Table 12.1 lists the common names and structures, along with the acidic properties, of the dicarboxylic acids containing 2–10

☐■TABLE 12.1

DICARBOXYLIC ACIDS: NAMES AND STRUCTURES

Name	Formula
Acetic* (L., *acetum*, vinegar)	CH_3COOH
Oxalic (Gr., *oxys*, sharp)	$HOOC{-}COOH$
Malonic (L., *malum*, apple)	$HOOC{-}CH_2{-}COOH$
Succinic (L., *succinum*, amber)	$HOOC{-}(CH_2)_2{-}COOH$
Glutaric (Composite of *glu*tamic + tar*taric*)	$HOOC{-}(CH_2)_3{-}COOH$
Adipic (L., *adipis*, fat)	$HOOC{-}(CH_2)_4{-}COOH$
Pimelic (Gr., *pimele*, fat)	$HOOC{-}(CH_2)_5{-}COOH$
Suberic (L., *suber*, cork)	$HOOC{-}(CH_2)_6{-}COOH$
Azelaic (Fr., *azote*, nitrogen; Gr. *elaion*, olive oil)	$HOOC{-}(CH_2)_7{-}COOH$
Sebacic (L., *sebum*, tallow)	$HOOC{-}(CH_2)_8{-}COOH$
o-Phthalic (Composite of na*phthal*ene + *ic*)	⬡—COOH ⬡—COOH
Maleic	$HOOC{-}\overset{H}{\underset{}{C}}{=}\overset{H}{\underset{}{C}}{-}COOH$
Fumaric (L., *fumus*, smoke)	$HOOC{-}\overset{H}{\underset{H}{C}}{=}\overset{}{\underset{H}{C}}{-}COOH$

*Included for reference value.

The first two members of the dicarboxylic acid family are much stronger acids than acetic acid. The presence of a second carboxyl group adjacent to, or near another, appears to withdraw electrons from the first. This inductive effect becomes weaker if the carboxyl functions are farther separated by intervening methylene groups. An electron withdrawal on the part of one carboxyl group tends to promote ionization of the other carboxyl group. The ionization of the second carboxyl group, once the first has been accomplished, is then rendered more difficult because the attraction of the negative charge on the first anion now must be overcome. The value of the second ionization constant, for this reason, is much smaller than that of the first.

□■ TABLE　12.1 *Continued*

DICARBOXYLIC ACIDS: MELTING POINTS AND ACID PROPERTIES

Name	M.P. (°C)	Ionization Constants, 25°	
		K_1	K_2
Acetic	16.6	1.8×10^{-5}	
Oxalic	187	3.5×10^{-2}	7×10^{-5}
Malonic	135 (dec.)	1.6×10^{-3}	4.5×10^{-6}
Succinic	185	6.4×10^{-5}	
Glutaric	97.5	4.7×10^{-5}	
Adipic	151	4×10^{-5}	
Pimelic	105	4×10^{-5}	
Suberic	142	3×10^{-5}	
Azelaic	106	2.5×10^{-5}	
Sebacic	134	2×10^{-5}	
o-Phthalic	191	1.2×10^{-5}	K_2 is approximately the same for the C_4–C_{10} acids, 3×10^{-6}.
Maleic	130	1.2×10^{-2}	3.9×10^{-7}
Fumaric	287	9.3×10^{-4}	1.8×10^{-5}

12.3　PREPARATION AND REACTIONS OF THE DICARBOXYLIC ACIDS

Dicarboxylic acids usually can be prepared by adapting methods used for the preparation of the monocarboxylic acids. Functional groups easily convertible to carboxyl groups usually provide a route to the dicarboxylic acids. For example, the oxidation of diols (glycols), the oxidation of unsaturated acids, and the hydrolysis of nitriles are methods frequently used. The preparation of oxalic, malonic, and azelaic acids by such methods are illustrated in the following reactions.

Oxidation of a diol

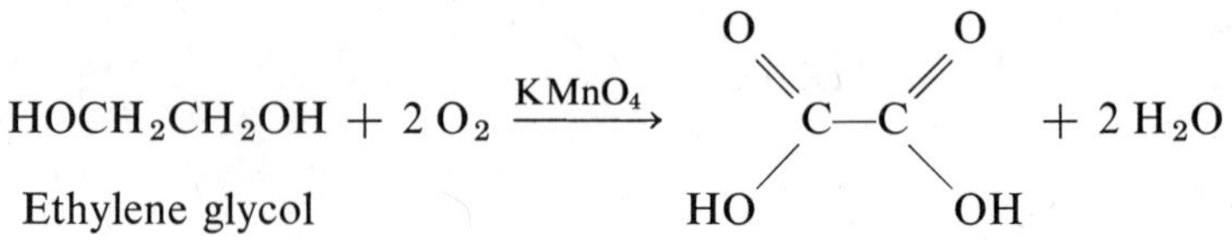

$$HOCH_2CH_2OH + 2\,O_2 \xrightarrow{KMnO_4} \underset{HO}{\overset{O}{\underset{\diagdown}{\overset{\parallel}{C}}}} - \underset{OH}{\overset{O}{\underset{\diagdown}{\overset{\parallel}{C}}}} + 2\,H_2O$$

Ethylene glycol

Oxalic acid

Oxidation of an unsaturated acid

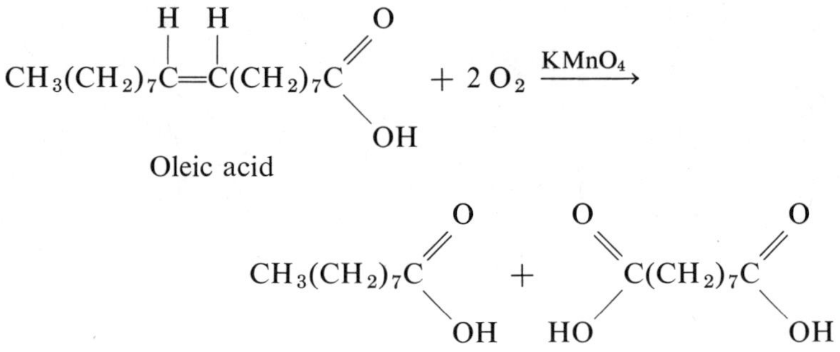

$$CH_3(CH_2)_7\overset{H}{\underset{|}{C}}=\overset{H}{\underset{|}{C}}(CH_2)_7\overset{O}{\underset{OH}{\overset{\parallel}{C}}} + 2\,O_2 \xrightarrow{KMnO_4}$$

Oleic acid

$$CH_3(CH_2)_7\overset{O}{\underset{OH}{\overset{\parallel}{C}}} + \underset{HO}{\overset{O}{\overset{\parallel}{C}}}(CH_2)_7\overset{O}{\underset{OH}{\overset{\parallel}{C}}}$$

Nonanoic acid   Azelaic acid

Hydrolysis of a nitrile

$$ClCH_2COOH + NaHCO_3 \rightarrow ClCH_2COO^-Na^+ + H_2O + CO_2$$
Chloroacetic   Sodium
acid   chloroacetate

$$ClCH_2COO^-Na^+ + K^+CN^- \rightarrow N\equiv C—CH_2COO^-Na^+ + KCl$$
Sodium cyanoacetate

$$N\equiv C—CH_2COO^-Na^+ + 2\,HCl + 2\,H_2O \rightarrow$$

$$HOOC—CH_2—COOH + NH_4Cl + NaCl$$

Malonic acid

The derivatives of the dicarboxylic acids are, in general, the same as those produced from the monocarboxylic acids and include salts, esters, amides, and acid halides. The behavior of the dicarboxylic acids, when heated, is unique, however, and deserves special mention.

Oxalic acid, when strongly heated, undergoes decomposition according to the following equation.

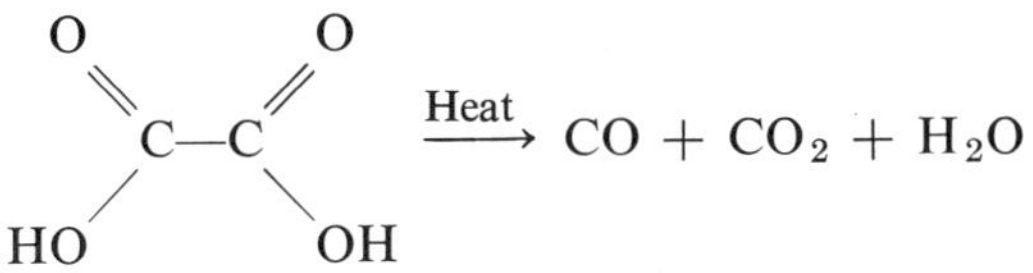

$$\underset{\underset{\text{Oxalic acid}}{HO}}{\overset{O}{\diagdown}}C - C\overset{O}{\underset{OH}{\diagup}} \xrightarrow{\text{Heat}} CO + CO_2 + H_2O$$

Malonic acid is so easily decomposed by heat that it is decarboxylated at its melting point (137°C).

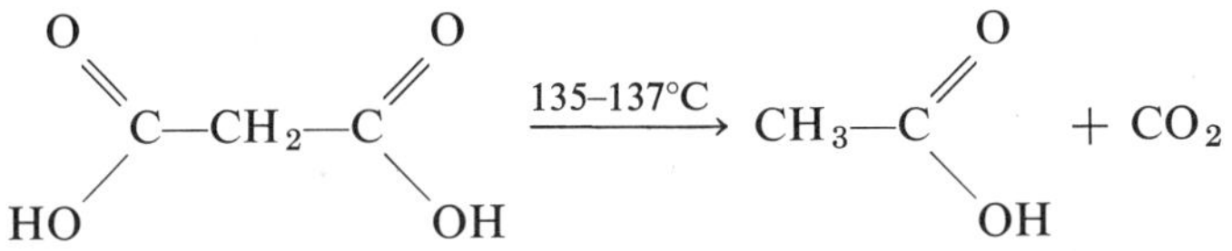

$$\underset{\underset{\text{Malonic acid}}{HO}}{\overset{O}{\diagdown}}C - CH_2 - C\overset{O}{\underset{OH}{\diagup}} \xrightarrow{135\text{–}137°C} \underset{\underset{\text{Acetic acid}}{}}{CH_3 - C}\overset{O}{\underset{OH}{\diagup}} + CO_2$$

Succinic and glutaric acids, when heated, lose water to produce their corresponding cyclic anhydrides.

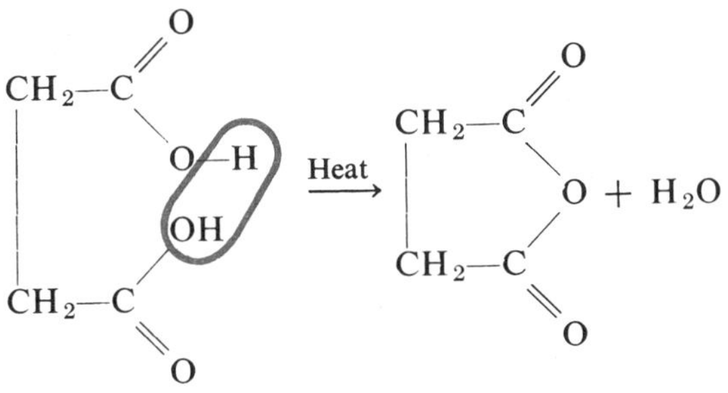

$$\begin{array}{c} CH_2 - C\overset{O}{\diagup} \\ | \qquad\quad O\!\!-\!\!H \\ | \qquad\quad OH \\ CH_2 - C\overset{}{\diagdown_{O}} \end{array} \xrightarrow{\text{Heat}} \begin{array}{c} CH_2 - C\overset{O}{\diagup} \\ | \qquad\quad O + H_2O \\ CH_2 - C\overset{}{\diagdown_{O}} \end{array}$$

Succinic acid   Succinic anhydride

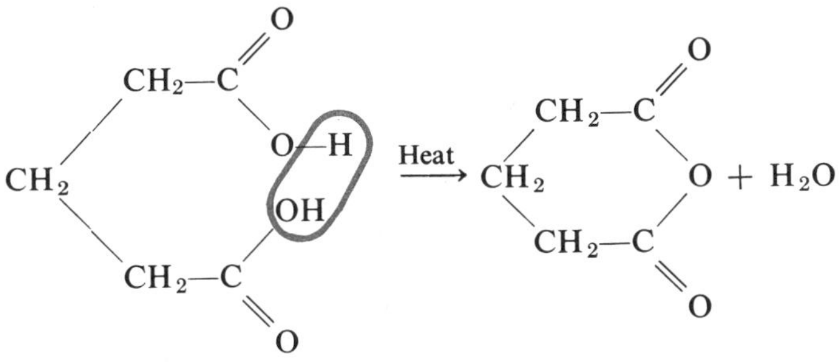

$$\begin{array}{c} CH_2 - C\overset{O}{\diagup} \\ CH_2 \qquad O\!\!-\!\!H \\ \qquad\quad OH \\ CH_2 - C\overset{}{\diagdown_{O}} \end{array} \xrightarrow{\text{Heat}} \begin{array}{c} CH_2 - C\overset{O}{\diagup} \\ CH_2 \qquad\quad O + H_2O \\ CH_2 - C\overset{}{\diagdown_{O}} \end{array}$$

Glutaric acid   Glutaric anhydride

Exercise 12.1   Why is it not possible to convert a halogen acid into a Grignard reagent and then, by carbonation of the Grignard reagent with anhydrous CO_2, form a second carboxyl group?

12.4   THE MALONIC ESTER SYNTHESIS

Substituted malonic acids, like malonic acid, also are easily decarboxylated. The ease with which carbon dioxide can be split out from only one carboxyl group of malonic acid makes it a very useful acid in a number of organic syntheses. A synthesis which involves a substituted malonic acid begins with its ethyl ester, diethyl malonate, or "malonic ester" as it usually is called. The methylene carbon of ethyl malonate is flanked on both sides by electron-withdrawing carbonyl groups. This dual influence makes the α-hydrogens especially mobile (acidic) and easily removed by a basic reagent, such as sodium ethoxide. The anion of sodiomalonic ester, when formed, is nucleophilic and reacts readily with alkyl halides.

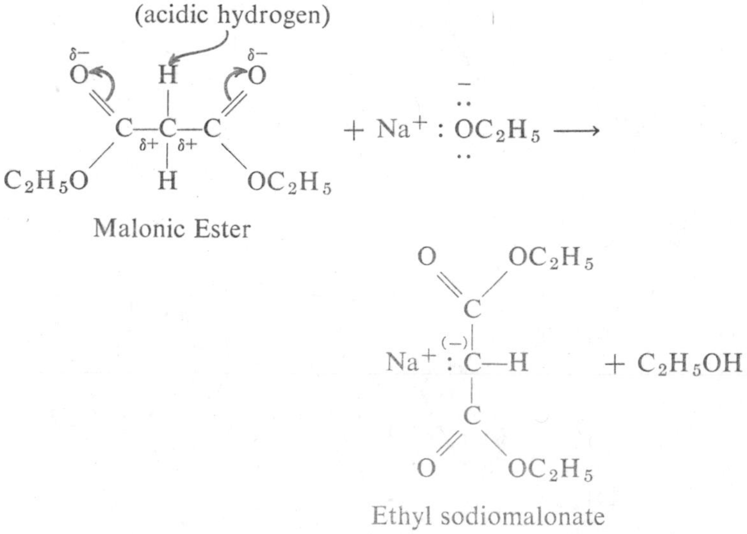

Malonic Ester

Ethyl sodiomalonate

Many synthetic organic compounds may be prepared *via* a substituted malonic ester. Indeed, the "malonic ester synthesis" often is the only route open to the preparation of a number of desirable

compounds. The usefulness of the malonic ester synthesis is illustrated by the following two reaction sequences. Sequence (A)
illustrates the preparation of one of the barbiturates (malonylureas)
commonly used in medicine as hypnotics (sleeping tablets). Sequence
(B) illustrates the formation of a branched-chain monocarboxylic
acid.

(A) *The Preparation of 5, 5-Diethylbarbituric acid.*

Step 1

$$
\begin{array}{c}
\text{O} \quad \text{OC}_2\text{H}_5 \\
\diagdown \diagup \\
\text{C} \\
|\\
\text{H}\!-\!\text{C}\!-\!\text{H} \\
|\\
\text{C} \\
\diagup\diagdown \\
\text{O} \quad \text{OC}_2\text{H}_5
\end{array}
\quad + \text{Na}^+\ {}^-\text{OC}_2\text{H}_5 \longrightarrow \text{Na}^+ :
\begin{array}{c}
\text{O} \quad \text{OC}_2\text{H}_5 \\
\diagdown \diagup \\
\text{C} \\
{}^{(-)}|\\
\text{C}\!-\!\text{H} \\
|\\
\text{C} \\
\diagup\diagdown \\
\text{O} \quad \text{OC}_2\text{H}_5
\end{array}
\quad + \text{C}_2\text{H}_5\text{OH}
$$

Step 2

$$
\text{Na}^+ :
\begin{array}{c}
\text{O} \quad \text{OC}_2\text{H}_5 \\
\diagdown \diagup \\
\text{C} \\
{}^{(-)}|\\
\text{C}\!-\!\text{H} \\
|\\
\text{C} \\
\diagup\diagdown \\
\text{O} \quad \text{OC}_2\text{H}_5
\end{array}
\quad \xrightarrow{\text{C}_2\text{H}_5\text{I}} \quad
\begin{array}{c}
\text{O} \quad \text{OC}_2\text{H}_5 \\
\diagdown \diagup \\
\text{C} \\
|\\
\text{C}_2\text{H}_5\!-\!\text{C}\!-\!\text{H} \\
|\\
\text{C} \\
\diagup\diagdown \\
\text{O} \quad \text{OC}_2\text{H}_5
\end{array}
$$

Ethyl malonic ester

Step 3

$$
\begin{array}{c}
\text{O} \quad \text{OC}_2\text{H}_5 \\
\diagdown \diagup \\
\text{C} \\
|\\
\text{C}_2\text{H}_5\!-\!\text{C}\!-\!\text{H} \\
|\\
\text{C} \\
\diagup\diagdown \\
\text{O} \quad \text{OC}_2\text{H}_5
\end{array}
\quad \xrightarrow[\text{2. C}_2\text{H}_5\text{I}]{\text{1. }^-\text{OC}_2\text{H}_5} \quad
\begin{array}{c}
\text{O} \quad \text{OC}_2\text{H}_5 \\
\diagdown \diagup \\
\text{C} \\
|\\
\text{C}_2\text{H}_5\!-\!\text{C}\!-\!\text{C}_2\text{H}_5 \\
|\\
\text{C} \\
\diagup\diagdown \\
\text{O} \quad \text{OC}_2\text{H}_5
\end{array}
$$

Diethyl malonic ester

Step 4

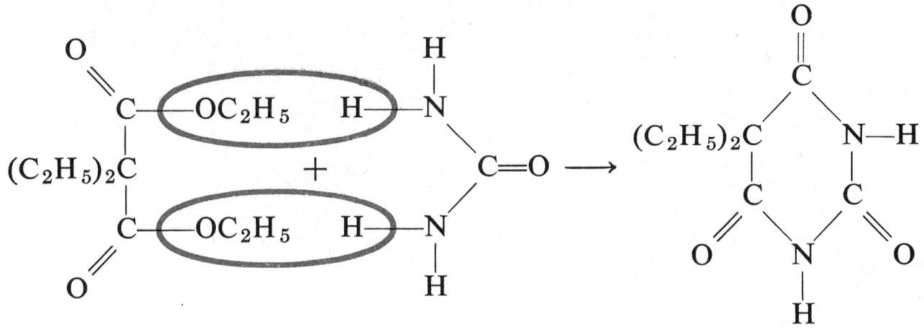

Urea

5, 5-Diethylbarbituric acid
(Barbital)

(B) *The Preparation of 4-Methylpentanoic acid.*

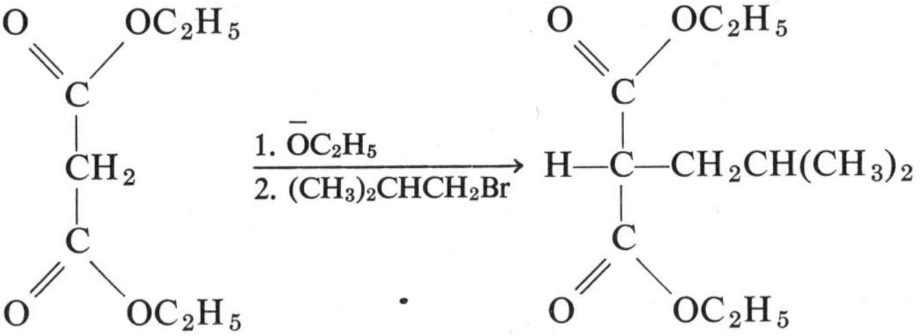

Ethyl isobutylmalonate

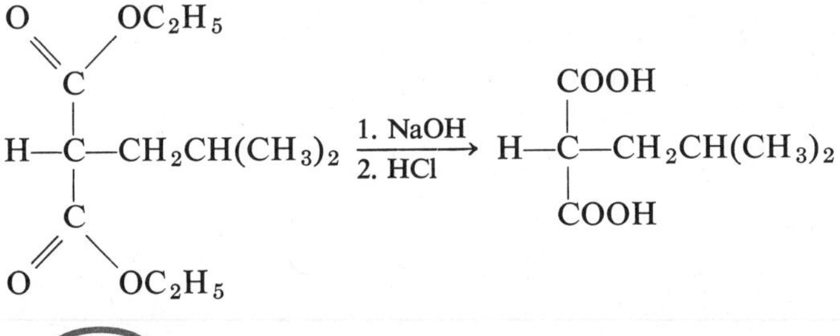

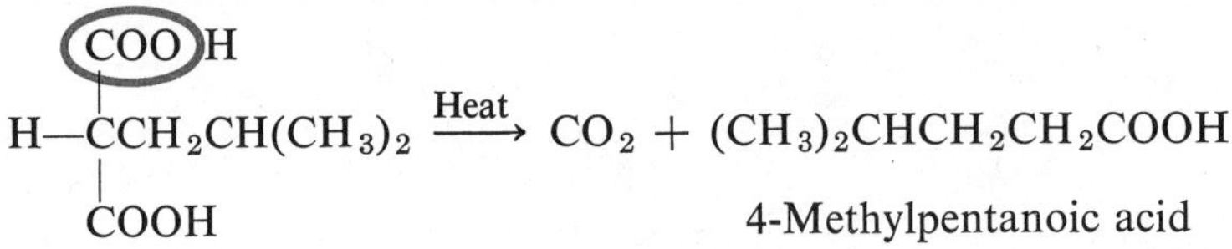

$$H-\underset{\underset{COOH}{|}}{\overset{\overset{\boxed{COOH}}{|}}{C}}CH_2CH(CH_3)_2 \xrightarrow{\text{Heat}} CO_2 + (CH_3)_2CHCH_2CH_2COOH$$

4-Methylpentanoic acid

Exercise 12.2   What product would you obtain if ethyl phenylmalonate were hydrolyzed in alkaline solution, then acidified and strongly heated?

1 2 . 5   OTHER IMPORTANT DICARBOXYLIC ACIDS

Adipic acid, used in large quantities for the production of nylon (Sec. 17.3), is an important industrial chemical. One commercial method for the production of adipic acid uses cyclohexanol as starting material. Cyclohexanol is oxidized to adipic acid according to the following reaction.

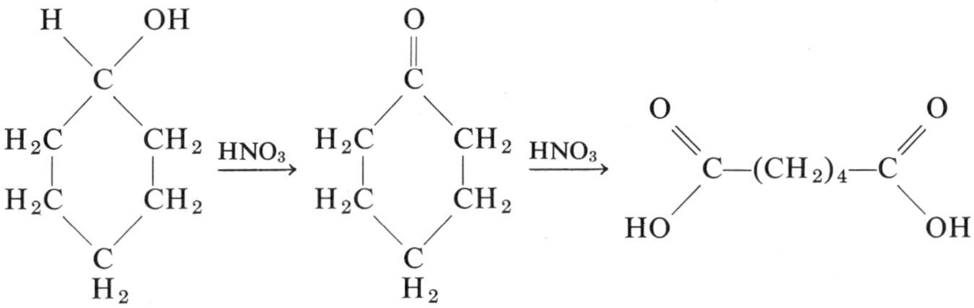

Cyclohexanol   Cyclohexanone   Adipic acid

Corn cobs and oat hulls provide another abundant source of raw material for the preparation of adipic acid. Furfural, an aromatic aldehyde obtainable from such agricultural wastes, can be converted into adipic acid through a series of reactions illustrated in Sec. 17.3.

o-Phthalic acid, or 1, 2-benzenedicarboxylic acid, is one of the more useful aromatic dicarboxylic acids. Phthalic acid, as it is simply called, is obtained by the vigorous oxidation of naphthalene (Sec. 10.5-A and 4.8). The *para* isomer, terephthalic acid, is prepared by the oxidation of the methyl groups of *p*-xylene.

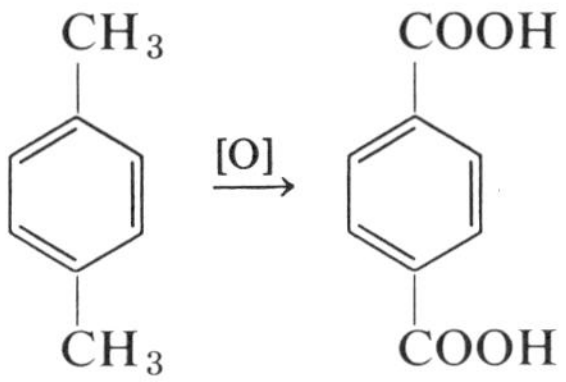

p-Xylene   Terephthalic acid
               (1, 4-Benzene-
               dicarboxylic acid)

Phthalic and terephthalic acids, when esterified with polyhydric alcohols, produce high molecular weight polyesters. The reaction of phthalic acid with ethylene glycol or with glycerol produces the **glyptal resins** (*gly*cerol + *phthal*ic acid) that are now widely used as synthetic auto finishes. The synthetic fiber known as "Dacron" or "Terylene" is a polyester of ethylene glycol and terephthalic acid. Dacron is not produced by the direct esterification of terephthalic acid, but rather by an ester interchange (alcoholysis) between methyl terephthalate and ethylene glycol.

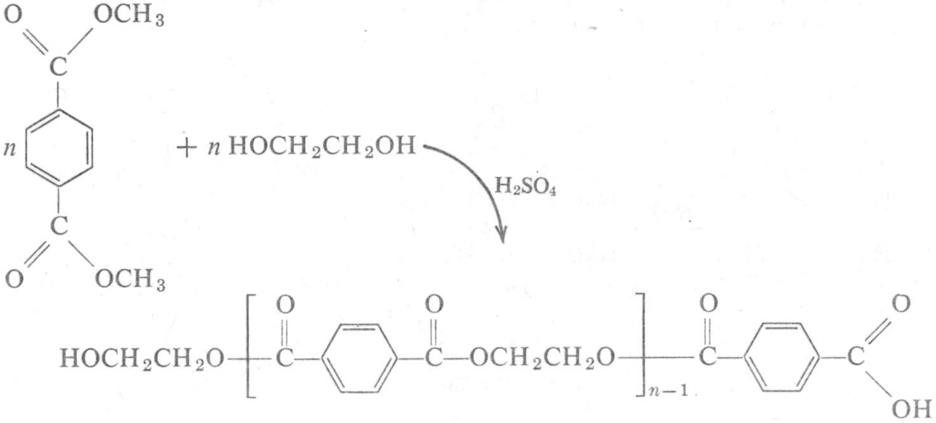

Dacron

The same polyester, when produced in the form of a film, is marketed under the trade name "Mylar."

Hydroxy and Halogen Acids

12.6 STRUCTURE AND NOMENCLATURE

Certain of the hydroxy acids are very common naturally occurring substances and usually are referred to by common names. The halogen acids, on the other hand, are mostly synthetic and are named systematically. Hydroxy and halogen substituents on the carbon chain can be located either by numbers or by Greek letters. The examples below illustrate both methods of nomenclature.

$$\overset{\beta}{\underset{(3)}{CH_3}}-\overset{\alpha}{\underset{(2)}{CH}}(OH)-\underset{(1)}{COOH} \qquad \overset{\beta}{\underset{(3)}{CH_3}}-\overset{\alpha}{\underset{(2)}{CH}}(Br)-\underset{(1)}{COOH}$$

2-Hydroxypropanoic acid α-Hydroxypropionic acid (Lactic acid)	2-Bromopropanoic acid α-Bromopropionic acid

Table 12.2 lists some of the more common hydroxy acids along with their structures and acidic properties.

PREPARATION AND REACTIONS OF SUBSTITUTED ACIDS

The chemistry of substituted acids is interrelated. A method that leads to the preparation of one substituted acid usually involves a reaction of another acid already bearing a different replaceable substituent.

Acids that have a halogen atom on the α-carbon atom are important starting materials for a number of substituted acids. Such

□■ TABLE 12.2

NATURALLY OCCURRING HYDROXY ACIDS

Common Name	Structure	Ionization Constants, 25°C
Glycolic (*Glycerol*)	$HOCH_2COOH$	1.5×10^{-4}
Lactic (L. *lactis*, milk)	$CH_3{-}CH{-}COOH$ $\qquad\quad\ \ \overset{\|}{OH}$	1.4×10^{-4}
Malic (L. *malus*, apple)	$\overset{H}{\overset{\|}{HO{-}C{-}COOH}}$ $\qquad\ \ \underset{CH_2COOH}{\|}$	$K_1\quad 4 \times 10^{-4}$ $K_2\quad 9 \times 10^{-6}$
Tartaric	$\overset{H}{\overset{\|}{HO{-}C{-}COOH}}$ $HO{-}\overset{\|}{\underset{\|}{C}}{-}COOH$ $\qquad\ \ \ H$	$K_1\ \ 9.6 \times 10^{-4}$ $K_2\ \ 2.9 \times 10^{-5}$
Citric (L. *citrum*, lemon, lime)	$CH_2{-}COOH$ $HO{-}\overset{\|}{C}{-}COOH$ $CH_2{-}COOH$	$K_1\ \ 8.7 \times 10^{-4}$ $K_2\ \ 1.8 \times 10^{-5}$ $K_3\quad 4 \times 10^{-6}$
Salicylic (L. *salix*, willow)	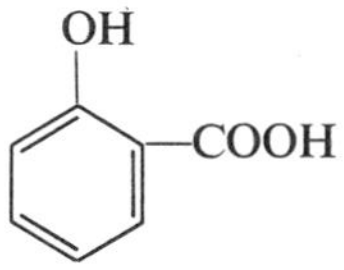	$K_1\quad 1 \times 10^{-3}$ $K_2\ \ 3.6 \times 10^{-14}$
Mandelic (Gr. *mandel*, almond)	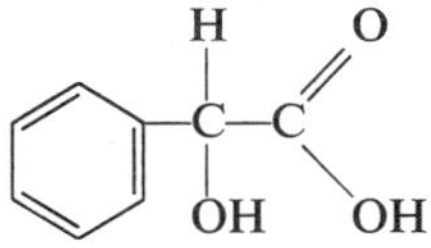	4.3×10^{-4}

α-halogen acids are easily prepared *via* the Hell-Volhard-Zelinsky reaction (Sec. 10.6-D). The reactions exhibited by halogen acids are similar in nature to those reviewed for the alkyl halides. For example, dehydrohalogenation with alcoholic potassium hydroxide converts a halogen acid to an unsaturated acid.

$$
\underset{\alpha\text{-Bromopropionic acid}}{
H-\overset{\displaystyle H}{\underset{\displaystyle H}{C}}-\overset{\displaystyle H}{\underset{\displaystyle Br}{C}}-C\overset{\displaystyle O}{\diagdown_{OH}}}
\xrightarrow[\text{KOH}]{\text{Alcoholic}}
\underset{\text{Acrylic acid}}{CH_2{=}\overset{\displaystyle H}{C}-COOH} + H_2O + K^+Br^-
$$

Now if we were to add hydrogen bromide to acrylic acid it would not, as you might expect, reform the original halogen acid. Markovnikov's rule (Sec. 3.9) is not followed when HBr is added to an α, β-unsaturated acid. The electrophilic nature of the carboxyl group diminishes the electron density around the β-carbon atom. The negative portion of the reagent, bromide ion in this case, bonds to the carbon with the greater number of hydrogens. A β-halogen acid thus may be obtained from an α-halogen acid through the elimination and subsequent addition of hydrogen halide.

$$
\underset{\text{Acrylic acid}}{H-\overset{\displaystyle H}{C}{=}\overset{\displaystyle H}{C}-COOH}
\xrightarrow{\text{HBr}}
\underset{\beta\text{-Bromopropionic acid}}{H-\overset{\displaystyle H}{\underset{\displaystyle Br}{C}}-CH_2-COOH}
$$

Hydrolysis of a halogen acid with dilute aqueous alkali produces the corresponding hydroxy acid.

$$
CH_3-\overset{\displaystyle H}{\underset{\displaystyle Br}{C}}-COOH + Na^+OH^- \rightarrow \underset{\text{Lactic acid}}{CH_3-\overset{\displaystyle H}{\underset{\displaystyle OH}{C}}-COOH} + Na^+Br^-
$$

Hydroxy acids also may be prepared by the hydrolysis of cyanohydrins (Sec. 9.7-A).

The hydroxy acids, when heated strongly, show a tendency to lose water. Strong heating converts α-hydroxy acids into cyclic diesters known as lactides. In the intermolecular action of two molecules of α-hydroxy acid to form a lactide, each molecule supplies both an alcohol and an acid function for the esterification of the other.

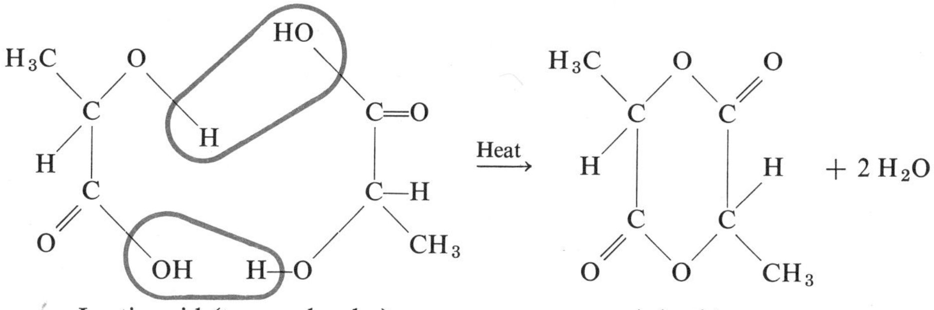

Lactic acid (two molecules)   A lactide

The β-hydroxy acids, when heated strongly, form α, β-unsaturated acids.

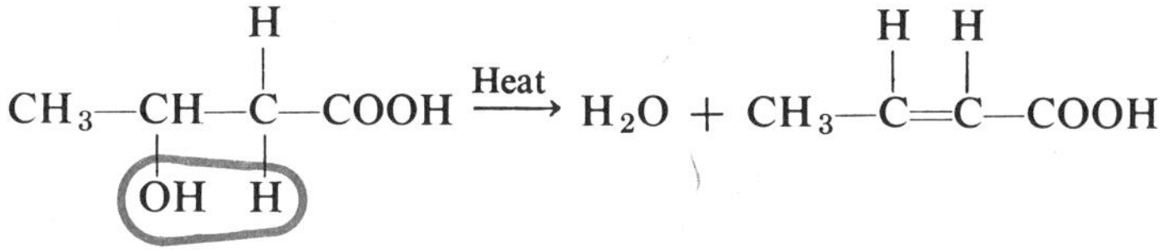

β-Hydroxybutyric acid   2-Butenoic acid
                                         (Crotonic acid)

The γ- and the δ-hydroxy acids can react intramolecularly to produce five- and six-atom cyclic inner esters known as γ- and δ-lactones.

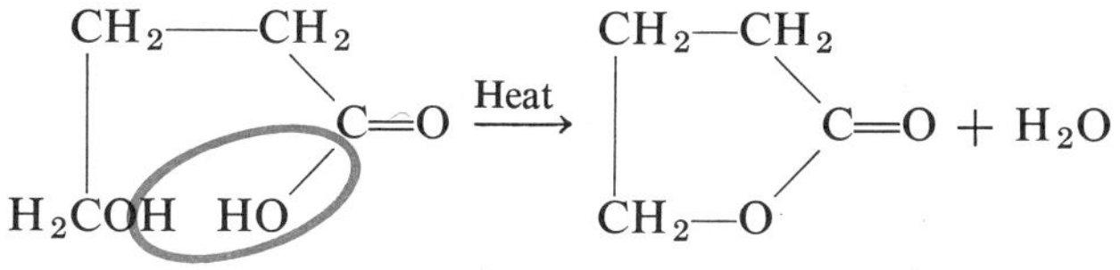

γ-Hydroxybutyric acid   γ-Butyrolactone

If, instead of the hydroxyl group, the amino group, (—NH₂), is a substituent in the γ or δ position, heating produces analogous compounds in which the nitrogen atom becomes part of the ring. Such compounds are called γ- and δ-lactams.

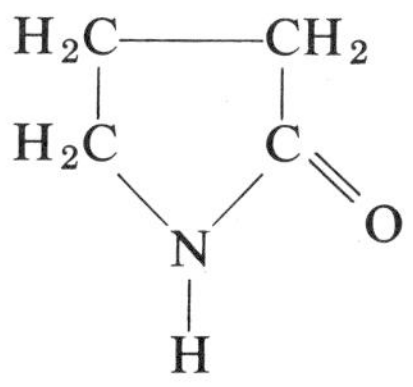

γ-Butyrolactam

One of the most important aromatic hydroxy acids, perhaps, is salicylic, or o-hydroxybenzoic, acid. The importance of salicylic acid and its derivatives lies in the fact that they are widely used as antipyretics and analgesics.

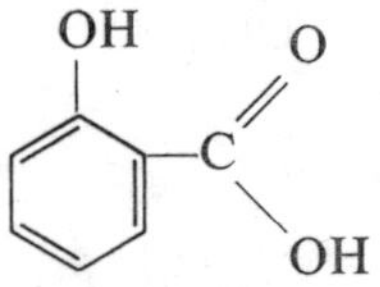

Salicylic acid

Salicylic acid is manufactured commercially in large quantities by heating sodium phenoxide with carbon dioxide under high pressure. The free acid is obtained from its sodium salt by treatment with mineral acid.

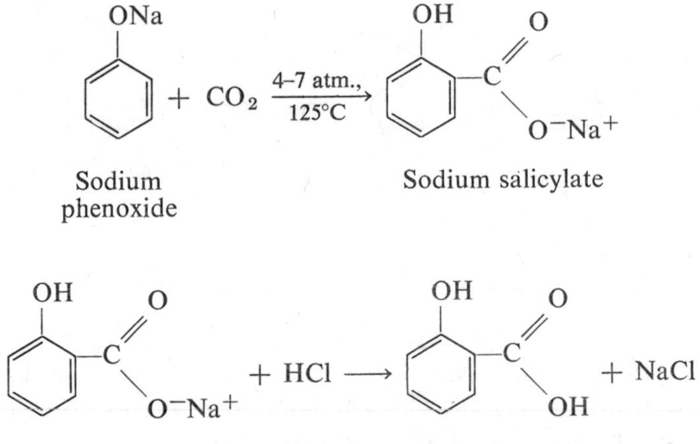

Sodium
phenoxide   Sodium salicylate

Salicylic acid

Salicylic acid is a stronger acid than benzoic due to the presence of the adjacent phenolic group. The ionization of salicylic acid is promoted because the salicylate ion, once formed, is stabilized by H-bonding between the phenolic hydrogen and one or the other of the oxygen atoms of the carboxylate group.

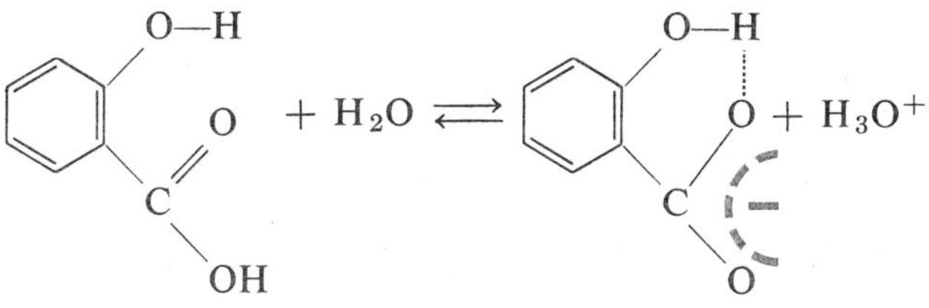

Salicylic acid   Salicylate ion

Salicylic acid is the starting material for the preparation of several very useful esters. In some of these the carboxyl group is involved, in others only the phenolic group. Esters formed from only the carboxyl group of salicylic acid are called *salicylates*. Methyl salicylate, a flavoring agent widely used in confections and in tooth pastes, and referred to as *oil of wintergreen*, is an example of such an ester. It is prepared by the direct esterification of salicylic acid by methyl alcohol.

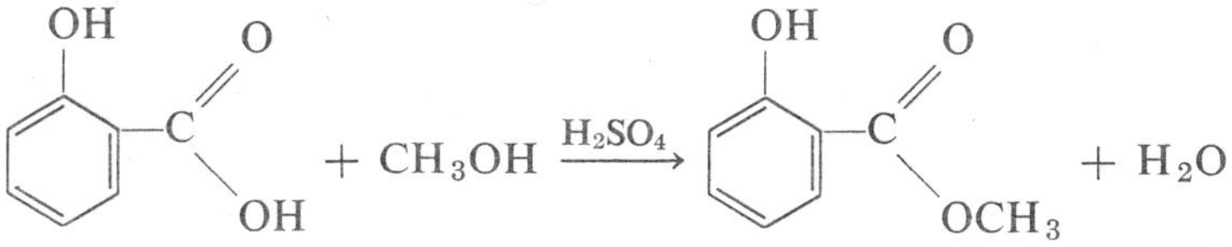

Methyl salicylate
(Oil of wintergreen)

Aspirin is by far the best example of an ester involving only the phenolic group of salicylic acid. Aspirin, or acetylsalicylic acid, is prepared by acetylation of the hydroxy group by acetic anhydride.

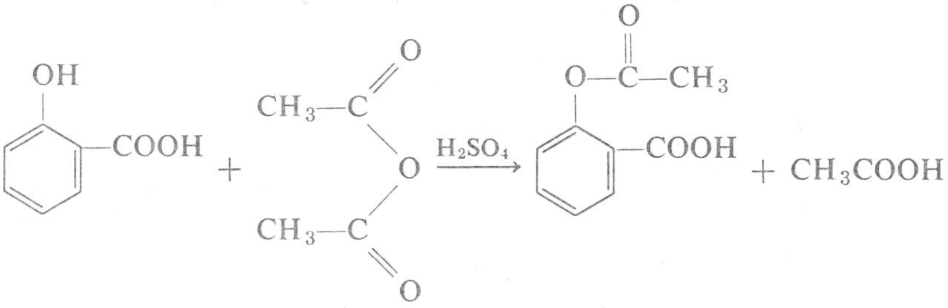

Acetic anhydride   Acetyl salicylic acid
(Aspirin)

Phenyl salicylate, or **Salol,** is used as an enteric coating for pills and tablets. An orally administered medicinal, if uncoated, is subject to hydrolysis in the acid environment of the stomach and either its effectiveness may be lost or a gastric disturbance may result. The coating of salol ensures safe passage into the intestine where, upon reaching an alkaline environment, the coating is hydrolyzed and the medicinal released.

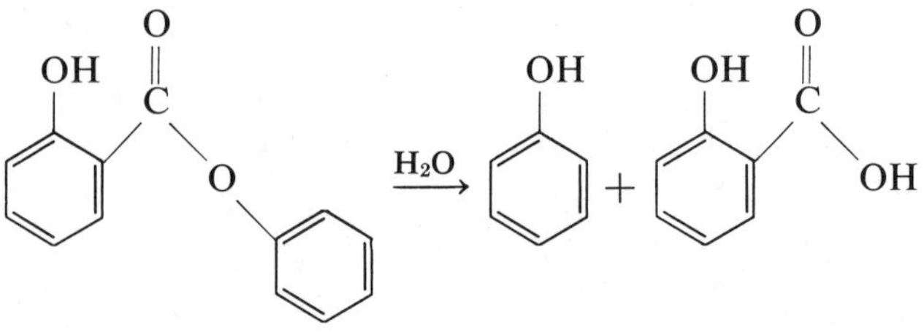

Phenyl salicylate   Phenol   Salicylic acid
(Salol)

12.8   KETO ACIDS

Certain of the keto acids play vital roles as metabolic intermediates in biological oxidation and reduction reactions. Pyruvic acid, $CH_3C—C—OH$, and acetoacetic acid are especially important. Pyruvic acid is a principal intermediate in the aerobic metabolism of carbohydrates and the precursor to oxalacetic acid, without which the tricarboxylic acid cycle will not operate (see Fig. 14.1). Inspection of the scheme outlined for the metabolism of fatty acids (Sec. 11.9) shows the CoA ester of acetoacetic acid also as an intermediate in the metabolic process. The abnormal metabolism of fatty acids by diabetics, if uncontrolled, releases an excess of acetoacetic acid into the blood stream. The tendency of β-keto acids to decarboxylate results in the release of acetone. The accumulation of acetoacetic acid and acetone in the blood may reach concentrations sufficient to cause death.

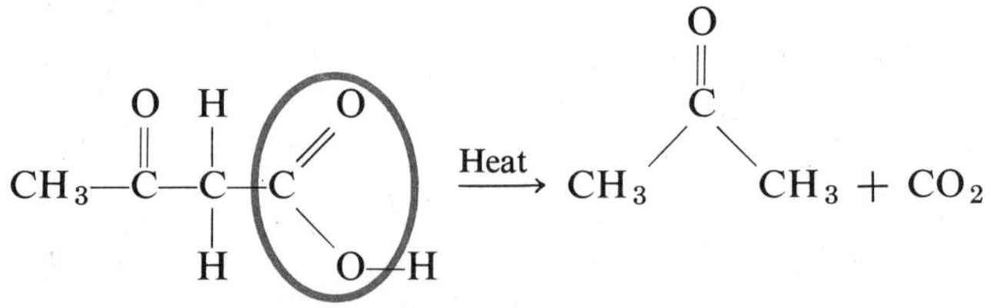

Acetoacetic acid   Acetone

The readiness with which a β-keto acid decarboxylates, when heated, makes it a useful intermediate in a number of organic syntheses. The α-hydrogen atoms of a β-keto ester are active and may be substituted in the same manner as those of malonic ester (Sec. 12.4). The substituted ester, when saponified, treated with a mineral acid, and heated, loses carbon dioxide to yield a ketone, one group of which is always methyl. This sequence of reactions, called the *acetoacetic ester synthesis*, is illustrated in the preparation of 2-hexanone.

$$CH_3\text{---}\overset{\overset{O}{\|}}{C}\text{---}CH_2C\overset{\overset{O}{/\!\!/}}{\underset{OC_2H_5}{\diagdown}} \quad \begin{Bmatrix} 1.\ C_2H_5O^-Na^+ \\ 2.\ n\text{-}C_3H_7Br \\ 3.\ Na^+\bar{O}H \\ 4.\ H_3\overset{+}{O},\ heat \end{Bmatrix} \longrightarrow CH_3\text{---}\overset{\overset{O}{\|}}{C}\text{---}CH_2CH_2CH_2CH_3$$

Ethyl acetoacetate   2-Hexanone

Exercise 12.3   In step (2) of the previous reaction sequence a tertiary alkyl halide may not be used. Why?

---

1 2 . 9   UNSATURATED ACIDS. GEOMETRICAL ISOMERISM

Malic acid, when strongly heated, loses the elements of water from adjacent carbon atoms to yield maleic and fumaric acids — two isomeric unsaturated dicarboxylic acids.

Malic acid

Maleic acid
(*cis*-Butenedioic acid)
M.P. 130°C

Fumaric acid
(*trans*-Butenedioic acid)
M.P. 287°C

Maleic acid when heated loses water to form an anhydride. Fumaric acid, on the other hand, is incapable of anhydride formation. However, when heated to a sufficiently high temperature (300°C), fumaric acid rearranges into maleic acid, which then yields the anhydride.

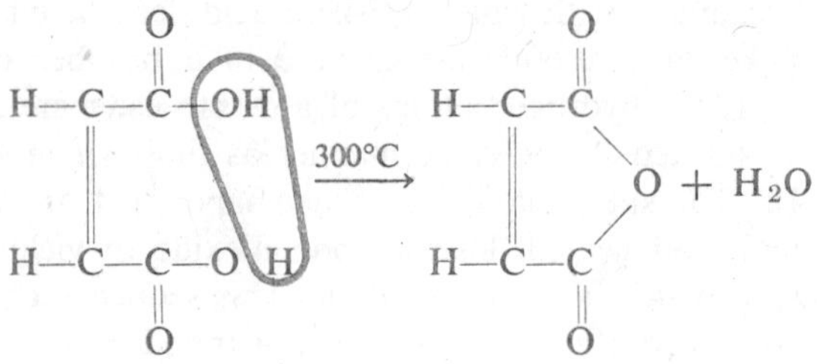

Maleic acid   Maleic anhydride

Both acids, when hydrogenated, yield succinic acid.

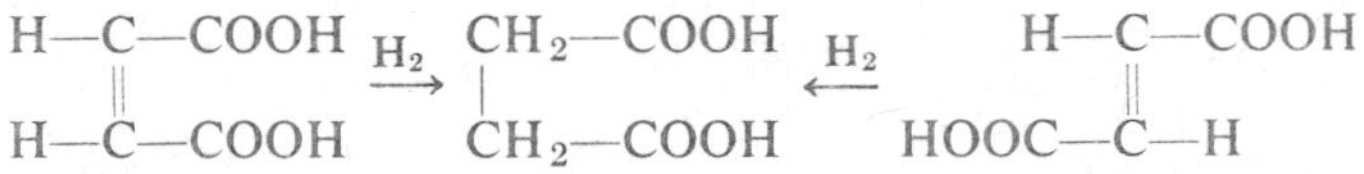

Maleic acid   Succinic acid   Fumaric acid

□□ *SUMMARY*

[1]   The bifunctional acids contain, in addition to a carboxyl group, one or more other functions. These may be, (a) a halogen, (b) a hydroxyl, (c) a carbon-carbon double bond, (d) a second carboxyl group, or (e) a keto group.

[2]   The chemical behavior of bifunctional acids, generally, is either that of the monocarboxylic acids or that usually associated with the second functional group.

[3]   The presence of a second functional group in an acid molecule may lead to cyclization, unsaturation, loss of carbon dioxide, or polymerization.

[4]   Dicarboxylic acids may be prepared by the same general methods used for the preparation of monocarboxylic acids. Such methods include

   a.   the oxidation of diols
   b.   the oxidation of unsaturated acids
   c.   hydrolysis of nitriles

[5]   Dicarboxylic acids usually are referred to by common names.

[6]   Adipic acid is used in the manufacture of "Nylon." Phthalic acid is used in the manufacture of *glyptal* resins, and terephthalic acid is used in the manufacture of "Dacron."

[7]   The chemistry of the halogen and hydroxy acids is interrelated.

[8] Halogen acids usually are prepared by

    a. the direct halogenation by the use of halogen and red phosphorus — e.g., the Hell-Volhard-Zelinsky reaction.

    b. the action of an inorganic halide upon a hydroxy acid

    c. the oxidation of a halohydrin

    d. the addition of hydrogen halide to an unsaturated acid

[9] Hydroxy acids may be prepared by

    a. the alkaline hydrolysis of the corresponding halogen acid

    b. the hydrolysis of a cyanohydrin

[10] Malic acid, when dehydrated, produces a pair of isomeric, unsaturated, dicarboxylic acids called **fumaric** and **maleic**. These acids are *cis-trans* isomers.

[11] The interrelationship of the bifunctional acids may be summarized by the following reaction sequences.

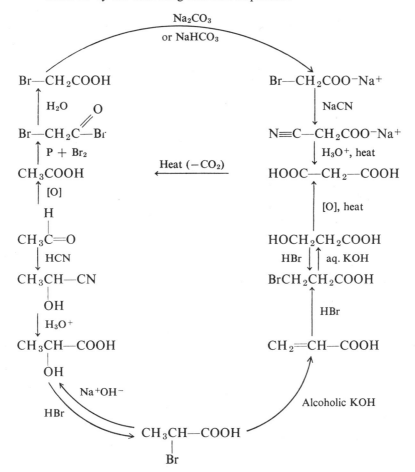

☐☐ *NEW TERMS*

[1] acetoacetic ester synthesis
[2] analgesic
[3] antipyretic
[4] barbiturates
[5] enteric coating
[6] glyptal resin

[7]   hypnotic
[8]   lactam
[9]   lactone
[10] malonic ester synthesis
[11] salol

■ ☐ SUPPLEMENTARY EXERCISES
▼   AND PROBLEMS

[1] Write structural formulas for each of the following.

(a) adipic acid
(b) tartaric acid
(c) terephthalic acid
(d) *cis*-butenedioic acid

(e) salicylic acid
(f) δ-valerolactone
(g) α-bromopropionic acid
(h) aspirin

[2] Name each of the following structures.

(a) 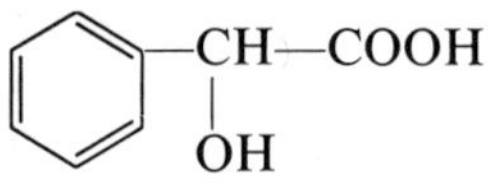
$$\text{(benzene ring)}-\underset{\underset{\text{OH}}{|}}{\text{CH}}-\text{COOH}$$

(c) 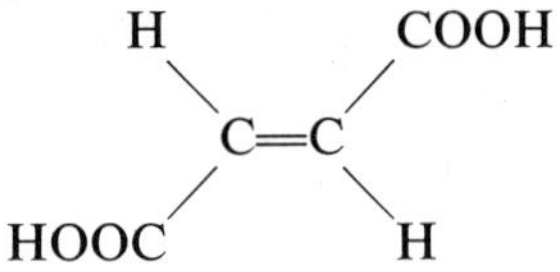
$$\underset{\text{HOOC}}{\overset{\text{H}}{\diagdown}}\text{C}=\text{C}\underset{\text{H}}{\overset{\text{COOH}}{\diagup}}$$

(b) 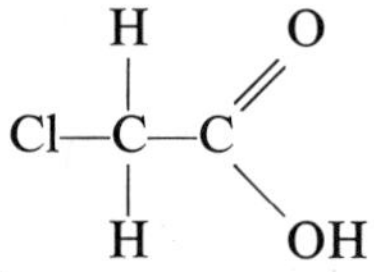
$$\text{Cl}-\underset{\underset{\text{H}}{|}}{\overset{\overset{\text{H}}{|}}{\text{C}}}-\text{C}\underset{\text{OH}}{\overset{\text{O}}{\diagup\!\!\!\diagup}}$$

(d) 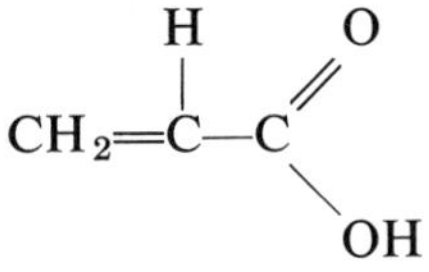
$$\text{CH}_2=\underset{\underset{\text{H}}{|}}{\text{C}}-\text{C}\underset{\text{OH}}{\overset{\text{O}}{\diagup\!\!\!\diagup}}$$

(e) 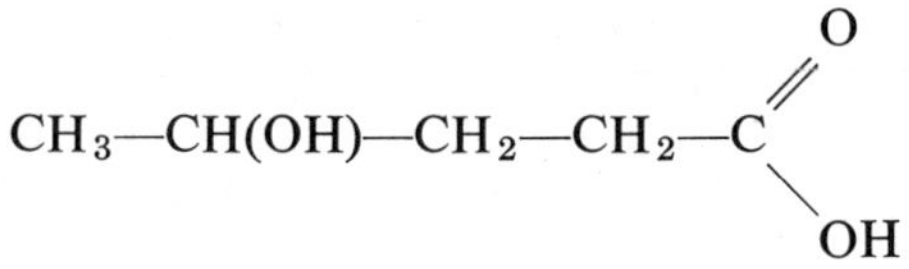
$$\text{CH}_3-\text{CH(OH)}-\text{CH}_2-\text{CH}_2-\text{C}\underset{\text{OH}}{\overset{\text{O}}{\diagup\!\!\!\diagup}}$$

(f) 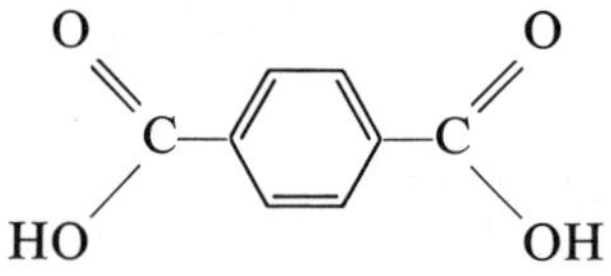
$$\underset{\text{HO}}{\overset{\text{O}}{\diagdown\!\!\!\diagdown}}\text{C}-\text{(benzene ring)}-\text{C}\underset{\text{OH}}{\overset{\text{O}}{\diagup\!\!\!\diagup}}$$

(g) 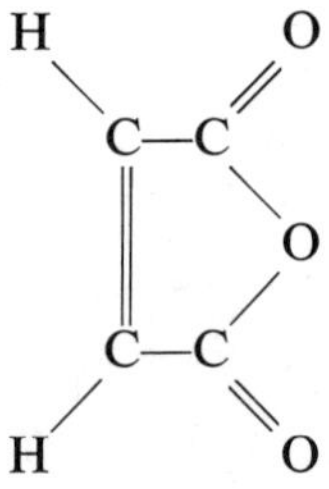
$$\begin{array}{c}\underset{\text{H}}{\overset{\text{H}}{\diagdown}}\text{C}-\text{C}\overset{\text{O}}{\diagup\!\!\!\diagup}\\ \| \qquad\qquad \text{O}\\ \text{C}-\text{C}\underset{\text{O}}{\diagdown\!\!\!\diagdown}\\ \underset{\text{H}}{\diagup}\end{array}$$

(h) 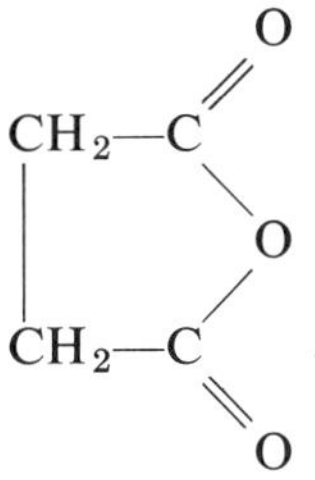
$$\begin{array}{c} CH_2-C \\ | \quad\quad\quad O \\ CH_2-C \end{array}$$
with two $C=O$ groups forming anhydride (O bridging)

(i) 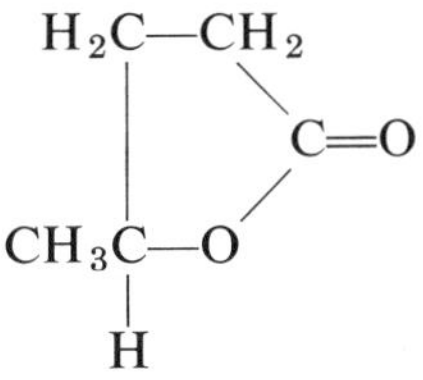
$$\begin{array}{c} H_2C-CH_2 \\ | \quad\quad\quad C=O \\ CH_3C-O \\ | \\ H \end{array}$$

[3] Complete the following reaction sequences and identify each lettered product.

(a) $H_2C\!=\!CH_2$ $\xrightarrow{HOCl}$ (A) $\xrightarrow{[O]}$ (B) $\xrightarrow[\substack{\text{1. NaOH}\\\text{2. NaCN}}]{}$ (C) $\xrightarrow{H_3O^+ \text{ heat}}$ (D)

(b) 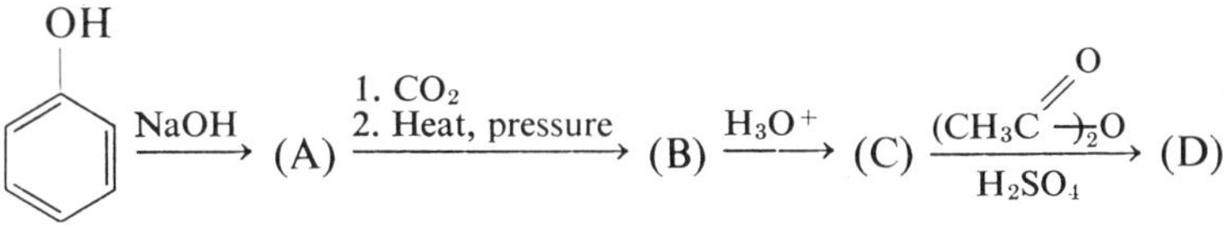 (phenol with OH) $\xrightarrow{NaOH}$ (A) $\xrightarrow[\substack{\text{1. CO}_2\\\text{2. Heat, pressure}}]{}$ (B) $\xrightarrow{H_3O^+}$ (C) $\xrightarrow[H_2SO_4]{(CH_3C\,\rightarrow\!_2O}$ (D)

(c) $CH_3\!-\!\overset{\overset{\displaystyle H}{|}}{C}\!=\!O$ $\xrightarrow{HCN}$ (A) $\xrightarrow{H_3O^+, \text{ reflux}}$ (B) $\xrightarrow{\text{Heat}}$ (C)

(d) $CH_3CH_2CH_2COOH$ $\xrightarrow[\substack{\text{1. Red P, Br}_2\\\text{2. H}_2O}]{}$ (A) $\xrightarrow{\text{Alcoholic KOH}}$ (B) $\xrightarrow{HBr}$ (C)

(e) $CH_2(COOC_2H_5)_2$ $\xrightarrow[\substack{\text{1. C}_2\text{H}_5\text{O}^-\text{Na}^+\\\text{2. C}_6\text{H}_5\text{OCH}_2\text{CH}_2\text{Br}}]{}$ (A) $\xrightarrow[\text{heat}]{48\% \text{ HBr,}}$ (B)

$+$ (C) $+$ CO_2;

(B) $+$ FeCl$_3$ $\longrightarrow$ red color

[4] Arrange the following in an order of increasing acidity.
(a) salicylic acid   (d) malonic acid
(b) chloroacetic acid   (e) mandelic acid
(c) oxalic acid

[5] Which of the following acids could exist as *cis-trans* isomers? Which as optical isomers?
(a) acrylic   (d) 1, 2-cyclopentanedicarboxylic acid
(b) 2-butenoic   (e) ricinoleic acid
(c) malic

[6] Suggest a simple chemical test for distinguishing between
(a) aspirin and phenyl salicylate.
(b) acetyl chloride and chloroacetic acid.
(c) maleic and malonic acid.

[7]   Beginning with ethyl alcohol as your only organic starting material, and any other reagents you might require, show how you might prepare:

(a)   acetic acid   (e)   2-butenoic acid
(b)   ethyl acetate   (f)   malonic acid
(c)   ethyl acetoacetate   (g)   2-pentanone
(d)   β-hydroxybutyric acid   (h)   n-butyric acid

[8]   A compound, $C_4H_8O_3$, responded to a series of tests as follows:

(a)   Water $\longrightarrow$ aqueous solution acid to litmus
(b) $Na_2Cr_2O_7 + H_2SO_4 +$ heat $\longrightarrow$ blue-green coloration
(c)   Strong heating $\longrightarrow C_4H_6O_2$
(d)   Product of (c) + dilute $KMnO_4 \longrightarrow$ decolorization
(e) $I_2 + NaOH \longrightarrow$ yellow solid
(f)   Rotated plane polarized light.

What was the compound?   Write equations for reactions (a) through (e).

chapter 13

Amines and Other Nitrogen Compounds

INTRODUCTION

> The amines are our principal organic bases. Structurally, they are related to ammonia and may be considered as derivatives of this simple substance. Amines have the general formulas RNH_2, R_2NH, and R_3N in which one, two, or all three of the hydrogen atoms of the ammonia molecule have been replaced by alkyl or aryl groups. Many useful amines are synthetic, but some occur naturally in the decomposition products of nitrogenous substances such as the proteins. Some of our most valuable drugs obtained from plant extracts are characterized by the presence of one or more basic nitrogen atoms in their structures. On the basis of this finding they are assigned the general name "alkaloids." Of course, not all alkaloids are useful drugs.

13.2

CLASSIFICATION AND NOMENCLATURE

Amines are classified as primary, secondary, or tertiary according to the number of hydrogen atoms of ammonia that have been replaced.

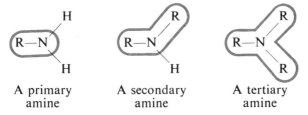

| A primary amine | A secondary amine | A tertiary amine |

Aliphatic amines of low molecular weight and the aromatic amines are generally known by their common names. These are established simply by prefixing the names of the nitrogen-attached alkyl groups to the word **amine.** If the substituents are identical, the prefixes *di* and *tri* are employed. Examples of each class and their names are given below.

Ammonia:

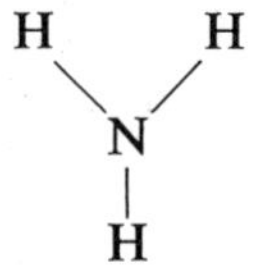

Primary amines:

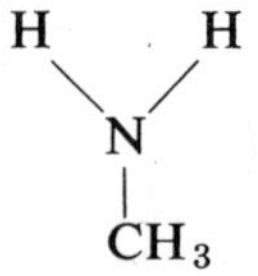

Methylamine

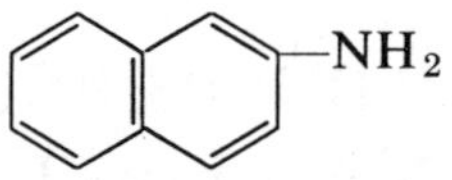

β-Naphthylamine

Secondary amines:

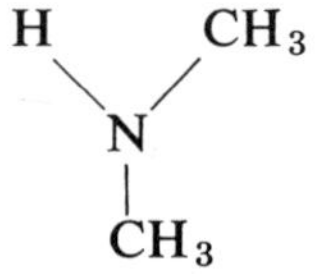

Dimethylamine

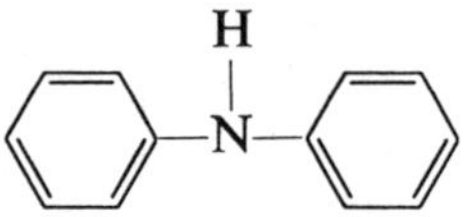

Diphenylamine

Tertiary amines:

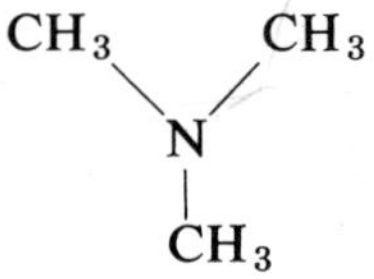

Trimethylamine

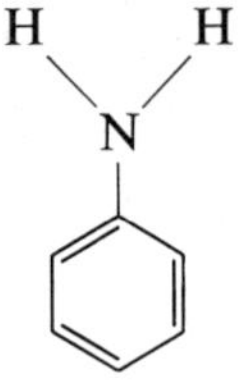

Aniline[1]

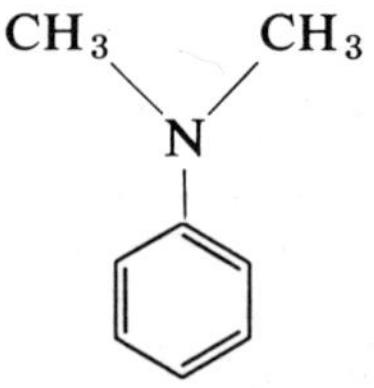

Dimethylaniline

---

[1]Aniline, the most important aromatic amine, is named after an early Spanish name for indigo (añil) from which it first was obtained by distillation.

The prefixes *sec* and *tert*, when part of the name of an amine, refer to the structure of an attached alkyl group, *not* to the class of the amine.

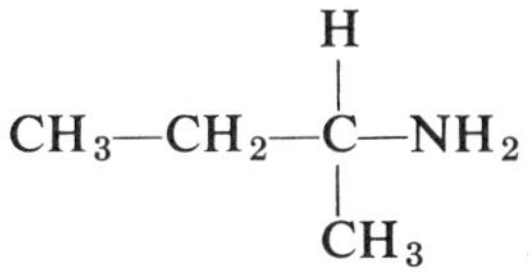

$$CH_3-CH_2-\overset{\overset{\displaystyle H}{|}}{\underset{\underset{\displaystyle CH_3}{|}}{C}}-NH_2$$

sec-Butylamine (a primary amine)

$$CH_3-\overset{\overset{\displaystyle CH_3}{|}}{\underset{\underset{\displaystyle CH_3}{|}}{C}}-NH_2$$

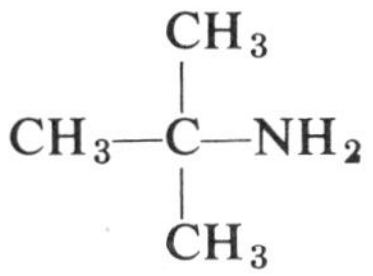

tert-Butylamine (a primary amine)

Frequently the amino group (—NH$_2$) is named simply as a substituent within another compound.

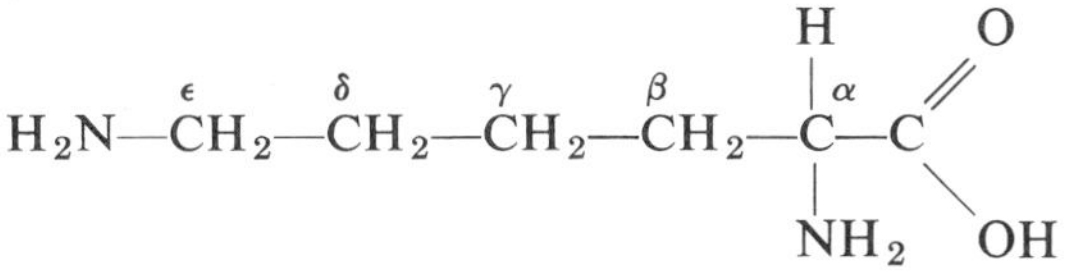

$$H_2N\overset{\epsilon}{-}CH_2\overset{\delta}{-}CH_2\overset{\gamma}{-}CH_2\overset{\beta}{-}CH_2\overset{\alpha}{-}\underset{\underset{\displaystyle NH_2}{|}}{\overset{\overset{\displaystyle H}{|}}{C}}-C\overset{\displaystyle O}{\underset{\displaystyle OH}{<}}$$

α, ϵ-Diaminocaproic acid (Lysine)
(2, 6-Diaminohexanoic acid)

$$H_2N-CH_2-CH_2-CH_2-CH_2-CH_2-CH_2-NH_2$$

1, 6-Diaminohexane
(Hexamethylenediamine)

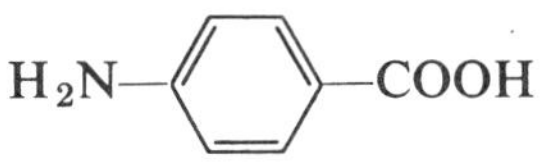

$$H_2N-\langle\!\!\bigcirc\!\!\rangle-COOH$$

p-Aminobenzoic acid

$$CH_3-CH_2-\overset{\overset{\displaystyle H}{|}}{\underset{\underset{\displaystyle NH_2}{|}}{C}}-CH_3$$

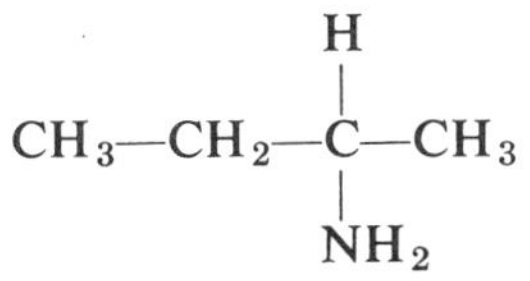

sec-Butylamine
(2-Aminobutane)

> **Exercise 13.1**   How many different alcohols of each class are obtainable from $C_4H_{10}O$? How many different amines of each class are obtainable from $C_4H_{11}N$?

13.3   PROPERTIES OF THE AMINES

The amines are basic compounds because only three of the five electrons in the valence shell of the nitrogen atom are used in covalent bonding. An amino nitrogen with two unshared electrons thus can function as an electron-pair donor (Lewis base). Structures deficient by an electron pair (Lewis acids) may combine with an amine and share in these two electrons to produce salts.

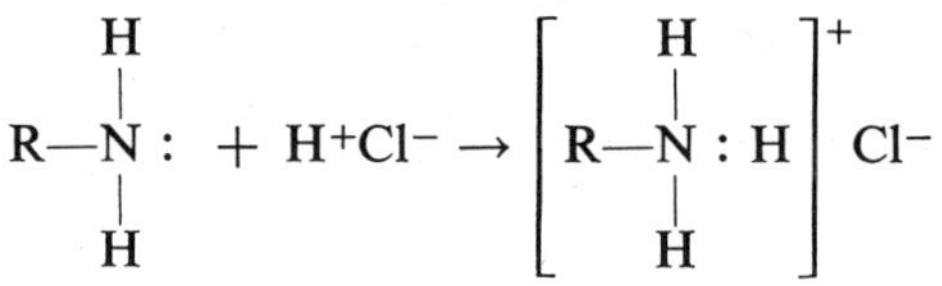

$$\begin{array}{c} H \\ | \\ R\!-\!N: \\ | \\ H \end{array} + H^+Cl^- \rightarrow \left[\begin{array}{c} H \\ | \\ R\!-\!N:H \\ | \\ H \end{array}\right]^+ Cl^-$$

An alkyl
ammonium chloride
(a salt)

Amine salts, for the most part, are water-soluble solids. Their formation from mineral acids thus affords an easy method for the separation of amines from a mixture of water-insoluble compounds. Extraction of a mixture of organic substances with an aqueous acid solution removes the basic amines. Amines, when separated in this manner, may be liberated as free bases from the acid solution by making it strongly alkaline.

$$RNH_3{}^+Cl^- + Na^+OH^- \longrightarrow RNH_2 + NaCl + H_2O$$

The solution of ammonia in water produces ammonium hydroxide, i.e., ammonium and hydroxide ions. Amines, similarly, combine reversibly with water to produce basic, substituted ammonium hydroxides.

$$NH_3 + H_2O \rightleftharpoons NH_4{}^+ + OH^-$$

$$K_b = \frac{[NH_4{}^+][OH^-]}{[NH_3]} = 1.8 \times 10^{-5}$$

$$R\text{—}\overset{\displaystyle H}{\underset{\displaystyle H}{\overset{\diagup}{N}}}\!: \;\; + \; H\text{—}\overset{..}{\underset{\displaystyle H}{O}}: \;\; \rightleftharpoons \left[R\text{—}\overset{\displaystyle H}{\underset{\displaystyle H}{N}}:H \right]^{+} \;\; :\overset{..}{\underset{..}{O}}H^{-}$$

$$CH_3NH_2 + H_2O \rightleftharpoons CH_3NH_3{}^{+}OH^{-}$$

Methylammonium
hydroxide

$$K_b = \frac{[CH_3NH_3{}^{+}][OH^{-}]}{[CH_3NH_2]} = 5 \times 10^{-4}$$

A comparison of the numerical values of their equilibrium constants, (K_b), reveals that methylamine, CH_3NH_2, is a stronger base than ammonia, NH_3. This increased basicity is explained in terms of an inductive effect. An alkyl substituent appears to provide a $+$ I effect when bonded to the nitrogen atom of an amine. The unshared electron pair of the amine nitrogen, through this effect, is more readily available for bonding and the basic strength of the amine is increased. The basicity of methylamine is greater than that of ammonia, and the strength of dimethylamine is greater than that of methylamine. A third methyl group, although adding to the inductive effect, appears to lessen the basic strength of the amine because of the space requirements of the three methyl groups. An electron-pair acceptor finds it more difficult to approach the nitrogen atom due to such crowding. On the other hand, an electron-withdrawing substituent bonded to the nitrogen atom of an amine diminishes the basic strength of the latter. For example, the dissociation constant for aniline (Table 13.1) is much smaller than that for the aliphatic amines due to the electron-withdrawing influence of the aromatic ring.

Resonance structures of aniline

Inductive and steric effects upon the basicity of a number of amines are indicated in the values of the equilibrium constants (K_b) in Table 13.1.

The lower molecular weight members of the amine family are water-soluble gases of an ammoniacal or fishlike odor. Those containing three to eleven carbons are liquids, and higher homologs are solids. Although the odors of most amines are unpleasant, their salts (called ammonium salts) are odorless.

☐■ TABLE 13.1

PHYSICAL PROPERTIES OF SOME AMINES

Name	Formula	B.P. (M.P.)°C	K_b
Ammonia	NH_3	−33.4	1.8×10^{-5}
Methylamine	CH_3NH_2	−6.5	5×10^{-4}
Dimethylamine	$(CH_3)_2NH$	7.4	7.4×10^{-4}
Trimethylamine	$(CH_3)_3N$	3.5	7.4×10^{-5}
Ethylamine	$C_2H_5NH_2$	16.6	5.6×10^{-4}
n-Propylamine	$CH_3CH_2CH_2NH_2$	48.7	4.7×10^{-4}
Isopropylamine	$(CH_3)_2CHNH_2$	34	5.3×10^{-4}
n-Butylamine	$CH_3CH_2CH_2CH_2NH_2$	77	4×10^{-4}
tert-Butylamine	$(CH_3)_3CNH_2$	43.8	3.4×10^{-4}
Aniline	$C_6H_5NH_2$	184	5.4×10^{-10}
Dimethylaniline	$C_6H_5N(CH_3)_2$	193.5	2.4×10^{-10}
p-Toluidine	$p\text{-}CH_3C_6H_4NH_2$	(43.7)	2×10^{-9}
o-Nitroaniline	$o\text{-}O_2NC_6H_4NH_2$	(71.5)	1.5×10^{-14}

13.4   PREPARATION OF AMINES

The amines may be prepared by a number of methods. The principal laboratory methods of preparation follow.

A.   Alkylation of Ammonia.   Alkyl groups may be introduced directly into the ammonia molecule by reaction with alkyl halides. The first product formed is an ammonium salt.

$$RX + \overset{\displaystyle H}{\underset{\displaystyle H}{:N-H}} \rightarrow \left[\overset{\displaystyle H}{\underset{\displaystyle H}{R:N-H}} \right]^{+} X^{-}$$

Alkylammonium
halide

Subsequent treatment of the ammonium salt with a stronger base (NaOH) liberates the free, primary amine.

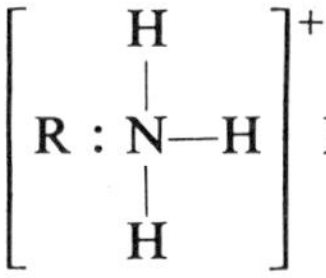

$$\left[R:\overset{\overset{\displaystyle H}{|}}{\underset{\underset{\displaystyle H}{|}}{N}}-H \right]^{+} X^{-} + OH^{-} \rightarrow RNH_2 + X^{-} + H_2O$$

A primary
amine

The reaction, unfortunately, does not stop at the first stage as illustrated above, but continues until replacement of hydrogen by alkyl groups yields not only the primary amine but the secondary and the tertiary as well. The tertiary amine, with no hydrogen remaining, then may react with a fourth molecule of alkyl halide to produce a quaternary ammonium salt. The following series of reactions illustrates the progressive alkylation of ammonia to produce all of the above products.

$$RNH_2 + RX \longrightarrow R_2NH_2{}^{+}X^{-}$$

$$R_2NH_2{}^{+}X^{-} + NaOH \longrightarrow R_2NH + NaX + H_2O$$

$$R_2NH + RX \longrightarrow R_3NH^{+}X^{-}$$

$$R_3NH^{+}X^{-} + NaOH \longrightarrow R_3N + NaX + H_2O$$

$$R_3N + RX \longrightarrow R_4N^{+}X^{-}$$

A quaternary
ammonium salt

B. Reduction of Unsaturated Nitrogen Compounds. Certain organic compounds that already contain nitrogen may be converted to primary amines by reduction methods. Most frequently used starting materials are oximes, nitriles, amides, and nitro compounds. The reduction can be accomplished either catalytically with hydrogen or directly with chemical reducing agents. The reactions below and on the next page illustrate how the same primary amine may be obtained from four different starting materials.

1. 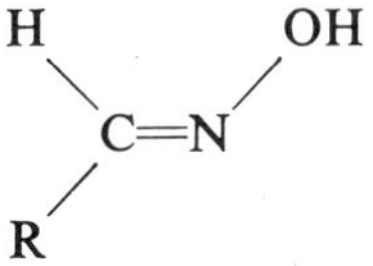
$$\underset{R}{\overset{H}{\diagdown}}C=N\overset{OH}{\diagup} + 4\,[H] \xrightarrow{\text{Na, C}_2\text{H}_5\text{OH}} R{-}CH_2NH_2 + H_2O$$

An aldoxime

2. $R-C \equiv N + 4\,[H] \xrightarrow[\text{heat, pressure}]{\text{H}_2,\ \text{Ni,}} RCH_2NH_2$

A nitrile

3. $R-\overset{\displaystyle O}{\underset{\displaystyle NH_2}{C}} + 4\,[H] \xrightarrow{\text{LiAlH}_4} R-CH_2NH_2 + H_2O$

An amide

4. $R-CH_2-NO_2 + 6\,[H] \xrightarrow{\text{Fe, +HCl}} R-CH_2NH_2$

A nitroalkane

Aniline, by far the most important aromatic amine, is prepared by the reduction of nitrobenzene. Industrially, the reaction is carried out with iron and steam. In the laboratory, tin and hydrochloric acid usually are used.

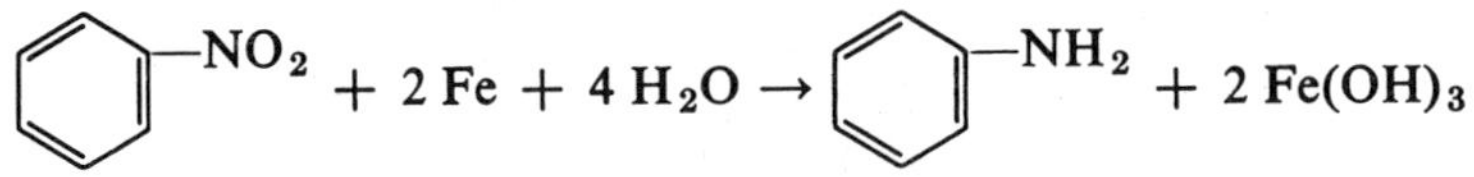

Nitrobenzene   Aniline

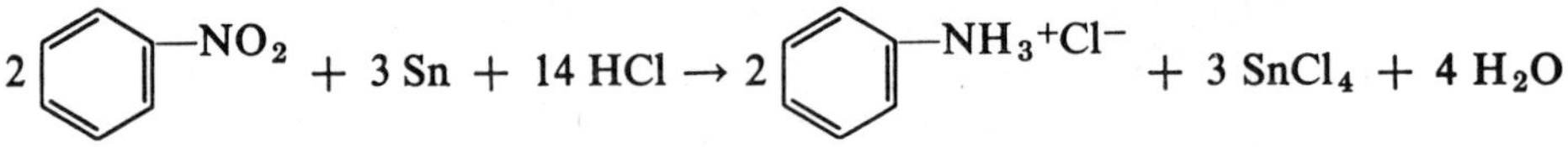

Anilinium chloride

The acid salt of aniline, when treated with sodium hydroxide, liberates the free amine.

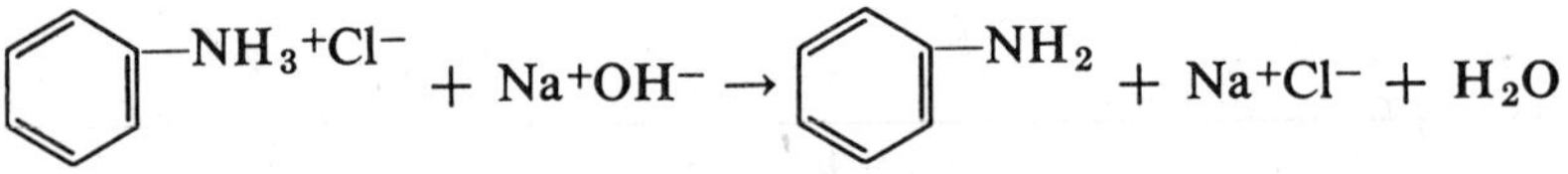

Exercise 13.2   A nitrile also may be reduced to a primary amine by treatment with sodium metal and absolute ethanol. Write a balanced equation for the reduction of ethyl cyanide by this method. *Note:* In determining polar numbers for carbon and nitrogen in both starting material and product, consider carbon the more electropositive of the two.

C. Special Methods for the Preparation of Primary Amines.
The German chemist Hofmann[2] discovered that primary amines
could be prepared by treating an amide with sodium hypobromite.
The reaction involves a rearrangement in which the alkyl group
(or aryl group) attached to the carbonyl carbon migrates to the
nitrogen atom. Inasmuch as the carbonyl carbon is eliminated as
carbon dioxide, the carbon chain of the amide is degraded to produce
a primary amine with one carbon atom less than the original amide.
The reaction is generally known as the **Hofmann Amide Hypohalite
Degradation.** The reaction is believed to proceed through the following steps.

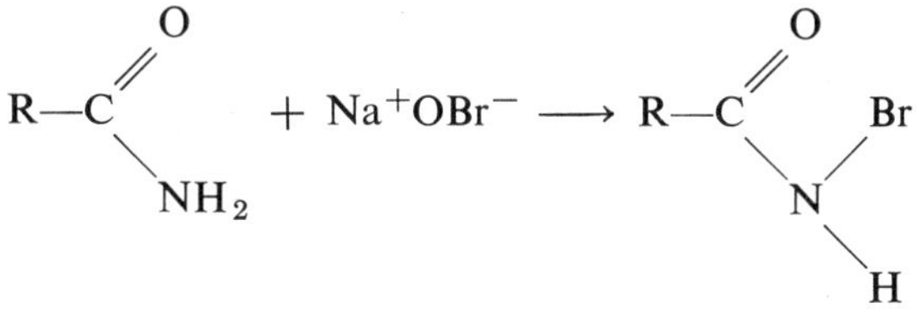

An amide   Sodium   An
                hypobromite   N-bromoamide

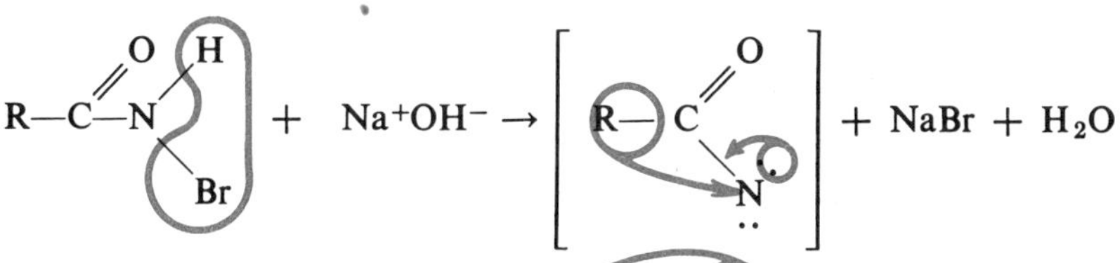

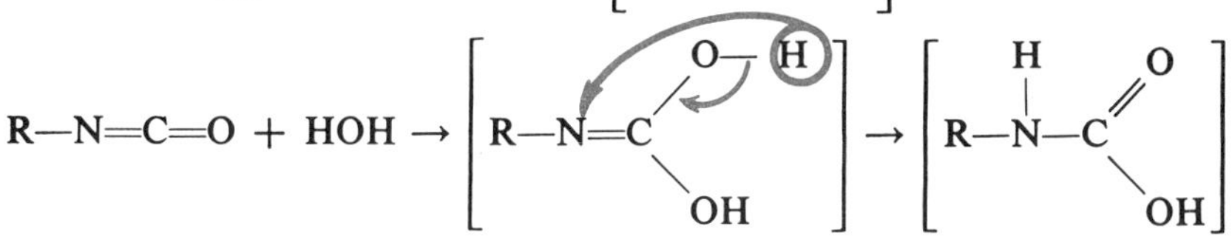

An isocyanate

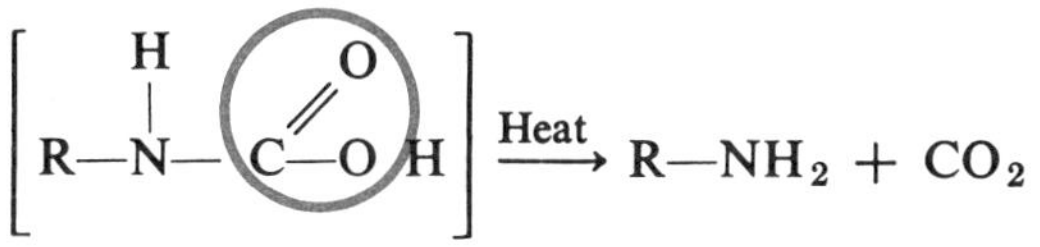

An alkyl substituted   A primary amine
carbamic acid (unstable)

[2]August Wilhelm von Hofmann (1818–1895) was one of the most cele-
brated chemists of his time. He was noted particularly for his research in the
chemistry of the amines. He was professor and the first director of the Royal
College of Chemistry at London (1845–1864), professor and director of the
laboratory, University of Berlin (1864–1895), and founder of the German
Chemical Society (1868).

Another useful method for the preparation of primary amines, known as Gabriel's phthalimide synthesis, utilizes the reaction of an alkyl halide with the potassium salt of phthalimide.

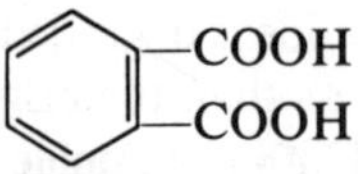

Phthalic acid 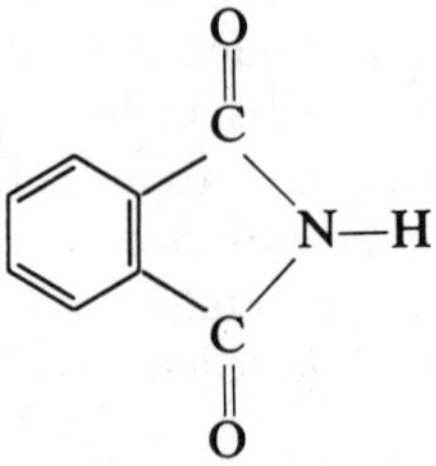   Phthalimide

The lone hydrogen atom bonded to the nitrogen of phthalimide is an active hydrogen due to the dual influence of the carbonyl groups. Salts can be formed from phthalimides and these salts are capable of reacting with alkyl halides.

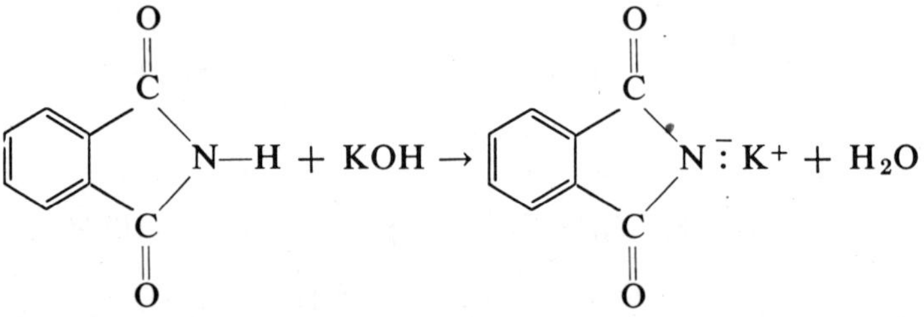

Phthalimide   N-Potassium phthalimide

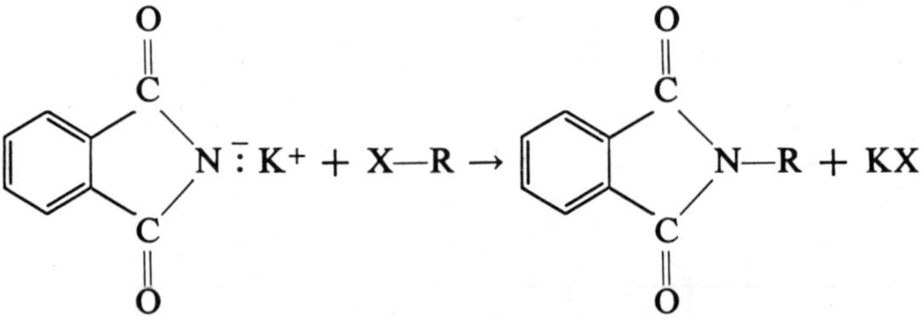

An N-alkyl
phthalimide

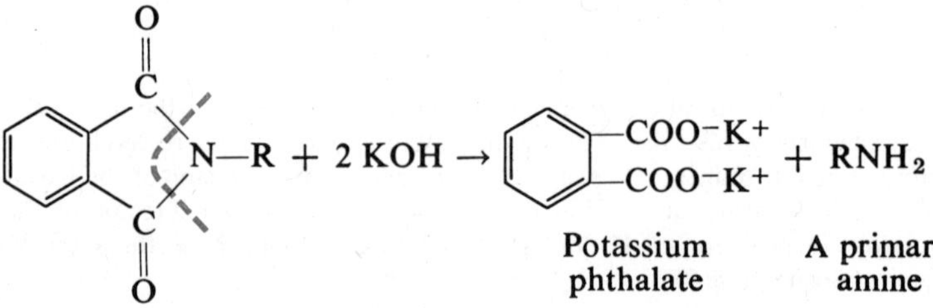

Potassium   A primary
phthalate   amine

Exercise 13.3   Which of the preparative methods outlined in Sec. 13.4 should be employed to accomplish the following conversions and to obtain the products indicated in a high state of purity, i.e., uncontaminated by traces of secondary and tertiary amines.

(a) $CH_2{=}CH{-}CH_2Cl \longrightarrow CH_2{=}CH{-}CH_2CH_2NH_2$

(b) $CH_3CH_2CH_2CH_2Br \longrightarrow CH_3CH_2CH_2CH_2NH_2$

What reaction mechanism does each of the above reactions illustrate?

13.5   REACTIONS OF AMINES

A.   Salt Formation.   As basic compounds, amines will react with acids to form water-soluble salts.   This is a characteristic property of the amines the usefulness of which has already been pointed out (Sec. 13.3).

B.   Alkylation.   · Primary amines, like ammonia, can be further alkylated with alkyl halides to give secondary and tertiary amines, and quaternary ammonium salts.   Hofmann discovered that a primary amine, when exhaustively methylated with methyl iodide, produced a quaternary ammonium iodide.   On treatment with silver oxide, the substituted ammonium iodide was converted to an ammonium hydroxide.   The ammonium base, when heated, decomposed to yield trimethylamine and an olefin with a terminal double bond.   The olefin thus had its origin in the alkyl group of the original amine.   From the structures of the decomposition products it was possible to deduce the formula of the original amine.   The steps in the reaction are illustrated using ethylamine.

$$C_2H_5NH_2 + 3\ CH_3I \rightarrow C_2H_5{-}\overset{\underset{\displaystyle CH_3}{|}}{\overset{\displaystyle CH_3}{\overset{|}{N}}}{}^{+}{-}CH_3I^- + 2\ HI$$

Ethylamine   Trimethylethylammonium
                                           iodide

$$2\ C_2H_5\overset{+}{N}(CH_3)_3I^- + Ag_2O + H_2O \longrightarrow 2\ C_2H_5\overset{+}{N}(CH_3)_3OH^- + 2\ AgI$$

Trimethylethylammonium
hydroxide

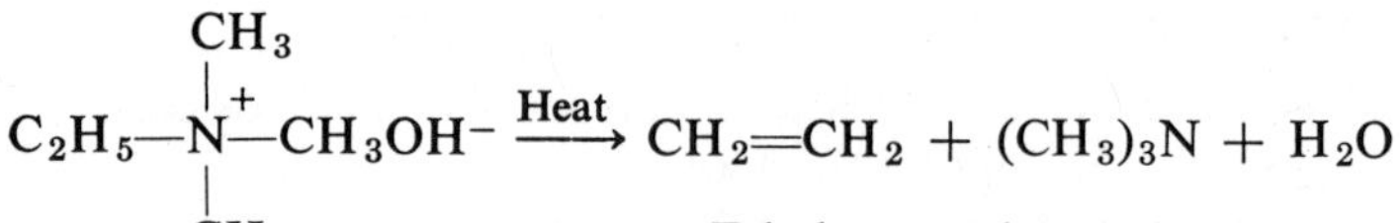

$$C_2H_5 - \overset{\overset{\displaystyle CH_3}{|}}{\underset{\underset{\displaystyle CH_3}{|}}{N}}{}^{+}\!\!-CH_3OH^- \xrightarrow{\text{Heat}} CH_2{=}CH_2 + (CH_3)_3N + H_2O$$

Ethylene   Trimethylamine

C.   Acylation.   The acyl group, $R{-}\overset{\overset{\displaystyle O}{\|}}{C}{-}$, may be substituted for hydrogen in both primary and secondary amines by reaction with acid anhydrides or acid chlorides. The use of either reagent produces an N-substituted amide. The reaction is illustrated below with ethylamine.

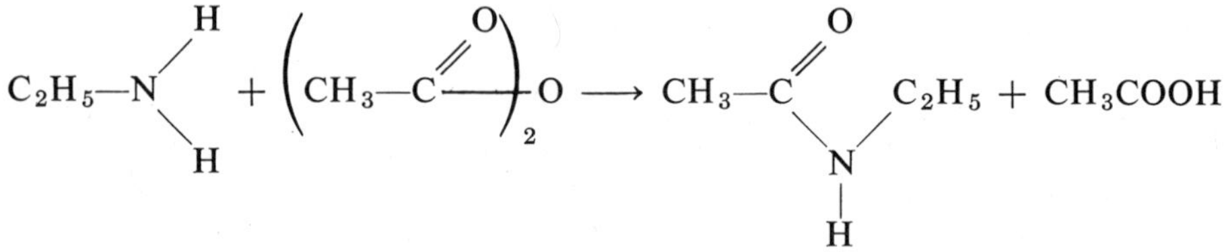

$$C_2H_5 - N\big\langle{}^{H}_{H} + \left(CH_3 - C\overset{O}{\underset{}{\diagdown}}\right)_2 O \longrightarrow CH_3 - C\overset{O}{\underset{\underset{\displaystyle H}{|}}{\underset{\displaystyle N}{\diagdown}}}C_2H_5 + CH_3COOH$$

Ethylamine   Acetic anhydride   N-Ethylacetamide

The acylation of aniline produces an **anilide**.

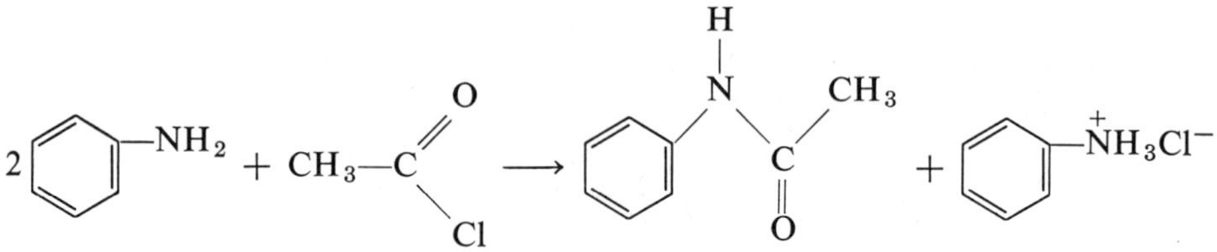

$$2\;\text{C}_6\text{H}_5{-}NH_2 + CH_3 - C\overset{O}{\underset{\displaystyle Cl}{\diagdown}} \longrightarrow \text{C}_6\text{H}_5{-}\overset{\overset{\displaystyle H}{|}}{N}{-}\overset{\overset{\displaystyle CH_3}{}}{\underset{\underset{\displaystyle O}{\|}}{C}} + \text{C}_6\text{H}_5{-}\overset{+}{N}H_3Cl^-$$

Aniline   Acetyl chloride   Acetanilide   Aniline
                                       (M.P. 114°C)   hydrochloride

Acetanilide is a very important compound medicinally. Not only is it used as an antipyretic, but it also is an important intermediate in the synthesis of other drugs. Tertiary amines, lacking hydrogen atoms bonded to the nitrogen, cannot be converted to amides. The ability to form substituted amides thus provides a method for classifying an amine as primary, secondary, or tertiary. The **Hinsberg test** is one such method. In the Hinsberg test benzenesulfonyl chloride, $C_6H_5SO_2Cl$, is the acid chloride used. Reaction of a primary amine with benzenesulfonyl chloride yields an N-alkyl sulfonamide that is soluble in an alkaline solution. The hydrogen atom that remains attached to the nitrogen atom of the amide is acidic due to the electron-withdrawing power of the sulfonyl group. The amide, therefore, is soluble in an alkaline solution.

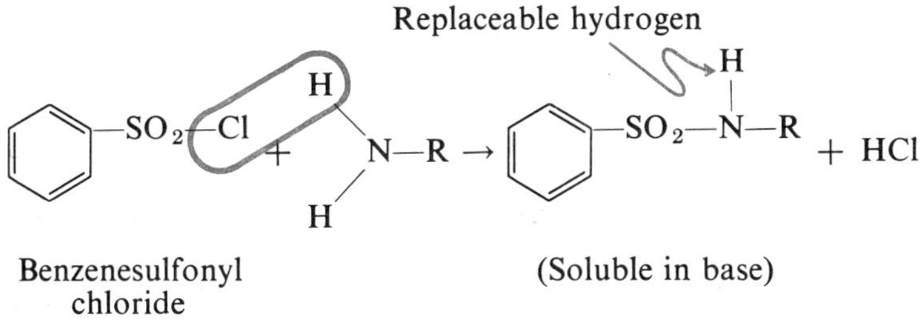

Replaceable hydrogen

Benzenesulfonyl
chloride   (Soluble in base)

A secondary amine, while reactive with benzenesulfonyl chloride, lacks the acidic hydrogen and forms an *alkali-insoluble* product.

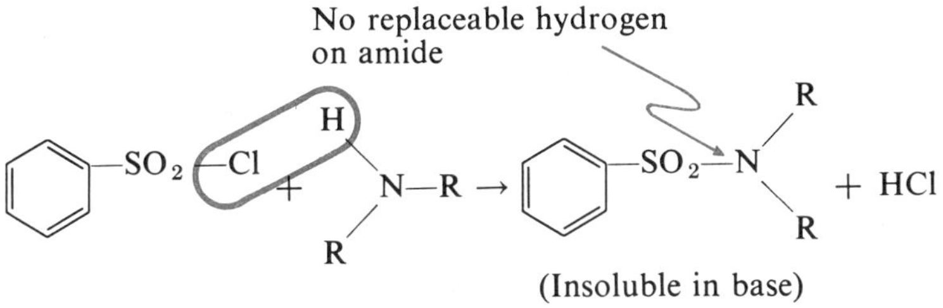

No replaceable hydrogen
on amide

(Insoluble in base)

Tertiary amines fail to react with benzenesulfonyl chloride for the same reason they failed to give acyl derivatives.

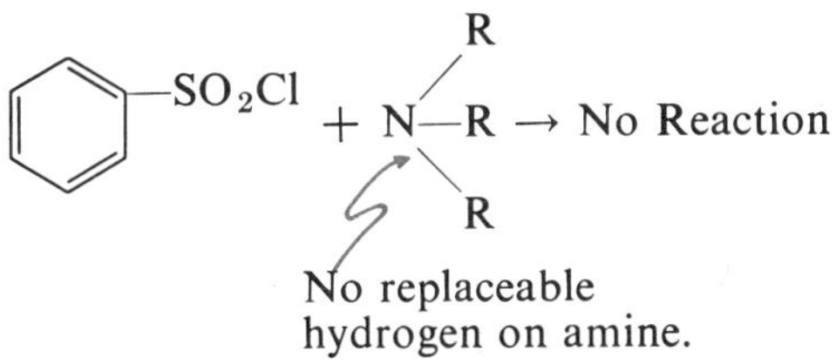

No replaceable
hydrogen on amine.

D.   Reaction with Nitrous Acid.   Nitrous acid is an unstable substance prepared in solution only when needed, by reaction between a mineral acid and sodium nitrite.

$$Na^+NO_2^- + H^+Cl^- \longrightarrow Na^+Cl^- + HNO_2$$

Nitrous acid

Ammonia, when treated with nitrous acid, forms ammonium nitrite which decomposes to nitrogen and water.

$$NH_3 + HNO_2 \longrightarrow NH_4NO_2$$

$$NH_4NO_2 \xrightarrow{\text{Heat}} N_2 + 2\,H_2O$$

An analogous reaction takes place with a primary amine to yield an alcohol as one product. The reaction is carried out by treating an acid solution of the amine (an amine salt solution) with an aqueous solution of sodium nitrite.

$$R-\boxed{N\left(H_2 + O\right)-N}-OH \rightarrow R-OH + H_2O + N_2$$

The above equation actually oversimplifies the true course of the reaction. The reaction of a primary amino group with nitrous acid appears to proceed through the initial formation of an unstable diazonium ion (see next equation). The latter, on decomposition, produces a nitrogen molecule and a carbonium ion. The carbonium ion then may react in several different ways. It either may combine with a base, or, by elimination of a proton, it may yield an olefin. It also may rearrange to a more stable carbonium ion before it follows either of these pathways. The routes leading to these different products are indicated by the following series of reactions.

$$CH_3-CH_2CH_2CH_2-NH_2 \cdot HCl + NaNO_2 \longrightarrow$$

n-Butylamine hydrochloride

$$CH_3-CH_2CH_2CH_2-\overset{\oplus}{N}{\equiv}N : \; + H_2O + OH^- + NaCl$$

A diazonium ion

$$CH_3-CH_2CH_2CH_2\overset{\oplus}{N}{\equiv}N \longrightarrow CH_3-CH_2CH_2-\overset{\overset{\textstyle H}{|}}{\underset{\underset{\textstyle H}{|}}{C}}\oplus \; + N_2$$

A carbonium ion

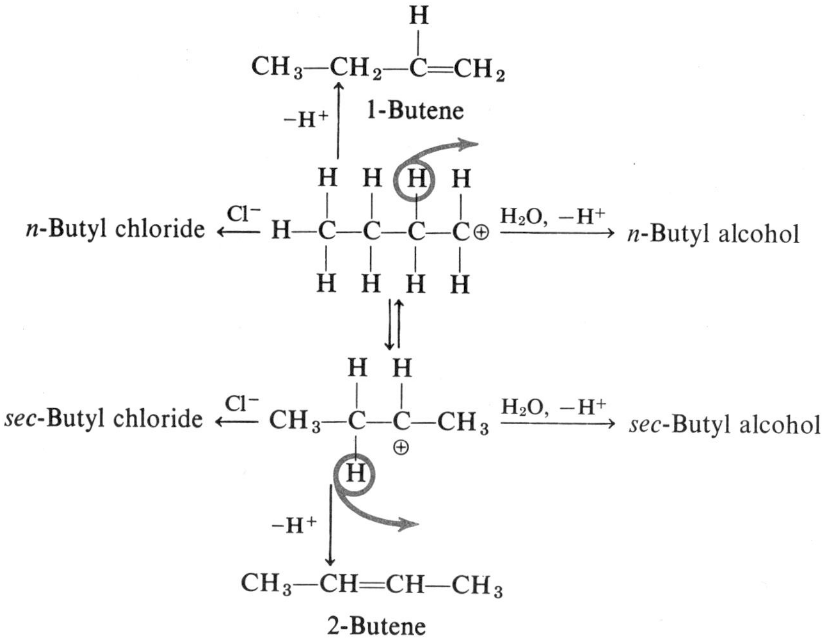

$$\text{CH}_3\text{—CH}_2\text{—}\overset{\overset{\displaystyle \text{H}}{|}}{\text{C}}\text{=CH}_2$$

1-Butene

n-Butyl chloride $\xleftarrow{\text{Cl}^-}$ H—C—C—C—C⊕ $\xrightarrow{\text{H}_2\text{O, } -\text{H}^+}$ n-Butyl alcohol

sec-Butyl chloride $\xleftarrow{\text{Cl}^-}$ $\text{CH}_3\text{—}\overset{\text{H}}{\underset{}{\text{C}}}\text{—}\overset{\text{H}}{\underset{⊕}{\text{C}}}\text{—CH}_3$ $\xrightarrow{\text{H}_2\text{O, } -\text{H}^+}$ sec-Butyl alcohol

$$\text{CH}_3\text{—CH}\text{=CH—CH}_3$$

2-Butene

Secondary amines react with nitrous acid to produce neutral N-nitroso compounds. These are yellow oils that may be separated from a solution containing other amines.

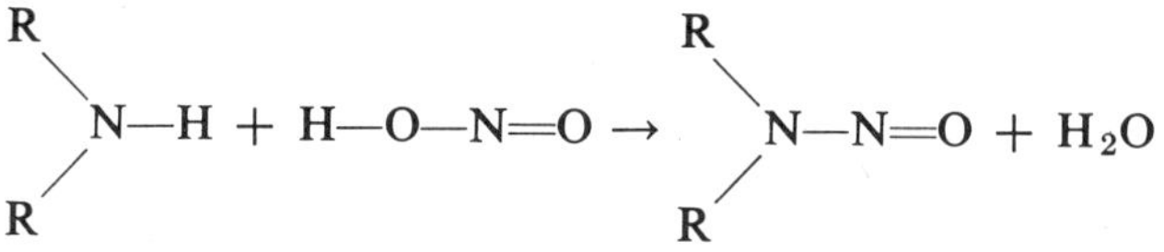

$$\begin{array}{c} \text{R} \\ \diagdown \\ \text{N—H} + \text{H—O—N}\text{=}\text{O} \rightarrow \\ \diagup \\ \text{R} \end{array} \quad \begin{array}{c} \text{R} \\ \diagdown \\ \text{N—N}\text{=}\text{O} + \text{H}_2\text{O} \\ \diagup \\ \text{R} \end{array}$$

An N-nitroso
compound

Tertiary amines do not react with nitrous acid other than to form substituted ammonium salts of nitrous acid. The amine may be recovered from solution by the addition of alkali.

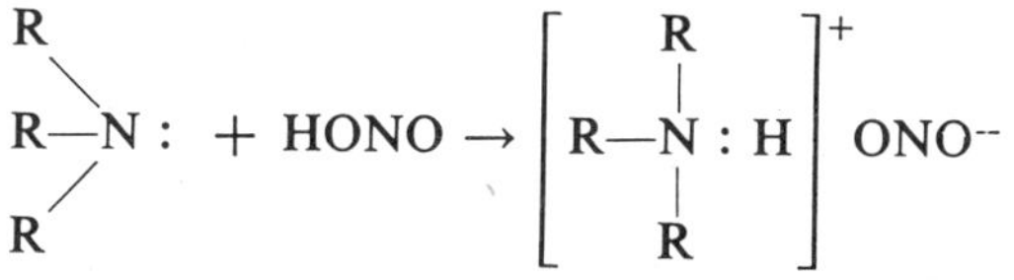

$$\begin{array}{c} \text{R} \\ \diagdown \\ \text{R—N :} + \text{HONO} \rightarrow \\ \diagup \\ \text{R} \end{array} \quad \left[\begin{array}{c} \text{R} \\ | \\ \text{R—N : H} \\ | \\ \text{R} \end{array} \right]^+ \text{ONO}^-$$

An amine nitrite salt

The reaction of aliphatic amines with nitrous acid has little value except as a diagnostic or as a separatory procedure. In either case, the primary amine is destroyed. On the other hand, the reaction of nitrous acid with aromatic primary amines produces intermediates known as diazonium salts.

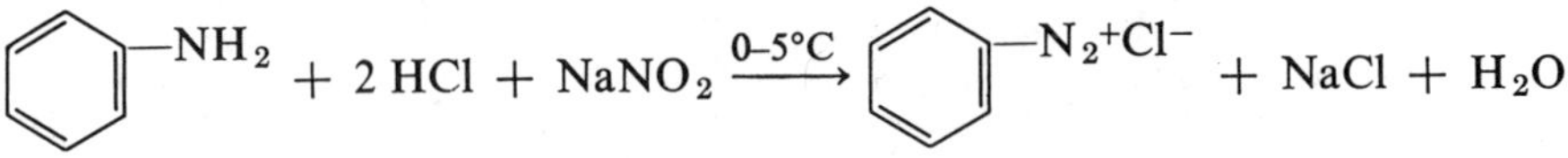

$$\text{C}_6\text{H}_5-\text{NH}_2 + 2\,\text{HCl} + \text{NaNO}_2 \xrightarrow{\text{0--5°C}} \text{C}_6\text{H}_5-\text{N}_2^+\text{Cl}^- + \text{NaCl} + \text{H}_2\text{O}$$

Benzenediazonium
chloride

A large number of very useful products, difficult, if not impossible to arrive at by any other route, are synthesized by way of a diazonium salt. We shall deal with the diazonium salts in a separate section.

Exercise 13.4   A primary aliphatic amine, when treated with nitrous acid, can form an olefin or an alcohol, whereas aniline under the same conditions yields only phenol. Explain.

E.   Ring Substitution in Aromatic Amines.   The primary amino group of aniline, like the hydroxyl group of a phenol, is very sensitive to oxidation. In order to preserve the amino group in the presence of an oxidizing reagent it must be "protected" prior to reaction. The amino group usually is protected by acetylation. For example, the nitration of aniline to *p*-nitroaniline requires this preliminary step.

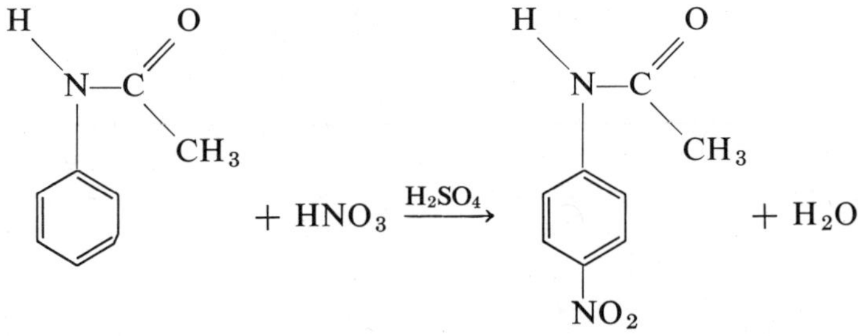

Acetanilide   *p*-Nitroacetanilide

Subsequent acid hydrolysis of *p*-nitroacetanilide removes the protecting acyl group.

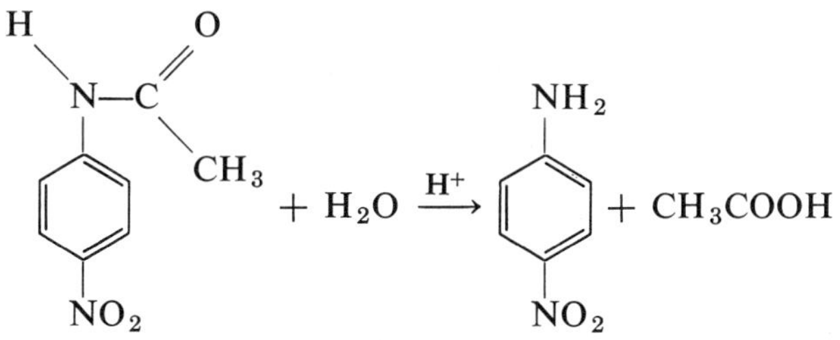

p-Nitroaniline

Exercise 13.5   Explain why the nitration of "unprotected" aniline with a nitrating mixture of nitric and sulfuric acids gives *m*-nitroaniline. (*Clue: See Table 4.2.*)

In all reactions involving ring substitution the powerful *ortho-para* directive influence of the amino group is manifest. The tribromo derivative of aniline, for example, may be prepared simply by shaking aniline with a solution of bromine in water.

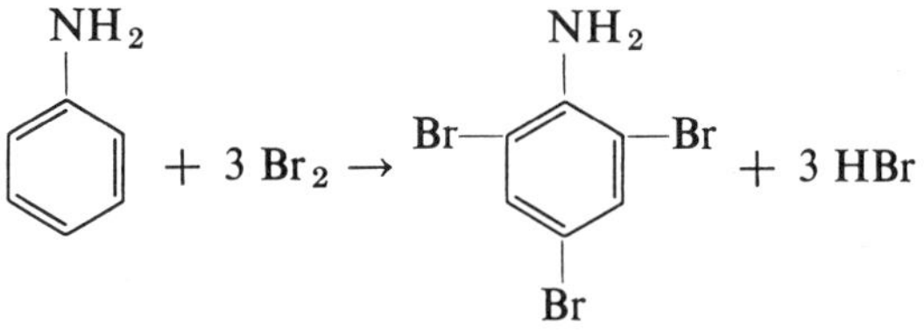

2, 4, 6-Tribromoaniline

Acetylation of aniline, besides protecting the amino group from oxidation, as explained under nitration, offers the additional advantage of diminishing the reactivity of aniline. For example, monobromoaniline is prepared by brominating acetanilide, followed by removal of the protecting group.

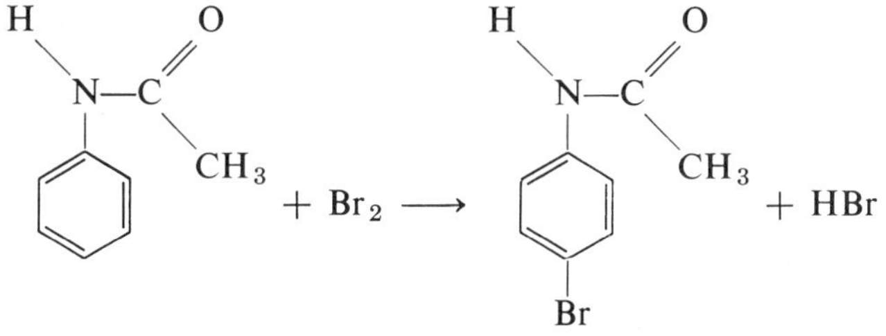

p-Bromoacetanilide

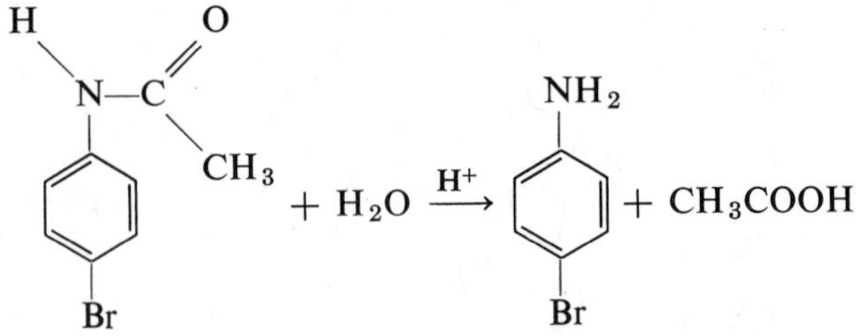

p-Bromoaniline

Sulfonation of aniline is a slow reaction in which the aniline hydrogen sulfate salt initially formed appears to undergo rearrangement upon further heating. The product is called sulfanilic acid.

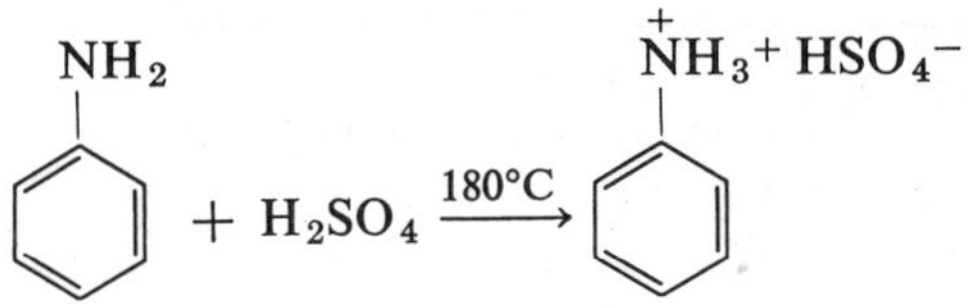

Aniline hydrogen sulfate

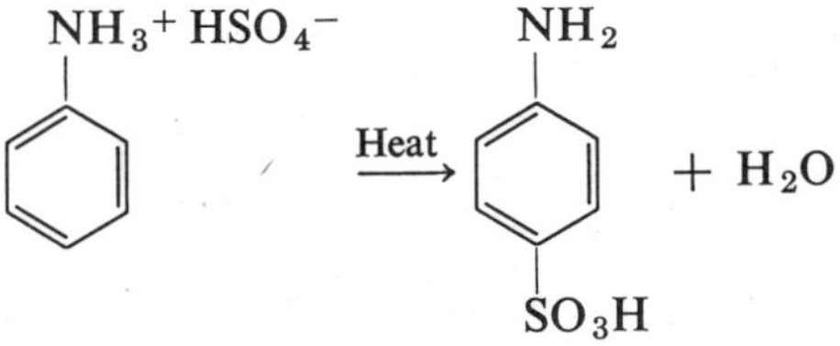

Sulfanilic acid

Sulfanilic acid appears to exist largely as an internal salt or a dipolar ion. Inner salts are possible when one group within a molecule is capable of acting as a proton donor (acid) to another within the same molecule capable of acting as a proton acceptor (base). The same phenomenon is shown by the amino acids (Sec. 15.5).

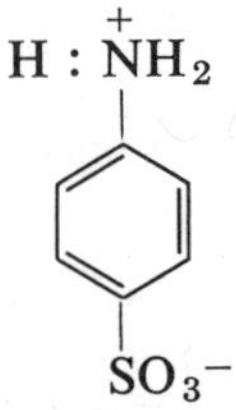

Inner salt of sulfanilic acid

Sulfanilic acid is an important intermediate in the synthesis of certain dyes and in the preparation of the *sulfa drugs*. The sulfa drugs were widely used during World War II to prevent infection in wounds and still find some application in medicine. They now have been replaced to a large extent by the antibiotics (Sec. 17.25, 17.26). Sulfanilamide is effective internally against streptococci and staphylococci infections. Other sulfa drugs are derivatives of sulfanilamide. In these "sulfas" some other group appears as an N-substituent in the amide portion of the parent compound. The following sequence of reactions illustrates how sulfanilamide is synthesized.

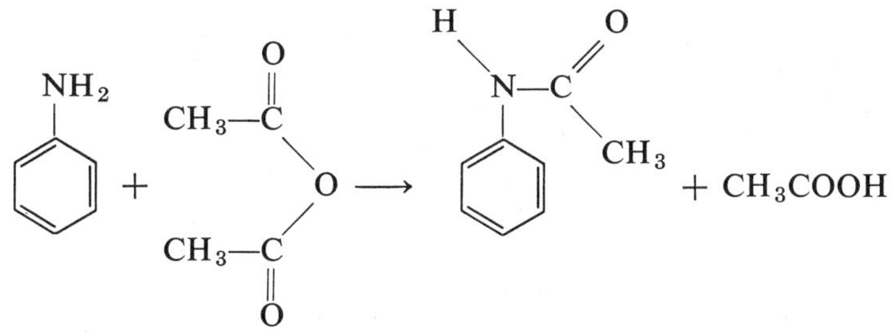

Aniline	Acetic anhydride		Acetanilide

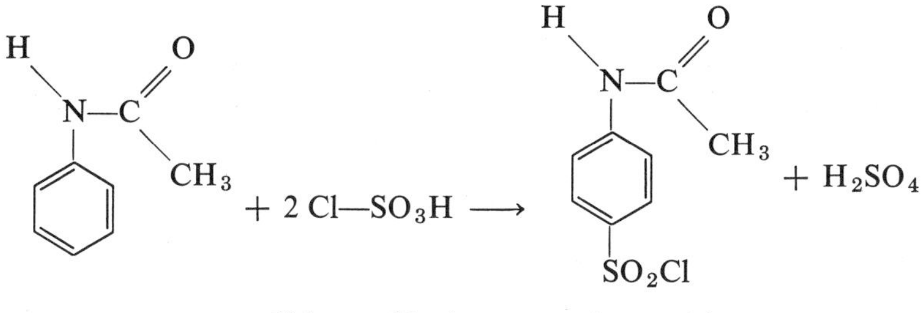

	Chlorosulfonic acid	p-Acetamido-benzenesulfonyl chloride

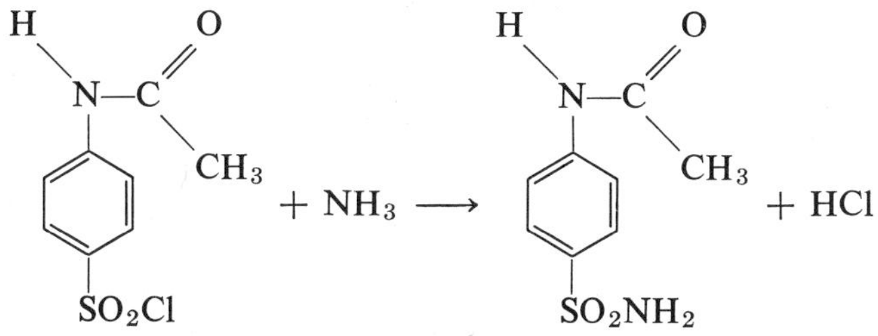

p-Acetamidobenzene-sulfonamide

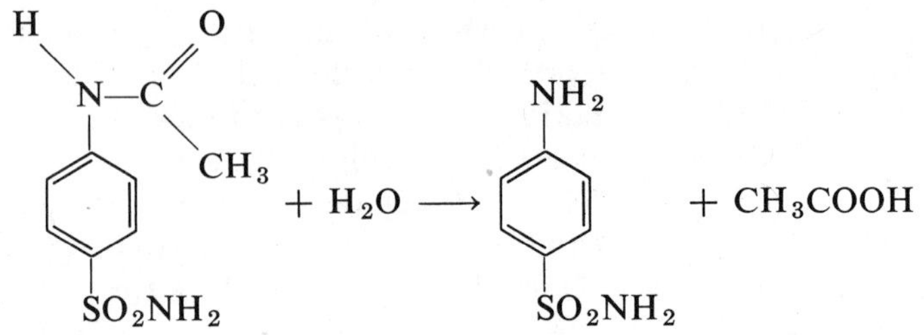

Sulfanilamide

13.6 DIAMINES

The diamines, compounds with two amino groups, can be prepared by methods similar to those employed for the preparation of the simple amines. The reaction of ammonia with dihalides, the reduction of dinitriles, and the Hofmann reaction of diamides all lead to the preparation of diamines. The primary requirement, in each case, is a bifunctional compound capable of being converted into one with two amino groups. Ethylene chloride, for example, reacts with ammonia to yield **ethylenediamine.**

$$ClCH_2CH_2Cl + 4\,NH_3 \longrightarrow H_2N-CH_2CH_2-NH_2 + 2\,NH_4Cl$$

Ethylenediamine

The ptomaines, tetramethylenediamine (putrescine) and pentamethylenediamine (cadaverine) are natural, malodorous products formed by bacterial decomposition of protein material. The amino acids ornithine and lysine on breakdown yield these respective diamines. Ethylenediaminetetraacetic acid (EDTA), a useful chelating[3] agent for certain divalent metals, is made from ethylenediamine and sodium chloroacetate.

$$4\,Cl-CH_2-COO^-Na^+ + H_2N-CH_2CH_2-NH_2 + 4\,NaOH \rightarrow$$

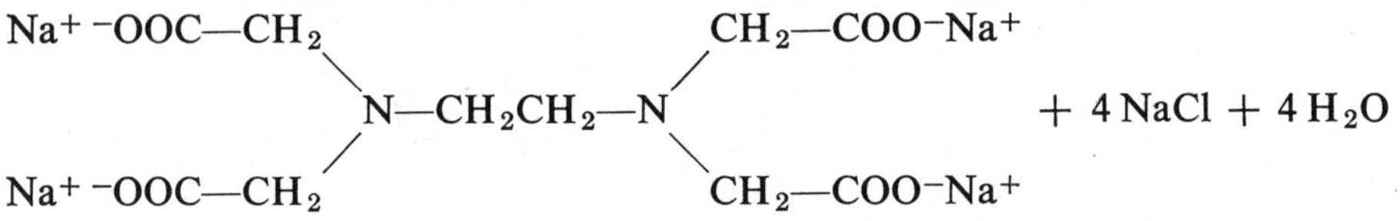

$$+\,4\,NaCl + 4\,H_2O$$

Sodium ethylenediaminetetraacetate (EDTA)

---

[3]A chelating agent (Gr., *chele*, claw) is a chemical compound capable of grasping a metallic ion in a clawlike manner. A ring closure results through a coordination of unshared pairs of electrons on the chelating agent with the metallic ion.

Sodium EDTA has the ability to sequester calcium and other metal ions to form soluble chelates and has been used with some success in the treatment of sclerosing diseases. The manner in which EDTA is able to chelate divalent metals is shown.

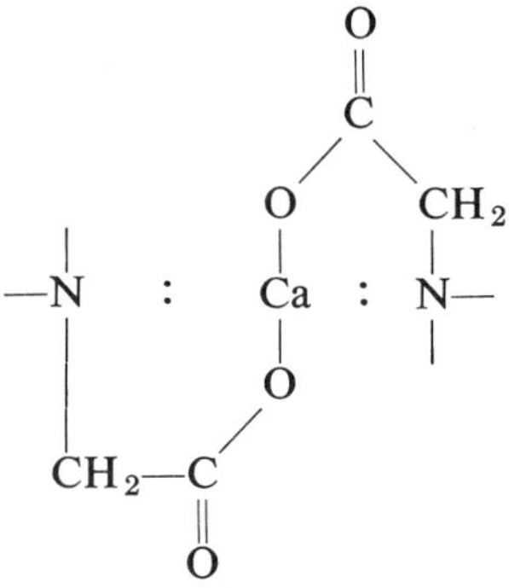

Hexamethylenediamine, used in the preparation of nylon, can be prepared from furfural (Sec. 17.3) by the following sequence.

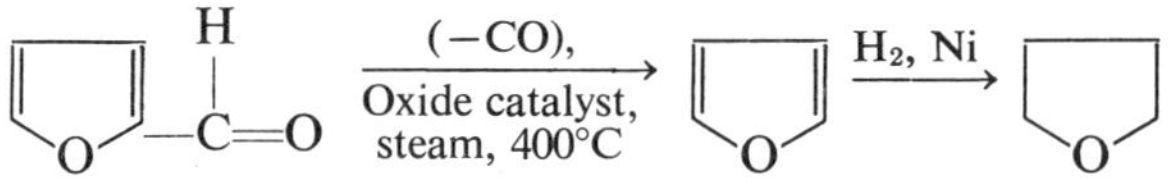

$$\text{Furfural} \quad\quad\quad \text{Furan} \quad \text{Tetrahydrofuran}$$

$+ \ HCl \rightarrow HOCH_2CH_2CH_2CH_2Cl$

Tetramethylene chlorohydrin

$$HO(CH_2)_4\text{—}Cl + HCl \rightarrow Cl(CH_2)_4Cl + H_2O$$

Tetramethylene
chloride

$$Cl\text{—}(CH_2)_4\text{—}Cl + 2\ NaCN \rightarrow NC\text{—}(CH_2)_4\text{—}CN + 2\ NaCl$$

Adiponitrile

The reduction of adiponitrile produces hexamethylenediamine.

$$NC\text{—}(CH_2)_4\text{—}CN + 4\ H_2 \xrightarrow{\text{Ni}} H_2N\text{—}(CH_2)_6\text{—}NH_2$$

Hexamethylenediamine

Adiponitrile on hydrolysis yields adipic acid. The condensation reaction between adipic acid and hexamethylenediamine produces the polyamide known as Nylon 66 (Sec. 17.3).

The aromatic diamines may be prepared by the reduction of the appropriate nitro compounds.

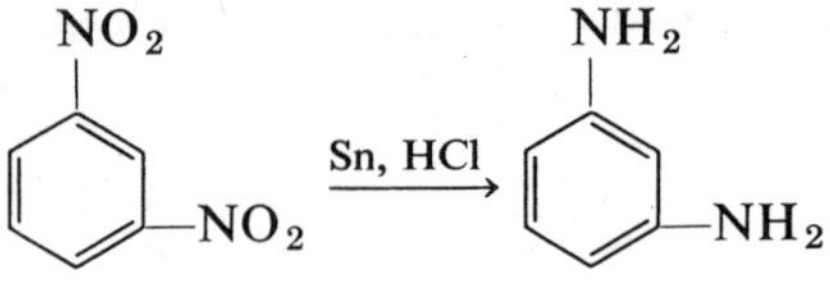

Benzidine, or p, p'-diaminobiphenyl, an important intermediate in the synthesis of dyes, is prepared *via* the rearrangement of hydrazobenzene. This reaction is known as the **benzidine rearrangement.**

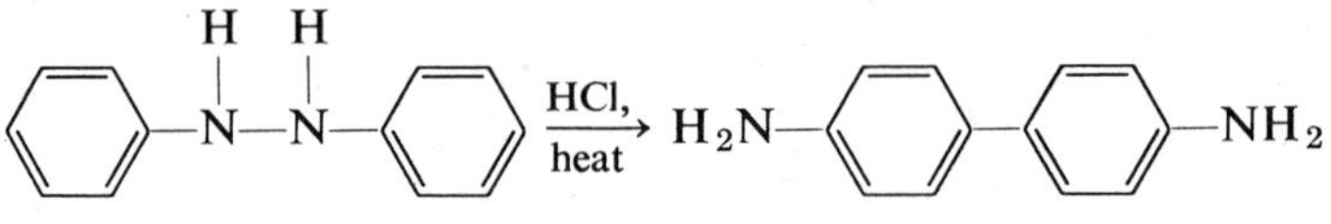

13.7   NITROGEN COMPOUNDS USED AS DIETARY SUGAR SUBSTITUTES

Certain individuals (diabetics) are incapable of producing sufficient insulin for the complete utilization of glucose (Sec. 14.3). Others, through an abnormal hormonal activity, overproduce glucose in the body. In either case, an abnormal amount of this sugar accumulates in the blood and results in a condition known as *hyperglycemia.* For these persons and for those who are overweight and wish to lower their caloric intake, a number of artificial sweeteners are available. These substances are nonnutritive agents with a sweetness many times that of sucrose. *Sucaryl,* the calcium salt of cyclohexylsulfamic acid, and *saccharin,* the imide of o-sulfobenzoic acid, are two of the more widely used sweetening agents. Both compounds are used in the form of water-soluble salts.

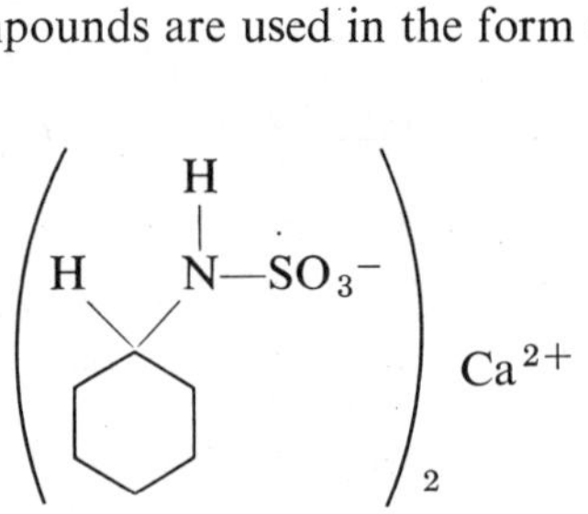

Sucaryl calcium
(Calcium cyclohexylsulfamate or "Cyclamate")

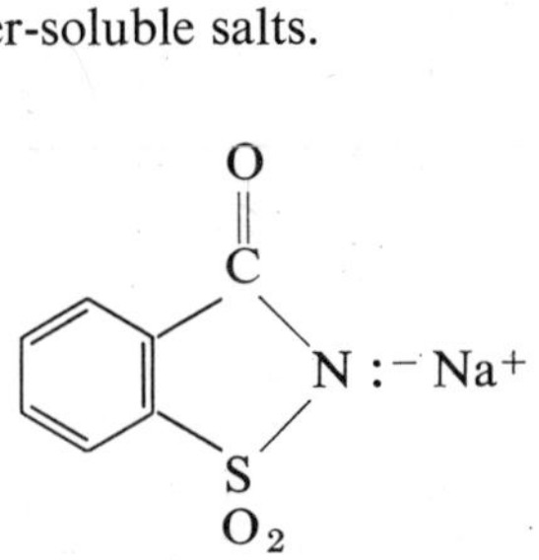

Saccharin sodium
(Sodium benzosulfimide)

Saccharin has a sweetness of approximately 500 times that of sucrose, which is assigned a sweetness of 1.0. The sweetness of sucaryl is approximately 30 when measured on the same scale.

13.8   AMINO ALCOHOLS AND SOME RELATED PHYSIOLOGICALLY
        ACTIVE COMPOUNDS

The aminoalcohols appear in a number of compounds of potent physiological activity.

Choline, $(CH_3)_3\overset{+}{N}CH_2CH_2OHOH^-$, trimethyl-$\beta$-hydroxyethyl ammonium hydroxide, forms part of the structure of lecithin (Sec. 11.6). Choline appears in lecithin with glycerol as a mixed ester of phosphoric acid and fatty acids. Acetylated choline or *acetylcholine*, plays a vital role in the generation and conduction of nerve impulses in the body.

$$\left[(CH_3)_3\overset{+}{N}\!-\!CH_2CH_2\!-\!O\!-\!C\overset{\displaystyle O}{\diagup}CH_3\right]OH^-$$

Acetylcholine

The ability of certain local anesthetics to mitigate pain appears to be due (in part at least) to their structural similarity to choline and an ability to replace acetylcholine for a short duration. A number of local anesthetizing agents have in their molecular architecture an aminoalcohol grouping in the form of either an ester or an ether unit. The local anesthetic *procaine*, to which most of us have been introduced while in a dentist's chair, is a synthetic replacement for the natural drug *cocaine* (Sec. 17.8).

Procaine hydrochloride
(Novocaine)

A large number of amines and amino alcohols, both naturally occurring and synthetic, have an effect upon the sympathetic nervous system and are known as **sympathomimetic agents.** These agents are powerful stimulants and dangerous if used promiscuously. Some may result in habituation when used for prolonged periods. The structures for a few of these are given on the next page.

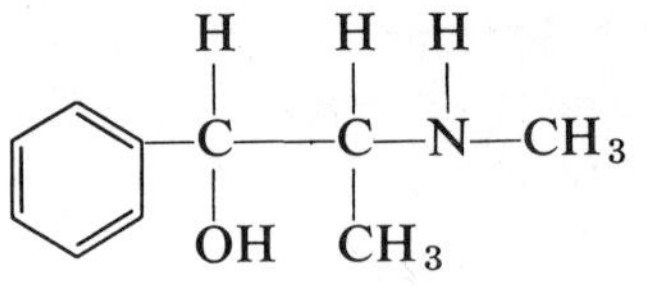

Ephedrine

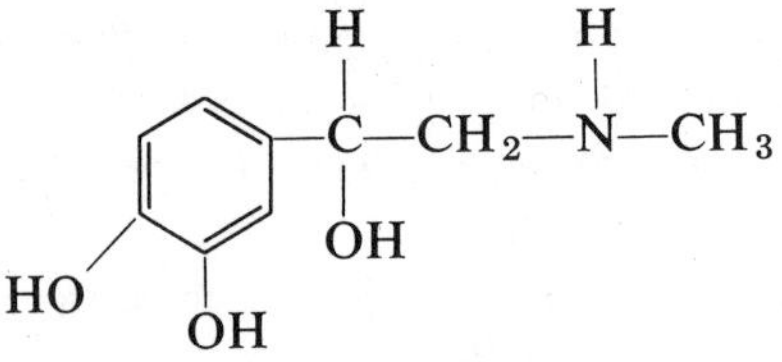

Epinephrine (Adrenalin)
(α, 3, 4-Dihydroxyphenyl-
β-methylaminoethanol)

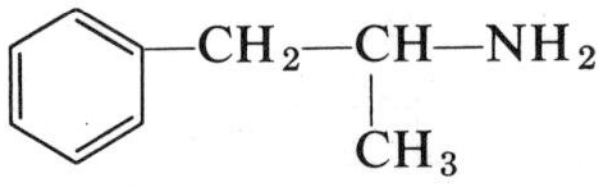

Benzedrine
(β-Aminopropylbenzene)

13.9 DIAZONIUM SALTS

As we have learned, the action of nitrous acid on primary aliphatic amines is of little importance as a preparative reaction. The action of nitrous acid on primary aromatic amines, on the other hand, has a number of applications, which lead to many useful products. The acid salt of an aromatic primary amine, when treated with a cold aqueous solution of sodium nitrite, does not liberate nitrogen as would an aliphatic primary amine. Instead, a water soluble **diazonium salt** is produced. This reaction is called **diazotization** and is an easy one to carry out.

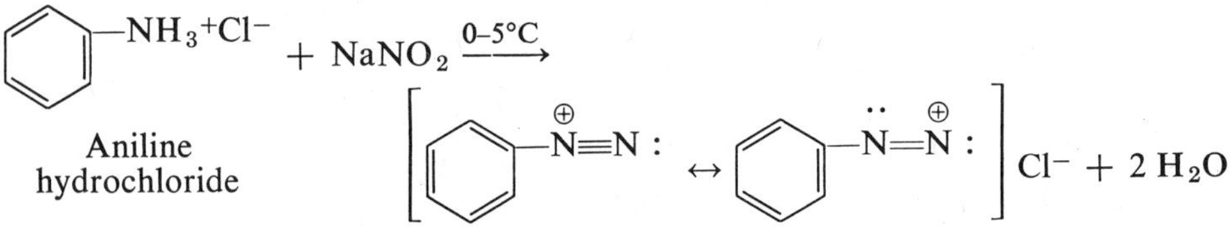

Aniline
hydrochloride

Benzenediazonium chloride

The benzenediazonium ion usually is written as

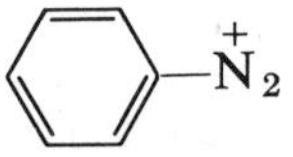

Although we have illustrated its formation from the hydrochloric acid salt of aniline, the sulfuric acid salt serves equally well, but produces the diazonium salt as the sulfate. The diazonium salt, once formed, is not isolated but instead is treated with the reagent required to give the product desired. The reactions of the diazonium salts may be divided into three principal types. In one type of reaction a displacement of the diazonium group by some other group takes place with an accompanying loss of nitrogen. In the second type, a coupling reaction takes place in which the nitrogen atoms are retained as an azo grouping, —N=N—, to become part of a new molecular structure. In the third type of reaction, a reduction, either partial or complete, of the diazonium group occurs. Reactions of each type are illustrated.

A.   Displacement Reactions of Diazonium Salts.   The following examples illustrate the usefulness of diazonium salts as reaction intermediates, where the diazonium group is replaced by some other group.

(1) $-N_2^+Cl^- + H_2O \xrightarrow{\text{Warm}}$ $-OH + N_2 + HCl$

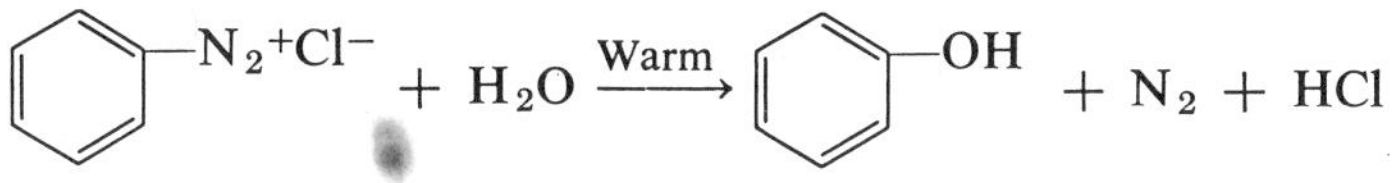

Phenol

(2)
(3)
(4) $-N_2^+Cl^- \left(\begin{array}{c} \text{CuCl} \\ \text{CuBr} \\ \text{CuCN} \end{array} \right) \rightarrow$

$-Cl$ or $(-Br)$ or $(-CN)$ $+ N_2$

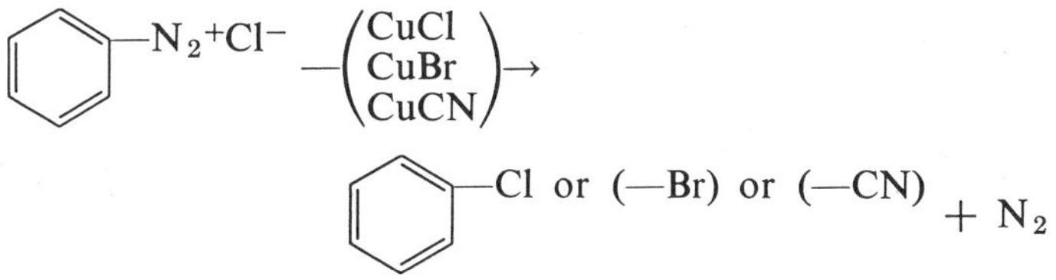

Chlorobenzene

(5) $-N_2^+Cl^- + KI \rightarrow$ $-I + N_2 + KCl$

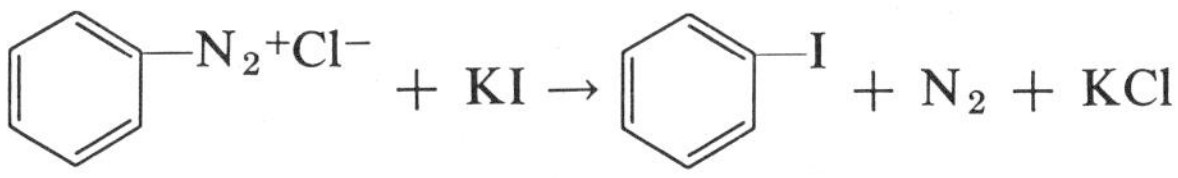

Iodobenzene

(6) $-N_2^+Cl^- + CH_3OH \rightarrow$

$-OCH_3 + N_2 + HCl$

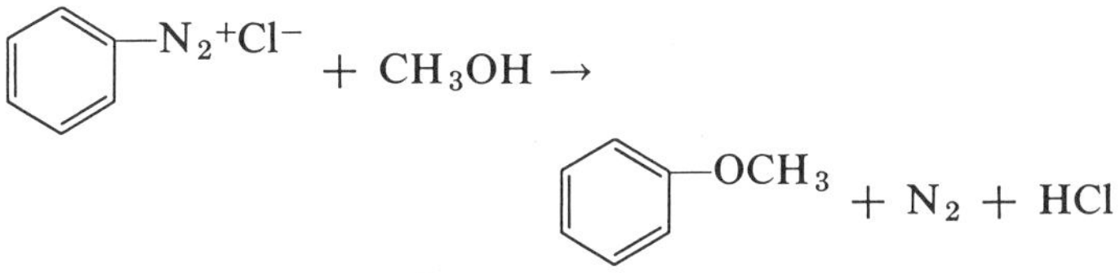

Methyl phenyl ether
(Anisole)

(7) 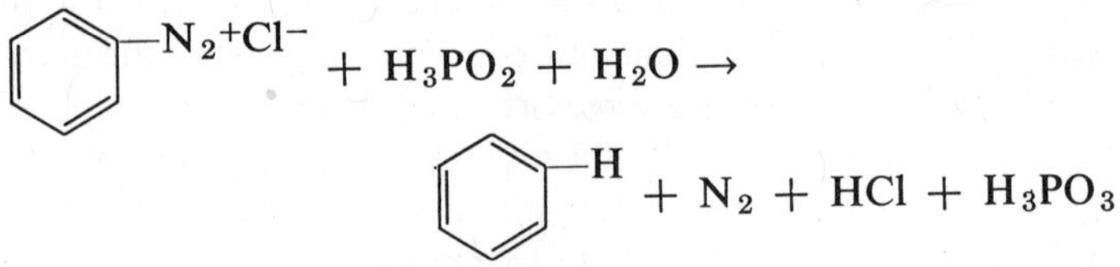 $-N_2^+Cl^-$ $+ H_3PO_2 + H_2O \rightarrow$

$-H$ $+ N_2 + HCl + H_3PO_3$

Benzene

The reactions of a benzenediazonium compound with cuprous salts, reactions (2), (3), and (4) above, usually are referred to as **Sandmeyer reactions.**

B.   Coupling Reactions of Diazonium Salts.   Diazonium salts undergo coupling reactions readily with phenols and aromatic amines. Since the coupling involves an attack of the positive diazonium ion on a center of high electron density in the benzene ring, the presence of substituents that increase the electron density of the ring enhances the coupling reaction.   Conversely, electron-withdrawing substituents on the ring inhibit the coupling reaction or prevent it entirely. Coupling takes place preferably in the position *para* to the activating group. Should the *para* position be occupied, coupling then occurs at one of the *ortho* positions. The coupling reaction is carried out by adding an amine or a phenol to a neutral, an alkaline, or a weakly acidic solution of the diazonium salt.

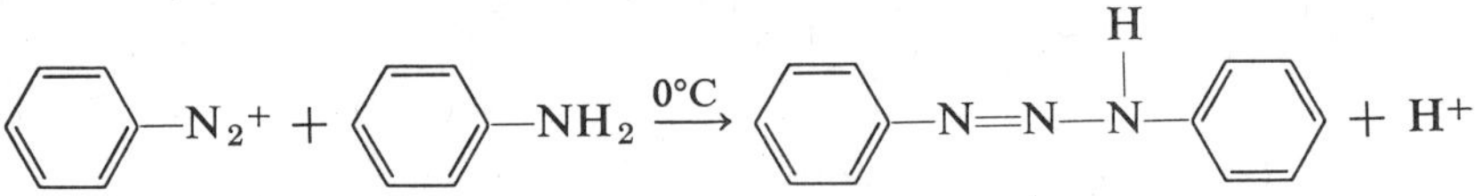

$-N_2^+ +$ $-NH_2 \xrightarrow{0°C}$ $-N{=}N-\overset{H}{\underset{|}{N}}-$ $+ H^+$

Aniline   Diazoaminobenzene

The diazoaminobenzene initially formed when aniline couples with the benzenediazonium ion rearranges on heating to *p*-aminoazobenzene.

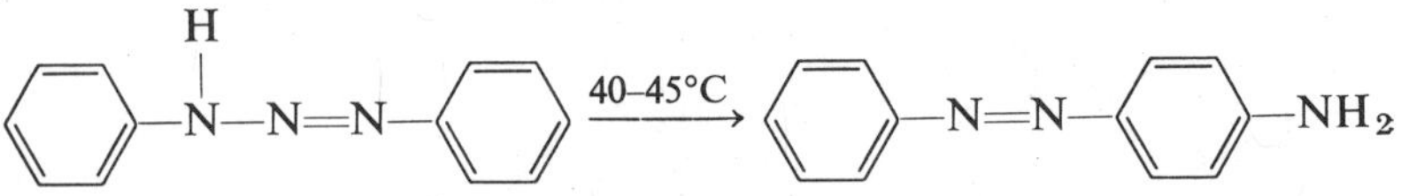

$-\overset{H}{\underset{|}{N}}-N{=}N-$ $\xrightarrow{40\text{–}45°C}$ $-N{=}N-$ $-NH_2$

p-Aminoazobenzene

Coupling will not take place with aniline in a strongly acid solution because in a strong acid environment the primary amino group of aniline becomes a positive anilinium ion which deactivates the ring.

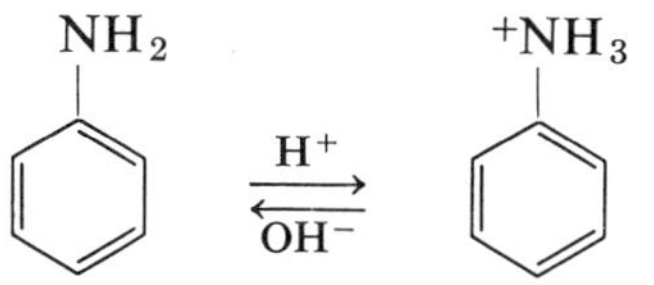

Ring active   Ring deactivated
(couples   (does not
readily)   couple)

Coupling with a phenol is inhibited in a strongly acid solution because the strong activating influence of the phenoxide ion is lacking. Phenols, you will recall, are acidic (Sec. 8.4) and for this reason would couple with the benzenediazonium ion most readily in a solution slightly alkaline.

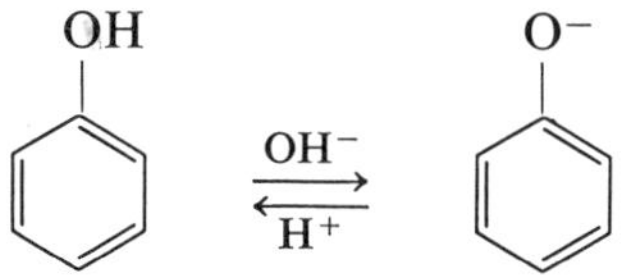

Weakly active   Strongly active
(couples   (couples
slowly)   readily)

When there is a choice of ring positions open to the benzene-diazonium ion, the group on the ring with the stronger directive influence prevails.

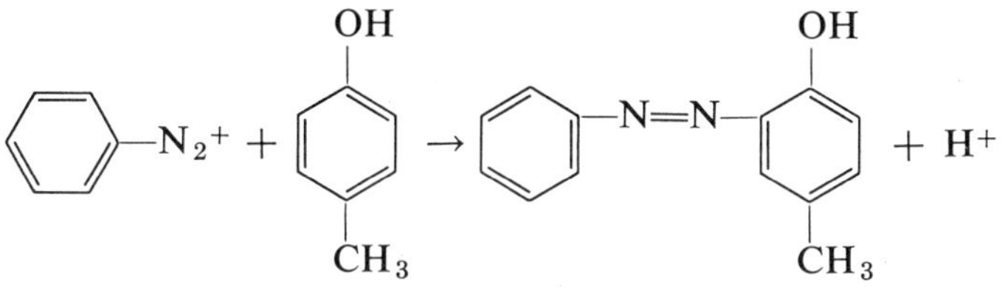

p-Cresol   Benzeneazo-p-cresol

The azo compounds, to a greater or less degree, are colored substances. The azo grouping, for this reason, is the structural feature in a wide variety of dyes called **azo dyes** (Sec. 16.4-B).

Exercise 13.6   Anisole, ⟨◯⟩—OCH₃, is not sufficiently active to couple with benzenediazonium chloride but will couple with 2, 4-dinitrobenzenediazonium chloride. Explain.

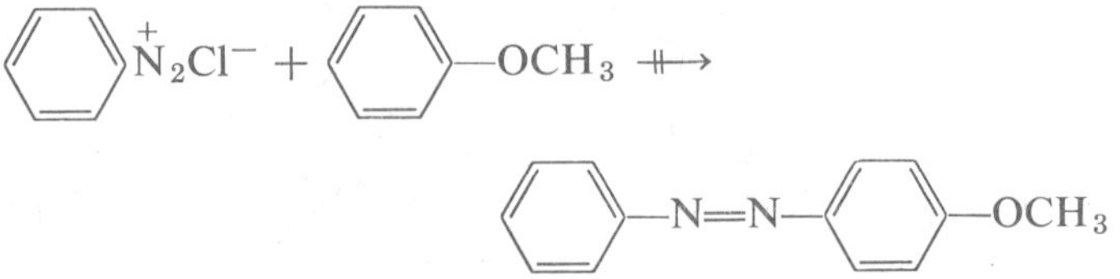

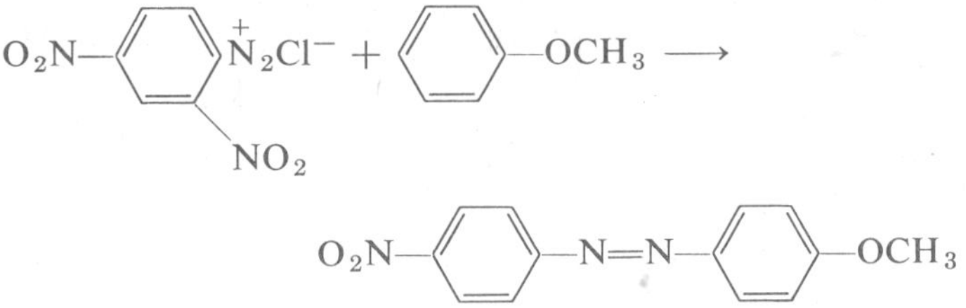

⟨◯⟩N₂Cl⁻ + ⟨◯⟩—OCH₃ ↛

⟨◯⟩—N=N—⟨◯⟩—OCH₃

O₂N—⟨◯⟩N₂Cl⁻ + ⟨◯⟩—OCH₃ ⟶
　　　NO₂

O₂N—⟨◯⟩—N=N—⟨◯⟩—OCH₃

C.   Reduction.   The partial reduction of a diazonium salt can be accomplished without the loss of nitrogen by the use of sodium sulfite as the reducing agent. The product of such a reduction is phenylhydrazine, a reagent useful in the identification of sugars (Sec. 14.9) and carbonyl compounds (Sec. 9.8).

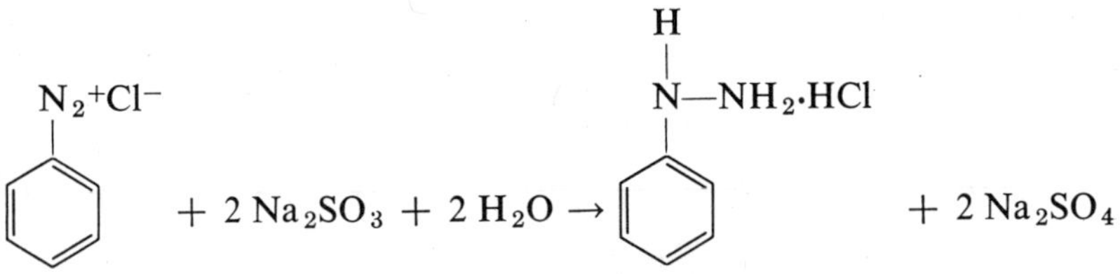

N₂⁺Cl⁻
⟨◯⟩ + 2 Na₂SO₃ + 2 H₂O →

$\overset{H}{\underset{}{N}}$—NH₂·HCl
⟨◯⟩   + 2 Na₂SO₄

Phenylhydrazine
hydrochloride

A complete reduction of a diazonium salt that results in its replacement by hydrogen is called **deamination**. Hypophosphorous acid, H_3PO_2, is an excellent reagent for this reaction (Sec. 13.9, Eq. A-7).

☐☐ *SUMMARY*

[1] Structure

Amines may be considered as ammonia derivatives. Amines are classified as primary, secondary or tertiary; also, as aliphatic or aromatic.

[2] Nomenclature

The amines usually are named by naming the alkyl or aryl groups attached to the nitrogen of the amino group, followed by the word "amine."

[3] Physical Properties

Amines are weakly basic compounds. The low molecular weight members (C_1-C_2) are gases and low boiling liquids. They are soluble in acids. Nearly all are foul-smelling.

[4] Preparation

The amines may be prepared by

a. The direct alkylation of ammonia

b. The reduction of nitriles ($-C\equiv N$), amides ($-\overset{\displaystyle O}{\overset{\|}{C}}-NH_2$), oximes ($-C=NOH$), and nitro ($-NO_2$) compounds
c. Hofmann's hypobromite degradation of amides
d. The Gabriel phthalimide synthesis

[5] Amines react with each of the following reagents to give the product indicated.

Amine		Reactant	Product
a.	RNH_2	+ acids $\longrightarrow$	salts
b.	RNH_2	+ acyl halides or (acid anhydrides) $\longrightarrow$	amides
c.	RNH_2	 + ⬡—$SO_2Cl \longrightarrow$	alkali-soluble benzenesulfonamide
d.	R_2NH	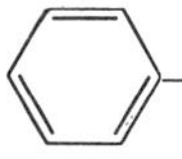 + ⬡—$SO_2Cl \longrightarrow$	alkali-insoluble benzenesulfonamide
e.	RNH_2	+ $HNO_2 \longrightarrow$	N_2 + alcohols + olefins
f.	R_2NH	+ $HNO_2 \longrightarrow$	N-nitroso compounds

g.  ⬡—NH_2 + HNO_2 $\xrightarrow[0-5°]{HCl,}$ diazonium salts

h.  ⬡—NH_2 + Br_2 ⟶ *ortho-para* substitution products

i. R—$CH_2CH_2NH_2$ + CH_3I ⟶ R—$CH_2CH_2\overset{+}{N}(CH_3)_3X^-$

$\xrightarrow[\text{heat}]{Ag_2O,}$ R—$CH{=}CH_2$ + $(CH_3)_3N$

[6] Diamines may be prepared by the same general methods used to prepare the simple amines.

[7] Amino ethanols can be prepared from ethylene oxide and ammonia. Physiologically-active compounds frequently contain an aminoalcohol unit.

[8] Diazonium salts formed from aromatic primary amines are useful intermediates in organic synthesis. The diazonium group may be

    a. Replaced by: halogen, cyanide, hydroxyl, and alkoxyl
    b. Coupled to: other aromatic rings
    c. Reduced to: phenylhydrazine, benzene (deamination)

□□ *NEW TERMS*

[1]	acetylcholine	[6]	Gabriel phthalimide synthesis
[2]	chelating agent	[7]	Hinsberg test
[3]	deamination	[8]	Hofmann amide degradation
[4]	diazonium salt	[9]	inner salts
[5]	diazotization	[10]	sympathomimetic agents

■ □SUPPLEMENTARY EXERCISES
▼   AND PROBLEMS

[1] Name the following compounds. If amines, classify each as primary, secondary, or tertiary.

(a) 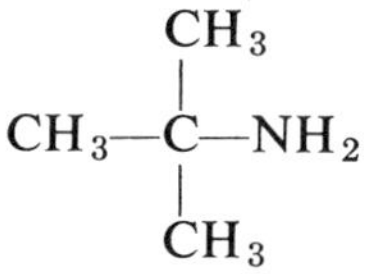
$$CH_3-\underset{\underset{CH_3}{|}}{\overset{\overset{CH_3}{|}}{C}}-NH_2$$

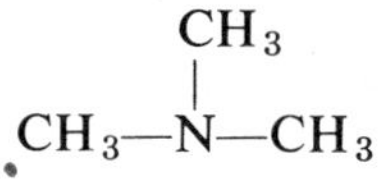

(b)
$$CH_3-\underset{\overset{\bullet}{}}{\overset{\overset{CH_3}{|}}{N}}-CH_3$$

(c)
naphthalene with NH_2

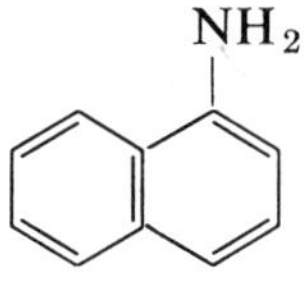

(d) 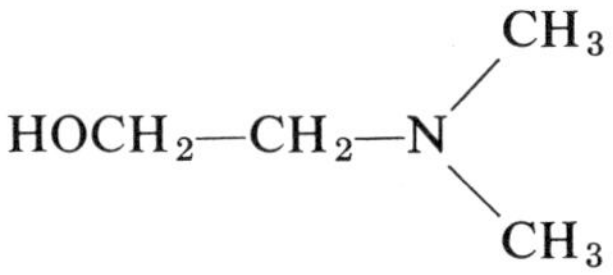
$$HOCH_2-CH_2-N\overset{\diagup CH_3}{\diagdown CH_3}$$

(e) 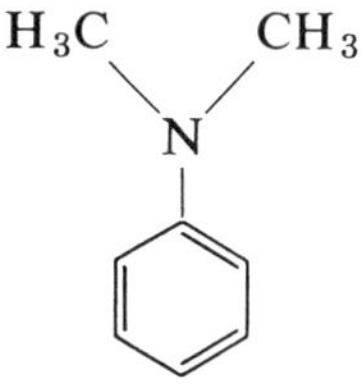
benzene ring with $\underset{\underset{N}{|}}{H_3C\diagdown \diagup CH_3}$

(f) 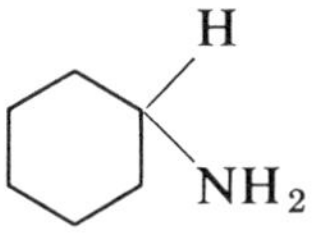
cyclohexane with $\overset{H}{\diagup}$ and NH_2

(g) $H_2N-CH_2-CH_2-CH_2-CH_2-CH_2-NH_2$

(h) 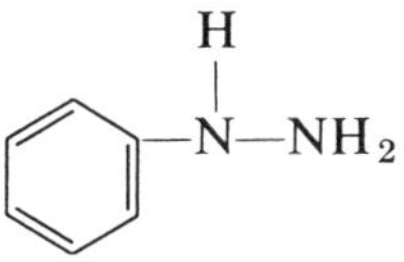
benzene ring with $\underset{\overset{|}{}}{\overset{H}{N}}-NH_2$

(i) 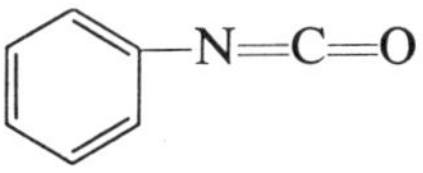
benzene ring with $-N{=}C{=}O$

[2] Write structures for the following.
(a) aniline
(b) benzenediazonium sulfate
(c) *p*-aminobenzenesulfonic acid (sulfanilic acid)
(d) tetramethylammonium chloride
(e) acetanilide
(f) β-diethylaminoethyl-*p*-aminobenzoate hydrochloride (Procaine).
(g) dimethylaniline
(h) *tert*-butylamine
(i) ethyldimethylamine

[3] Without consulting a table of ionization constants, arrange the following compounds in an order of diminishing basic strength.

(a) aniline   (b) ammonia   (c) dimethylamine   (d) ethylamine
(e) benzamide

[4] Taking advantage of acidic, basic, and other properties, outline a procedure for separating a mixture that includes (a) aniline, (b) benzoic acid, (c) acetophenone, and (d) bromobenzene.

[5] What reagents and conditions are required to accomplish each of the following conversions? (Some require more than one step.)

(a) 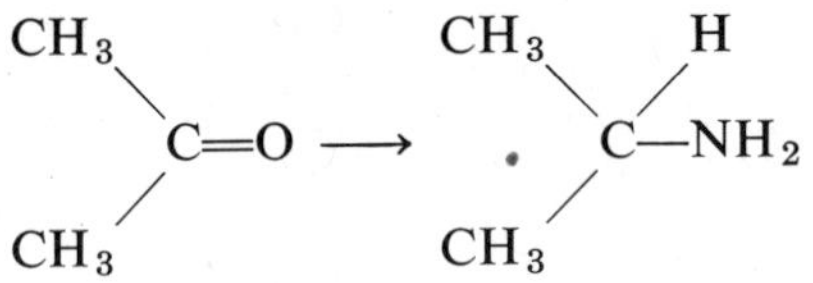 $\begin{array}{c} CH_3 \\ \diagdown \\ \diagup \\ CH_3 \end{array} C{=}O \longrightarrow$. $\begin{array}{c} CH_3 \quad H \\ \diagdown \diagup \\ C{-}NH_2 \\ \diagup \\ CH_3 \end{array}$

(b) $CH_3{-}CH_2{-}I \longrightarrow CH_3{-}CH_2{-}CH_2{-}NH_2$

(c) 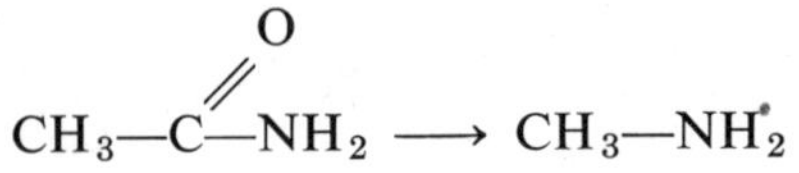 $CH_3{-}\overset{\overset{\displaystyle O}{\|}}{C}{-}NH_2 \longrightarrow CH_3{-}NH_2^{\bullet}$

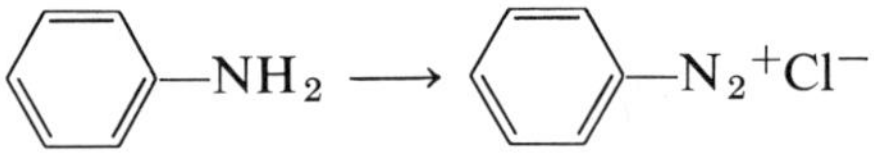

(d) $CH_3{-}CH_2{-}CH_2{-}CH_2{-}NH_2 \longrightarrow$
     $(CH_3)_3N + CH_3{-}CH_2{-}CH{=}CH_2$

(e) 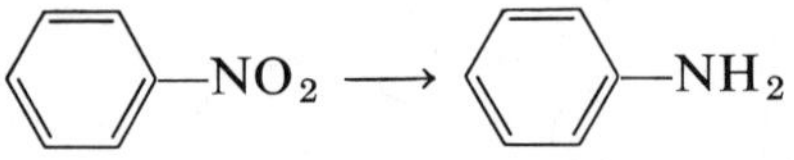 ⬡$-NO_2 \longrightarrow$ ⬡$-NH_2$

(f) 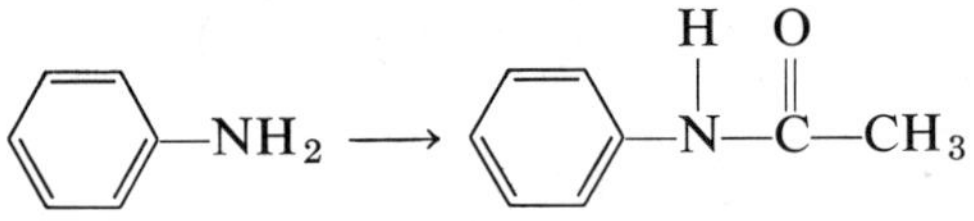 ⬡$-NH_2 \longrightarrow$ ⬡$-\overset{\overset{\displaystyle H}{|}}{N}{-}\overset{\overset{\displaystyle O}{\|}}{C}{-}CH_3$

(g) ⬡$-NH_2 \longrightarrow$ ⬡$-N_2^+Cl^-$

(h) ⬡$-N_2^+Cl^- \longrightarrow$ ⬡$-CN$

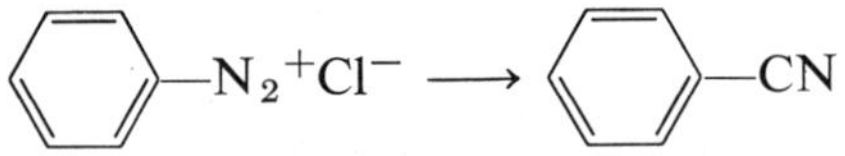

(i) 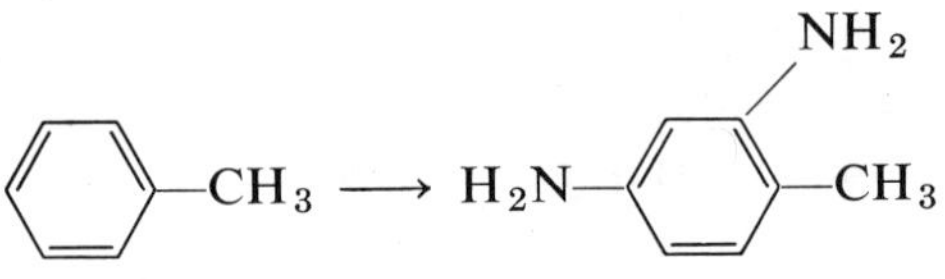 ⬡$-CH_3 \longrightarrow H_2N-$⬡$\overset{\overset{\displaystyle NH_2}{|}}{}-CH_3$

(j) 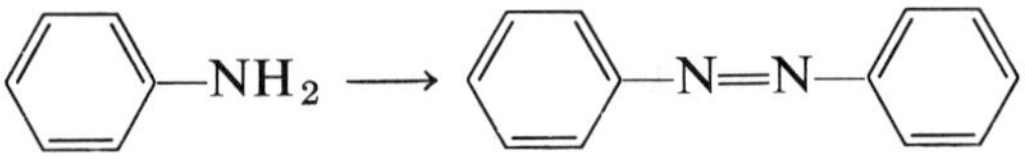 ⬡$-NH_2 \longrightarrow$ ⬡$-N{=}N-$⬡

[6] What simple test tube reactions would serve to distinguish between:

(a) *n*-butylamine and triethylamine
(b) aniline hydrochloride and benzamide
(c) *sec*-butyl alcohol and *sec*-butylamine
(d) aniline and benzylamine

[7] When 1.83 g of an unknown amine was treated with nitrous acid, the evolved nitrogen, corrected to standard temperature and pressure, measured 560 ml. The alcohol isolated from the reaction mixture gave a positive iodoform reaction. What is the structural formula of the unknown amine?

[8]   A white solid compound, $C_{13}H_{11}NO$, was insoluble in water but appeared to go into solution when heated with sodium hydroxide. Continued heating produced an oily layer which was acid-soluble. The mixture was cooled, and acidified with hydrochloric acid. This treatment caused the precipitation of a white acid whose neutralization equivalent was found to be 122 ± 1. Draw and name the original compound.

[9]   Draw reasonable structures for the isomeric compounds A, B, and C, $C_{10}H_{13}NO_2$, if:

A

(a) it is a white solid that is insoluble in cold, dilute acid or base;
(b) refluxing with an alkaline solution produces a gas with a strong ammoniacal odor;
(c) acidification of the hydrolysis mixture liberates an acid with a N.E. of 152 ± 1.

B

(a) it is a white solid insoluble in cold, dilute acid or base;
(b) refluxing with sodium hydroxide solution produces an oily layer. The oily layer, when separated and purified, can be diazotized.
(c) acidification of the alkaline hydrolysis mixture, followed by extraction with ether isolated a compound with a neutralization equivalent of 74 ± 1.

C

(a) it is an oil insoluble in water, acid, or base;
(b) oxidation with sodium dichromate and concentrated sulfuric acid produced a solid compound, $C_8H_5NO_6$, that was soluble in hot water and in cold, dilute base;
(c) strong heating of the compound caused it to melt only.

chapter 14

Carbohydrates

INTRODUCTION

> The name **carbohydrate** originated from the French "hydrate de carbon." Early analyses of a number of naturally occurring compounds of this class gave empirical formulas in which the ratios of carbon, hydrogen, and oxygen appeared to indicate hydrates of carbon of the type $C_xH_{2y}O_y$ or $C_x(H_2O)_y$ where x and y may be the same or different. For example, the simple sugar **glucose** (grape sugar) has a molecular formula of $C_6H_{12}O_6$, and **sucrose** (cane sugar) the formula $C_{12}H_{22}O_{11}$, but such definite ratios of water to carbon are not to be found in every carbohydrate. Therefore the name carbohydrate, as often is the case in chemical nomenclature, is not descriptive but has persisted and probably will be with us for a long time.
>
> The carbohydrates comprise a great class of natural substances which includes the sugars, starches, cellulose and related products. Carbohydrates may be described as polyhydroxy aldehydes or polyhydroxy ketones, or substances which, when hydrolyzed, give polyhydroxy aldehydes or polyhydroxy ketones.

14.2   CLASSIFICATION AND NOMENCLATURE

The carbohydrates may be subdivided conveniently into three principal classes: monosaccharides, oligosaccharides (Gr., *oligos*, a few), and polysaccharides.

Monosaccharides include all sugars that contain a single carbohydrate unit — that is, one incapable of producing a simpler carbohydrate on further hydrolysis. Most of the monosaccharides are five- and six-carbon structures. The five-carbon monosaccharides are called **pentoses** and those of six-carbons are called **hexoses.**

The suffix -*ose* is a generic designation of any sugar. The monosaccharides frequently are referred to as simple sugars and are either polyhydroxy aldehydes or polyhydroxy ketones. If an aldehyde, the name **aldose** is applicable; if a ketone, the name **ketose** frequently is used to describe the sugar.

Oligosaccharides consist of two or more (but a relatively small number) monosaccharide units joined by acetal linkages between the aldehyde or ketone group of one simple sugar and a hydroxy group of another. This kind of coupling in sugar chemistry gives rise to what is called a **glycosidic** linkage. Hydrolysis of an oligosaccharide yields the simple sugar components. **Disaccharides** are composed of two simple sugar units, **trisaccharides** of three, etc.

Polysaccharides consist of hundreds or even thousands of monosaccharide units joined together through glycosidic linkages to form macro molecules, or polymers.

14.3   GLUCOSE: A TYPICAL MONOSACCHARIDE

Glucose (frequently called dextrose because of its dextrorotation) is the most important of the monosaccharides. Not only is it the most widely occurring sugar, but in free or combined form it is perhaps the most abundant of organic compounds. Glucose is the end product of the hydrolysis of starch and cellulose and is closely associated with the metabolic processes. Glucose is a main source of energy for all living organisms. It comprises 0.08–0.1% of the blood content of all normal mammals and is one of the few organic compounds which may be injected as a food directly into the blood stream. Our best introduction to carbohydrate chemistry is offered by a review of the chemical and physical properties of glucose.

14.4   THE STRUCTURE OF GLUCOSE

The experimental evidence which led to the elucidation of the glucose structure provides one of the most fascinating chapters in organic chemistry. Combustion analysis and a molecular weight determination established the molecular formula of glucose as $C_6H_{12}O_6$. Structural evidence was supplied by the following: (a) reaction with acetic anhydride produced a crystalline pentacetate and suggested the presence of five hydroxyl groups; (b) reaction with hydroxylamine (Sec. 9.8) produced an oxime and suggested the presence of a carbonyl group; (c) mild oxidation with bromine in an aqueous solution yielded a 6-carbon acid, $C_5H_{11}O_5COOH$, and indicated an aldehyde function as one end of the molecule. This observation was reënforced when the addition of HCN yielded a cyanohydrin; (d) hydrolysis of the cyanohydrin, followed by reduction, produced heptanoic acid.

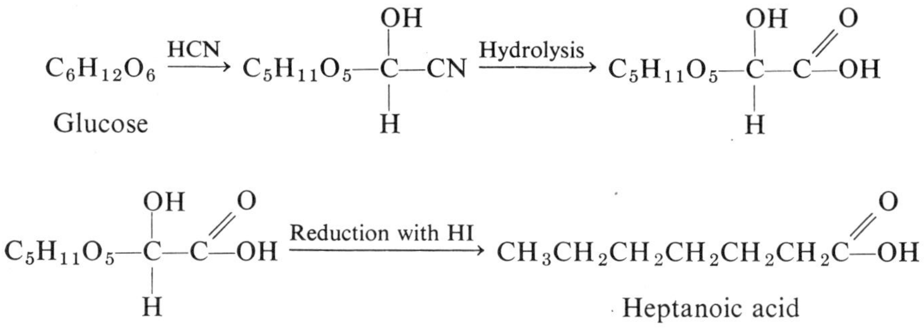

$$C_6H_{12}O_6 \xrightarrow{HCN} C_5H_{11}O_5-\overset{\overset{\displaystyle OH}{|}}{\underset{\underset{\displaystyle H}{|}}{C}}-CN \xrightarrow{Hydrolysis} C_5H_{11}O_5-\overset{\overset{\displaystyle OH}{|}}{\underset{\underset{\displaystyle H}{|}}{C}}-\overset{\displaystyle O}{C}-OH$$

Glucose

$$C_5H_{11}O_5-\overset{\overset{\displaystyle OH}{|}}{\underset{\underset{\displaystyle H}{|}}{C}}-\overset{\displaystyle O}{C}-OH \xrightarrow{Reduction\ with\ HI} CH_3CH_2CH_2CH_2CH_2CH_2\overset{\displaystyle O}{C}-OH$$

Heptanoic acid

The above reactions indicate a six-carbon chain with a terminal aldehyde group. A six-carbon aldehyde with five hydroxyl groups can have a stable structure only if each hydroxyl group is attached to a different carbon atom. The structure of glucose thus was proposed as the following:

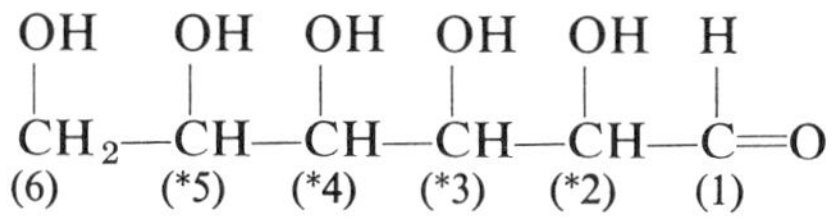

$$\underset{(6)}{\overset{\overset{\displaystyle OH}{|}}{CH_2}}-\underset{(*5)}{\overset{\overset{\displaystyle OH}{|}}{CH}}-\underset{(*4)}{\overset{\overset{\displaystyle OH}{|}}{CH}}-\underset{(*3)}{\overset{\overset{\displaystyle OH}{|}}{CH}}-\underset{(*2)}{\overset{\overset{\displaystyle OH}{|}}{CH}}-\underset{(1)}{\overset{\overset{\displaystyle H}{|}}{C}}=O$$

Glucose

14.5   THE CONFIGURATION OF GLUCOSE

Inspection of the above formula reveals the presence of four different asymmetric carbon atoms. No less than sixteen ($2^4 = 16$) optical isomers with the above structure are possible. Only two other aldohexoses (mannose and galactose) occur in nature. Which of the sixteen possible structures is glucose? Which is mannose? Which is galactose? The answers to these perplexing questions were obtained through a brilliant series of syntheses and degradation studies performed by a research group headed by Emil Fischer, 1891–1896.[1] Most of the remaining thirteen aldohexoses were synthesized and the configurations of all known isomers elucidated. To review all the chemistry which finally led to this great accomplish-

[1]Emil Fischer (1852–1919), Professor of Chemistry, University of Berlin. Winner of the Nobel Prize in Chemistry, 1902.

ment is beyond the scope of this text[2] but a simplified scheme may be written to show how all eight D-forms of the aldohexoses were obtained.

The reference standard chosen for relating configurations of optically active compounds is D-glyceraldehyde (Sec. 6.5). The carbon chain of D-glyceraldehyde can be lengthened into a sugar molecule through repeated cyanohydrin formation. A lengthening of the carbon chain in this manner is known as the **Kiliani synthesis.**

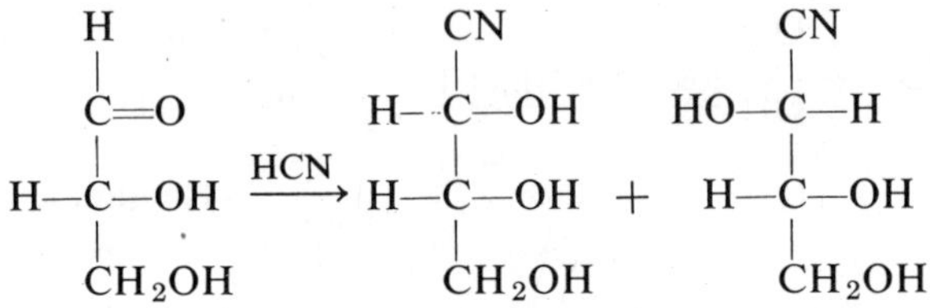

$$
\begin{array}{ccc}
\text{H} & \text{CN} & \text{CN}\\
| & | & |\\
\text{C}=\text{O} & \text{H}-\text{C}-\text{OH} & \text{HO}-\text{C}-\text{H}\\
| \quad \xrightarrow{\ \text{HCN}\ } & | & |\\
\text{H}-\text{C}-\text{OH} & \text{H}-\text{C}-\text{OH}\ + & \text{H}-\text{C}-\text{OH}\\
| & | & |\\
\text{CH}_2\text{OH} & \text{CH}_2\text{OH} & \text{CH}_2\text{OH}
\end{array}
$$

D (+) Glyceraldehyde   (A mixture of optically active diastereoisomers. Both retain the D configuration.)

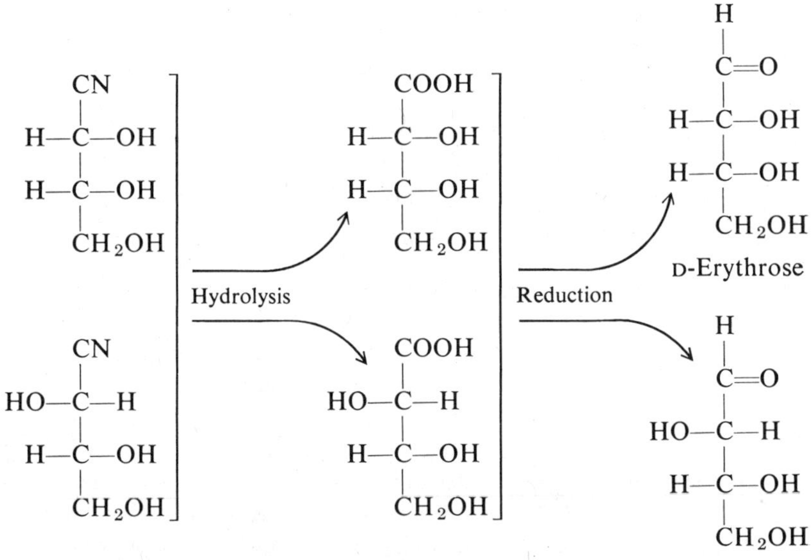

$$
\begin{array}{ccccc}
\text{CN} & & \text{COOH} & & \begin{array}{c}\text{H}\\|\\\text{C}=\text{O}\end{array}\\
| & & | & & \\
\text{H}-\text{C}-\text{OH} & & \text{H}-\text{C}-\text{OH} & & \text{H}-\text{C}-\text{OH}\\
| & & | & & |\\
\text{H}-\text{C}-\text{OH} & & \text{H}-\text{C}-\text{OH} & & \text{H}-\text{C}-\text{OH}\\
| & & | & & |\\
\text{CH}_2\text{OH} & & \text{CH}_2\text{OH} & & \text{CH}_2\text{OH}\\
& \text{Hydrolysis} & & \text{Reduction} & \text{D-Erythrose}\\
\text{CN} & & \text{COOH} & & \begin{array}{c}\text{H}\\|\\\text{C}=\text{O}\end{array}\\
| & & | & & \\
\text{HO}-\text{C}-\text{H} & & \text{HO}-\text{C}-\text{H} & & \text{HO}-\text{C}-\text{H}\\
| & & | & & |\\
\text{H}-\text{C}-\text{OH} & & \text{H}-\text{C}-\text{OH} & & \text{H}-\text{C}-\text{OH}\\
| & & | & & |\\
\text{CH}_2\text{OH} & & \text{CH}_2\text{OH} & & \text{CH}_2\text{OH}\\
& & & & \text{D-Threose}
\end{array}
$$

The following scheme shows how the configurations of the pentoses are related to those of their parent structures, the tetroses.

---

[2] An excellent discussion of the methods employed by Fischer to determine the spatial configuration about each of the four asymmetric carbon atoms of glucose may be found in Morrison and Boyd, *Organic Chemistry*, 2nd ed., Chapter 33. Boston: Allyn and Bacon, Inc., (1966).

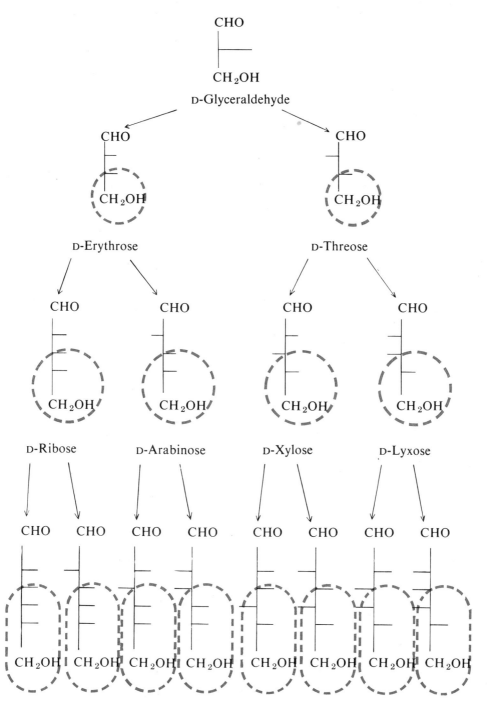

D-Allose D-Altrose D-Glucose D-Mannose D-Gulose D-Idose D-Galactose D-Talose

Similarly, the configurations of the hexoses may be related to those of their antecedents, the pentoses. The hydroxyl groups in each structure are denoted by a short horizontal spur and the carbon chain as a vertical line. The dotted line encloses only that portion of each structure that has a configuration identical with that of its parent. Mirror images of all structures shown would have resulted had we used L-glyceraldehyde as our starting material.

Exercise 14.1   The oxidation of glucose by strong nitric acid converts both the aldehyde and the primary alcohol group into carboxyl groups. The resulting dicarboxylic acid, called **glucaric acid**, was found to be optically active. Why did this result eliminate the structure shown for galactose as being that of glucose?

The projection formula for glucose usually is written as shown below and assigned a D-configuration (Sec. 6.5). The "tail" or lower extremity of the formula is $HOCH_2$—, that is, the hydroxymethyl group.

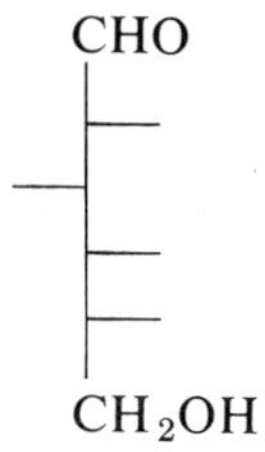

CHO

CH_2OH

14.6   THE CYCLIC STRUCTURE OF SUGARS. MUTAROTATION

Several properties of glucose are not explainable by the open-chain formula. For example, when D-glucose is heated with methanol in the presence of hydrogen chloride, the expected dimethyl acetal is not obtained. Instead, two optically active isomeric compounds result, each containing but *one* methoxyl group. Ethers such as those shown in structures **II** and **III** are named **glycosides.** If glycosides are formed from a sugar and a nonsugar hydroxy compound, the nonsugar component is called an **aglycone. Glucoside**

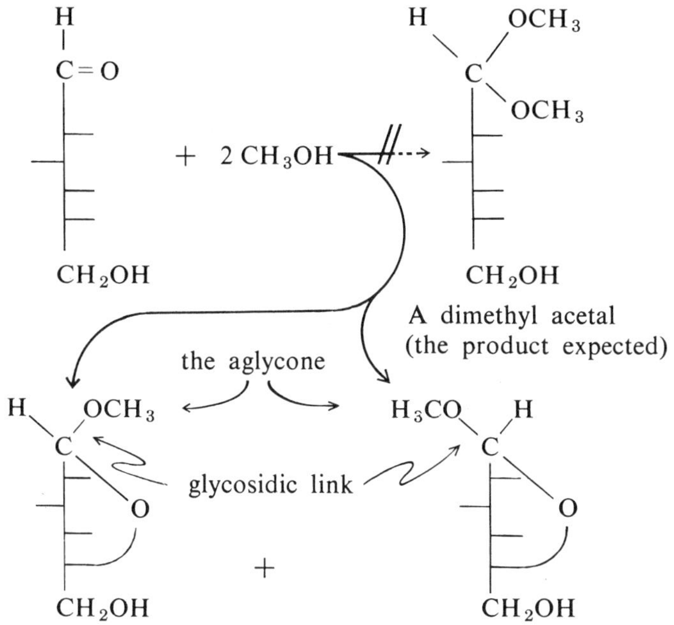

H
|
C=O
⊢
⊣
⊢
CH₂OH

+ 2 CH₃OH —//--→

H   OCH₃
 \ /
  C
  \
   OCH₃
⊢
⊣
⊢
CH₂OH   **I**

A dimethyl acetal
(the product expected)

the aglycone

H   OCH₃
 \ /
  C
⊢   O
⊢
⊣
CH₂OH

α-Methylglucoside

$[\alpha]_D^{20} = +159°$

II

glycosidic link

+

H₃CO   H
    \ /
     C
  O ⊢
     ⊢
     ⊣
CH₂OH

β-Methylglucoside

$[\alpha]_D^{20} = -34°$

III

is a name specifically assigned to a glycoside produced from glucose. The easily oxidized aldehyde group no longer exists in a glucoside. The methyl glucosides (structures **II** and **III**), therefore, are incapable of reducing Fehling's solution or Tollens' reagent. A second observation, unexplainable by the straight-chain formula, was that two crystalline forms of D-glucose could be isolated. One form, designated the α-form, crystallized from a concentrated aqueous solution at 30°C, decomposed at its melting point (147°C) and, in a freshly prepared solution, showed a specific rotation of +113°. The other form, designated the β-form, crystallized from a hot, glacial acetic acid solution, melted at 148–150°C, and, in a freshly prepared solution showed a specific rotation of +19°. The rotation of an aqueous solution of either the α- or the β-form of glucose, when allowed to stand, was found to change. The rotation of each solution reached the equilibrium value of +52°. Such a change in rotation on standing is called **mutarotation.** Mutarotation is caused by a change in configuration of one asymmetric center in each isomer. The explanation for this behavior for glucose rests in the fact that the glucose molecule exists largely in one of two cyclic hemiacetal forms. Ring closure can result easily through intramolecular acetal formation when the hydroxyl group of carbon (5) is brought into close proximity to the carbonyl group. Zigzag carbon chains, as illustrated in structures **IV** and **V** (below), provide this condition. You will note that two different modes of addition are possible.

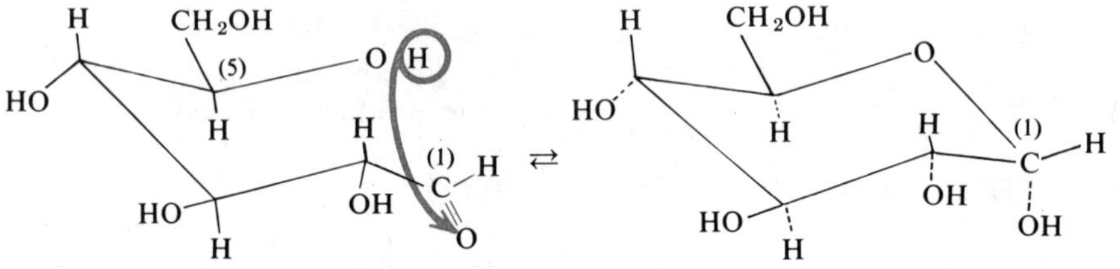

D-Glucose   **IV** α-D-Glucose

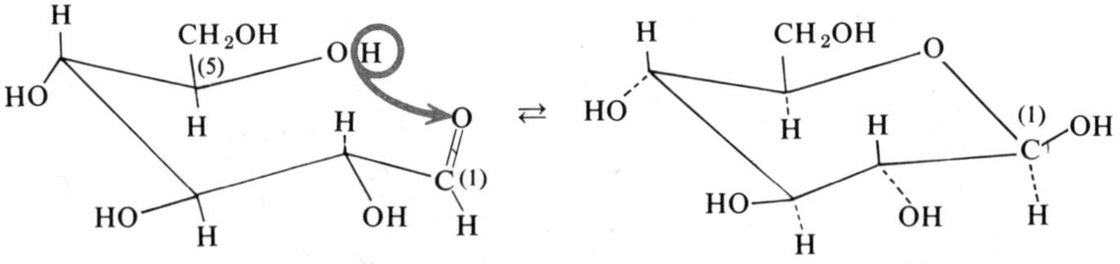

D-Glucose   **V** β-D-Glucose

Carbon (1) in each of the cyclic hemiacetal structures shown represents a new asymmetric center, and two diastereoisomers thus are possible: α- and β-D-glucose. Enough of the open chain (about

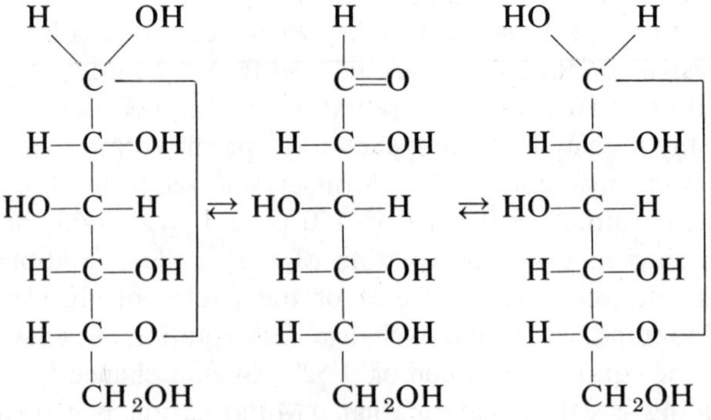

α-D-Glucose   D-Glucose β-D-Glucose

1%) form of glucose is present in the equilibrium mixture to give some of the reactions typical of the aldehyde group, but glucose exists preferentially in the cyclic form. The structures below represent typical ways of formulating the glucose molecule.

The Haworth[3] formulas for the cyclic forms of glucose are drawn as planar, hexagonal slabs with darkened edges toward the viewer. Hydroxyl groups and hydrogen atoms are shown either as above (solid bonds) or below (dotted bonds) the plane of the hexagon.

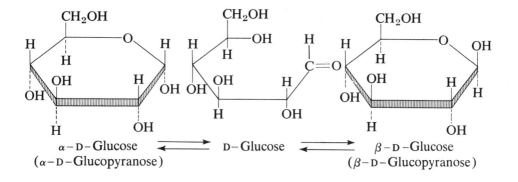

α-D-Glucose $\rightleftarrows$ D-Glucose $\rightleftarrows$ β-D-Glucose

(α-D-Glucopyranose)   (β-D-Glucopyranose)

The *pyranose* designation for the cyclic forms of glucose indicates a structural similarity to the six-membered, heterocyclic **pyran** ring, . A *furanose* designation for a sugar indicates a five-membered ring with a structural relationship to the heterocycle, **furan,** (Sec. 17.3). The Haworth structures are easy to draw, but one must not forget that the six-membered ring is very much like that of cyclohexane and can pucker (Sec. 2.12). Correct cyclic structures for glucose are indicated by the chair representations that follow. Of the two structures shown on page 388 for α-D-glucopyranose, the conformation in which most of the bulkier groups are bonded equatorially (structure **II**) appears to be the more stable one. Similar conformations for β-D-glucopyranose can be drawn by interchanging the positions of the hydrogen atom and the hydroxyl group on carbon (1).

[3]Walter Haworth (1883–1950), Professor of Chemistry, University of Birmingham. Winner of the Nobel Prize in Chemistry in 1937.

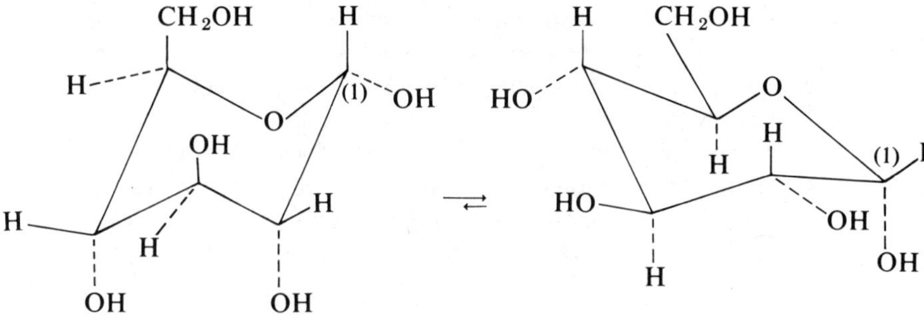

I   α-D-Glucopyranose   II

FRUCTOSE

Fructose, $C_6H_{12}O_6$, also called *levulose* because it is levorotatory, is the most widely distributed ketose. Fructose is found along with glucose in the juices of ripe fruits and in honey. It also occurs with glucose as a component of the disaccharide *sucrose*.

A comparison of the structures of glucose and fructose shows that fructose has only three asymmetric carbon atoms, and the configurations about these are identical to those of corresponding carbon atoms in the glucose chain.

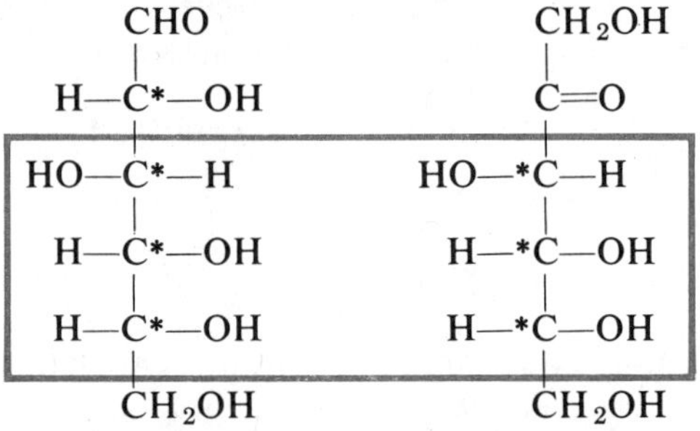

D(+)Glucose   D(−)Fructose

Fructose, unlike glucose, can not be oxidized by aqueous bromine and, as a keto sugar, one would not expect fructose to reduce Fehling's solution. However, the alkalinity of Fehling's solution is sufficient to cause a rearrangement of fructose to glucose or mannose, both easily oxidizable sugars.

The cyclic form of fructose may be either that of a pyranose or a furanose. In more complicated structures of which fructose is a part, it is found in the furanose form.

β-D-Fructopyranose   β-D-Fructofuranose

14.8   REACTIONS OF THE HEXOSES

A number of reactions involving both the carbonyl and hydroxylic groups of the monosaccharides were reviewed in previous sections. Oxidation by bromine, Tollens' reagent, and Fehling's solution, the addition of hydrogen cyanide, the formation of acetals and acetates, all were reactions helpful in elucidating the structure of glucose. In addition to the preceding reactions, the following also are important in sugar chemistry.

14.9   REACTION WITH PHENYLHYDRAZINE. OSAZONE FORMATION

The carbonyl function in a sugar molecule will, if free to react, condense with phenylhydrazine to produce a phenylhydrazone. The phenylhydrazones of sugars, unlike the phenylhydrazones of simple compounds containing a carbonyl function, usually are difficult to isolate. On the other hand, when an excess of phenylhydrazine is used it forms with sugars a diphenylhydrazone derivative called an **osazone.** The osazones of sugars are easily crystallized and can be used for identification purposes. When excess phenylhydrazine is used the carbinol adjacent to the carbonyl, that is, carbon No. 2 in aldoses but carbon No. 1 in ketoses, becomes oxidized to a second carbonyl group. The carbonyl formed by this oxidation, along with the one originally present, condenses with phenylhydrazine to produce the osazone. The mechanics of the oxidation step are not entirely clear but it appears that for osazone formation to occur, the ratio of phenylhydrazine to sugar in the reaction mixture must be at least 3:1 because one molecule of phenylhydrazine is changed to aniline and ammonia. Inasmuch as only carbons (1) and (2) are involved in osazone formation, D-glucose, D-mannose, and D-fructose all form identical osazones.

The configurations of carbon atoms (3), (4), and (5) in each of these three sugars thus are revealed to be identical. A pair of aldoses that differ only in the configuration about the No. 2 carbon atom such as glucose and mannose are called **epimers.**

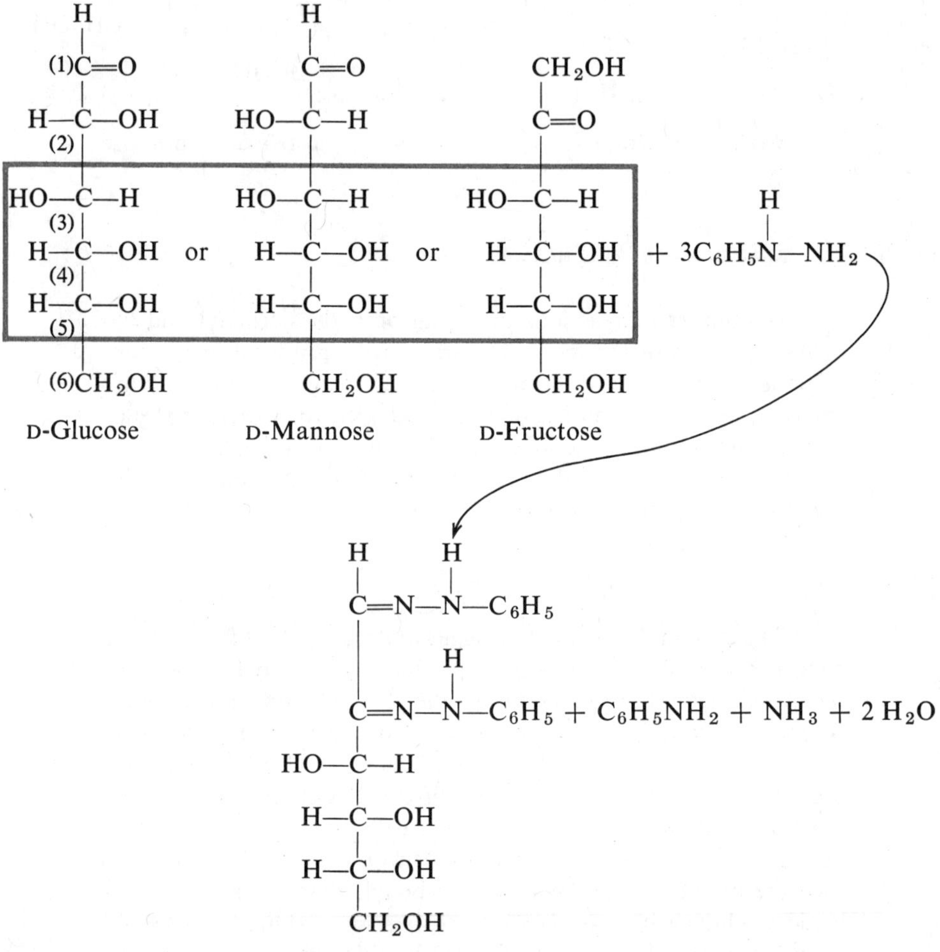

D-Glucose   D-Mannose   D-Fructose

Osazone of D-Glucose,
D-Mannose, and D-Fructose

Exercise 14.2   Criticize the following statement: "Two hexoses that react with phenylhydrazine and yield identical osazones are epimers."

14.10   THE FERMENTATION OF SUGARS

Emil Fischer found that of the sixteen aldohexoses only those found in nature (D-glucose, D-mannose, and D-galactose) could be fermented by yeast. The three simple sugars just named, along with D-fructose, are acted upon by the enzyme **zymase** to yield the same decomposition products — ethyl alcohol and carbon dioxide. The reactions by which alcohol is produced from a sugar are complex but the net result may be indicated by the equation below.

$$C_6H_{12}O_6 \xrightarrow{\text{Zymase}} 2\,C_2H_5OH + 2\,CO_2$$

The fermentation of sugar, the oldest chemical reaction known, provided the ancients with wine and the leavening action for making bread.

14.11   OLIGOSACCHARIDES

Disaccharides, the most important of the oligosaccharides, may be regarded as glycosides. However, unlike the simple methylglucosides (Sec. 14.6), the hydroxylic compound that is coupled through the glycosidic link is a second monosaccharide unit — not an aglycone. A molecule of water is split out from two monosaccharide units to form a disaccharide. Restoration of the water by hydrolysis of the disaccharide reforms the two monosaccharide components. Hydrolysis may be effected by dilute acids or by enzymes. The most important of the disaccharides and the only ones we shall consider are *sucrose, maltose, cellobiose,* and *lactose.*

14.12   SUCROSE

Sucrose, ordinary table sugar, is obtained from the juices extracted from sugar cane and sugar beets. The juice from either source contains about 14–25% of sucrose. To a small extent, sucrose is obtained from the sap of certain species of maple trees. Maple sugar is marketed largely as a syrup. Sucrose is dextrorotatory but on hydrolysis produces equimolar quantities of D-glucose (dextrose), and D-fructose (levulose). During the hydrolysis of sucrose the sign of the specific rotation changes from positive to negative, or is said to **invert**. The hydrolysis mixture is called *invert sugar*. The enzyme *invertase*, carried by the bee, is able to accomplish the same result in the production of honey.

$$C_{12}H_{22}O_{11} \xrightarrow[\text{(or \textit{invertase})}]{\text{Acid hydrolysis}} \text{D-Glucose} + \text{D-Fructose}$$

$$\text{Sucrose} \qquad\qquad \underbrace{[\alpha]_D^{20} = +52° \quad [\alpha]_D^{20} = -92°}$$

$$[\alpha]_D^{20} = +66.5° \qquad\qquad\qquad \text{Invert sugar}$$

$$\frac{+52 - 92}{2} = [\alpha]_D^{20} = -20°$$

The sweetness of honey is largely due to the presence of fructose which is approximately three times as sweet as glucose. Invert sugar shows less tendency to crystallize than does sucrose and for this reason is used to a large extent in the manufacture of candy. Sucrose will not reduce Fehling's solution and therefore is classified as a *nonreducing* disaccharide. The α-D-glucopyranose ring, as shown in the sucrose structure below, is joined to the β-D-fructofuranose ring through a glycosidic link. Carbon (1) of glucose and carbon (2) of fructose are involved in this union. A "head-to-head" arrangement of this type leaves no potential aldehyde function to be oxidized and explains why sucrose is nonreducing. A junction at these ring positions further explains why sucrose fails to form an osazone with phenylhydrazine and why it fails to show mutarotation.

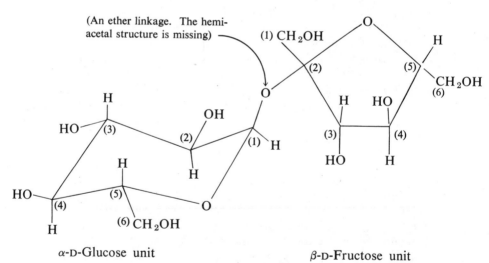

α-D-Glucose unit   β-D-Fructose unit

Sucrose
(α-D-Glucopyranosyl β-D-fructofuranoside)

14.13   MALTOSE

Maltose, or malt sugar, is a disaccharide produced when starch is hydrolyzed by malt *diastase*, an enzyme found in sprouting barley.

Another enzyme, *maltase*, selectively splits the alpha-glycosidic link and completely hydrolyzes maltose to yield two D-glucose units. Maltose is a *reducing sugar*. This chemical evidence suggests the presence of an aldehyde group either uncombined or in equilibrium with the hemiacetal form. In agreement with this, maltose forms an osazone and also exhibits mutarotation. Maltose is dextrorotatory and gives at equilibrium a specific rotation value of $+136°$. The structure of maltose is that of two glucose units in a "head-to-tail" arrangement joined through an α-linkage from carbon (1) of one glucose unit to carbon (4) of a second glucose unit.

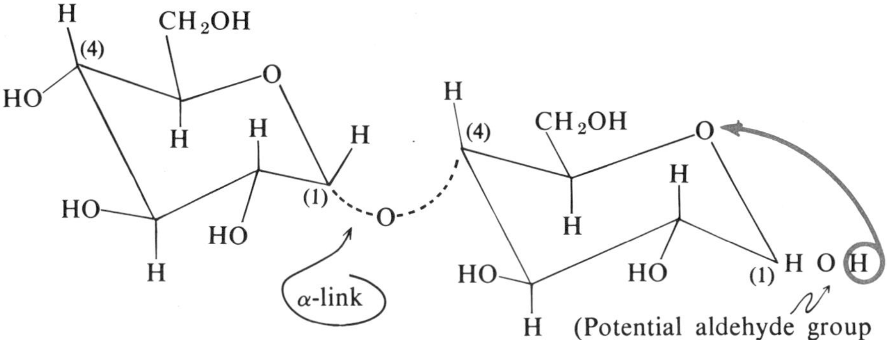

$[\alpha]_D^{20} = +136°$ Maltose   (Potential aldehyde group in hemiacetal structure.)

14.14   CELLOBIOSE

Cellobiose is a disaccharide which is obtained by the hydrolysis of cellulose. It is a reducing sugar consisting of two glucose units joined as in maltose, *but through a β-linkage*. The enzyme maltase is incapable of hydrolyzing cellobiose. In all other respects the behavior of cellobiose is identical to that described for maltose.

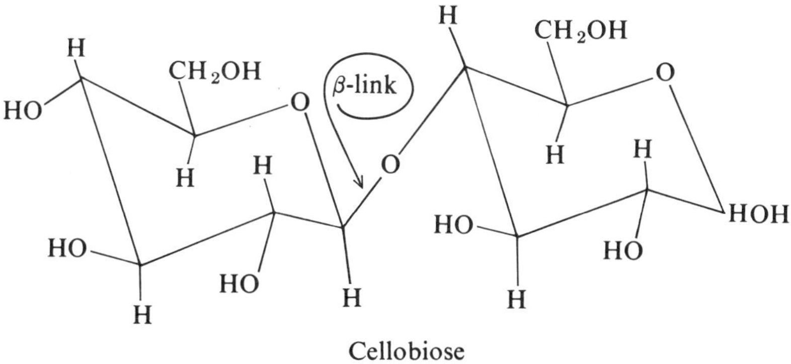

Cellobiose

14.15   LACTOSE

Lactose is known as milk sugar because it is present in the milk of mammals. It is present in cows' milk to the extent of about 5% and in human milk to about 7%. It is produced commercially as a by-product in the manufacture of cheese. Lactose is a reducing sugar, forms an osazone, and exhibits mutarotation. Lactose is dextrorotatory and, at equilibrium, gives a specific rotation of +55°. Lactose, when hydrolyzed by mineral acids or by the action of the enzyme *lactase*, produces equimolar quantities of D-glucose and D-galactose. Lactose is a β-galactoside in which the number (1) carbon of galactose is joined through a β-linkage to the number (4) carbon of glucose in a "head-to-tail" arrangement. This is shown below.

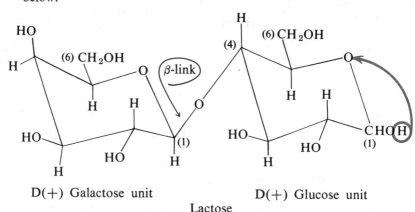

D(+) Galactose unit   D(+) Glucose unit

Lactose

14.16   POLYSACCHARIDES

The polysaccharides are high molecular weight (25,000– 15,000,000) natural polymers in which hundreds (or even thousands) of pentose or hexose units have been joined through glycosidic linkages. The most important polysaccharides are starch, glycogen, inulin, and cellulose.

14.17   STARCH, GLYCOGEN, AND INULIN

Starch is the reserve carbohydrate of most plants. It comprises the major part of all cereal grains and most plant tubers, where it is stored. Starch is used as a principal food source throughout the world. Glycogen is the reserve carbohydrate of animals and a relatively small amount is stored in the liver and muscles. Structurally, starch and glycogen are similar. Both have the empirical formula $(C_6H_{10}O_5)_n$ and both, when completely hydrolyzed, yield glucose. Starch and glycogen are only partially hydrolyzed to maltose by the enzyme amylase. When a paste made of starch and water is heated, two fractions may be separated. One, called the **amylose fraction,** is water soluble and has a molecular weight range of 20,000–225,000. A second fraction, called **amylopectin,** is water insoluble and has a molecular weight range of 200,000–1,000,000.

Amylose can be hydrolyzed almost completely to maltose by the enzyme β-amylase. This hydrolysis indicates that the maltose units arise from glucose units joined through alpha 1-4 linkages. Amylopectin, on the other hand, is hydrolyzed to maltose to a much lesser degree by the same enzyme. Chemical evidence indicates that considerable branching occurs in the amylopectin fraction of the starch molecule. Such branches are formed from glucose units linked through carbon atoms (1) and (6). The glycosidic link at these positions resists hydrolysis by β-amylase. A segment of a branched starch molecule is shown.

A segment of the starch molecule

Inulin is a polysaccharide comparable to starch. It is found in the underground stems (tubers) of the Jerusalem artichoke and in dahlia roots. Inulin, on hydrolysis, yields fructose as its end product.

14.18   CELLULOSE

Cellulose comprises the skeletal material of plants and is the most abundant organic substance found in nature. It is the chief constituent of wood and cotton. Cotton, almost pure cellulose, is the principal source of cellulose used as fiber for fabrics. The cellulose content of wood is approximately 50 per cent. The separation of cellulose from other plant components is an important commercial process upon which the textile, paper, and plastics industries are largely dependent.

The general formula for cellulose, like that for starch, may be written $(C_6H_{10}O_5)_n$, but the numerical value of n in the formula for cellulose is much larger than that for starch. Methylation studies indicate that the structure of cellulose, unlike that of starch, is largely unbranched.

Complete hydrolysis of cellulose produces D-glucose. Partial hydrolysis produces cellobiose (Sec. 14.14), cellotriose, and higher oligosaccharides. The presence of β-glycosidic linkages establishes the structure of cellulose as

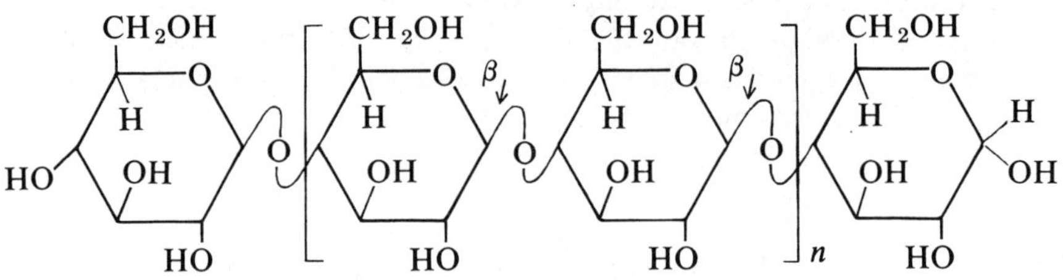

Structure of cellulose unit

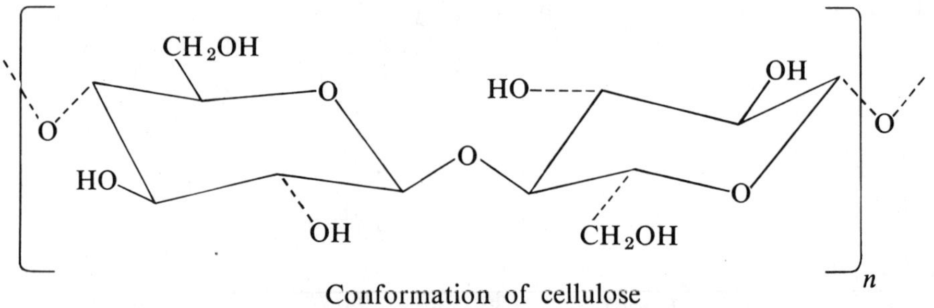

Conformation of cellulose

Man is incapable of utilizing cellulose for food because his digestive juices lack enzymes capable of hydrolyzing the β-glycosidic linkage. Ruminants (cud-chewing animals), are able to digest cellulose because certain microorganisms present in their compartmented stomachs cause a preliminary hydrolysis of cellulose before it reaches the intestine. Certain lower orders of animals (snails, termites) having similar assistance also are able to feed upon cellulose.

14.19   DERIVATIVES OF CELLULOSE

The derivatives of cellulose, like those of any polyhydric alcohol, are principally esters and ethers. Each $(C_6H_{10}O_5)$ unit of cellulose has three hydroxyl groups available. The conversion of some or all of these groups to ethers or to ester functions alters the properties of cellulose remarkably.

Cellulose nitrates are formed when cellulose is nitrated in the presence of sulfuric acid. A product known as *pyroxylin* is formed when cellulose is nitrated under conditions which esterifies approximately two-thirds of the available hydroxyl groups.

$$[C_6H_7O_2(OH)_3]_n \xrightarrow{2nHNO_3,\ H_2SO_4} [C_6H_7O_2(OH)(ONO_2)_2]_n$$

Cellulose   Pyroxylin

Pyroxylin is used in plastics and in lacquers. Unlike cellulose, pyroxylin is very soluble in a number of highly volatile organic solvents and can be used in such solutions as a quick-drying finish. Evaporation of the solvent, after application of such finishes, leaves a thin, hard, glossy film of cellulose nitrate deposited upon a surface. A product known as "patent leather" is produced when solutions of pyroxylin are applied to cloth. *Celluloid* (*cellul*ose + *oid*), one of the earliest plastics, is made by mixing pyroxylin and camphor with alcohol. The gelatinous mass which results hardens after evaporation of the solvent.

Guncotton is a product obtained when cellulose is almost completely nitrated under conditions carefully controlled to prevent degradation of the cellulose molecule. Guncotton contains about 12–13% of nitrogen, is explosive, and is used in the manufacture of smokeless powder.

Cellulose acetate is obtained by the reaction of cellulose with acetic anhydride. Like the nitrates, cellulose acetate also is an ester but is not explosive. A viscous solution of cellulose acetate when extruded through the fine openings of a die, called a "spinneret," produces thin fibers. From such fibers the popular "acetate" fabrics are woven. Photographic film also is prepared from cellulose acetate. Cellulose from cotton linters or wood pulp, when treated with sodium hydroxide and carbon disulfide, can be converted into a product known as a **xanthate**. Xanthates with dilute alkali form a heavy, viscous solution called "viscose." Cellulose in the form of *rayon* is regenerated when viscose is extruded through a spinneret into a bath of dilute mineral acid.   Extrusion of viscose through a long, thin slit produces *cellophane*. The chemical steps involved in the formation of viscose rayon may be illustrated by applying the same reactions to a simple alcohol.

$$ROH + NaOH + CS_2 \longrightarrow RO-\overset{\displaystyle S}{\overset{\|}{C}}-S^-Na^+ + H_2O$$

A xanthate

$$RO\overset{\displaystyle S}{\overset{\|}{C}}-S^-Na^+ + H_2SO_4 \longrightarrow ROH + CS_2 + NaHSO_4$$

Ethyl cellulose is a cellulose ether prepared by a modified Williamson synthesis (Sec. 8.12). Alkali-cellulose (produced as in the viscose process) is treated with ethyl chloride to produce the ether.

Two or three hydroxyl groups per six-carbon unit are converted into ethoxy ethers. The cellulose ethers are widely used in the plastics and textile industries.

14.20   MERCERIZED COTTON

Mercerized cotton is cotton fiber modified by treatment with sodium hydroxide while the yarn is under tension. Subsequent washing and drying produces a smooth fiber with a lustrous finish and greatly improved tensile strength. The process, called **mercerization,** was discovered by an English chemist, John Mercer, in 1814.

14.21   PAPER

Most paper is made from wood pulp. The cellulose of wood is separated from a noncellulosic substance called lignin. The latter is converted into an alkali-soluble substance by treatment with calcium hydrogen sulfite, $Ca(HSO_3)_2$, and removed from the insoluble cellulose fibers. The cellulose fibers, after removal of lignin, are washed and removed from the mixture as a matting on a large, flat filter. Compression of the matting, followed by drying, produces paper. Additional treatment produces paper products for every purpose — stationery, newsprint, hardboard, tissue, and wax paper. The paper industry, which depends upon cellulose as its raw material, is one of the country's largest consumers of forest products.

THE TRICARBOXYLIC ACID CYCLE.

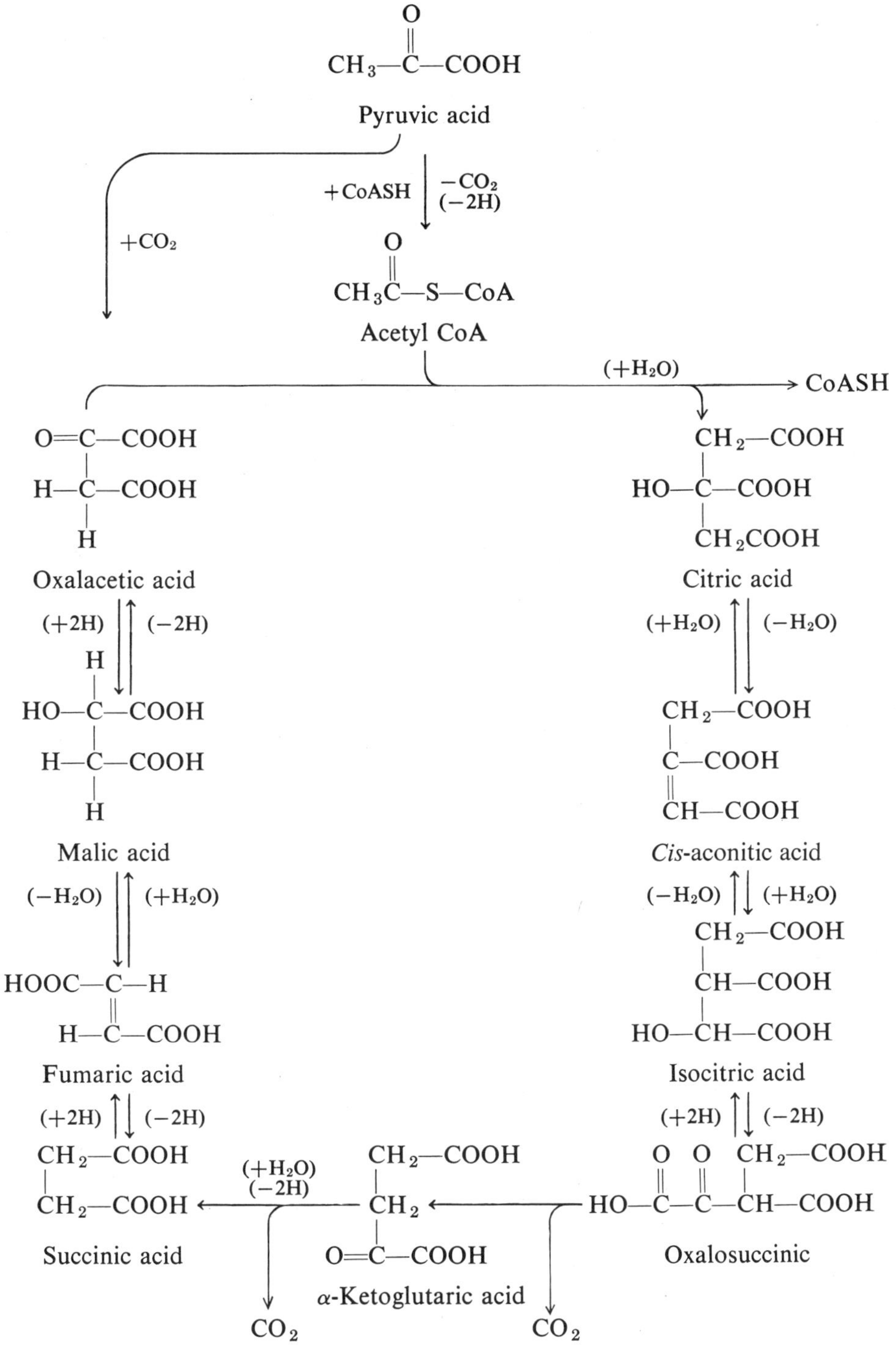

$$CH_3-\overset{\overset{\displaystyle O}{\|}}{C}-COOH$$

Pyruvic acid

$+CoASH$ $\begin{array}{c} -CO_2 \\ (-2H) \end{array}$

$+CO_2$

$$CH_3\overset{\overset{\displaystyle O}{\|}}{C}-S-CoA$$

Acetyl CoA

$(+H_2O)$ $\longrightarrow$ CoASH

$$\begin{array}{l} O=C-COOH \\ H-C-COOH \\ \quad\;\; H \end{array}$$

Oxalacetic acid

$(+2H) \Big\Uparrow\Big\Downarrow (-2H)$

$$\begin{array}{l} \quad\;\; H \\ HO-C-COOH \\ H-C-COOH \\ \quad\;\; H \end{array}$$

Malic acid

$(-H_2O) \Big\Uparrow\Big\Downarrow (+H_2O)$

$$\begin{array}{l} HOOC-C-H \\ \quad\quad\;\; \| \\ H-C-COOH \end{array}$$

Fumaric acid

$(+2H) \Big\Uparrow\Big\Downarrow (-2H)$

$$\begin{array}{l} CH_2-COOH \\ CH_2-COOH \end{array}$$

Succinic acid

$\xleftarrow{\begin{array}{c}(+H_2O)\\(-2H)\end{array}}$

$$\begin{array}{l} CH_2-COOH \\ CH_2 \\ O=C-COOH \end{array}$$

α-Ketoglutaric acid

CO_2

$$\begin{array}{l} CH_2-COOH \\ HO-C-COOH \\ CH_2COOH \end{array}$$

Citric acid

$(+H_2O) \Big\Uparrow\Big\Downarrow (-H_2O)$

$$\begin{array}{l} CH_2-COOH \\ C-COOH \\ \| \\ CH-COOH \end{array}$$

Cis-aconitic acid

$(-H_2O) \Big\Uparrow\Big\Downarrow (+H_2O)$

$$\begin{array}{l} CH_2-COOH \\ CH-COOH \\ HO-CH-COOH \end{array}$$

Isocitric acid

$(+2H) \Big\Uparrow\Big\Downarrow (-2H)$

$$\begin{array}{l} \quad O\;\; O \;\; CH_2-COOH \\ \quad \| \;\;\; \| \\ HO-C-C-CH-COOH \end{array}$$

Oxalosuccinic

CO_2

The digestion of carbohydrates involves the enzymatic hydrolysis of carbohydrates to produce the simple sugars: glucose, fructose, and galactose. These simple sugars are absorbed into the blood stream and are transported first to the liver and eventually to the muscles. At these sites, glycogen can be synthesized and temporarily stored. These carbohydrate stores, when called upon to supply energy, are hydrolyzed to glucose. A series of enzymatic reactions cleaves the 6-carbon glucose chain into two 3-carbon

$$CH_3-\overset{\displaystyle O}{\overset{\displaystyle \|}{C}}-COOH$$

pyruvic acid molecules, $CH_3-C-COOH$. Oxidative decarboxylation of pyruvic acid, in association with CoA (Sec. 11.9), forms acetyl CoA, which then enters the tricarboxylic acid cycle as shown in Fig. 14.1. All carbohydrates, in meeting the energy requirements of the body, ultimately are oxidized to carbon dioxide and water.

□□ *SUMMARY*

[1]   Carbohydrates are polyhydroxy aldehydes or polyhydroxy ketones.

[2]   Carbohydrates, in general, may be classified as: mono-, oligo-, and polysaccharides. Monosaccharides may be classified functionally, as aldoses or ketoses; according to chain length, as pentoses or hexoses.

[3]   Glucose is the most important monosaccharide. It is an aldohexose but exists largely in a cyclic hemiacetal structure. It exhibits *mutarotation* and has an equilibrium rotation value of $+52°$.

[4]   Important reactions of glucose include

a. Reduction of Fehling's solution.
b. Formation of a hemiacetal (glucoside) with an alcohol.
c. Formation of an osazone with phenylhydrazine.
d. Formation of a pentacetate with acetic anhydride.
e. Addition of HCN to form a cyanohydrin.
f. Fermentation to ethyl alcohol and carbon dioxide.

[5]   The disaccharides sucrose, maltose, cellobiose, and lactose are the most important oligosaccharides. Sucrose and maltose are α-glucosides. Lactose is a β-galactoside. Maltose and lactose reduce Fehling's solution, form osazones, and exhibit muta-rotation; sucrose does none of these. The hydrolysis of sucrose "inverts," or changes, its rotation value from $(+)$ to $(-)$. Invert sugar is hydrolyzed sucrose.

[6]   Polysaccharides are high molecular weight polymers in which thousands of basic pentose or hexose units are combined. The most important polysaccharides are starch, glycogen, and cellulose.

[7]   Starch (cereal grains, plant roots and tubers) is composed of thousands of glucose units joined predominantly through α-linkages at carbons (1) and (4). It is the reserve carbohydrate of plants.

[8]   Glycogen is the reserve carbohydrate of animals. It is stored in the liver and muscle.

[9]   As with starch, cellulose is composed of glucose units, but the connection between glucose molecules in cellulose are β-linkages. Moreover, cellulose appears to be an unbranched structure.

[10] Cellulose derivatives (esters and ethers) are useful plastics. Among these are

  a. Cellulose nitrates, which are used in smokeless powder, in lacquers, and other surface coatings.
  b. Cellulose acetate, which is used in textiles and photographic film.
  c. Ethyl cellulose, which is used in a variety of plastic articles.

[11] Cellulose which has been regenerated from viscose (a cellulose xanthate) may be formed into *rayon* and *cellophane*.

[12] Mercerized cotton is cotton yarn treated with sodium hydroxide to make the fiber smooth and stronger.

[13] The manufacture of paper products is one of the principal uses for cellulose.

[14] The digestion of carbohydrates results in the production of simple sugars.

[15] The metabolism of simple sugars involves a series of degradation reactions *via* the tricarboxylic acid cycle.

□□ *NEW TERMS*

[1]	aglycone	[9]	mercerization
[2]	aldohexose	[10]	mutarotation
[3]	epimer	[11]	nonreducing sugar
[4]	glucopyranose	[12]	oligosaccharide
[5]	glucopyranoside	[13]	polysaccharide
[6]	glycoside	[14]	pyroxylin
[7]	guncotton	[15]	xanthate
[8]	invert sugar		

■ □ SUPPLEMENTARY EXERCISES
▼   AND PROBLEMS

[1]   Write open-chain projection formulas for D-glucose and D-fructose. Draw cyclic structures for each and show the manner in which they are joined to form sucrose, maltose, and lactose.

[2]   Write balanced equations to show the products formed when glucose is caused to react with each of the following.

(a)	phenylhydrazine	(e)	acetic anhydride
(b)	Fehling's solution	(f)	zymase in yeast
(c)	CH_3OH, anhydrous HCl	(g)	Br_2 (aqueous)
(d)	HNO_3	(h)	hydroxylamine

[3]   Explain why both maltose and lactose are reducing sugars but sucrose is not.

[4]   Explain the apparent contradiction in the following statement:

"Fructose is not a reducing sugar but may be oxidized by Fehling's solution"

[5]   Draw structures for each of the following.

(a)	methyl α-D-glucoside	(c)	a structural unit of starch
(b)	sucrose	(d)	a structural unit of cellulose

[6]   Using R—OH to represent a cellulose unit, write equations illustrating the preparation of

(a)	cellulose acetate	(c)	viscose rayon
(b)	smokeless powder	(d)	ethyl cellulose

[7] Which of the following tests would serve to distinguish between the sugars in each of the pairs listed below: (a) bromine (aqueous), (b) Fehling's solution, (c) phenylhydrazine, (d) a polarimetric measurement.

(A) glucose and fructose
(B) glucose and mannose
(C) maltose and lactose
(D) sucrose and maltose

[8] An optically active hexose, (A), $C_6H_{12}O_6$, was degraded to an optically active pentose (B), $C_5H_{10}O_5$, by the following series of reactions:

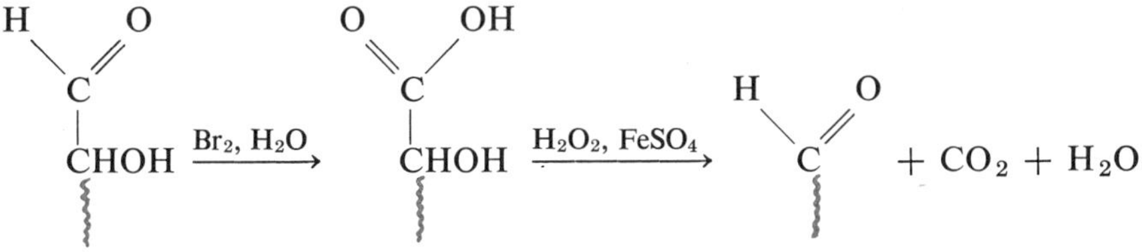

$$(B) + HNO_3 \longrightarrow C_5H_8O_7 \text{ (optically active)}$$

Compound (B) was degraded to an optically active tetrose (C), $C_4H_8O_4$, through the same series of reactions as shown above.

$$(C) + HNO_3 \longrightarrow \textit{meso} \text{ tartaric acid}$$

Give possible structures for (A) and (B).

chapter 15

Amino Acids, Peptides, and Proteins

INTRODUCTION

The name protein has its origin in the Greek word *proteios*, meaning "of first importance." The name is well chosen for proteins are the basis of protoplasm and comprise the underlying structure of all living organisms. Proteins, in the form of muscle, skin, hair, and other tissue, make up the bulk of the body's nonbony structure. In addition to providing such structural material, proteins have many other functions. Proteins, as enzymes, catalyze biochemical reactions; as hormones, they regulate metabolic processes; as antibodies, they resist and nullify the effects of toxic substances. Such specialized functions illustrate the great importance of proteins.

Proteins are high molecular weight, long-chain polymers made up largely of various amino acids linked together. The constituent amino acids are obtained when a protein is hydrolyzed by dilute acids, by dilute alkalis, or by protein-digesting enzymes. It would be difficult to consider the properties of molecules as complex as the proteins without first examining the properties of the α-amino acids from which they are constructed.

Amino Acids

15.2   STRUCTURE OF AMINO ACIDS

Nearly all amino acids obtained from plant and animal proteins have an amino group on the carbon atom alpha (α) to the carboxyl function. An α-amino acid has the following general formula.

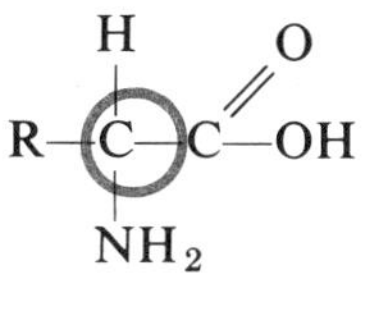

$$R-\underset{\underset{NH_2}{|}}{\overset{\overset{H}{|}}{C}}-\overset{\overset{O}{\parallel}}{C}-OH$$

The R in the general formula for an α-amino acid may be a hydrogen, a straight- or branched-chain aliphatic group, an aromatic ring, or a heterocyclic ring (Sec. 17.1). Most amino acids have one amino group and one carboxyl group and usually are classified as neutral amino acids. A few have a second amino group joined to other carbon atoms in the molecule and show basic properties. Others contain a second carboxyl group and behave as acids. With the exception of glycine (aminoacetic acid) all amino acids contain at least one center of asymmetry and are optically active. Amino acids of protein origin all possess the L-configuration. With few exceptions, the body is able to utilize completely only the L-isomers of those amino acids which it is not able to synthesize itself.

15.3   NOMENCLATURE AND CLASSIFICATION BY STRUCTURE

Of the known α-amino acids, about twenty have been found to be constituents of the more common plant and animal proteins. The structures for these, together with their names and abbreviations, are given in Table 15.1.

□■ TABLE 15.1

AMINO ACIDS DERIVED FROM PROTEINS

A. Neutral Amino Acids	
NAME (ABBREVIATION)	FORMULA
1. **Glycine (Gly)** (Aminoacetic acid)	$$\begin{array}{c} H \\ \mid \\ H-C-COOH \\ \mid \\ NH_2 \end{array}$$
2. **Alanine (Ala)** (α-Aminopropionic acid)	$$\begin{array}{c} H \\ \mid \\ CH_3-C-COOH \\ \mid \\ NH_2 \end{array}$$
3. **Valine (Val)** (α-Aminiosovaleric acid)	$$\begin{array}{c} CH_3 \quad H \\ \mid \qquad \mid \\ CH_3-C\!-\!-\!-\!C-COOH \\ \mid \qquad \mid \\ H \qquad NH_2 \end{array}$$
4. **Leucine (Leu)** (α-Aminoisocaproic acid)	$$\begin{array}{c} CH_3 \;\; H \;\; H \\ \mid \quad\;\; \mid \;\;\; \mid \\ CH_3-C\!-\!-\!-\!C\!-\!C-COOH \\ \mid \quad\;\; \mid \;\;\; \mid \\ H \quad\;\; H \;\; NH_2 \end{array}$$

A. Neutral Amino Acids — *continued*

5. Isoleucine (Ileu)
(α-Amino-β-methylvaleric)

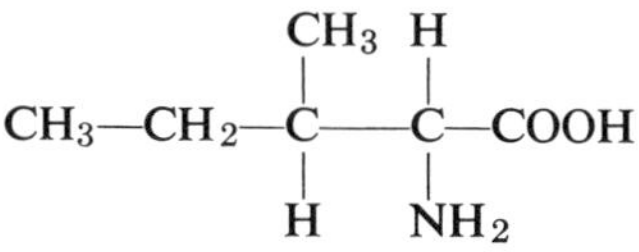

$$CH_3-CH_2-\overset{\displaystyle CH_3}{\underset{\displaystyle H}{C}}-\overset{\displaystyle H}{\underset{\displaystyle NH_2}{C}}-COOH$$

6. Serine (Ser)
(α-Amino-β-hydroxypropionic acid)

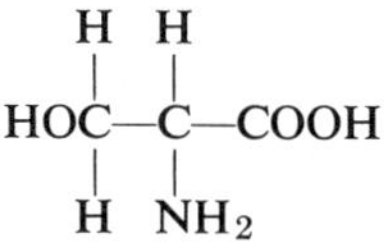

$$HO\overset{\displaystyle H}{\underset{\displaystyle H}{C}}-\overset{\displaystyle H}{\underset{\displaystyle NH_2}{C}}-COOH$$

7. Threonine (Thre)
(α-Amino-β-hydroxybutyric acid)

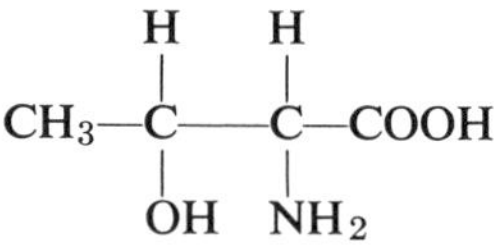

$$CH_3-\overset{\displaystyle H}{\underset{\displaystyle OH}{C}}-\overset{\displaystyle H}{\underset{\displaystyle NH_2}{C}}-COOH$$

8. Phenylalanine (Phe)
(α-Amino-β-phenylpropionic acid)

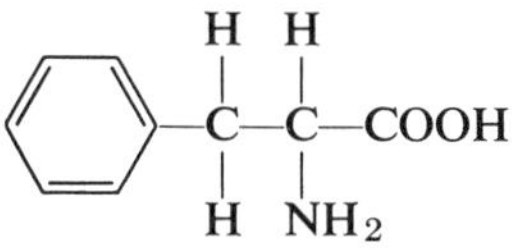

9. Tyrosine (Tyr)
(α-Amino-
    p-hydroxyhydrocinnamic acid)

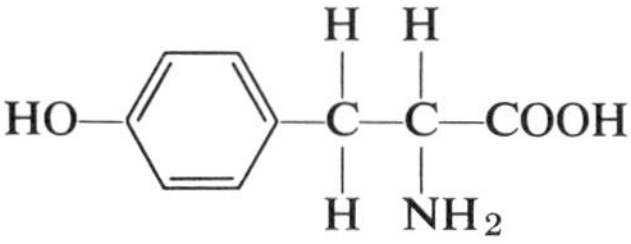

10. Tryptophan (Try)
(α-Amino-β-(3-indolyl) propionic
    acid)

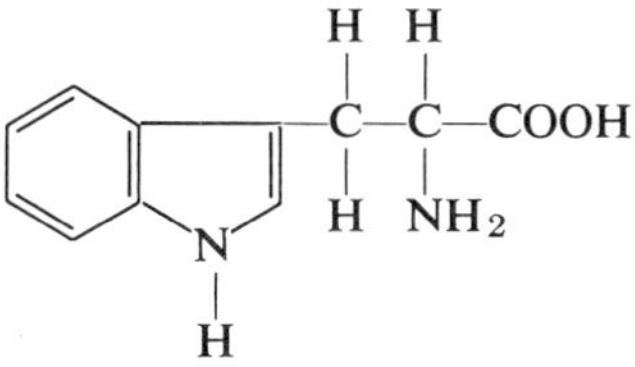

11. Proline (Pro)[1]
(2-Pyrrolidine carboxylic acid)

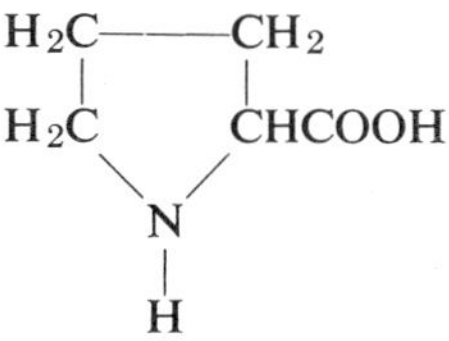

12. Hydroxyproline (HPro)[1]
(4-Hydroxy-
    2-pyrrolidine carboxylic acid)

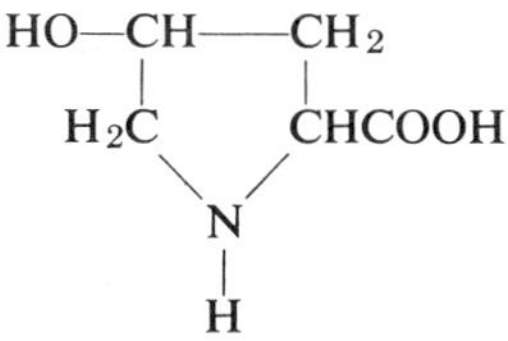

[1]Proline and hydroxyproline are *imino acids*. The nitrogen atom, although joined to the α-carbon, is part of a ring. An imino nitrogen bears only one hydrogen atom but can still take part in the formation of proteins.

NAME (ABBREVIATION)	FORMULA
B. Basic Amino Acids	

13. **Histidine (His)** (α-Amino- β-4-imidazolylpropionic acid)	$$\overset{\displaystyle \underset{\displaystyle H-C=\!\!\!=C-CH_2-\overset{\displaystyle H}{\underset{\displaystyle NH_2}{C}}-COOH}{\underset{N\;\;\;\;\;NH}{}}}{\overset{H}{\underset{\|}{C}}}$$
14. **Lysine (Lys)** (α, ϵ-Diaminocaproic acid)	$CH_2-CH_2-CH_2-CH_2-\overset{\displaystyle H}{\underset{\displaystyle NH_2}{C}}-COOH$ $\;\;NH_2$
15. **Arginine (Arg)** (α-Amino-δ-guanidinovaleric acid)	$H_2N-\overset{\displaystyle \overset{H}{\underset{\|}{N}}}{\underset{\|}{C}}-N-CH_2CH_2CH_2-\overset{\displaystyle H}{\underset{\displaystyle NH_2}{C}}-COOH$

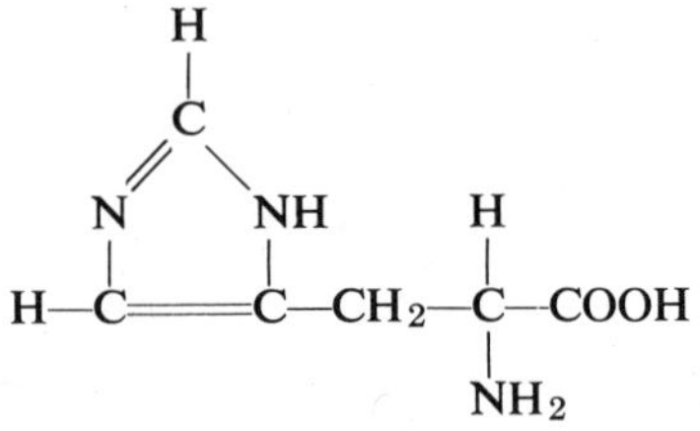

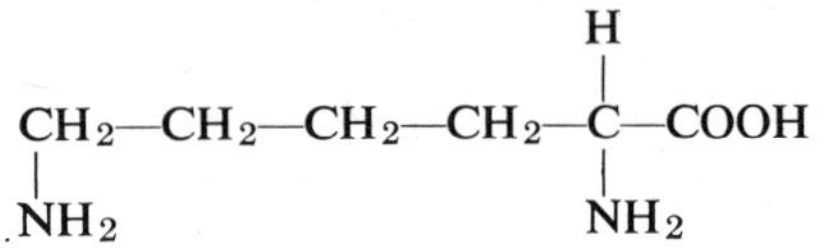

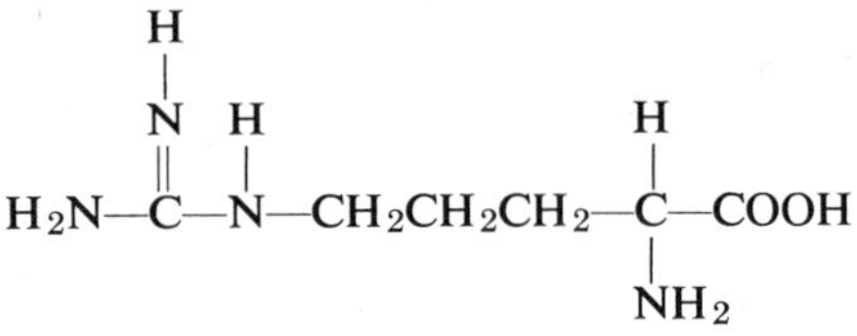

C. Acidic Amino Acids	

16. **Aspartic acid (Asp)** (Aminosuccinic acid)	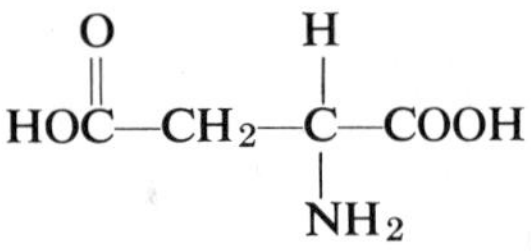 $HO\overset{\displaystyle O}{\overset{\|}{C}}-CH_2-\overset{\displaystyle H}{\underset{\displaystyle NH_2}{C}}-COOH$
17. **Glutamic (Glu)** (α-Aminoglutaric acid)	$HO\overset{\displaystyle O}{\overset{\|}{C}}-CH_2-CH_2-\overset{\displaystyle H}{\underset{\displaystyle NH_2}{C}}-COOH$

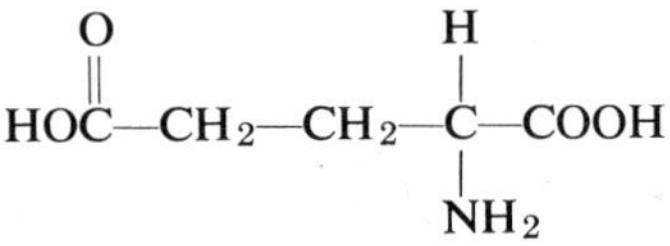

D. Sulfur-Containing Amino Acids	

18. **Methionine (Met)** (α-Amino-γ-methylthiobutyric acid)	$CH_3-S-CH_2-CH_2-\overset{\displaystyle H}{\underset{\displaystyle NH_2}{C}}-COOH$
19. **Cysteine (Cys)** (α-Amino-β-mercaptopropionic acid)	$HS-CH_2-\overset{\displaystyle H}{\underset{\displaystyle NH_2}{C}}-COOH$

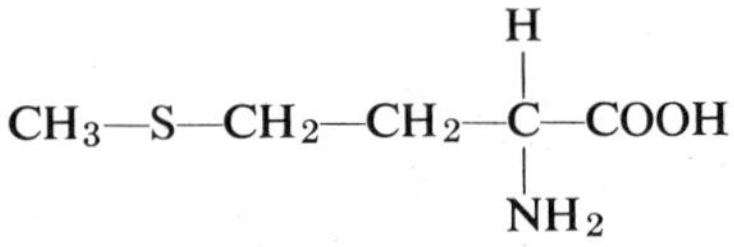

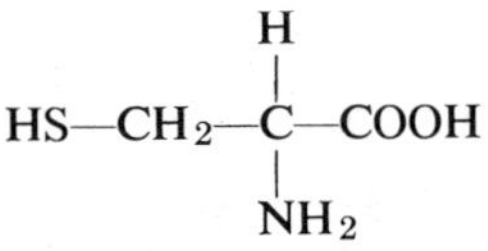

20. **Cystine (Cys-SCy)**		$$S-CH_2-\overset{\overset{\displaystyle H}{\displaystyle |}}{\underset{\underset{\displaystyle NH_2}{\displaystyle |}}{C}}-COOH$$ $$S-CH_2-\overset{\overset{\displaystyle H}{\displaystyle |}}{\underset{\underset{\displaystyle NH_2}{\displaystyle |}}{C}}-COOH$$

15.4   NUTRITIVE CLASSIFICATION OF AMINO ACIDS

A nutritive classification of the α-amino acids has resulted from nutritional experiments carried out on laboratory animals. It is not a strict classification but varies with the requirements of the different species of animals tested. The omission of certain amino acids in the diet of some animals prevents their normal growth and development. The animal organism either is incapable of synthesizing certain amino acids or is incapable of synthesizing them in sufficient quantity to maintain a normal state of good health. The effects of such malnutrition disappear when the missing amino acids are supplied in the diet. On the basis of such studies, α-amino acids are divided into two categories as **essential** or **nonessential.** Table 15.2 lists the α-amino acids in these two general classes.

□■ TABLE 15.2

CLASSIFICATION OF THE AMINO ACIDS ACCORDING TO NUTRITIONAL REQUIREMENTS

Essential (indispensable)	Nonessential (dispensable)
Arginine[2]	Alanine
Glycine[3]	Aspartic acid
Histidine[4]	Cysteine
Isoleucine[5]	Cystine
Leucine[5]	Glutamic acid
Lysine[5]	Hydroxyproline
Methionine[5]	Proline
Phenylalanine[5]	Serine
Threonine[5]	Tyrosine
Tryptophan[5]	
Valine[5]	

[2]Required for optimum growth in the rat and chick.
[3]Required for optimum growth in the chick.
[4]Required by all subhuman species tested and by infants, but not by adult man.
[5]Required by all species tested, including adult man.

The amino acids are colorless crystalline solids and have melting points (with decomposition) in excess of 200°C. Most amino acids are soluble in water but sparingly soluble in organic solvents. These properties are not characteristic of most simple organic acids or simple amines but are more like those of salts.

A neutral amino acid possesses an amino group and a carboxyl group and thus can behave either as a base or an acid. An amino acid in an alkaline solution reacts like an acid to produce a *metal salt*.

$$
\underset{\substack{|\\ NH_2}}{\overset{\substack{H\\ |}}{R-C}}-\overset{\substack{O\\ \diagup\diagup}}{C}\diagdown_{OH} \;+\; Na^+OH^- \;\longrightarrow\; \underset{\substack{|\\ NH_2}}{\overset{\substack{H\\ |}}{R-C}}-\overset{\substack{O\\ \diagup\diagup}}{C}\diagdown_{O^-} \;+\; Na^+ \;+\; H_2O
$$

An amino acid anion

If an alkaline solution of an amino acid is electrolyzed, the anion of the amino acid salt migrates toward the anode or positive electrode.

An amino acid in an acidic solution behaves like a base to form an *amine salt*.

$$
\underset{\substack{|\\ N:\\ \diagup\;\diagdown\\ H\quad H}}{\overset{\substack{H\\ |}}{R-C}}-\overset{\substack{O\\ \diagup\diagup}}{C}\diagdown_{OH} \;+\; H^+Cl^- \;\longrightarrow\; \underset{\substack{|\\ \overset{+}{N}:H\\ \diagup\;\diagdown\\ H\quad H}}{\overset{\substack{H\\ |}}{R-C}}-\overset{\substack{O\\ \diagup\diagup}}{C}\diagdown_{OH} \;+\; Cl^-
$$

An amino acid cation

If an acidic solution of an amino acid is electrolyzed, the cation of the amine salt migrates to the cathode or negative electrode.

The hydrogen ion concentration at which the amino acid shows no tendency to migrate to either electrode is called the **isoelectric point.** Isoelectric points are given in pH values and vary from low values for acidic amino acids (pH 3 for aspartic acid) to high values for basic amino acids (pH 10.8 for arginine). Neutral amino acids do not have isoelectric points at the neutral figure (pH 7.0), as might be expected, but slightly on the acid side. At its isoelectric point, a "neutral" amino acid is completely ionized, with the proton shifting from the carboxyl group to the amino group to produce an inner salt or **dipolar ion.**

Exercise 15.1   The amino acid cation (second equation Sec. 15.5) has two acidic groups. What are they? Which group is more acidic — that is, will give up a proton more readily when base is added to a solution of the amino acid hydrochloride? (*Hint: Observe the changes in the dipolar ion* (*same section*) *with a change in pH.*)

$$
\underset{\substack{| \\ \overset{/ \; \backslash}{H \quad H}}}{R-\overset{\overset{H}{|}}{\underset{\underset{}{N:}}{C}}-C\overset{O}{\underset{O^-}{\diagup}} \; + \; H_2O \; \underset{OH^-}{\overset{H^+}{\rightleftharpoons}} \; R-\overset{\overset{}{}}{\underset{\underset{\overset{/ \; \backslash}{H \quad H}}{N:H}}{C}}-C\overset{O}{\underset{O^-}{\diagup}} \; \underset{OH^-}{\overset{H^+}{\rightleftharpoons}} \; R-\overset{\overset{H}{|}}{\underset{\underset{+}{NH_3}}{C}}-C\overset{O}{\underset{OH}{\diagup}}
$$

Dipolar ion

Dipolar ions, as the preceding equation illustrates, are *amphoteric* and can act either as acids or bases.

15.6   SYNTHESIS OF AMINO ACIDS

Interest in obtaining the individual amino acids in pure form for use in nutrition experiments has led to a number of synthetic procedures for the preparation of amino acids. Some of these are adaptations of methods previously reviewed for the preparation of simple primary amines (Sec. 13.4). Of the many methods that have been employed for the preparation of amino acids, we shall consider only three. These three methods are general methods and are satisfactory for the preparation of *some* amino acids. No single method has been developed for the synthesis of *all* amino acids.

A.   Direct Amination[6] of α-Halogen Acids.   In this method the halogen atom of an α-halo acid is replaced by an amino group directly by treating the acid with ammonia. In practice, a large excess of ammonia is used to prevent the formation of a disubstituted ammonia derivative.

---

[6]A reaction that introduces the amino group into the molecule is called *amination*.

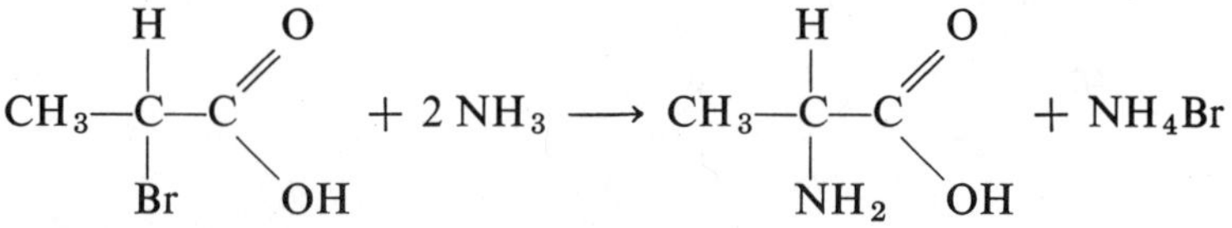

$$CH_3-\underset{\underset{Br}{|}}{\overset{\overset{H}{|}}{C}}-\overset{\overset{O}{\parallel}}{C}\diagdown OH \quad + 2\,NH_3 \longrightarrow CH_3-\underset{\underset{NH_2}{|}}{\overset{\overset{H}{|}}{C}}-\overset{\overset{O}{\parallel}}{C}\diagdown OH \quad + NH_4Br$$

α-Bromopropionic acid   D, L-Alanine

B.   Indirect Amination of α-Halogen Acids.   The halogen of
α-halo acids may be replaced by the —NH₂ group indirectly by
adaptation of Gabriel's primary amine synthesis (Sec. 13.4-C). In
this synthesis, an α-halo ester is condensed with the potassium salt
of phthalimide.

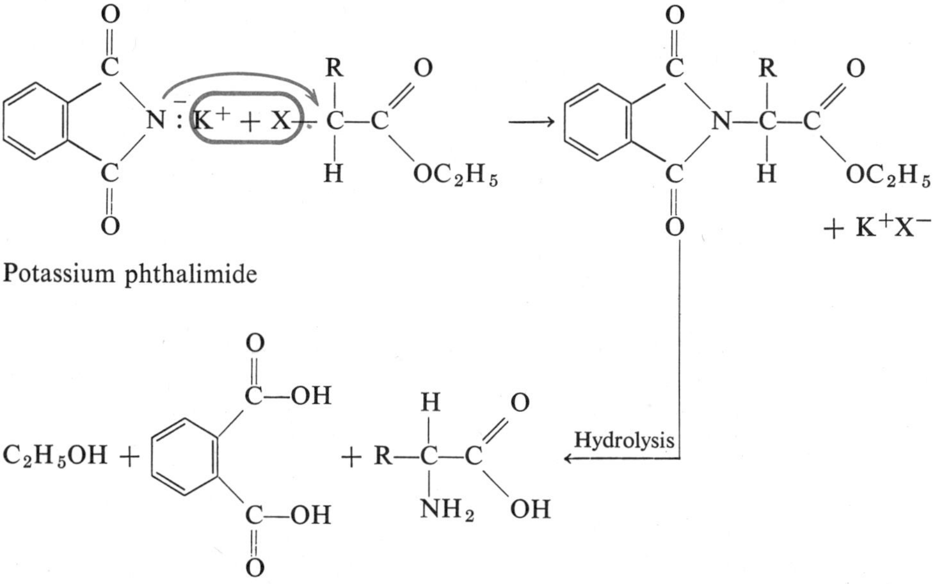

Potassium phthalimide

$$+ K^+X^-$$

o-Phthalic acid

C.   The Hydrolysis of α-Amino Nitriles (Strecker Synthesis).   In
the **Strecker synthesis** of an amino acid, an aldehyde is treated with
ammonium cyanide (ammonia and hydrogen cyanide). The aminonitrile that results from this reaction then is hydrolyzed to the amino
acid. The method lends itself very well to the preparation of simple
neutral amino acids. The preparation of D, L-alanine by the Strecker
synthesis begins with acetaldehyde.

$$CH_3\!-\!\overset{\displaystyle H}{\underset{}{C}}\!\!=\!\!O + HCN + NH_3 \rightarrow CH_3\!-\!\overset{\displaystyle H}{\underset{\displaystyle NH_2}{C}}\!-\!CN + H_2O$$

Acetaldehyde   Aminonitrile

$$CH_3\!-\!\overset{\displaystyle H}{\underset{\displaystyle NH_2}{C}}\!-\!CN + 2\,H_2O \longrightarrow CH_3\!-\!\overset{\displaystyle H}{\underset{\displaystyle NH_2}{C}}\!-\!\overset{\displaystyle O}{C}\!\diagdown_{OH} + NH_3$$

D, L-Alanine

Any synthesis of amino acids (except glycine) leads to a racemic mixture and must be followed by resolution if the natural form of the amino acid is required.

Exercise 15.2   Using acrylic acid, $CH_2\!=\!CHCOOH$, and any other reagents you might require, outline a synthesis leading to aspartic acid.

15.7   REACTIONS OF THE AMINO ACIDS

The reactions of the amino acids are, in general, reactions characteristic of both carboxylic acids and primary amines.

A.   Esterification.   All amino acids can be esterified. Emil Fischer utilized this reaction as early as 1901 as a technique for the separation of the constituent amino acids obtained from a protein hydrolysate. The protein was hydrolyzed to its constituent amino acids, the mixture was esterified, and the liquid amino acid esters separated by fractional distillation. Fischer's method is illustrated by the following equations.

$$CH_3\!-\!\overset{}{\underset{\displaystyle NH_2}{CH}}\!-\!\overset{\displaystyle O}{C}\!\diagdown_{OH} + HCl + C_2H_5OH \longrightarrow CH_3\!-\!\overset{\displaystyle H}{\underset{\displaystyle \overset{NH_3}{+}}{C}}\!-\!\overset{\displaystyle O}{C}\!\diagdown_{OC_2H_5} + H_2O + Cl^-$$

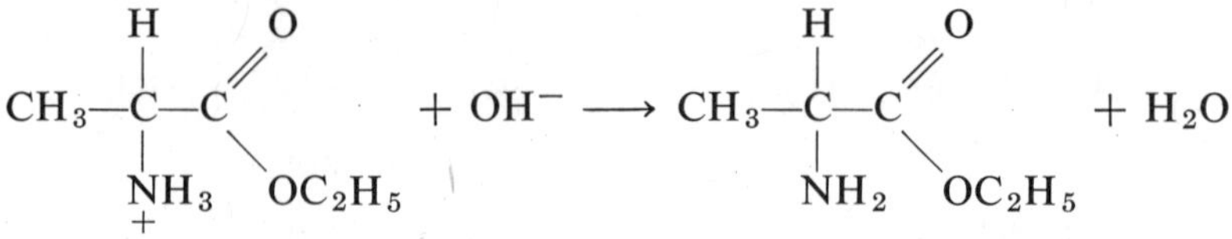

$$\underset{\substack{\overset{|}{NH_3}\\+}}{CH_3-\overset{\overset{\displaystyle H}{|}}{C}-C}\overset{\displaystyle O}{\diagup}{\diagdown}{OC_2H_5} \quad + OH^- \longrightarrow \quad \underset{\substack{\overset{|}{NH_2}}}{CH_3-\overset{\overset{\displaystyle H}{|}}{C}-C}\overset{\displaystyle O}{\diagup}{\diagdown}{OC_2H_5} \quad + H_2O$$

Ethyl ester of Alanine

B.   Reaction with Nitrous Acid.   The amino acids, with the exception of proline and hydroxyproline, react with nitrous acid to liberate nitrogen gas. This reaction is the basis for the **Van Slyke method** for determining "free" amino groups (uncombined α-amino groups) in protein material. The reaction gives an index to the number of uncombined $-NH_2$ groups such as would be provided by certain basic amino acids.

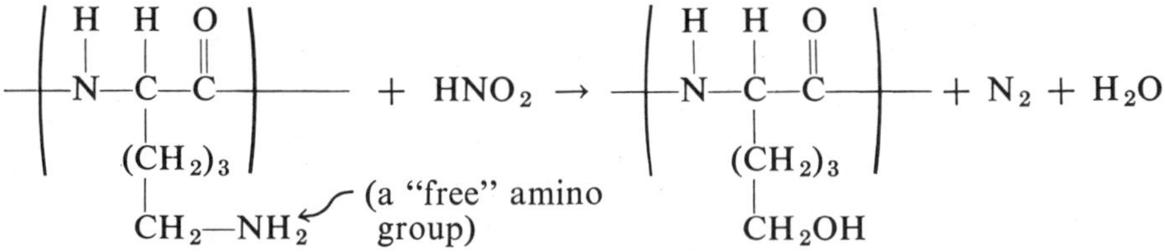

$$\left\{ \underset{\substack{(CH_2)_3\\ \\CH_2-NH_2}}{-N-\overset{\overset{H}{|}}{C}-C} \right\} + HNO_2 \rightarrow \left\{ \underset{\substack{(CH_2)_3\\ \\CH_2OH}}{-N-\overset{\overset{H}{|}}{C}-C} \right\} + N_2 + H_2O$$

(a "free" amino group)

Lysine unit

C.   Reaction with Acid Halides or Acid Anhydrides.   The amino group of amino acids is readily converted to an amide by reaction with an acid halide or anhydride. Thus, glycine reacts with benzoyl chloride to produce hippuric acid. Benzoates, when ingested, are rendered water-soluble and voided from the body in the urine as hippuric acid.

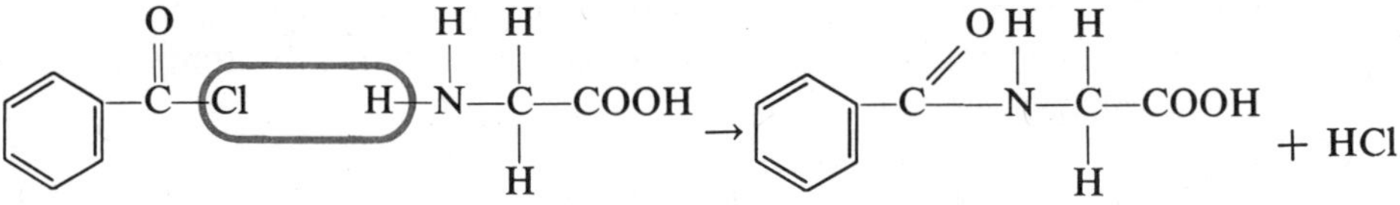

Benzoyl chloride   Glycine   Hippuric acid

D.   Reaction with Ninhydrin.   Amino acids react with a ninhydrin solution (triketohydrindene hydrate) to produce purple compounds. The reaction is of value in the assay of protein material and can be used for the quantitative determination of amino acids. The following sequence of reactions illustrates how ninhydrin converts an amino acid into an aldehyde and carbon dioxide.

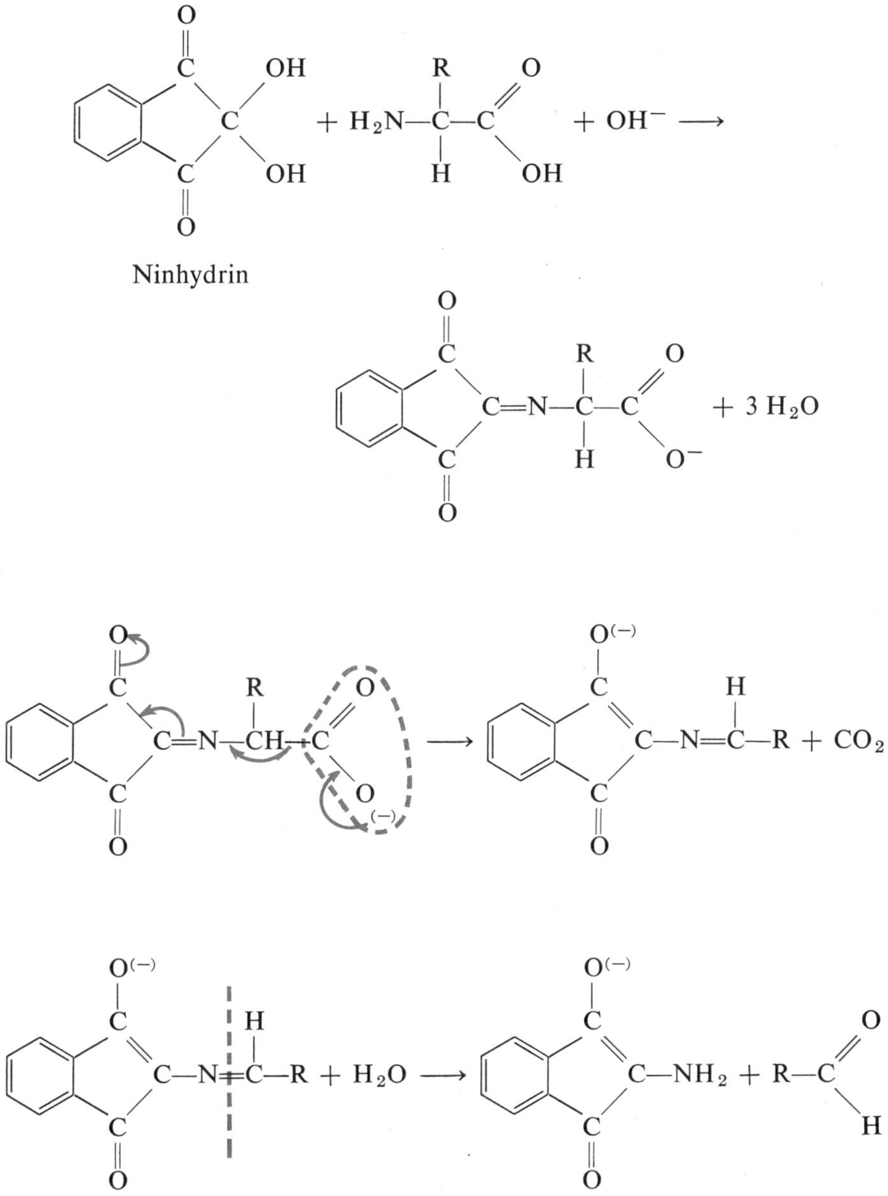

Ninhydrin

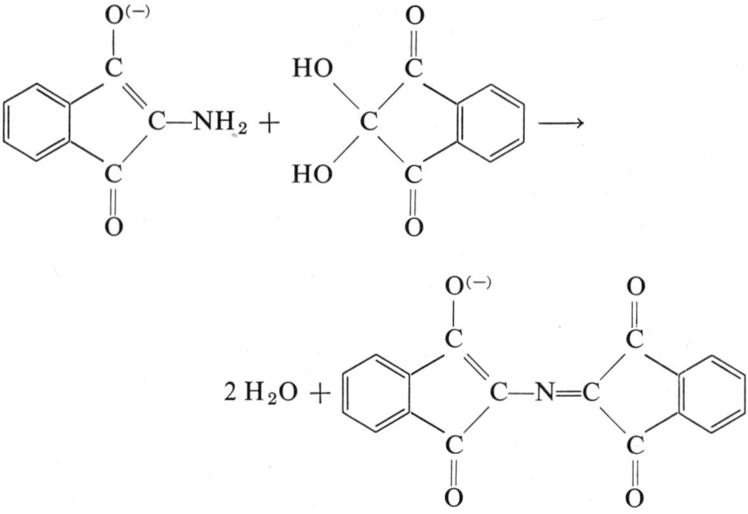

$$2 \text{ H}_2\text{O} +$$

(Colored product)

E.   Peptide Formation.   Amino acids can be condensed with each other to form peptides (Sec. 15.8). However, the sequence of the individual amino acids in a peptide cannot be controlled unless steps are taken to block reaction at an amino group or at a carboxyl function. Without such protective measures, random condensation can occur. In practice, when amino acids are to be joined into peptides, the amino acid to appear first in the peptide chain (counting from left to right) must have its amino group protected. The protecting group is removed after condensation is completed. The method is illustrated in the preparation of the dipeptide, alanylglycine (Ala-Gly).

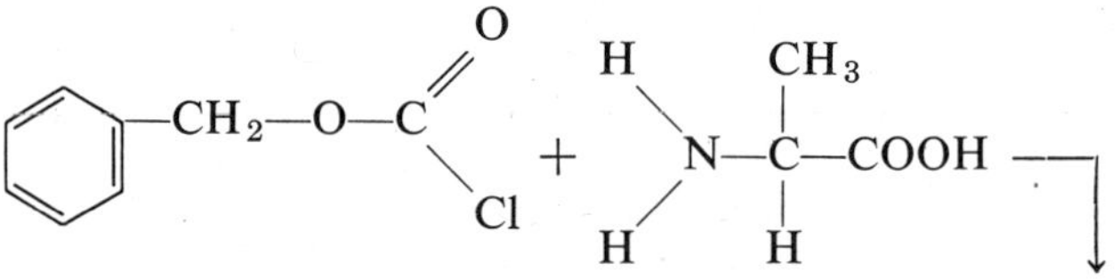

Benzylchloroformate   Alanine

Step 1.

Amino group of alanine
protected.

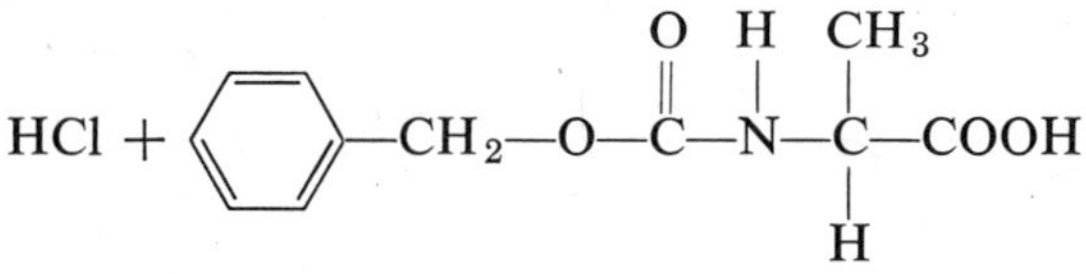

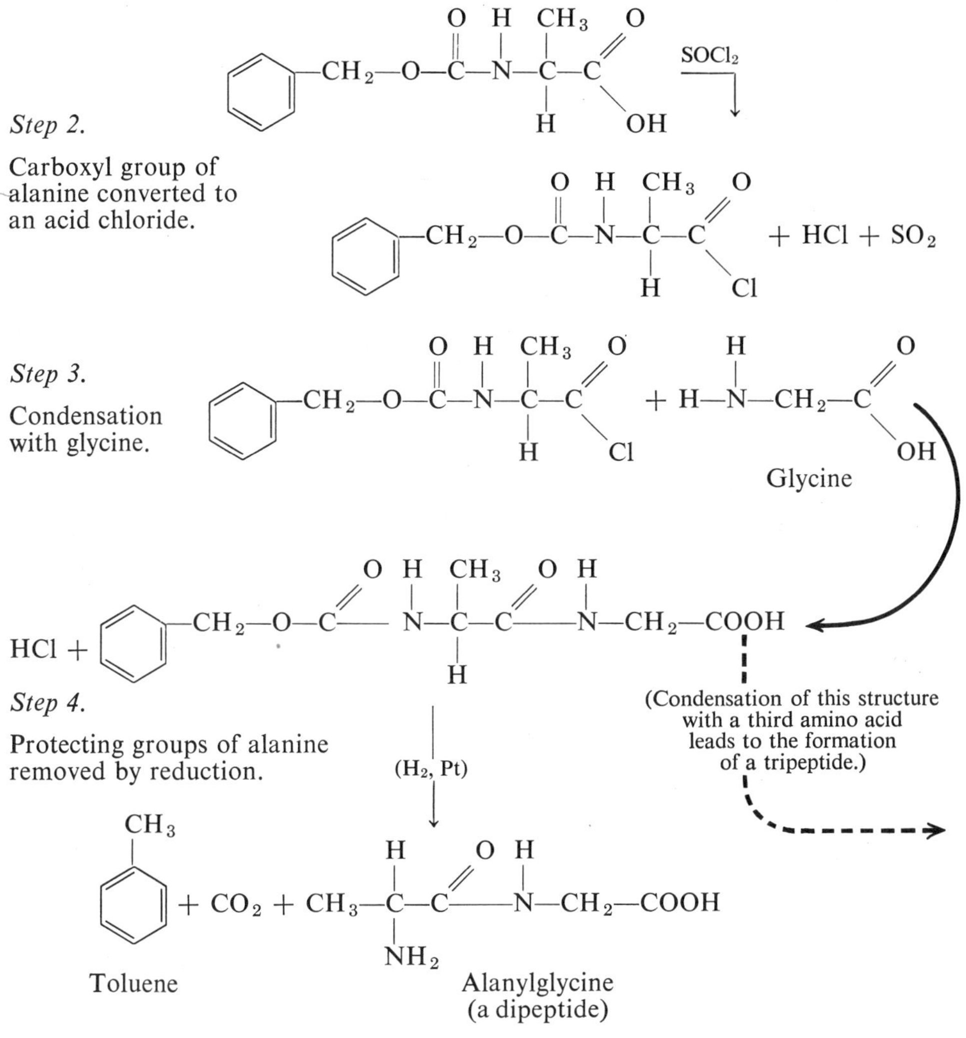

Step 2.

Carboxyl group of alanine converted to an acid chloride.

$$\text{C}_6\text{H}_5\text{—CH}_2\text{—O—C(O)—N(H)—C(CH}_3\text{)(H)—C(O)—OH} \xrightarrow{\text{SOCl}_2}$$

$$\text{C}_6\text{H}_5\text{—CH}_2\text{—O—C(O)—N(H)—C(CH}_3\text{)(H)—C(O)—Cl} + \text{HCl} + \text{SO}_2$$

Step 3.

Condensation with glycine.

$$\text{C}_6\text{H}_5\text{—CH}_2\text{—O—C(O)—N(H)—C(CH}_3\text{)(H)—C(O)—Cl} + \text{H—N(H)—CH}_2\text{—C(O)—OH}$$

Glycine

$$\text{HCl} + \text{C}_6\text{H}_5\text{—CH}_2\text{—O—C(O)—N(H)—C(CH}_3\text{)(H)—C(O)—N(H)—CH}_2\text{—COOH}$$

(Condensation of this structure with a third amino acid leads to the formation of a tripeptide.)

Step 4.

Protecting groups of alanine removed by reduction.

$$(\text{H}_2, \text{Pt})$$

$$\text{C}_6\text{H}_5\text{—CH}_3 + \text{CO}_2 + \text{CH}_3\text{—C(H)(NH}_2\text{)—C(O)—N(H)—CH}_2\text{—COOH}$$

Toluene

Alanylglycine
(a dipeptide)

Peptides and Proteins

15.8   STRUCTURE AND NOMENCLATURE

In a protein molecule the α-amino acids are joined together through amide linkages formed between the amino group of one acid molecule and the carboxyl group of another. Such amide linkages are called peptide links and serve to unite hundreds of amino acid residues in a protein molecule. When only two α-amino acids are joined, as in alanylglycine (Sec. 15.7-E), the product is a dipeptide. A dipeptide, with free amino and carboxyl groups on opposite ends of the chain, can unite at either end with a third α-amino acid to form a tripeptide. A tripeptide can form a tetrapeptide, and so on, until finally a long-chain polypeptide results. If n is the number of different amino acids in a polypeptide, the number of possible sequences (and isomers) is n *factorial*, $(n!)$. Thus, three different amino acids could combine in one of six different sequences, $(3 \times 2 \times 1 = 6)$. . One such sequence is illustrated below.

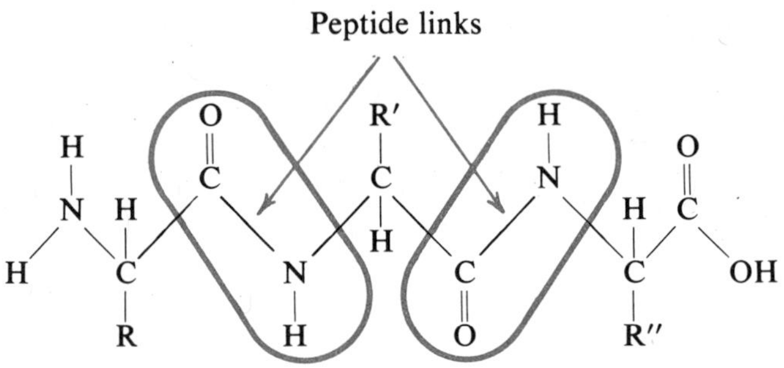

Peptide links

A variation in sequence, as well as a variation in the number and kind of amino acids joined, makes possible an infinite number of arrangements. It must not be thought, however, that the manner in which amino acids are joined in nature to form the polypeptide links in proteins is a haphazard one. On the contrary, the amino acids which comprise a protein are joined in a uniform manner to give specificity to certain types of tissue within each organism.

Peptides are named as derivatives of the C-terminal amino acid which still has a free carboxyl group. The C-terminal amino acid is the last one, counting from left to right. The method of naming is illustrated by the following tetrapeptide.

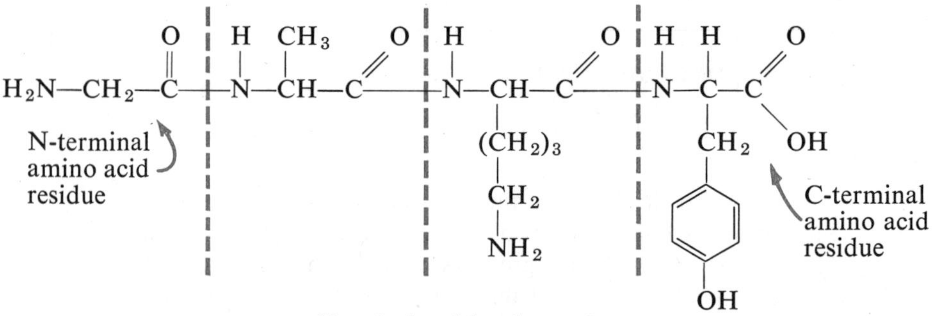

Glycyl-alanyl-lysyl-tyrosine

15.9   THE SEQUENCE OF AMINO ACIDS IN PEPTIDES

Determination of the amino acid sequence of a natural peptide is a tedious and laborious process but has been accomplished in a few cases. In practice, the N-terminal group of a peptide is "tagged" by reaction with 2, 4-dinitrofluorobenzene before the peptide is hydrolyzed.

The tagged amino acid, when liberated by hydrolysis, is colored and easily distinguished from the other amino acids that comprise the peptide structure. The different amino acids and the number of each that make up the peptide chain is determined by repeated tagging of the N-terminus of each fragmentary peptide that results when the original peptide is subjected to only a partial hydrolysis. To illustrate the method let us review the work that led to the elucidation of the *glutathione* structure.

Glutathione is a tripeptide isolated from yeast. A complete enzymatic or acid hydrolysis of the peptide revealed that it was composed of only three α-amino acids: L-glutamic acid, L-cysteine, and glycine. If each of these α-amino acids had but one amino group and one carboxyl group, the number of possible sequences would be six (Sec. 15.8). However, glutamic acid (see Table 15.1) has two carboxyl groups. This increases the total number of possible sequences to twelve for we do not know whether the α-carboxyl or the γ-carboxyl group of glutamic acid is involved in a peptide link. Mild hydrolysis of glutathione gave two dipeptides. One of these, on further treatment, yielded cysteine and glutamic acid, the other gave cysteine and glycine. This much is now known about glutathione: the cysteine structure is linked to both glycine and glutamic acid. But how? A little pencil work now will show that only the three sequences I, II, and III could possibly fit that of glutathione.

Cys-Glu

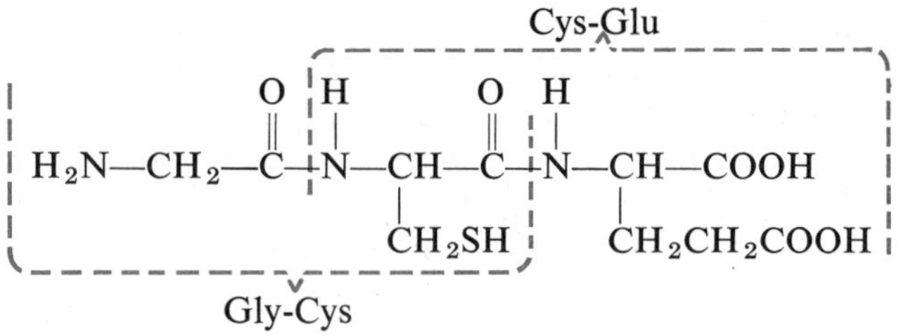

I $H_2N-CH_2-\overset{\overset{O}{\|}}{C}-\overset{\overset{H}{|}}{N}-CH-\overset{\overset{O}{\|}}{C}-\overset{\overset{H}{|}}{N}-CH-COOH$

with CH₂SH and CH₂CH₂COOH substituents below

Gly-Cys

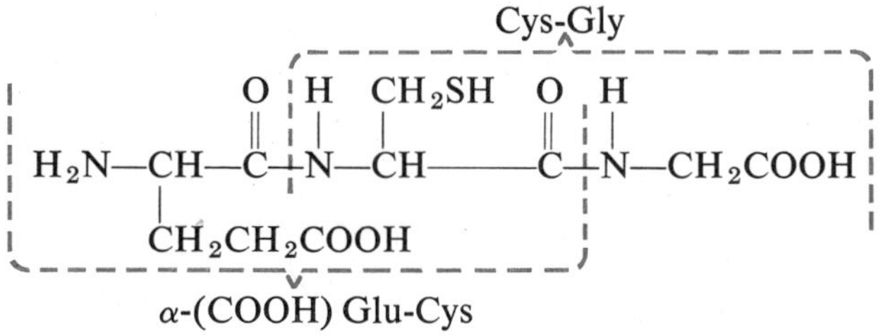

Cys-Gly

II $H_2N-CH-\overset{\overset{O}{\|}}{C}-\overset{\overset{H}{|}}{N}-CH-\overset{CH_2SH}{}-C-\overset{\overset{H}{|}}{N}-CH_2COOH$

with CH₂CH₂COOH substituent below

α-(COOH) Glu-Cys

Cys-Gly

III $H_2N-CH-CH_2CH_2\overset{\overset{O}{\|}}{C}-\overset{\overset{H}{|}}{N}-CH-\overset{CH_2SH}{}-\overset{\overset{O}{\|}}{C}-\overset{\overset{H}{|}}{N}-CH_2COOH$

with COOH substituent below

γ-(COOH) Glu-Cys

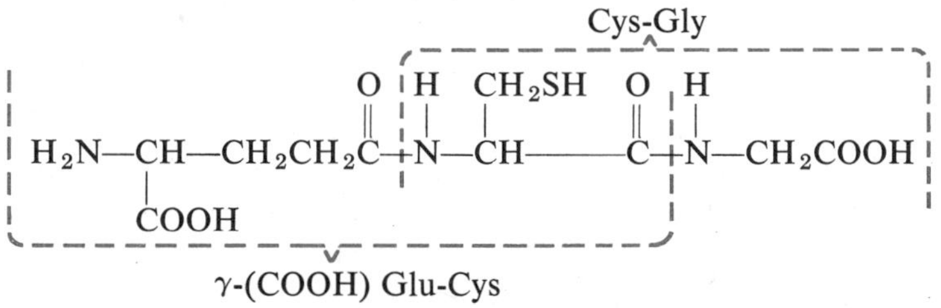

The tagging technique identified glutamic acid as the N-terminal amino acid. This finding eliminates structure I as a possibility. The synthesis of the remaining two dipeptides is now in order. In one of these the α-carboxyl of glutamic acid must be linked to cysteine, and in the other the γ-carboxyl must be joined. The latter structure proved to be identical with that of the dipeptide obtained by hydrolysis. The correct structure for glutathione is thus established as that shown by the tripeptide III.

Once the proper sequence of amino acids in a peptide is known, a synthesis for it usually follows. The historic accomplishment of duVigneaud[7] and his co-workers in determining the oxytocin structure provides such an outstanding example.

Oxytocin is a peptide hormone produced by the posterior lobe of the pituitary gland. It has the function of causing a contraction

---

[7] Vincent duVigneaud (1901–   ), Cornell University College of Medicine. Winner of the Nobel Prize in Chemistry, 1955.

of smooth muscle, particularly uterine muscle, and finds application in obstetrics. In addition to this function, the hormone also promotes the flow of milk from the mammary glands.

Oxytocin, on hydrolysis, produced one molecule each of leucine, isoleucine, proline, glutamic acid, tyrosine, aspartic acid, cystine, glycine, and three equivalents of ammonia. The sequence of the α-amino acids in oxytocin was determined and the structure shown in Fig. 15.1 was assigned to it. The research team subsequently synthesized an octapeptide of the same sequence. This outstanding achievement represents the first synthesis of a peptide hormone.

■□FIGURE 15.1 OXYTOCIN

(SHADED AREAS INDICATE THE FREE AMINO GROUPS OF THE AMIDES OF GLYCINE, GLUTAMIC, AND ASPARTIC ACIDS.)

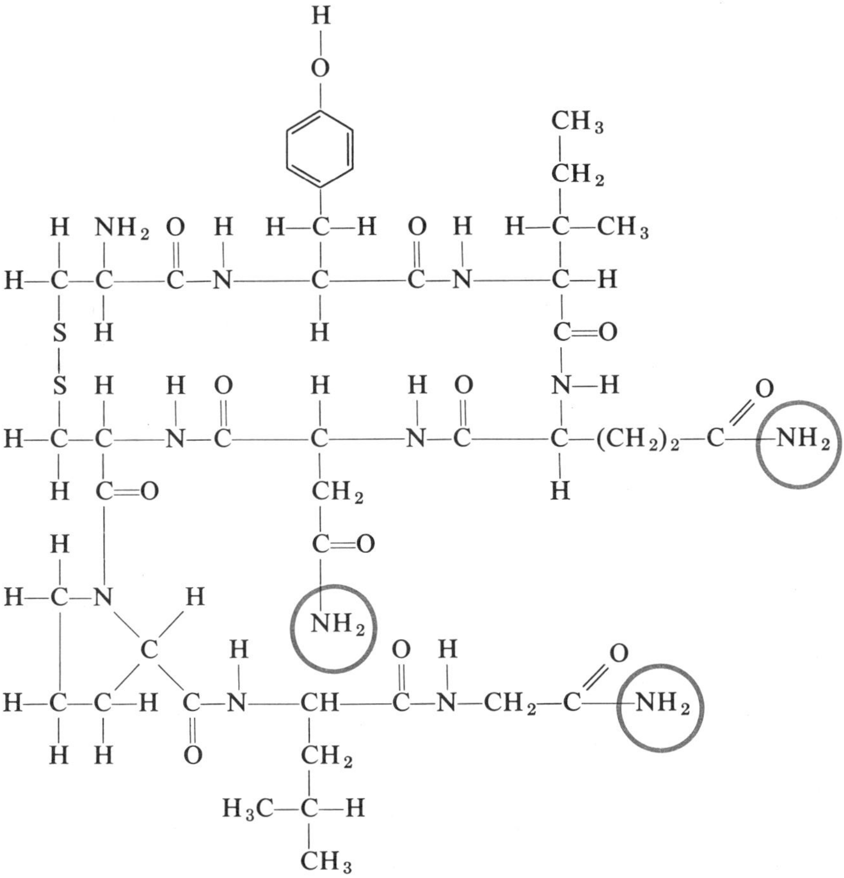

Another brilliant example of determining the sequence of amino acids in a natural polymer was that performed by Sanger[8] of England. He and his associates, after years of diligent investigation and by the use of ingenious techniques, were able to elucidate the amino acid sequence of the hormone insulin. Until about 1955 the amino acid sequence in any polypeptide within the protein range was unknown. The molecular weight of beef insulin was determined to be 5,734 and its composition that of forty-eight amino acid residues of sixteen different kinds!

Exercise 15.3   Why could not bromobenzene be used for tagging the N-terminal α-amino acid of a peptide? (*Hint: See Section 7.6.*)

15.10   THE COMPOSITION AND STRUCTURE OF PROTEINS

Proteins differ from carbohydrates and fats in elementary chemical composition. All proteins contain, in addition to carbon, hydrogen, and oxygen, other elements in the approximate percentages as follows: nitrogen (15%), sulfur (1.0%), and phosphorus (0.5%). The molecular weights of proteins are unbelievably high, ranging from 10,000 to 10,000,000.

Acceptance of the peptide hypothesis of protein structure, first proposed in 1902 by Fischer and Hofmeister, has led to many other questions regarding protein structures. How are peptide chains held together? How are they arranged in space? X-ray analysis and the persistent efforts of numerous investigators have revealed the answer to some of these questions.

The long polypeptide chains which comprise some protein molecules appear to be grouped together in bundles with adjacent chains joined by hydrogen bonds. The amide hydrogen atom in the peptide link of one chain is attracted to an oxygen atom in the peptide link of another. Fibrous proteins which constitute the hair and nails appear to have a longitudinal structure of the type shown on the next page in which dotted lines indicate hydrogen bonding.

---

[8]Frederick Sanger (1918–   ), Cambridge University. Winner of the Nobel Prize in Chemistry, 1958.

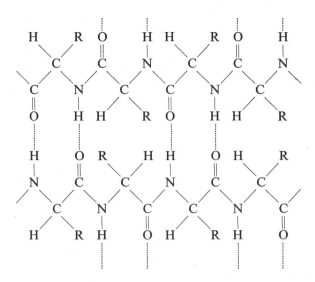

Other proteins appear to have a helical structure. Hydrogen bond formation between approximately every fourth amide grouping within the chain has the effect of pulling it into a coil. The drawing below, in which hydrogen bonding is indicated by dotted lines, illustrates graphically the effects of such internal attraction. A coil produced in this manner is called an α-helix.

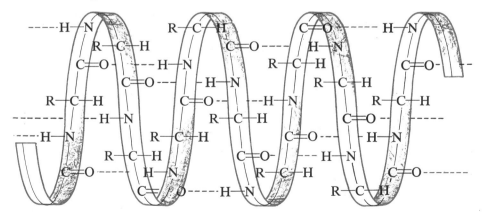

Proteins may be classified as simple proteins or as conjugated proteins. Simple proteins are those which yield, on hydrolysis, only α-amino acids. Albumin in eggs, gluten in wheat, keratin in hair, and collagen in connective tissue are examples of simple proteins. Conjugated proteins are those which, on hydrolysis, yield other compounds in addition to α-amino acids. Such nonprotein materials are called **prosthetic** groups. Hemoglobin is an example of a conjugated protein. The prosthetic group, in this case, is the iron-containing porphyrin structure called heme (Sec. 17.3).

Proteins when heated coagulate, or precipitate. The protein albumin, found in egg white, is a common example of a protein easily coagulated by heat. The salts of certain heavy metals (silver, mercury, lead) also cause proteins to precipitate. The immediate ingestion of protein material such as egg white as an antidote for accidental heavy metal poisonings is based on this behavior. The cauterizing action of silver nitrate is another application. Proteins also are precipitated by certain acids. Precipitation of protein by any agent is an irreversible change and the precipitated protein is said to be **denatured.**

A number of chemical tests on proteins produce color reactions. One of these, the **biuret test,** produces a pink or purple color when an alkaline solution of protein material is treated with a very dilute cupric sulfate solution. The test is specific for multiple peptide links and is not given by α-amino acids. It is a convenient test and often is used on a protein hydrolysate to determine the completeness of hydrolysis.

The **xanthoproteic test** is a yellow color reaction produced when a protein is treated with concentrated nitric acid. The test is simply a nitration of the aromatic ring of certain amino acids (tyrosine, phenylalanine, and tryptophan) and is one recognized by every student as the familiar nitric acid stain. Another color test for proteins is the **Millon test.** The reagent used for this test is a mixture of mercuric and mercurous nitrates. A protein when treated with Millon's reagent and heated produces a red color. Any phenolic compound will give the reaction, and the Millon test, like others which give colored reactions, is dependent upon the presence of certain individual amino acids in the protein molecule.

> **Exercise 15.4**   Suggest a reason why it is a legal require-
> ment that the eyes of newborn infants be treated with a silver
> nitrate solution.

15.13   NUTRITIONAL IMPORTANCE OF PROTEINS

Proteins provide one of the major nutrients for the body, but their utilization differs from that of the fats and carbohydrates. Whereas fats and carbohydrates are used primarily to supply heat and energy, the proteins are used mainly to repair and replace worn-out tissue. Such repairs and replacements are made of protein material which the animal organism has synthesized from other ingested proteins. Unlike certain of the lower plants, animals are not capable of "fixing"[9] atmospheric nitrogen, or converting ammonium or nitrate salts into proteins. Animals obtain their protein by eating plants that have synthesized protein material, or by eating other animals that have eaten such plants. The digestion of proteins to α-amino acids by the body supplies the required building material from which the animal's own protein can be formed. So far as is known, and in contrast to carbohydrates and fat depots, there are no body depots of proteins which serve as stores and have no other function.

15.14   METABOLISM OF PROTEINS

The digestion of proteins leads to mixtures of simple amino acids and polypeptides of varying lengths. Digestion destroys the specificity of a protein and frees the constituent amino acids for the synthesis of new proteins that suit the requirements of the individual. Amino acids not required for such syntheses are converted to other necessary foods such as carbohydrates and fat and ultimately are oxidized to yield energy. The metabolic changes involved in these conversions are very complex.

The amino acids produced by the digestion of a protein are absorbed through the intestinal wall into the blood and are transported to the liver. Certain of the amino acids then proceed from the liver to other tissues. Amino acids are required by the cells for

[9]The conversion of atmospheric nitrogen into nitrates or nitrogenous compounds. Certain free-living soil bacteria and others that live in nodules on the roots of leguminous plants (peas, beans, clover) are able to "fix" and store nitrogen in the form of nitrates.

the synthesis of proteins, enzymes, certain hormones, and other nitrogen-containing substances. Body tissues are capable of synthesizing
some amino acids (nonessential) by removing the required amino
groups from other amino acids. The amino group taken from one
acid is transferred to an α-keto analogue of the amino acid to be
synthesized. This transfer is called **transamination** and is illustrated
below.

$$
\underset{\text{Alanine}}{\begin{array}{c} CH_3 \\ | \\ H_2N-C-H \\ | \\ COOH \end{array}}
+
\underset{\substack{\alpha\text{-Ketoglutaric} \\ \text{acid}}}{\begin{array}{c} COOH \\ | \\ CH_2 \\ | \\ CH_2 \\ | \\ C=O \\ | \\ COOH \end{array}}
\rightleftharpoons
\underset{\substack{\text{Pyruvic} \\ \text{acid}}}{\begin{array}{c} CH_3 \\ | \\ C=O \\ | \\ COOH \end{array}}
+
\underset{\text{Glutamic acid}}{\begin{array}{c} COOH \\ | \\ CH_2 \\ | \\ CH_2 \\ | \\ H_2N-C-H \\ | \\ COOH \end{array}}
$$

The amino group of α-amino acids, if not required for the
synthesis of new amino acids, can be oxidatively removed. This
process is called **deamination.**

$$
\underset{\text{Alanine}}{\begin{array}{c} CH_3 \\ | \\ H_2N-C-H \\ | \\ COOH \end{array}}
+ \tfrac{1}{2}O_2 \rightarrow
\underset{\text{Pyruvic acid}}{\begin{array}{c} CH_3 \\ | \\ C=O \\ | \\ COOH \end{array}}
+ NH_3
$$

The ammonia formed by deamination combines with carbon dioxide
through a series of enzymatic reactions to produce urea.

$$
2\,NH_3 + CO_2 \rightarrow \underset{\text{Urea}}{H_2N-\overset{\displaystyle O}{\overset{\|}{C}}-NH_2} + H_2O
$$

Urea is eliminated from the body by way of the urine and is a major
end-product of protein metabolism.

The carbon skeleton of an amino acid, after the amino group
is removed by either of the processes described above, may be used
to synthesize other amino acids or it may enter the pathways of
carbohydrate and fatty acid metabolism. The latter course proceeds

by way of the tricarboxylic acid cycle (Sec. 14.22). Thus the deaminated amino acid, like a fat or a carbohydrate, may ultimately be converted to carbon dioxide, water, and energy.

15.15   IMPROPER METABOLISM OF PROTEINS. ALLERGIES

The inability of some persons to accomplish complete hydrolysis of certain protein material may result in the absorption of minute amounts of unchanged protein from the intestinal tract.   Such metabolic failures cause the individual to become extremely sensitive or allergic to certain foods.   When present even in minute amounts and eaten unknowingly as ingredients in other foods, the effects of such allergens can be very distressing.   Sneezing, hives, eczema, and general discomfort result.   The old phrase "one man's food is another's poison" has some basis in fact.   Proteins injected as serums or as antibiotics sometimes, when incompatible with the individual, produce even more serious results.   Incompatibilities of the kind described appear to be genetically related and part of the heredity of the individual.   The complex chemistry that controls heredity rests in the area of nucleoproteins and is currently the area of greatest excitement to biochemists.   We can only hope that with advancements in techniques, chemists will be able to reveal more of the secrets of the life processes.

□□ *SUMMARY*

[1]   Proteins are high molecular weight natural polymers made up largely by combination of various α-amino acids.

[2]   Approximately twenty amino acids comprise the bulk of plant and animal protein.   Names and structures for the common amino acids are listed in Table 15.1.

[3]   Amino acids may be classified according to properties as (a) neutral (one amino group and one carboxyl group), (b) acidic (more than one carboxyl group per amino group), and (c) basic (more than one amino group per carboxyl function).

[4]   The α-amino acids with the exception of glycine are optically active.

[5]   The α-amino acids obtained from plant or animal sources have the L-configuration.

[6]   Amino acids may be grouped under a nutritive classification into two categories: (a) **essential** (required in the diet because the animal organism is incapable of synthesizing it), and (b) **nonessential** (not required in the diet).

[7]   Amino acids have both the properties of carboxylic acids and primary amines. Amino acids form inner salts or dipolar ions.

[8]   Amino acids have an isoelectric point.

[9]   Individual amino acids can be separated from protein hydrolysates. Amino acids can be synthesized by (a) amination of α-halogen acids with ammonia, (b) an adaptation of the Gabriel primary amine synthesis, and (c) the Strecker synthesis.

[10]   Amino acids generally show reactions characteristic of both the primary amines and the carboxylic acids. The principal reactions of amino acids are

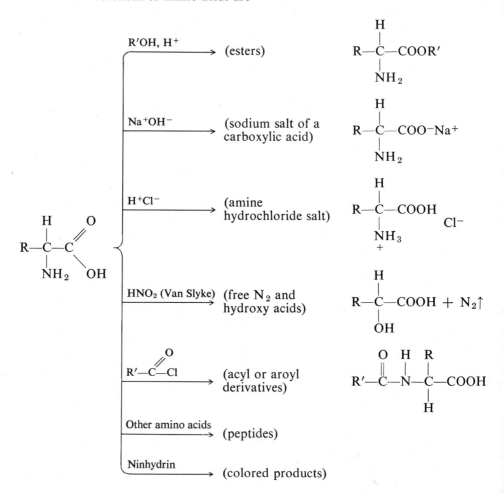

[11] Two or more amino acids joined through amide linkages form peptides. A peptide is named as a derivative of the amino acid with a C-terminal carboxyl function.

[12] Proteins, when hydrolyzed, yield amino acids and polypeptides.

[13] Proteins are classified as simple proteins or conjugated proteins. Simple proteins on complete hydrolysis give only amino acids. Conjugated proteins on hydrolysis give, in addition to amino acids, nonprotein *prosthetic* groups.

[14] Proteins are easily precipitated, or coagulated, by heat, by acids, and by certain heavy metals. Such coagulation is irreversible and is called *denaturation.*

[15] Proteins are used in the body mainly to repair and replace worn-out tissue.

[16] The digestion and metabolism of protein material begins with its hydrolysis to α-amino acids. The α-amino acids, by **transamination** and/or **deamination,** are converted into other α-amino acids or become oxidized to carbon dioxide and water.

□□ *NEW TERMS*

[1]	conjugated protein	[6]	isoelectric point
[2]	deamination	[7]	peptide
[3]	denaturation	[8]	prosthetic group
[4]	dipolar ion	[9]	simple protein
[5]	essential amino acid	[10]	transamination

■ □ SUPPLEMENTARY EXERCISES
▼   AND PROBLEMS

[1]   Draw the structures and name three sulfur-containing α-amino acids.

[2]   Draw the structures of three amino acids which would give a yellow color with concentrated nitric acid.

[3]   Beginning with a 3-carbon alcohol outline all necessary steps in the preparation of D, L-alanine. Include as one step an adaptation of Gabriel's method for the preparation of primary amines.

[4]   Complete the following equations.

(a) 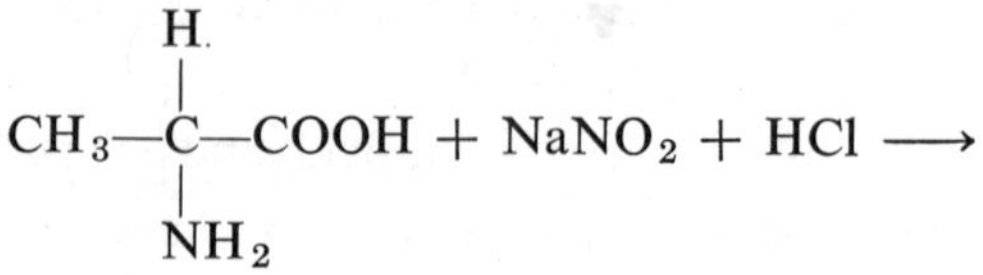 $CH_3-\overset{\displaystyle H}{\underset{\displaystyle NH_2}{C}}-COOH + NaNO_2 + HCl \longrightarrow$

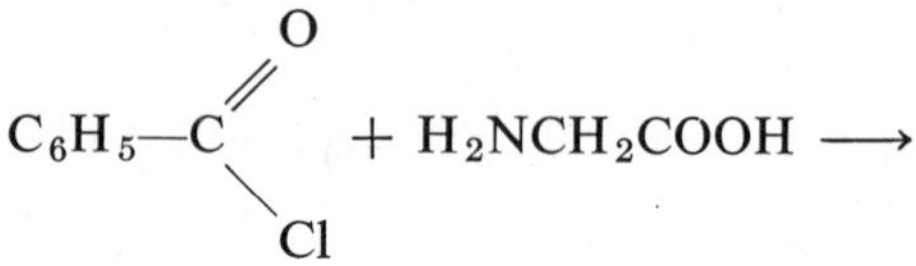

(b) $C_6H_5-\overset{\displaystyle O}{\underset{\displaystyle Cl}{C}} + H_2NCH_2COOH \longrightarrow$

(c) $CH_3-\overset{\displaystyle H}{\underset{\displaystyle NH_2}{C}}-COOH + HCl \longrightarrow$

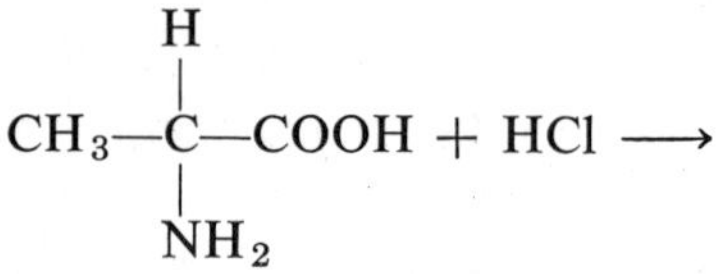

(d) 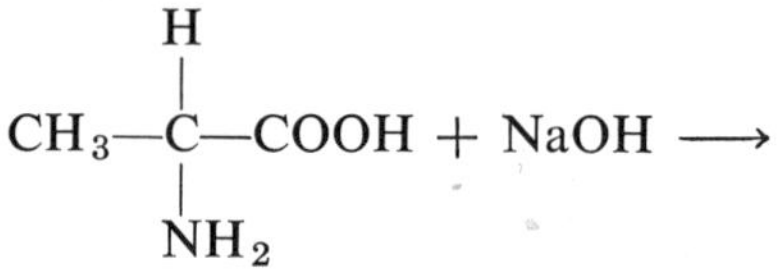 $CH_3-\overset{\displaystyle H}{\underset{\displaystyle NH_2}{C}}-COOH + NaOH \longrightarrow$

(e) 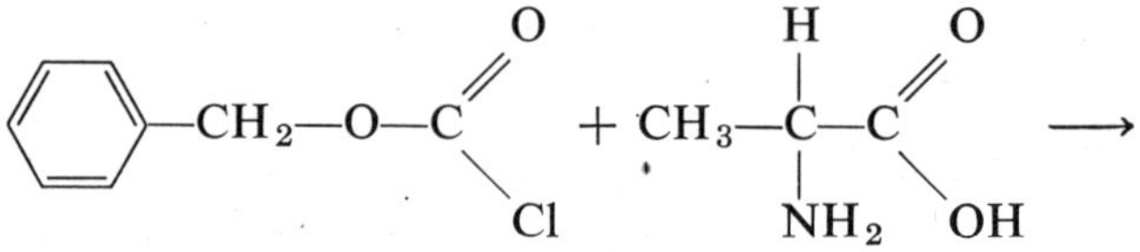 $\bigcirc-CH_2-O-\overset{\displaystyle O}{C}{\diagdown}_{Cl} + CH_3-\overset{\displaystyle H}{\underset{\displaystyle NH_2}{C}}-\overset{\displaystyle O}{C}{\diagdown}_{OH} \longrightarrow$

(f)   Product of (e) $+$ $SOCl_2$ $\longrightarrow$

(g)   Product of (f) $+$ alanine $\longrightarrow$

[5]   Draw all tripeptides that could possibly be synthesized from glycine, alanine, and phenylalanine.

[6]   A solution turns pink litmus blue and the indicator phenol-phthalein slightly pink. Would glycine, if dissolved and electrolyzed in this solution, migrate to the cathode or anode? (The isoelectric point of glycine is 6.1.)

[7]   A kilogram of human hemoglobin contains approximately 3.33 grams of iron. If each molecule of hemoglobin contains four heme structures (the iron-containing prosthetic group), what is the minimum molecular weight of this protein?

[8]   A Van Slyke nitrogen determination made on a solution of 8.74 mg of an unknown amino acid liberated 2.50 ml of N_2 at 740 mm and 25°. What is the minimum molecular weight of the amino acid? If the isoelectric point of this unknown amino acid occurs at a pH value of 10.8, what amino acid could it be?

[9]   A peptide on complete hydrolysis yielded five different amino acids in the following amounts: one unit each of serine and glycine, two units each of arginine and phenylalanine, and three units of proline. The N-terminal amino acid was identified as arginine. Partial hydrolysis liberated di- and tripeptides of the following compositions:

Ser-Pro-Phe	Gly-Phe-Ser	Pro-Gly
Phe-Ser-Pro	Pro-Phe-Arg	Arg-Pro

Deduce and write out the structure of this nonapeptide.

chapter 16

Color in Organic Compounds, Dyes

INTRODUCTION

Light is composed of electromagnetic vibrations of varying wavelengths, but only those within the relatively narrow range of 4,000–7,800 Å, called the **visible** region, are perceptible to the human eye and are responsible for the sensation of color.

The proper mixture of all wavelengths within the visible region results in white light, but when radiation of a certain wavelength within the visible region is absent — that is, has been absorbed or removed by interference in any manner — the resultant light is colored. The color perceived by the eye is produced by a composite of all wavelengths not absorbed and is the complementary color of the particular wavelengths that were absorbed. For example, absorption of the longer wavelengths (red, orange, yellow) results in a blue or blue-green color; absorption of the shorter wavelengths (violet, blue) results in an orange or yellow color. Table 16.1 lists the complementary colors produced when various wavelengths within the visible region of the spectrum are absorbed.

☐ ■ TABLE 16.1

ABSORPTION OF VISIBLE LIGHT AND COMPLEMENTARY COLORS

Wave Length Absorbed (Å)	Color Absorbed	Complementary Color
4,000–4,250	violet	yellow-green
4,250–4,750	blue	yellow
4,750–4,900	blue-green	orange
4,900–5,000	green-blue	red
5,000–5,500	green	purple
5,500–5,750	yellow-green	violet
5,750–5,950	yellow	blue
5,950–6,050	orange	green-blue
6,050–7,800	red	blue-green

The amount and intensity of the color produced when a molecule absorbs in the visible region of the spectrum is a function of molecular structure. In an attempt to correlate color with structure early chemists noted that certain groups, when present in a molecule, nearly always produced color. Such groups, usually multiple-bonded, electron-attracting structures, were called **chromophores** (Gr., *chroma*, light; *phorein*, to bear). The following are examples of common chromophoric groups:

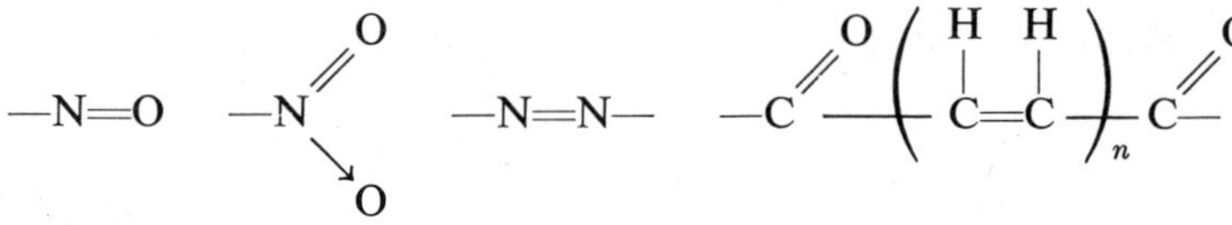

Nitroso	Nitro	Azo	Dicarbonyl
			($n = 0$ or some integer)

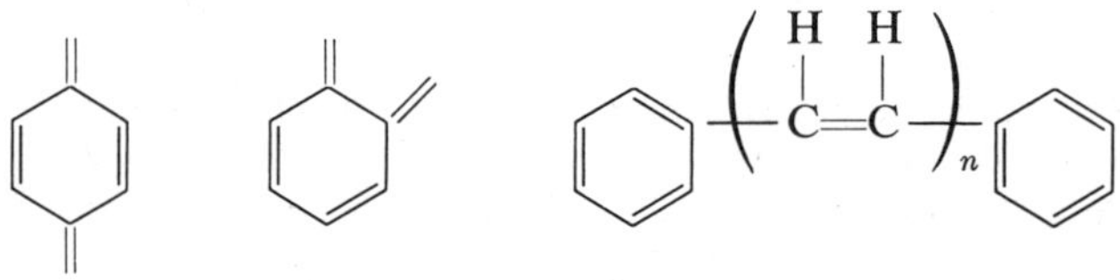

p-Quinoid	*o*-Quinoid	Diphenylpolyenes
		($n = 3$ or more)

Certain electron-donor groups, when present in a molecule with a chromophore, appeared to intensify or augment the color. Such color-assisting groups were called **auxochromes** (Gr., *auxanein*, to increase). Auxochromes usually are acidic or basic groups which form with the chromophore an extended, conjugated system. The hydroxyl group is the auxochrome in many colored organic compounds. For example, nitrobenzene is so pale yellow as to appear almost colorless, but *o*- and *p*-nitrophenols are very bright yellow. On the other hand, *m*-nitrophenol lacks the intensity of its *ortho* and *para* isomers because the chromophore and the auxochrome, if *meta* to each other cannot form part of the same conjugated system. The resonance structures possible for all three isomeric mononitrophenols are shown:

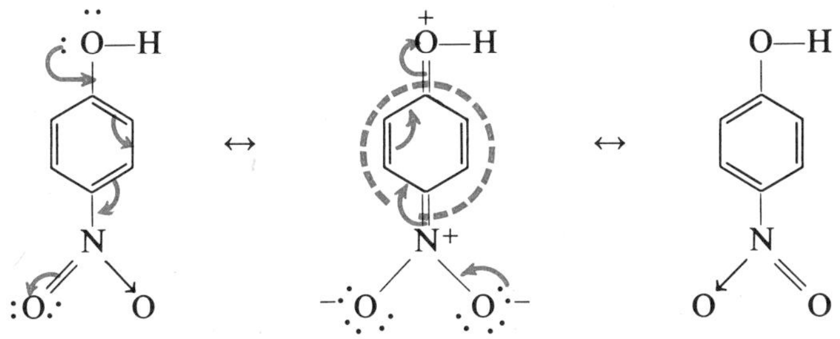

Resonance forms of *p*-Nitrophenol
(*p*-quinoid structure outlined by dotted line).

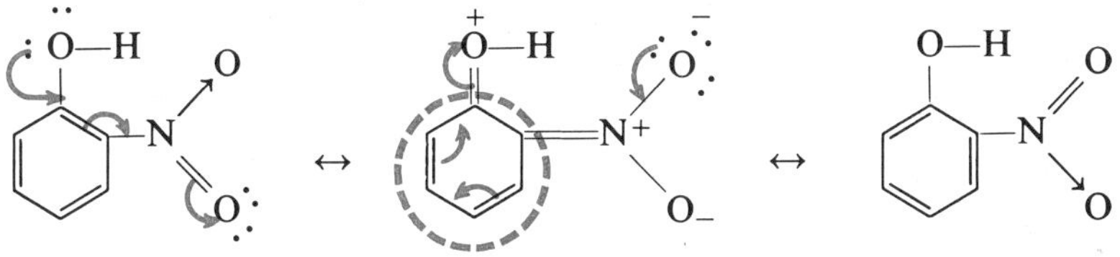

Resonance forms of *o*-Nitrophenol
(*o*-quinoid structure outlined by dotted line).

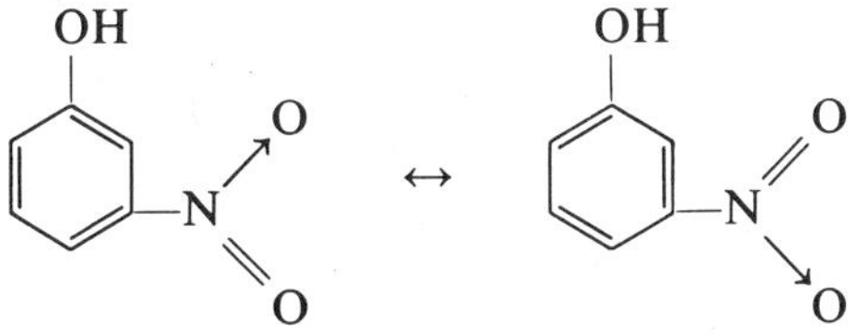

Resonance forms of *m*-Nitrophenol.
(A conjugated system of alternate double and single bonds
between chromophore and auxochrome is not possible.)

Other common auxochromes besides the hydroxyl groups are
—OR, —NH$_2$, —NHR, and —NR$_2$. In these color-assisting groups
you will observe that each has one thing in common — namely, one
or more pairs of electrons which may interact with and extend the
conjugation already present.   Although the chromophore-auxo-
chrome theory has been a useful one, color in an organic compound
is now recognized as the result of extensive conjugation, not the
function of any particular group.   If an organic compound is to be
used as a dye, a third grouping, in addition to the chromophore and
auxochrome, must be present.   Such groups make possible salt
formation and provide better water solubility.   Sulfonic and carboxylic acid salts usually are employed for this purpose.

Exercise 16.1   Explain why the color of a *p*-nitrophenol solution changes from a light yellow to orange when made basic with sodium hydroxide.

Color and Dyes

16.3   HISTORICAL

A compound to be used as a dye must possess, besides color, the ability to attach itself firmly to fabric, to leather, or to whatever is to be colored. Moreover, it must be fast to light and resistant to washing. Natural compounds which possess all the qualities cited above have never been plentiful or easily obtained, yet color has been so important in the life of man that it has been used since the beginning of civilization. One of the earliest dyes used by the ancients was indigo blue which occurs as a glucoside (Sec. 14.6) in the leaf of the indigo plant. Cloth samples taken from the tombs of the pharaohs revealed that indigo was known to the Egyptians as early as 2000 B.C., but the synthesis of indigo was not accomplished until 1880 by Baeyer. Another early dye, an object of commerce for thousands of years, was Tyrian purple. Although structurally similar to indigo, it is not of plant origin. It was obtained by the ancients from a snail (*Murex brandaris*) found on the small Mediterranean island of Tyre off the coast of present day Lebanon. Such large numbers of this small mollusk were required to produce but a little of the highly prized dye, that the use of this color by any but the nobility was forbidden. Hence the expression "born to the purple." Another ancient dye is alizarin, which is found in the root of the madder plant. It was used to dye cotton and linen red. Its synthesis was accomplished in 1870. Unlike indigo, Tyrian purple and alizarin are no longer important as dyes. The structures of these three ancient dyes are given below. You will be able to recognize in each the color-bearing and the color-assisting groups.

Indigo

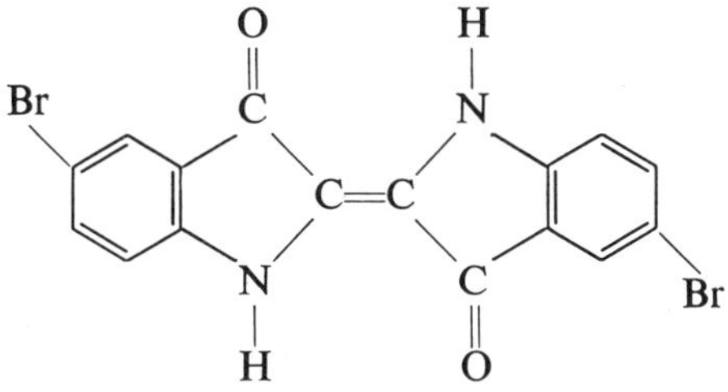

Tyrian purple (6, 6'-dibromoindigo)[1]

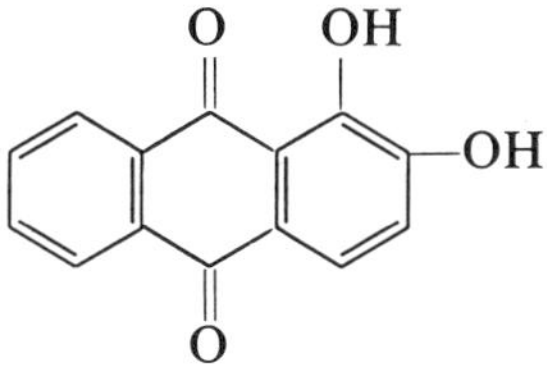

Alizarin

Progress in the production of synthetic dyes from coal-tar derivatives has been comparatively recent. The first synthetic dye to be produced commercially was mauve. It was accidentally discovered only a little more than a hundred years ago. In 1856, William Perkin, an eighteen-year-old assistant in Hofmann's (Sec. 13.4-C) laboratory, tried to oxidize an aniline derivative in the hope of obtaining quinine. Although the structures of neither starting material nor hoped-for product were known at the time, their molecular formulas were. Perkin reasoned that the reaction could possibly proceed as follows.

$$2\,C_{10}H_{13}N + 3\,O \longrightarrow C_{20}H_{24}N_2O_2 + H_2O$$

Allyltoluidine   Quinine

The black product which the reaction yielded contained a violet substance which had all the desirable properties of a dye. Perkin called the dye "mauveine," and, recognizing the commercial possibilities of his discovery, began to manufacture it in quantity. The aniline which Perkin used was not pure but contained some o- and p-toluidines. Mauveine since has been found to have the polycylic structure shown on page 438.

[1]The numbering of heterocyclic ring systems is illustrated in Table 17.1.

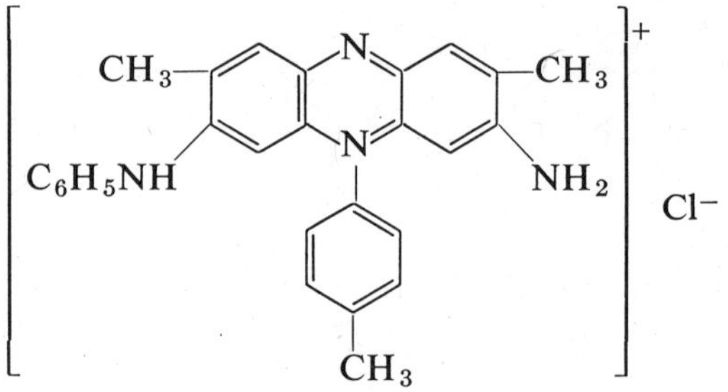

Mauveine

Perkin's discovery stimulated further research that led not only to the preparation of many other dyes, but, equally important, to the preparation of many other useful organic compounds. The impetus provided by the search for dyestuffs led to a period of intense chemical research so productive that it has been referred to as "the golden age of organic chemistry." Many of the synthetic dyes produced today are far superior to the naturally occurring ones used by the ancients. Not only our garments, but a host of other commodities throughout the market place, are now available in a wide variety of color — purple included.

16.4   CLASSIFICATION OF DYES BY STRUCTURE

Dyes may be classified in two ways. The organic chemist classifies them according to a common parent structure. The dyer who is primarily interested in anchoring the dye to the fiber classifies them according to the method of application. The first, or chemical classification, includes the following principal types along with examples of each.

A.   Nitro and Nitroso Dyes.   Dyes of this class are the o- or p-nitroso, nitrophenols, and the nitroso and nitronaphthols. One of the oldest nitro dyes is the high explosive, trinitrophenol (picric acid (Sec. 8.9-D).

Names assigned to the hundreds of dyes in everyday use usually indicate a color and often the method of application, but seldom do the names of dyes reveal their chemical structures. Other examples of nitro and nitroso dyes are shown.

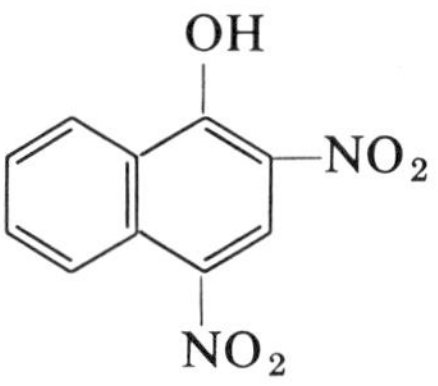

Martius yellow

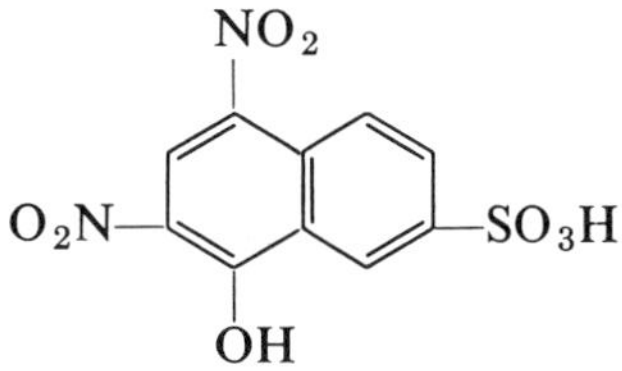

Naphthol yellow S

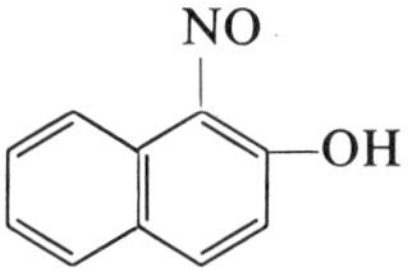

Naphthol green Y

B.   Azo Dyes.   This class represents the largest and most important group of dyes. The characteristic feature of each dye in this class is the chromophoric azo group (—N=N—), which forms part of the conjugated system and joins two or more aromatic rings. Azo dyes are prepared by coupling a diazotized aromatic amine with another aromatic amine or with a phenol or a naphthol (see Sec. 13.9-B). This simple reaction can be carried out directly within the fabric, and results in a product complete with chromophore, auxochrome, and conjugated system.   One of the first azo dyes to be prepared was *para red*, obtained from diazotized *p*-nitroaniline and β-naphthol.

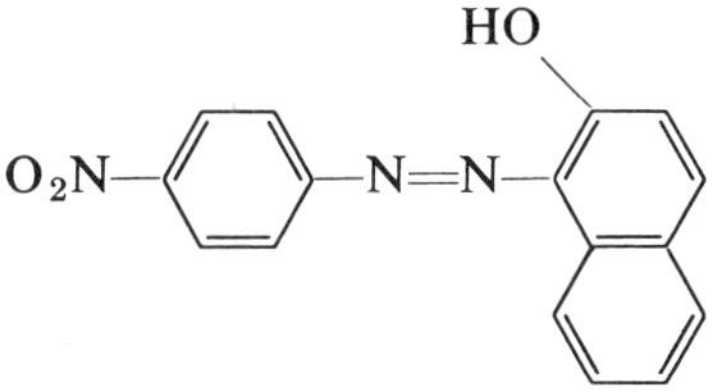

Para red

A similar coupling reaction with diazotized sulfanilic acid and β-naphthol produces *Orange II*.

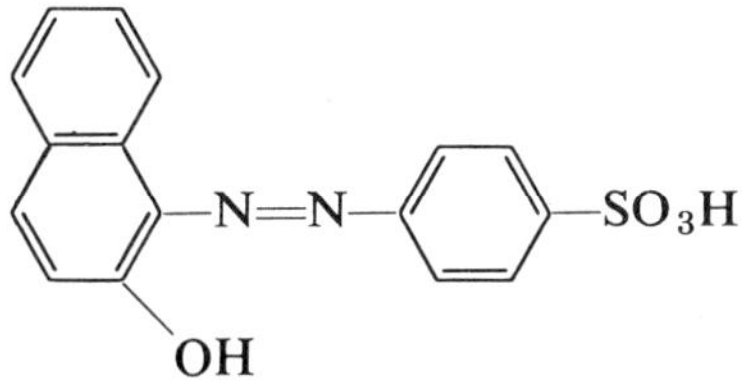

Orange II

More than one aromatic ring, when included in the coupling reaction, extends the conjugated system and deepens the color of a dye. For example, diazotized benzidine (4, 4'-diaminobiphenyl) will couple with 1-naphthylamine-4-sulfonic acid to produce a dye called *congo red*. Congo red also is used as a chemical indicator.

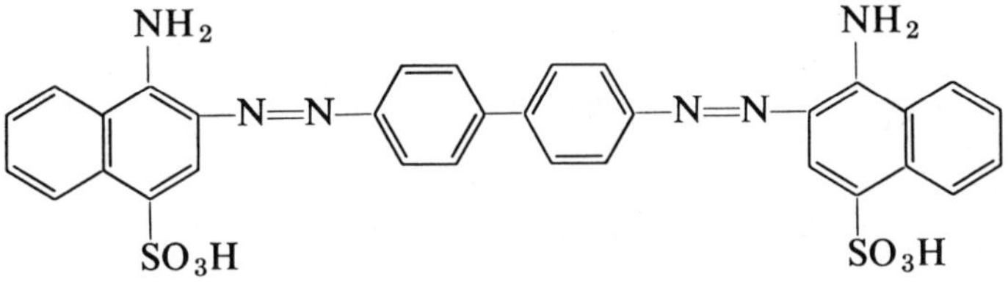

Congo Red

C.   Triphenylmethane Dyes.   The triphenylmethane dyes can be identified from a common structural feature in which a central carbon atom is joined to two benzene rings and to a *p*-quinoid group.

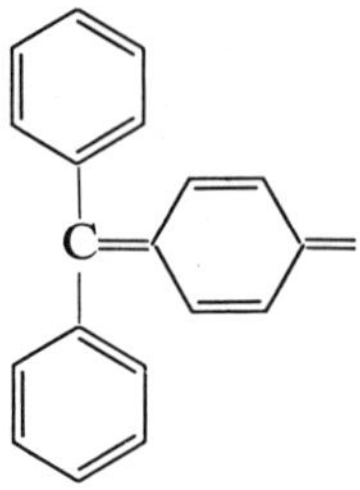

Malachite green is an example of a dye in this class and is one which has been prepared as a laboratory exercise by students for many years. It has been said that the best measure of a student's laboratory technique may be had from his preparation of malachite green. If he can accomplish this synthesis without dyeing the laboratory bench, his books and papers, his neighbors, and himself all a brilliant green, he is indeed a first-rate technician. Malachite green is prepared by condensing benzaldehyde with dimethylaniline to give a colorless **leuco base.** (Gr., *leuco*, white.) Oxidation of the leuco base followed by acid treatment yields the dye.

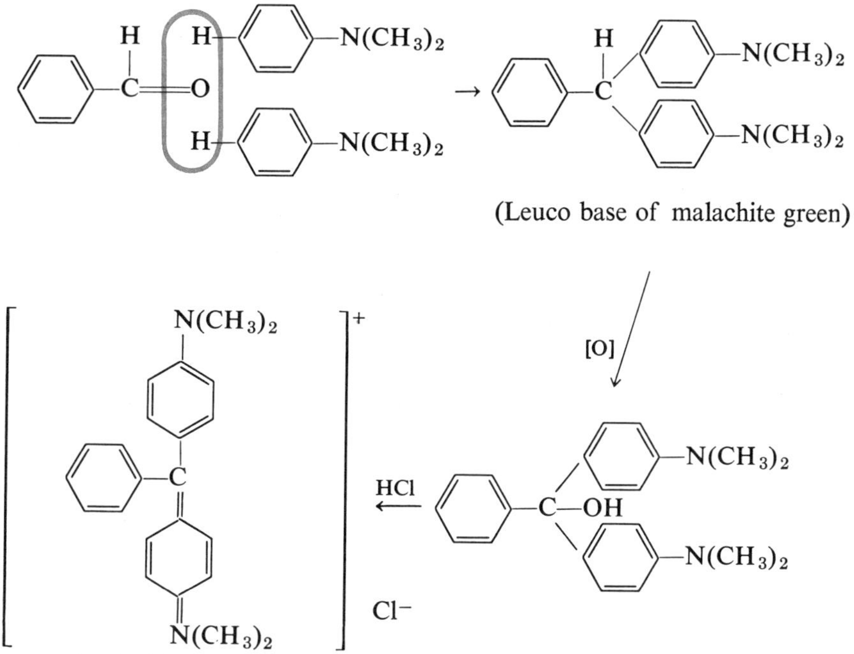

(Leuco base of malachite green)

Malachite green

Other triphenylmethane dyes with structures very similar to that of malachite green are *crystal violet* and *rosaniline*. Crystal violet is used as a biological stain and, until recently, has been widely used medicinally as an anthelmintic.

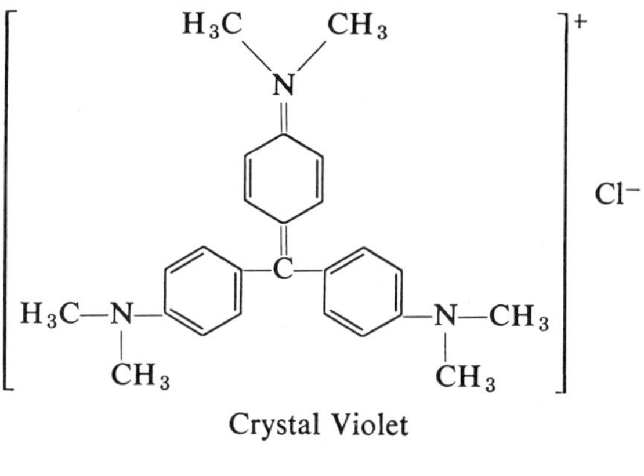

Crystal Violet

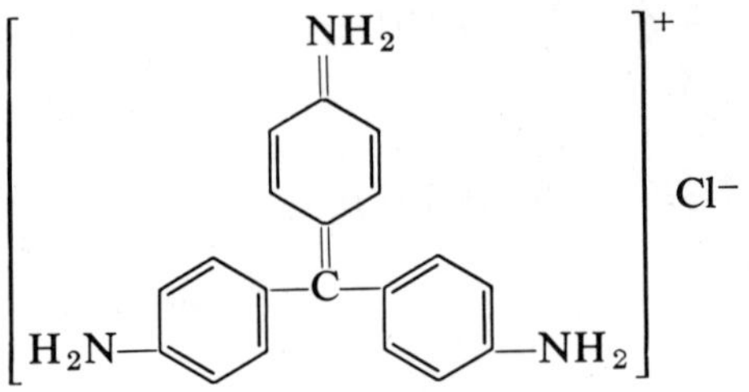

Rosaniline

The familiar phenolphthalein, an acid-base indicator rather than a dye, also has a triphenylmethane structure. It is prepared by condensing phthalic anhydride with phenol.

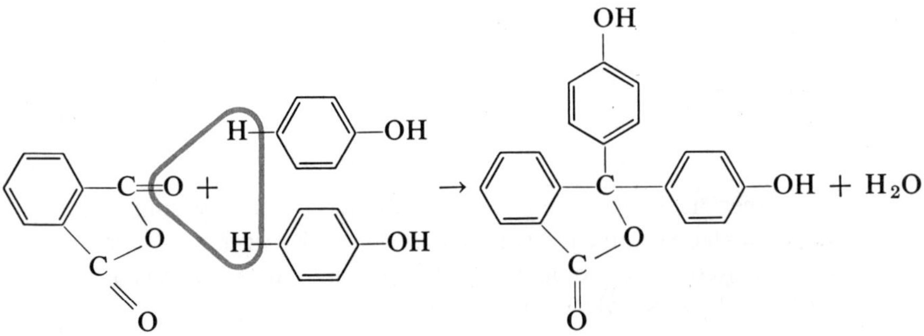

Phenolphthalein (colorless)

Indicators and some dyes are able to change color with a change in the hydrogen ion concentration of their solutions. Such changes in color are possible because an indicator is itself a weak acid or a weak base and enters into a salt-producing reaction. Phenolphthalein in acid solutions is colorless but turns red in alkaline solutions. A strong alkaline solution converts the indicator into a triphenylcarbinol derivative. Without an extended conjugated system the compound again is colorless.

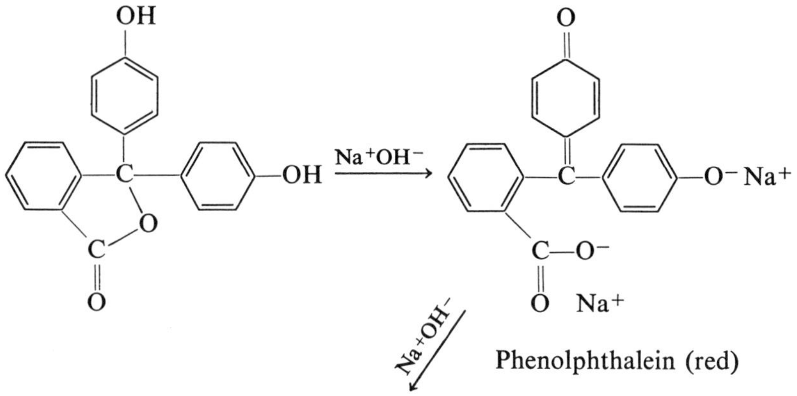

Phenolphthalein (red)

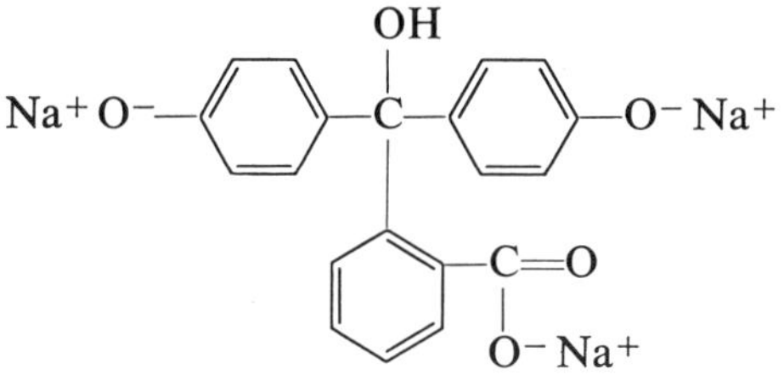

Phenolphthalein (colorless)

D. Indigoid Dyes. The indigoid dyes have as their identify-ing feature two conjugated carbonyl groups, $-\overset{\overset{\textstyle O}{\|}}{C}-CH=CH-\overset{\overset{\textstyle O}{\|}}{C}-$. Indigo is our best example of a dye of this class. It does not occur naturally in a colored form but rather as a colorless plant glucoside, *indican*. The latter yields glucose and *indoxyl* when hydrolyzed. Indoxyl, when exposed to air, oxidizes to indigo.

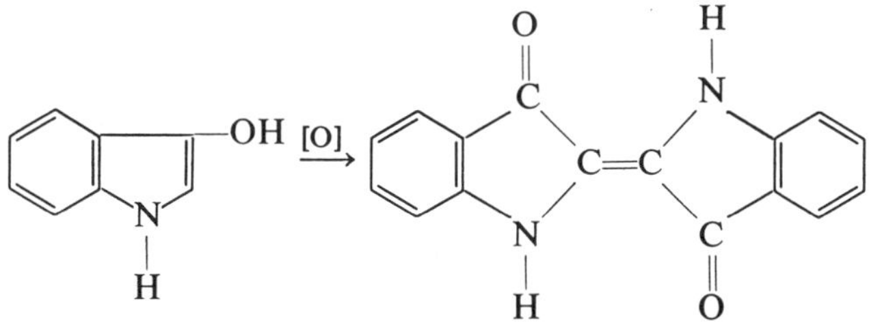

Indoxyl   Indigo

Exercise 16.2   Cloth to be dyed with indigo is first dipped in a hot solution of *indigo white* and then exposed to air for oxidation to indigo. Indigo white is actually a bright yellow compound. Why is it colored? Why is it water soluble?

Indigo white

E.   Anthraquinone Dyes.   The anthraquinone dyes have a *p*-quinoid structure in common with two other benzene rings in a *fused ring* molecule. An example of an anthraquinone dye is alizarin (Sec. 16.3).

16.5   CLASSIFICATION OF DYES BY METHOD OF APPLICATION

The mechanics of dyeing vary with the nature of the material to be dyed. A dye process suitable for animal fibers such as wool or silk may be entirely unsatisfactory for dyeing cotton. Wool and silk are proteins and contain many basic and acidic groups. These groups serve as points of attachment for a dye because it also has acidic and basic functions. On the other hand, cotton is a carbohydrate and provides only neutral ether linkages and hydroxyl groups as points of attachment for hydrogen bonds. Affixing color to synthetic fibers such as the polyolefins — hydrocarbons entirely lacking in polar groups — requires still other techniques. One point is clear: a dye must do more than simply color the surface of a fiber. It should become a *part of the fiber*, and wear and wash with the fiber. A number of dyes fulfil these conditions very well when used on some materials but not when used on others. In all cases the nature of the material will determine the process and the dye to be employed in dyeing it. A number of different dyeing methods and dyes adaptable to each method are described in the following sections.

A.   Direct or Substantive Dyes.   Dyes of this class contain polar groupings — acidic or basic — which are able to combine with polar groups in the fiber. Such dyes color a fabric directly when the latter is immersed in a hot, aqueous solution of the dye. Direct dyes are particularly well adapted to the dyeing of silk and wool. Picric acid and Martius yellow (Sec. 16.4-A) are two examples of direct dyes. Both compounds are acids and can combine with the free amino groups found in protein fibers. Nylon, a polyamide (Sec. 17.3), also may be dyed by this method.

B.   Mordant Dyes.   This class of dyes includes those which can form an insoluble, colored salt (called a lake) with certain metallic oxides. Mordant dyeing is one of the earliest methods practiced for anchoring color to a fabric. Mordant dyes can be used on silk and wool or on cotton fibers. The fabric appears colored because the colored precipitate is bound to and envelops each fiber. The oxides of aluminum, chromium, and iron usually are used for mordanting colors. Alizarin is an example of a mordant dye.

Alizarin

C.   Vat Dyes.   A vat dye is a substance which, in a reduced form, is water soluble and may be colorless. In this form it is introduced into the fabric. The fabric, after the dye is absorbed, is removed from the "vat" and exposed to air or treated with a chemical oxidizing agent. This step oxidizes the dye to a colored, insoluble form. The ancient dyes, indigo and Tyrian purple, are classic examples of vat dyes.

D.   Ingrain Dyes.   Ingrain dyes, sometimes called developed dyes, are dyes which develop within the fabric itself. The azo dyes are good examples of ingrain dyes. The cloth to be dyed first is immersed in an alkaline solution of the compound to be coupled — usually a phenol or naphthol. A second immersion in a cold solution of a diazotized amine causes the coupling reaction to take place within the fabric. Dyes produced in this manner were referred to at one time as *ice colors* because of the low temperature requirement for stability on the part of the diazonium salt.

E.   Disperse Dyes.   Dyes classified under this category are those which are soluble in the fiber but not in water. Disperse dyes are used in the coloring of many of the newer synthetic fibers. These sometimes are referred to as hydrophobic (water-fearing) fibers and usually are lacking in polar groups. The dye, in the form of a finely divided dispersion, is dissolved in some organic compound, (often a phenolic) and the absorption into the fiber is carried out in a surface-active bath (soap solution) at high temperatures and pressures. Examples of disperse dyes used for acetate rayons, Dacron, Nylon and other synthetic fibers are Celliton Fast Pink B (1-amino-4-hydroxyanthraquinone) and Celliton Fast Blue B (1, 4-N, N'-dimethylaminoanthraquinone).

Celliton Fast Pink   Celliton Fast Blue B

16.6   ORGANIC PIGMENTS

Our discussion of color in organic compounds would not be complete without a brief reference to colored pigments not used as dyes. A dye must be absorbed by the material to be colored, a pigment is applied to the surface. Pigments are not water soluble but, like the pigments in paints (Sec. 11.7), are suspended in the vehicle. Pigments are used mainly in decorative coatings, in printing inks, and for imparting color to plastics. If the chemical structure of a pigment can be modified to confer upon it water solubility, then it may serve as a dye.

The *phthalocyanines* comprise an important group of pigments. One of these, copper phthalocyanine is prepared by heating phthalonitrile with copper at 200°.

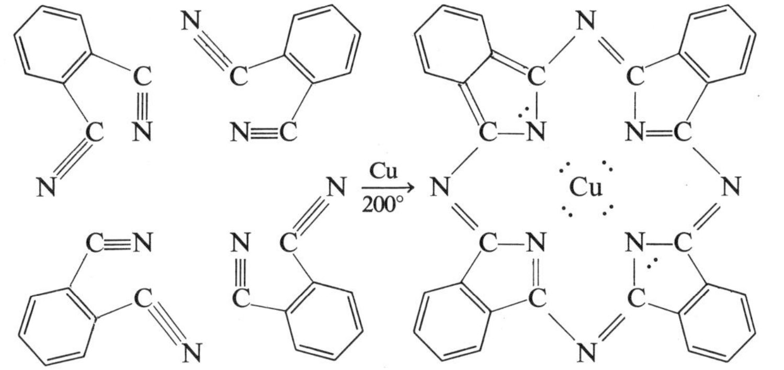

Copper phthalocyanine

□□ *SUMMARY*

[1] Organic molecules can absorb energy from electromagnetic vibrations (light) in the ultraviolet, in the visible, or in the infrared regions of the spectrum.

[2] Absorption of light in the visible region produces color. Early chemists attributed color in organic molecules to the presence of multiple-bonded, electron-attracting groups which they called **chromophores.** Common chromophores are

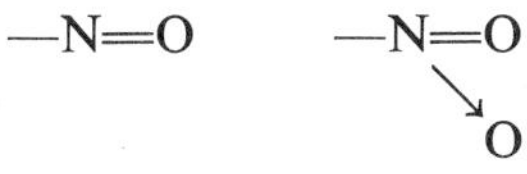

Nitroso   Nitro

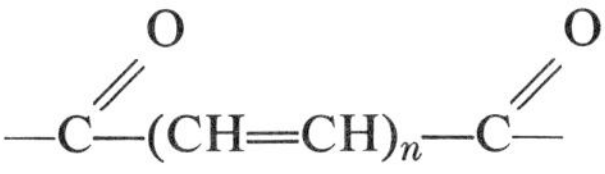

Dicarbonyl

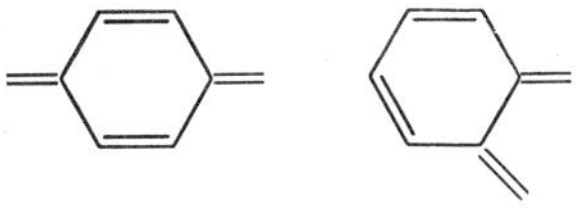

p- and *o*-quinoid 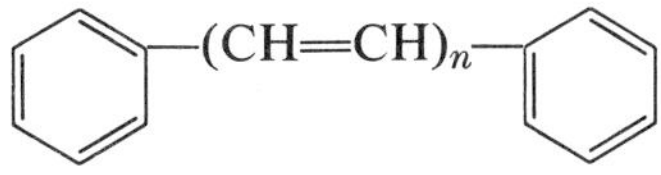   Diphenylpolyenes

[3] Groups capable of extending the conjugation of a colored compound are electron-donating, color-intensifying groups called **auxochromes.** Common auxochromes are —OH, —OR, —NH$_2$, —NHR, —NR$_2$.

[4] A colored organic compound may be used as a dye if it can be anchord to a fiber, is reasonably fast to light, and is resistant to washing.

[5] Dyes can be classified according to structure as

    a. Nitroso or nitro dyes
    b. Azo dyes
    c. Triphenylmethane dyes
    d. Indigoid dyes
    e. Anthraquinone dyes

[6] Dyes can be classified according to use as

    a. Direct dyes
    b. Mordant dyes
    c. Vat dyes
    d. Ingrain dyes

□□ *NEW TERMS*

[1]	auxochrome	[5]	ingrain dye
[2]	azo dye	[6]	leuco compound
[3]	chromophore	[7]	mordant
[4]	complementary color	[8]	a phthalocyanine

■ □ SUPPLEMENTARY EXERCISES
▼   AND PROBLEMS

[1] A molecule absorbs strongly at 5.9 μ. Would any change resulting from this absorption be perceptible to the human eye?

[2] A drop of colorless mineral oil when allowed to spread on the surface of water produces a changing color pattern. Explain.

[3] An organic compound absorbs radiation of wavelengths 5,960–6,000 Å. What color region of the visible spectrum is this? What color is the compound likely to be?

[4] *β-Carotene*, $C_{40}H_{56}$, is a $(C{=}C)_8$ system that imparts a yellow color to carrots. Its open-chain isomer, *lycopene*, is a $(C{=}C)_{11}$

system responsible for the color of ripe tomatoes and watermelon. Explain why one is yellow and the other red. Consult Table 16.1 and suggest wavelength regions where absorption by each natural substance might take place.

[5]   Draw structures for the following compounds.

(a)   2, 4-dinitrophenylhydrazine   (c)   *p*-nitrobenzoic acid

(b)   diacetyl, $(CH_3-C)_2$ (d)   quinone
        with $\parallel$ O below

Would these compounds be colored? Could any one be used satisfactorily as a dyestuff? Explain.

[6]   A dye called Vat Blue B is actually 5, 5', 7, 7'-tetrabromoindigo. Draw its structure.

[7]   In each of the dyes whose structures are given below, (a) outline the part of the structure considered to be the chromophore; (b) circle that part of each structure responsible for deepening the color — i.e., the auxochrome. Classify each according to structure and according to use.

(a)

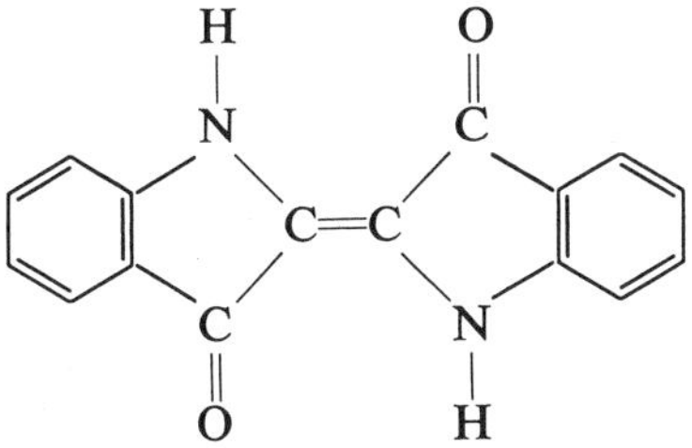

(b)

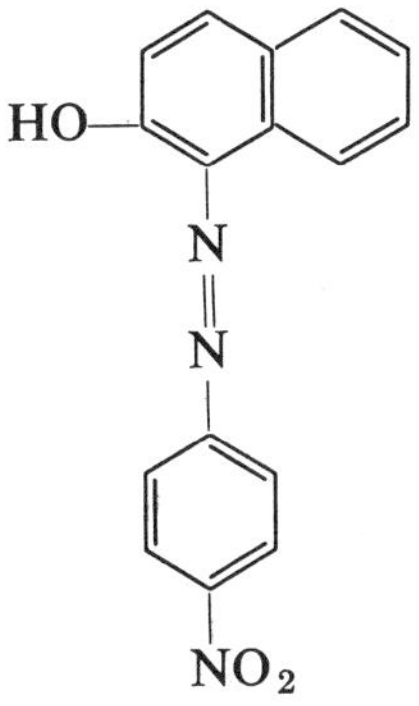

(c)

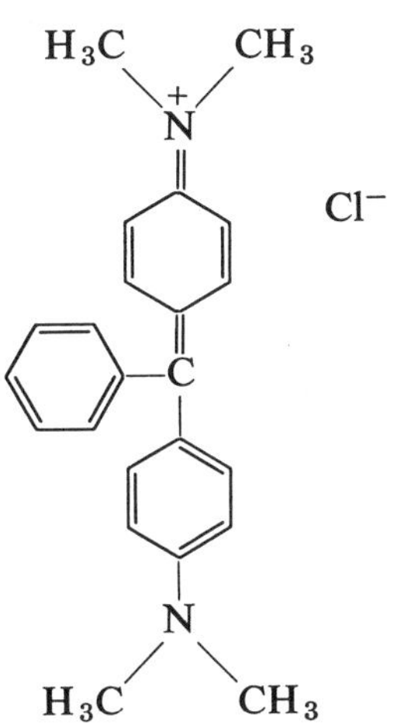

[8]   Explain the following phenomena:

(a)   phenolphthalein is colorless in acid solutions, red in weakly alkaline solutions, and again colorless in strongly alkaline solutions.

(b)   an aqueous solution of p-nitrodimethylaniline is yellow but becomes colorless when the solution is made acidic.

chapter 17

Heterocyclic Compounds — Natural Products

INTRODUCTION

> The cyclic compounds studied up to this point were largely ring systems in which only carbon atoms were joined together. Such ring systems are spoken of as **carbocyclic.** Cyclic compounds which contain, in addition to carbon, one or more other atoms in the ring are called **heterocyclic** (Gr., *heteros*, other). The hetero atoms which occur most frequently in heterocyclic rings are nitrogen, sulfur, and oxygen. A number of cyclic structures containing nitrogen and oxygen as ring atoms have been discussed or at least mentioned in earlier sections — e.g., ethylene oxide, cyclic acid anhydrides, lactones, imides, and the hemiacetal carbohydrate structures. Strictly speaking, the preceding examples are heterocycles, but each is converted rather easily into a noncyclic form. The heterocycles which we refer to in this section are much more stable. The five- and six-membered heterocycles are nearly free of strain and possess a stability which is characteristic of the benzene nucleus. In fact, some heterocyclic compounds are even more stable than benzene. Heterocyclic compounds are very abundant in nature, and a study of plant and animal products would be difficult without at least a brief survey of the common heterocyclic ring systems.

17.2   HETEROCYCLIC RING SYSTEMS

Natural products that contain one or more heterocyclic rings in their molecular structures are so numerous and their properties, in many cases, are so complex that we can consider only a very few of them in the present chapter. The names and structures of the five- and six-membered heterocyclic ring systems most frequently encountered in natural products are given in Table 17.1. You will note that numbering the ring members begins with the hetero atom.

COMMON HETEROCYCLIC RING SYSTEMS

Structure	Name	Occurs in These Examples
(A) *Five-membered Rings*		
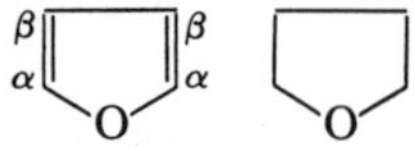 (a) (b)	(a) Furan (b) Tetrahydrofuran	Furfural Morphine
	Thiophene	
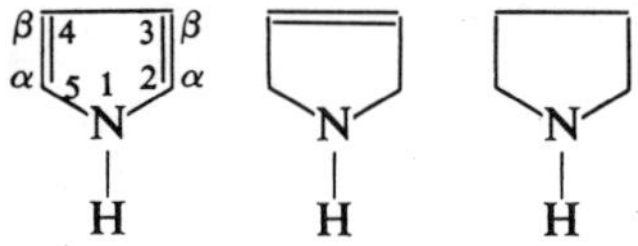 (a) (b) (c)	(a) Pyrrole (b) Pyrroline (c) Pyrrolidine	Vitamin B_{12} Chlorophyll-a, Heme Nicotine, Tryptophan, Proline
	Thiazole	Penicillins Vitamin B_1
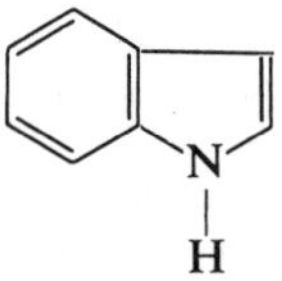	Indole	Tryptophan, Strychnine, Reserpine
(B) *Six-membered Rings*		
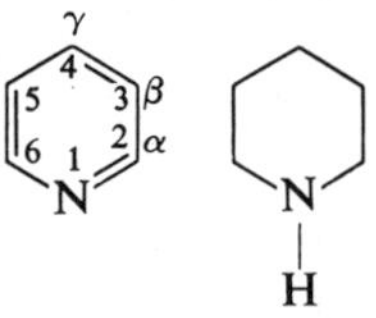 (a) (b)	(a) Pyridine (b) Piperidine	NAD, Nicotine, Vitamin B_{12}, Quinine, Morphine, Cocaine, Coniine, Reserpine
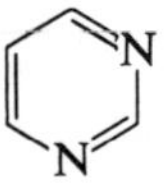	Pyrimidine	Vitamin B_1 Barbiturates
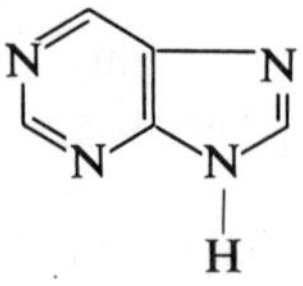	Purine	CoA enzyme NAD enzyme
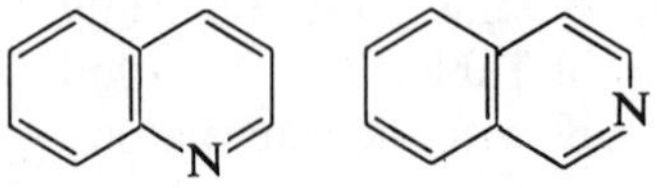 (a) (b)	(a) Quinoline (b) Isoquinoline	Curare

Other ring members (in rings with but one hetero atom) often are designated in nonsystematic nomenclature as α, β and γ. The α atom is the ring member adjacent to the hetero atom. For example, β-picoline (Sec. 17.13-b) is 3-methylpyridine. There are three isomeric picolines. The other two, of course, are α- and γ-picoline.

17.3   FIVE-MEMBERED HETEROCYCLES

The simplest five-membered heterocycles are those with only one hetero atom. We shall consider only three: furan, pyrrole, and thiophene.

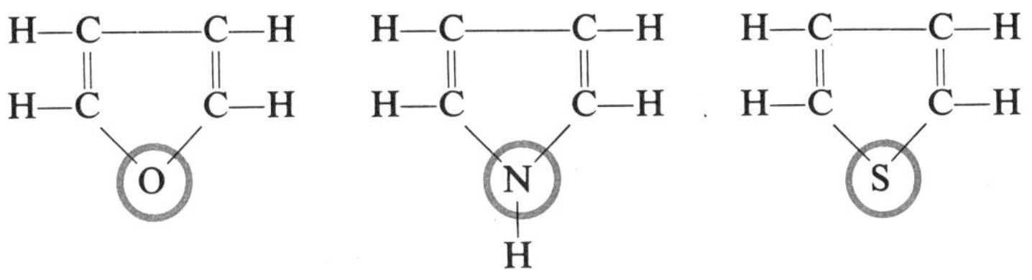

Furan   Pyrrole   Thiophene

Furan, C_4H_4O, appears as part of the skeletal structure of a number of natural products but is most readily available as the α-aldehyde, *furfural*. Furfural is obtained from corn cobs, oat hulls, bran, and straw. These agricultural wastes are a rich source of polymeric pentoses known as *pentosans*. Hydrolysis of the latter to pentoses, followed by treatment with hot, dilute sulfuric acid yields furfural.

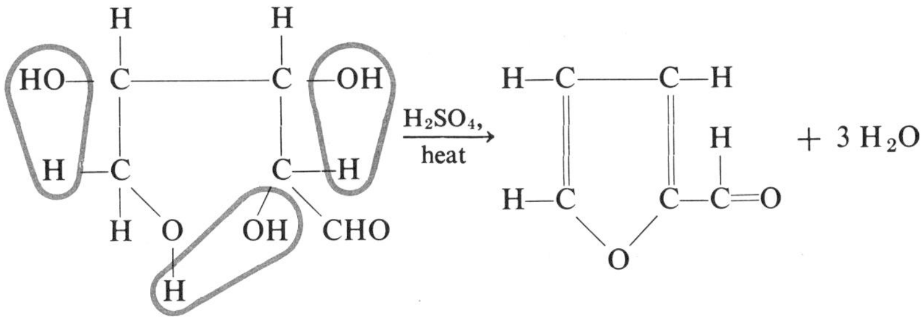

A pentose   Furfural
                         (B.P. 162°C)

The ready availability of large quantities of furfural from low-cost raw materials has led to a number of industrial applications. Foremost among these is the manufacture of nylon. The reactions by which furfural is converted into this valuable synthetic polyamide are shown below.

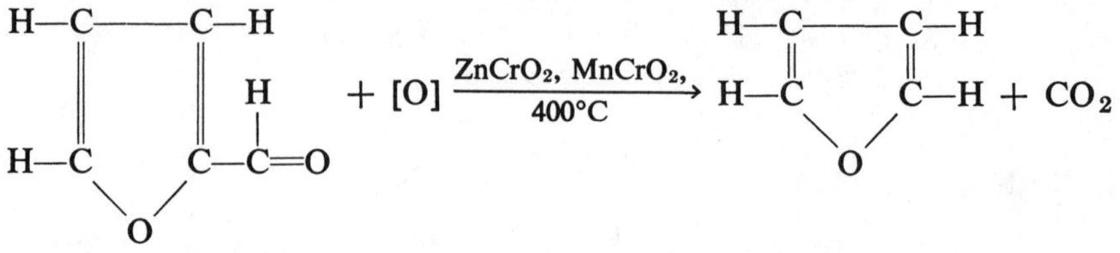

$$
\text{Furfural} + [O] \xrightarrow[400°C]{\text{ZnCrO}_2,\ \text{MnCrO}_2,} \text{Furan} + CO_2
$$

Furfural   Furan

$$
\text{Furan} + 2\,H_2 \xrightarrow{\text{Ni}} \text{Tetrahydrofuran}
$$

Tetrahydrofuran

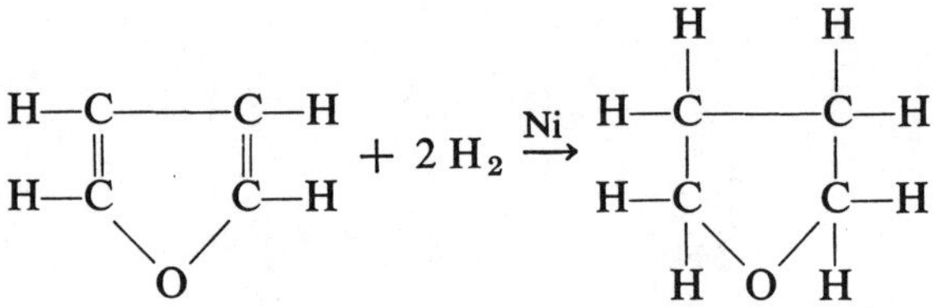

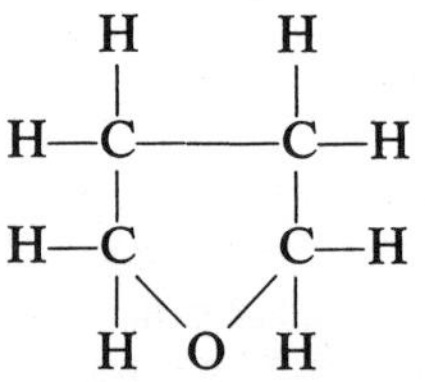

$$
\text{Tetrahydrofuran} + 2\,HCl \rightarrow Cl-CH_2CH_2CH_2CH_2-Cl + H_2O
$$

1, 4-Dichlorobutane

$$
Cl-CH_2CH_2CH_2CH_2-Cl + 2\,NaCN \rightarrow
$$
$$
NC-CH_2CH_2CH_2CH_2-CN + 2\,NaCl
$$

Adiponitrile

$$
NC-CH_2CH_2CH_2CH_2-CN + 4\,H_2O + 2\,H^+ \rightarrow
$$
$$
HO-\underset{\text{O}}{C}(CH_2)_4\underset{\text{O}}{C}-OH + 2\,NH_4^+
$$

Adipic acid
(A)

$$
NC-CH_2CH_2CH_2CH_2-CN + 4\,H_2 \xrightarrow{\text{Catalyst}} H_2N-(CH_2)_6-NH_2
$$

Hexamethylenediamine
(B)

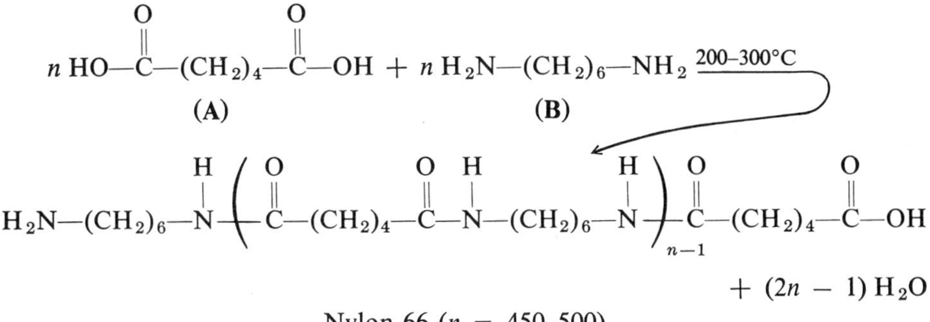

$$n \; HO—\overset{\overset{\displaystyle O}{\|}}{C}—(CH_2)_4—\overset{\overset{\displaystyle O}{\|}}{C}—OH \; + \; n \; H_2N—(CH_2)_6—NH_2 \xrightarrow{200–300°C}$$

(A)   (B)

$$H_2N—(CH_2)_6—\overset{\overset{\displaystyle H}{|}}{N}\left(\overset{\overset{\displaystyle O}{\|}}{C}—(CH_2)_4—\overset{\overset{\displaystyle O}{\|}}{C}—\overset{\overset{\displaystyle H}{|}}{N}—(CH_2)_6—\overset{\overset{\displaystyle H}{|}}{N}\right)_{n-1}\overset{\overset{\displaystyle O}{\|}}{C}—(CH_2)_4—\overset{\overset{\displaystyle O}{\|}}{C}—OH$$

$$+ \; (2n - 1) \, H_2O$$

Nylon 66 (n = 450–500)

Pyrrole, (Gr., *pyrros*, fiery + L. *oleum*, oil), C_4H_5N, is found in coal tar and in bone oil. The latter is obtained by the dry distillation, or pyrolysis, of animal by-products such as horns, hooves, and bones.

The pyrrole structure, as well as its partial and completely reduced forms, *pyrroline*, C_4H_7N, and *pyrrolidine*, C_4H_9N, are part of many natural products.

A union of four pyrrole rings makes up the **porphyrin structure** which appears in both the heme of blood and in chlorophyll-a. You will note that both of these natural products are chelates (Sec. 13.6).

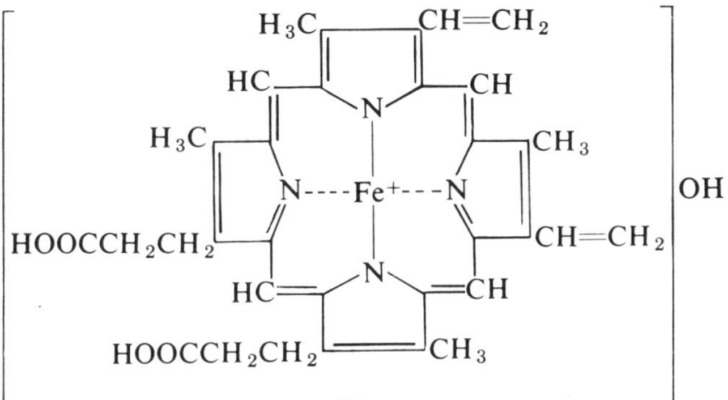

Heme

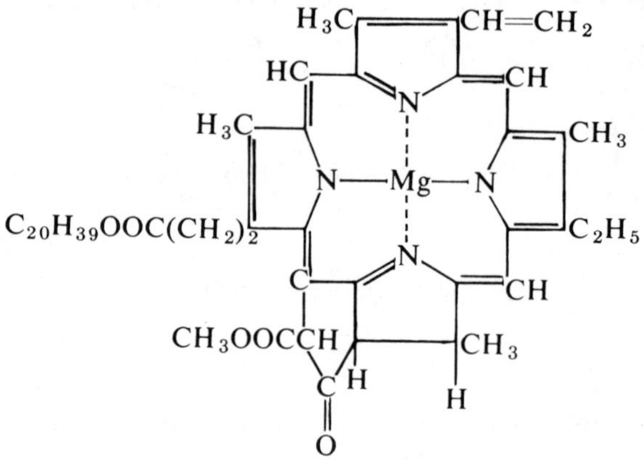

Chlorophyll-a

Indole, C_8H_7N, also a coal tar constituent, is found as part of the total structure of a number of alkaloids (Sec. 17.7, 17.8, 17.9). Indole, or 2-benzopyrrole,[1] and its 3-methyl derivative, skatole, are degradation products of the α-amino acid tryptophan. These two compounds are largely responsible for the odor of feces.

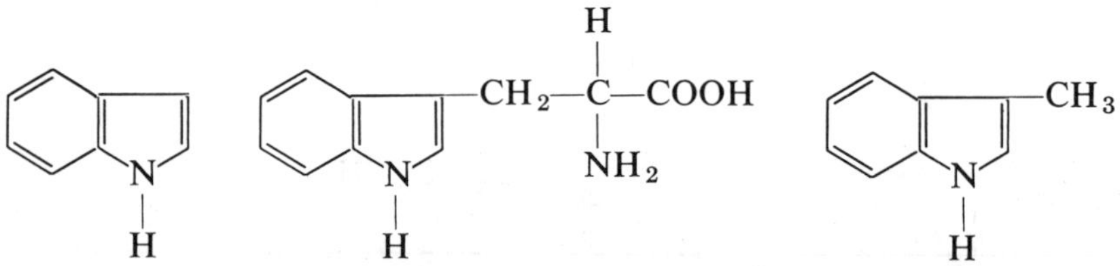

| Indole (2-Benzopyrrole) | Tryptophan [α-Amino-β-(3-indolyl) propionic acid] | Skatole (3-Methylindole) |

[1] A cyclic structure which has part of its ring in common with a benzene ring sometimes is called a *benzo* compound.

Thiophene, C_4H_4S, like many of the nitrogen-containing heterocycles, also is found in coal tar. Because its boiling point (87°C) is so near that of benzene (80°C), thiophene invariably appears as an impurity in any benzene obtained from coal tar.

17.4   PROPERTIES OF THE FIVE-MEMBERED HETEROCYCLES

The chemical properties of furan, pyrrole, and thiophene are very much like those of benzene. All three five-membered heterocyclic ring systems have an electron cloud — i.e., the aromatic sextet (Sec. 4.3), above and below the plane of the ring and engage in reactions characteristic of the benzene nucleus. Furan, pyrrole, and thiophene undergo nitration, sulfonation, halogenation, and the Friedel-Crafts reaction. Substitution on the ring in each case takes place preferentially at the 2, 5-positions.

17.5   SIX-MEMBERED HETEROCYCLES

The most widely occurring six-membered heterocycle is *pyridine*, C_5H_5N. Pyridine occurs along with pyrrole in bone oil but commercially is obtained from coal tar. Pyridine is a malodorous liquid, soluble in water and in most organic solvents. Chemically, it is less reactive than benzene and undergoes substitution with difficulty. The pyridine ring, its reduced form, *piperidine*, $C_5H_{11}N$, or one of the derivatives of pyridine can be found in a great many plant products. A number of these are described in the section devoted to the alkaloids (Sec. 17.6). Pyridine, along with the purine and pyrimidine structures, also is found in nucleic acids — the prosthetic groups of nucleoproteins. The nucleoproteins are of particular interest to the biochemist because they are intimately related to the life processes in both plants and animals. For example, an important enzyme necessary for a large number of metabolic reactions to occur, is *nicotinamide-adenine-dinucleotide*[2] (NAD), or sometimes referred to as diphosphopyridine nucleotide (DPN).

---

[2]A nucleotide is a phosphoric acid ester. The alcohol portion of the ester is a carbohydrate (usually D-ribose or a related sugar) that occurs as an N-glycoside with a natural base.

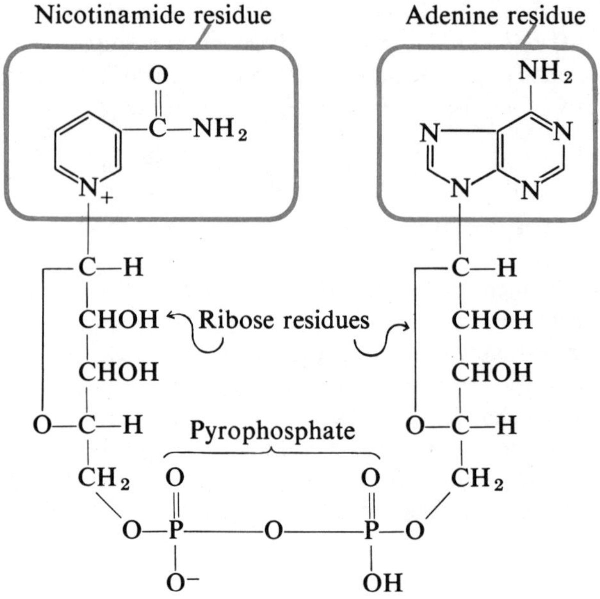

Nicotinamide residue   Adenine residue

NAD

The nicotinamide residue (upper left-hand part of structure) is the amide of nicotinic acid. Nicotinic acid, commonly called *niacin*, is the anti-pellagra vitamin (Sec. 17.13). The fused ring heterocycle adenine (upper right-hand part of structure) may be recognized as the purine part of the coenzyme A molecule (Sec. 11.9).

The Alkaloids

17.6   INTRODUCTION

The alkaloids are naturally occurring nitrogenous substances of plant origin that possess marked physiological properties. The term alkaloid means "alkalilike" and originates in the fact that nearly all alkaloids are nitrogen heterocycles with basic properties. Alkaloid chemistry represents an extremely complex study and one to which volumes have been devoted. In this book we can examine only a few members of each general class.

17.7   ALKALOIDS WITH ISOLATED FIVE- AND SIX-MEMBERED HETEROCYCLIC SYSTEMS

Coniine, 2-*n*-propylpiperidine, has a relatively simple structure when compared to those of other alkaloids.

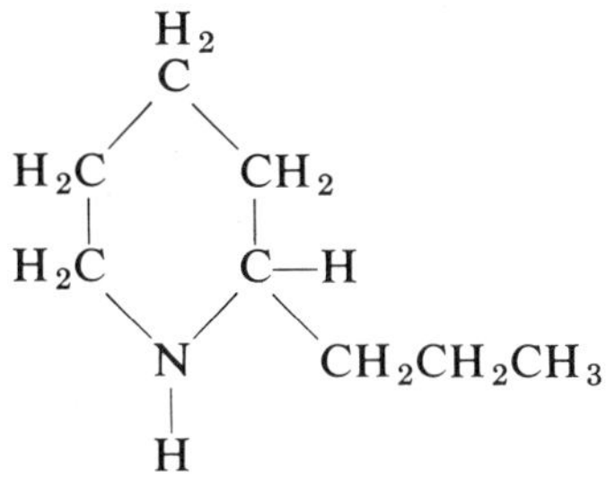

Coniine

Coniine is the toxic substance in *Conium maculatum* and certain other closely related herbs. Its common name is "hemlock," but, of course, this is not the hemlock tree of our forests. Students of history will remember reading of hemlock as the death potion Socrates was forced to drink.

Meperidine, a synthetic phenylpiperidine sometimes called "Demerol," has a physiological action similar to, but less marked than, that of morphine (Sec. 17.9). The analgesic property of meperidine was accidentally discovered when an injection into a rat caused the animal to manifest the same symptoms as those produced by morphine.

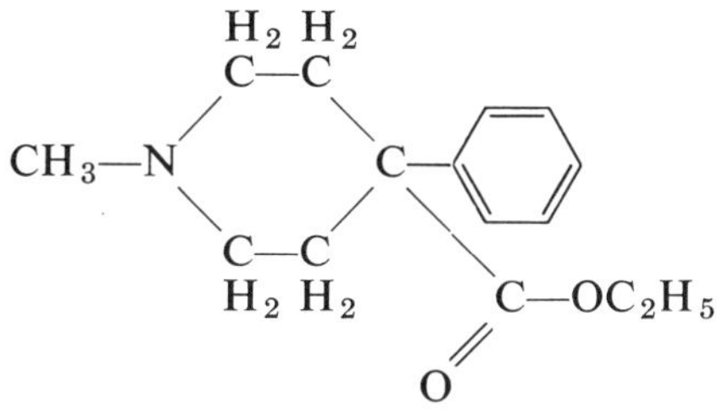

Meperidine

Nicotine, one of the principal alkaloids found in the tobacco plant, is a β-pyridine derivative in which N-methylpyrrolidine is joined at its 2-position to the pyridine ring.

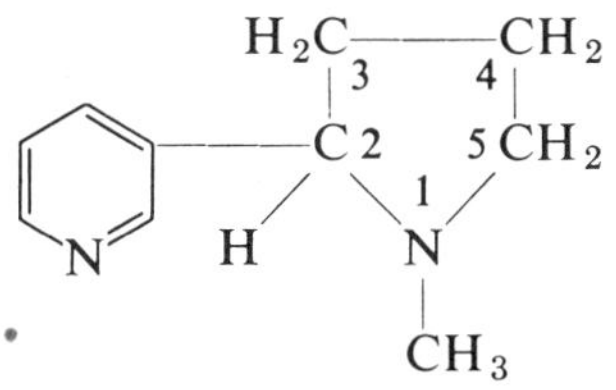

Nicotine

Nicotine is extremely toxic to animals when ingested. It kills a number of insects on contact and is used in sprays against a number of leaf-sucking pests.

17.8   ALKALOIDS CONTAINING BRIDGED HETEROCYCLIC SYSTEMS

Cocaine, and *atropine* belong to a class of alkaloids known as the **tropane alkaloids.** Cocaine is obtained from coca leaves and is a powerful anesthetic but has the disadvantages of being very toxic and habit forming. A synthetic substitute, *procaine,* (sometimes called novocaine) incorporates the beneficial properties of cocaine without the undesirable side effects. The part of the cocaine structure enclosed in the formula (solid line) appeared to be responsible for its anesthetic property and served as a pattern in early attempts to synthesize local anesthetics.

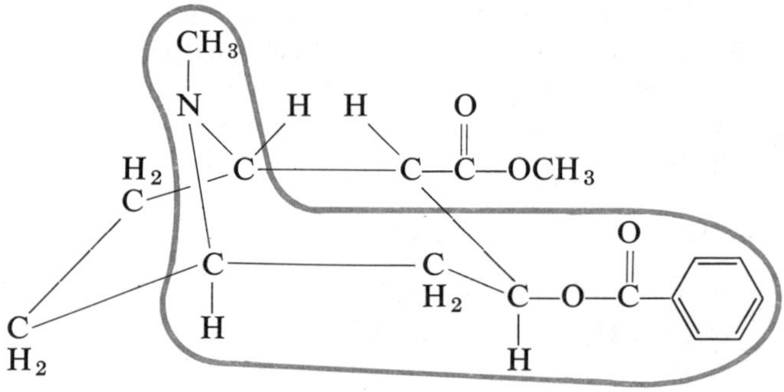

Cocaine

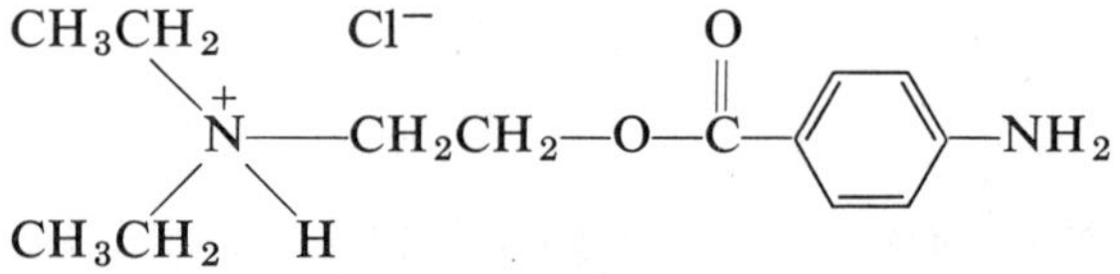

β-Diethylaminoethyl-*p*-aminobenzoate hydrochloride
(Procaine)

However, in the evolution of hundreds of compounds sought for their anesthetic properties, it was discovered that a benzoic acid ester is not necessarily a requisite for anesthetic action. *Xylocaine,* and more recently *mepivacaine,* are amides that retain certain structural similarities to cocaine.

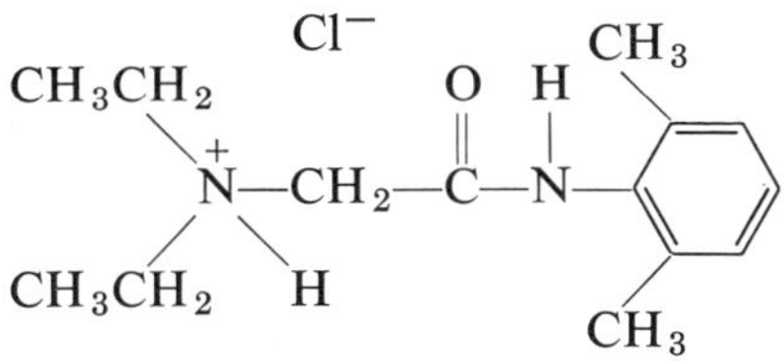

$$CH_3CH_2$$
$$CH_3CH_2$$
$$\overset{+}{N}-CH_2-\overset{\overset{O}{\|}}{C}-\overset{\overset{H}{|}}{N}-$$

Cl⁻ ... O H CH₃ ... CH₃

2, 6-Dimethyl-α-diethylaminoacetanilide hydrochloride
(Xylocaine)

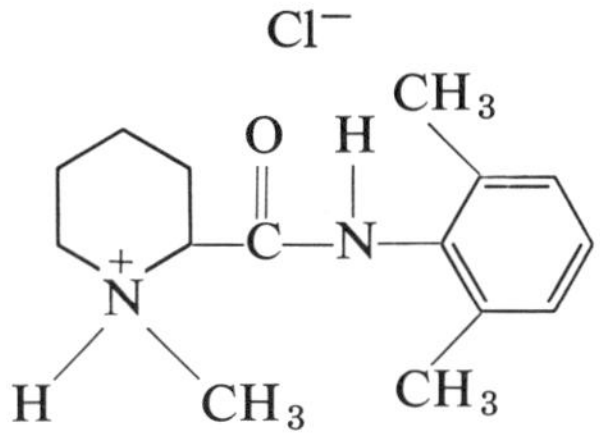

Cl⁻

O H CH₃

C—N—

N CH₃ CH₃

H

d, l-1-Methyl-2', 6'-pipecoloxylidide hydrochloride
(Mepivacaine)

Atropine occurs in the dried roots, leaves, and tops of the belladonna plant, *Atropa belladonna*. It is used in the form of its sulfate salt as a mydriatic for the dilation of the pupil of the eye. The action of the drug was known to early Europeans, and the belladonna plant, supposedly, was named "beautiful lady" in reference to the cosmetic effects of enlarged pupils. Structurally, atropine is very similar to cocaine.

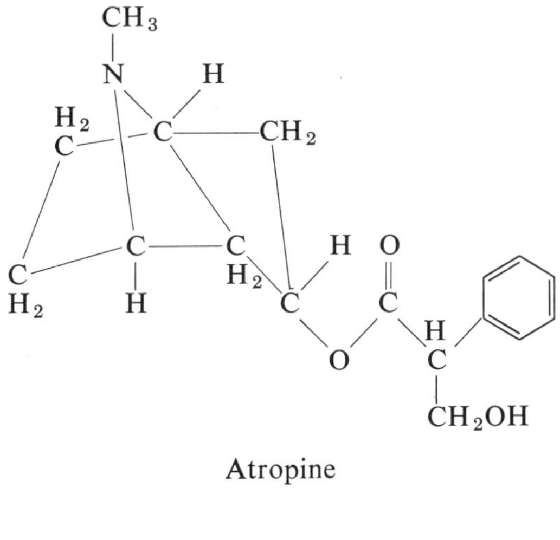

$$CH_3$$

N H

$$H_2\atop C$$ C CH₂

C C H O
$$H_2\atop C$$ H C C

C H O
H C
CH₂OH

Atropine

17.9 ALKALOIDS WITH FUSED HETEROCYCLIC SYSTEMS

Morphine, one of the most useful of drugs, occurs along with twenty-four other alkaloids in the dried latex of the opium poppy, *Papaver somniferum*. Morphine is a powerful analgesic, but its use, like that of other narcotics, leads to addiction.

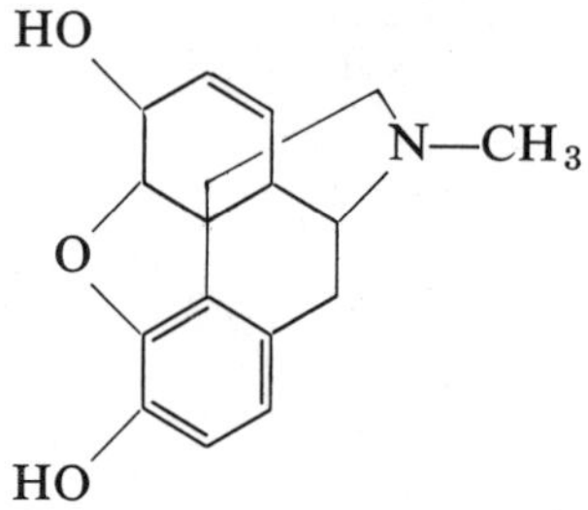

Morphine

Codeine is an ether derivative of morphine in which the phenolic hydroxyl has been replaced by a methoxyl group. Codeine is widely used as a cough depressant.

Heroin is not a component of opium but is the diacetyl derivative of morphine produced by acetylating both phenolic and alcoholic hydroxyl groups. Its manufacture in the United States is forbidden.

Ergot alkaloids are alkaloids produced by the fungus *ergot*, a parasitic growth on rye and other cereals. They are amides of lysergic acid, a structure which includes the indole nucleus. Perhaps the most notorious of the ergot alkaloids is the synthetic diethyl amide of lysergic acid known as LSD. The oral administration of as little as 50 μ g (0.000,050 g) of this amide produces psychotic symptoms in man resembling schizophrenia. It is believed by psychopharmacologists that the drug is antagonistic to serotonin, a substance naturally present in brain tissue.

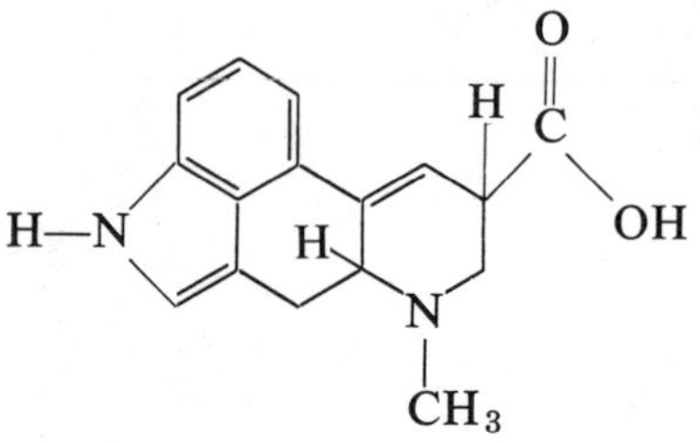

Lysergic acid

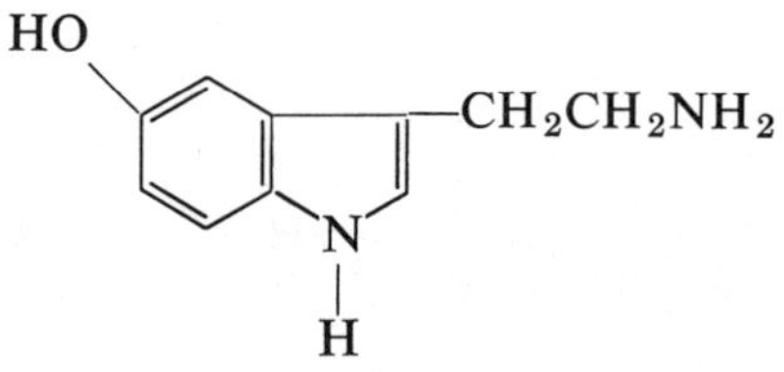

Serotonin

Reserpine is a complex polycyclic system which, like the ergot alkaloids, also includes the indole nucleus. Reserpine is one of the alkaloids obtained from the extracts of a species of Indian snake root called *Rauwolfia serpentina.* Such extracts have been used for centuries by the natives of southern Asia to treat a variety of disorders including snake bite, dysentery, insanity, and epilepsy. Reserpine has remarkable tranquilizing powers and is called a behavioral drug. Its synthesis was accomplished by Woodward[3] in 1956.

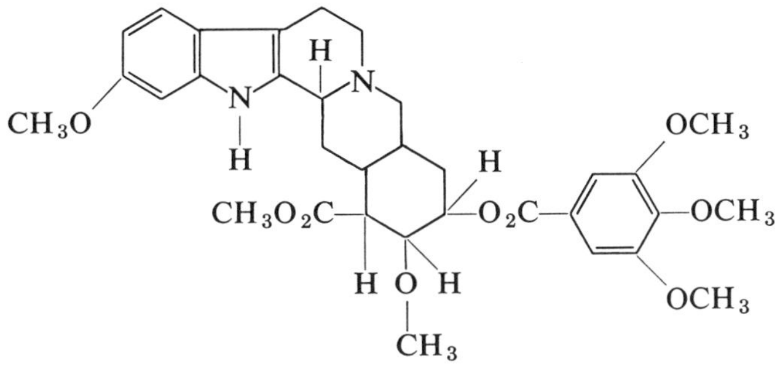

Reserpine

Tubocurarine is an alkaloid which contains two isoquinoline residues. It is the active principle of curare, a paralyzing arrow and dart poison used by South American aborigines. Tubocurarine and other curariform drugs act as skeletal muscle relaxants and have been used as valuable aids during surgery. A lethal dose of the drug results in respiratory failure. The tubocurarine structure includes two quaternary ammonium ions and in this respect bears a functional similarity to choline (Sec. 13.8).

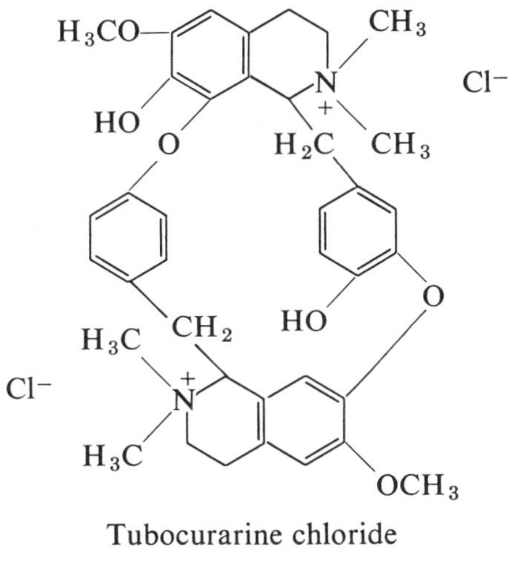

Tubocurarine chloride

[3]Robert B. Woodward (1917–   ), Professor of Chemistry, Harvard University. Winner of the Nobel Prize in Chemistry (1965).

Vitamins

17.10 INTRODUCTION

The major nutrients (fats, carbohydrates, proteins) comprise the bulk of the animal diet, but certain other nutrients in minute amounts also are necessary constituents of the diet. The lack of these trace nutrients in the animal diet results in deficiency diseases manifested by improper growth, metabolism, and behavior. These essential dietetic constituents are called **vitamins.** The vitamins may be defined simply as abundant, potent, naturally-produced substances that the animal organism requires, but usually is incapable of synthesizing. The need for a certain vitamin varies with the species, and a vitamin required by one animal may not always be required by another. Vitamin research is one of several areas in which organic chemistry and nutrition are interrelated. It is a vast and complex field of study and our discussion will be limited to only a brief review of the principal vitamins.

17.11 HISTORICAL

One of the major hardships encountered by the early explorers — Columbus, Vasco da Gama, Jacques Cartier, Henry Hudson and others — on their expeditions into the new world was the disease *scurvy*. Scurvy, caused by a lack of vitamin C, was especially common among sailors on long voyages without fresh food. It was recognized as early as 1750 to be a deficiency disease, and British naval surgeons, in their attempts to treat it, observed the beneficial effects of fruit juices — especially, citrus fruits. They recommended fruit as a regular part of a sailor's ration, but the recommendation went unheeded by the British Admiralty for almost fifty years. Finally, the inclusion of limes in ships provisions eliminated scurvy as one of a British seaman's hazards. The name "limey" in reference to a British seaman is still heard today.

The first serious inquiry into the cause and effects of a vitamin deficiency began with the observations of Dr. Eijkman, a Dutch physician working in Java. In 1897, he observed that a diet of polished rice caused beriberi among the natives. This disease is characterized by a polyneuritis, muscular atrophy, and a general debilitation. The protective principle against this disease, now known as thiamine, appeared to have been removed in the rice polishings. The symptoms of beriberi disappeared when the rice polishings were restored to the diet. Funk, in 1911, succeeded in isolating from rice polishings the vital substance. On analysis, it was found to contain nitrogen, and Funk concluded that the chemical structures of these essential agents were those of amino compounds. He therefore named them **vitamines** (vital amines). The name since has been shortened by dropping the final "e." As used today the term designates a number of substances some of which lack nitrogen entirely.

17.12   THE FAT-SOLUBLE VITAMINS

The fat-soluble vitamins are those soluble in fats and in fat solvents. Included in this classification are vitamins A, D, E, and K. The role of vitamins as food accessories usually is considered in relation to nutritional deficiencies. It should be pointed out that doses of the fat-soluble vitamins, when given far in excess of normal requirements, also can have toxic effects. Vitamin poisoning occurred in a number of arctic explorers who became seriously ill after eating polar bear liver. There also have been numerous cases of vitamin poisoning in infants. Young mothers, eager to fulfill all vitamin requirements of their first offspring, sometimes give overdoses of fat-soluble vitamins. Poisoning by water-soluble vitamins is not possible because any amounts not required are voided from the body in urine.

Each of the fat-soluble vitamins is discussed briefly in the following sections.

(a) **Vitamin A** may be obtained from the coloring matter of many green and yellow vegetables. Vitamin A, as such, is not found in plants, only β-carotene, its precursor or *provitamin*. The β-carotene molecule (Sec. 3.12), when cleaved in the center of the linear chain and converted at each end to a carbinol, yields two molecules of vitamin A. Other sources of vitamin A[4] are fish-liver oil, the livers of other animals, eggs, butter, and cheese.

A deficiency of vitamin A causes night blindness — an inability to see in dim light or to adjust to decreased intensity of light. Another disease of the eye known as *xerophthalmia*, in which the tear glands cease to function, results from a lack of vitamin A.

---

[4]There are two vitamins A. One is known as vitamin A_1 or retinol, and the other as vitamin A_2, or 3-dehydroretinol. Vitamin A_2 is found in the liver oils of fresh water fish and differs structurally from vitamin A_1, found in the livers of cod and other salt-water fish, by having a second double bond between carbons 3 and 4. Physiologically, the two vitamins have the same activity and both are called vitamin A.

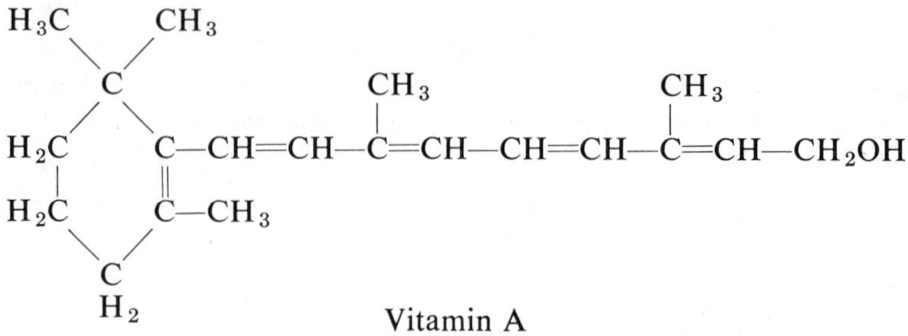

Vitamin A

(b) **Vitamin D** is sometimes referred to as the "antirachitic" vitamin. It is related to the proper deposition of calcium phosphate and controls the normal development of the teeth and bones. There are ten or more compounds which have antirachitic properties and are designated D_1, D_2, D_3, etc. Vitamin D from fish oils is D_3, while that produced by irradiation of the skin with ultraviolet or sunlight is D_2. Vitamin D_2 is known as *calciferol* and is derived from ergos-terol, a plant sterol (Sec. 17.22). Milk, by irradiation, is fortified with vitamin D. Vitamin D is produced in or on the skin by irradia-tion of the sterols present there. Sunlight supplies *not* the vitamin, only the necessary radiation. Vitamin D_2 has the following structure.

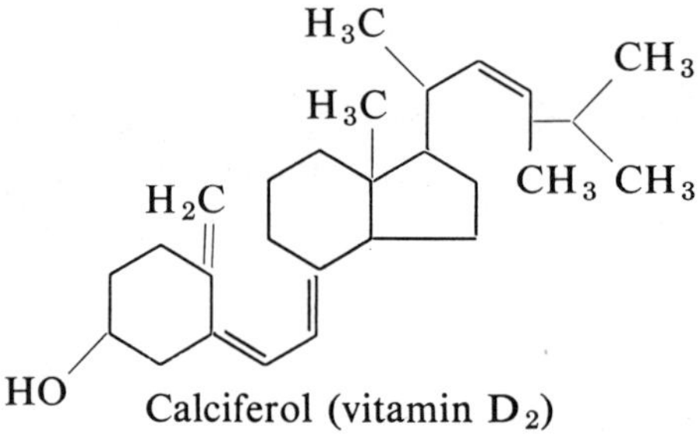

Calciferol (vitamin D_2)

(c) **Vitamin E,** sometimes called the fertility factor, is related to the proper functioning of the reproductive system. Vitamin E is found in the nonsaponifiable fraction of vegetable oils such as corn-germ oil, cottonseed oil, wheat-germ oil, and peanut oil. It also occurs in green leafy vegetables. As in the case of the A and D vita-mins, there also is more than one form of vitamin E. Four different structures called *tocopherols* have vitamin E activity. These are designated α-, β-, γ-, and δ-tocopherols. The structure of α-tocoph-erol, the most potent, is shown.

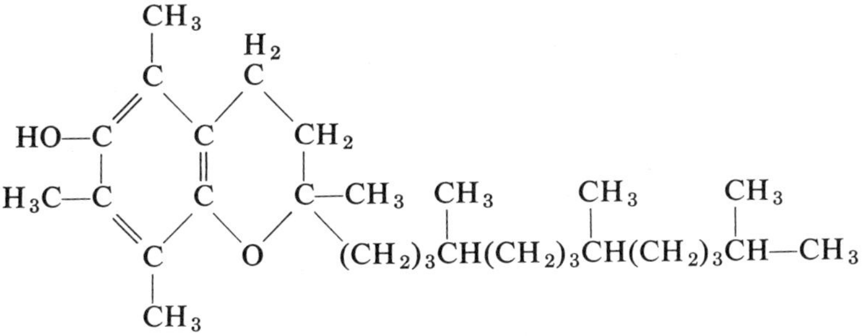

α-Tocopherol

Vitamin E, as was pointed out earlier (Sec. 11.6), also is used as an antioxidant for the prevention of oxidative rancidity in vegetable oils.

(d) **Vitamin K** is the antihemorrhagic factor related to the bloodclotting mechanism. This vitamin is important especially from a surgical standpoint. There are two K vitamins. Vitamin K_1 is obtained from the alfalfa leaf; vitamin K_2 is produced by bacterial action in the intestinal canal. The structure of vitamin K_1 is shown.

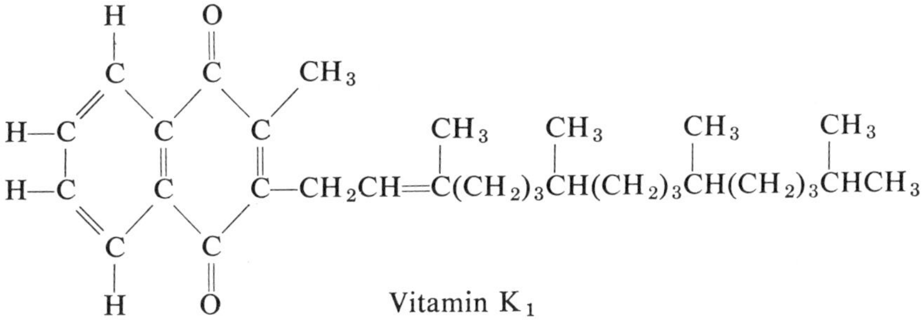

Vitamin K_1

17.13   THE WATER-SOLUBLE VITAMINS

The water-soluble vitamins include vitamin C and all other vitamins designated B. The latter are collectively referred to as the vitamin B complex. The water-soluble vitamins bear less resemblance to each other than do the fat-soluble vitamins. Whereas the fat-soluble vitamins are isoprenoid structures (Sec. 17.14) and largely of hydrocarbon composition, the water-soluble vitamins all possess polar groupings to render them water-soluble.

(a) **Vitamin C,** now called **ascorbic acid,** is the vitamin which prevents scurvy. A person with scurvy suffers pains in the joints and hemorrhages from the mucous membranes of the mouth. The gums especially are affected and become red, ulcerated, and even gangrenous. Ascorbic acid is abundantly found in citrus fruits, tomatoes, green peppers, and parsley. It should be obtained from fresh sources for it loses its potency when heated or when exposed to air for any length of time. Ascorbic acid is a hexose derivative with the following structure.

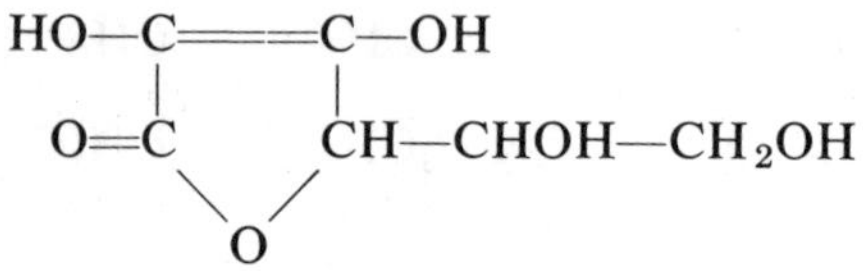

$$HO-C\!\!=\!\!=\!\!C-OH$$
$$O\!\!=\!\!C \qquad CH-CHOH-CH_2OH$$
$$\diagdown O \diagup$$

Ascorbic acid

(b) **The B Vitamin Complex.** Vitamins designated as B vitamins were at one time all thought to be the same. The isolation of each new factor from vitamin B preparations has led to a designation of B_1, B_2, B_3, etc., for each new factor. The B vitamins appear to play an important role in energy metabolism. A brief discussion of the principal B vitamins is given in the following sections.

Vitamin B_1 (thiamine), a deficiency of which causes beriberi in man, is present in whole cereal grains, legumes, lean meat, nuts, and yeast. The vitamin has been found to contain both the pyrimidine and thiazole heterocyclic systems. The structure of thiamine has been determined and the vitamin has been prepared. Thiamine usually is prepared in the form of an acid salt.

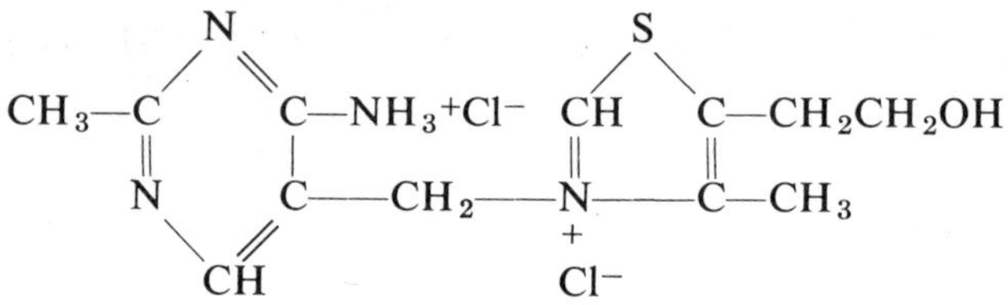

$$CH_3-C \qquad C-NH_3^+Cl^- \quad CH \qquad C-CH_2CH_2OH$$
$$N \qquad C-CH_2-N-C-CH_3$$
$$CH \qquad\qquad Cl^-$$

Thiamine hydrochloride
(Vitamin B_1)

Thiamine occurs in nature either as the pyrophosphoric acid ester or as the free vitamin.

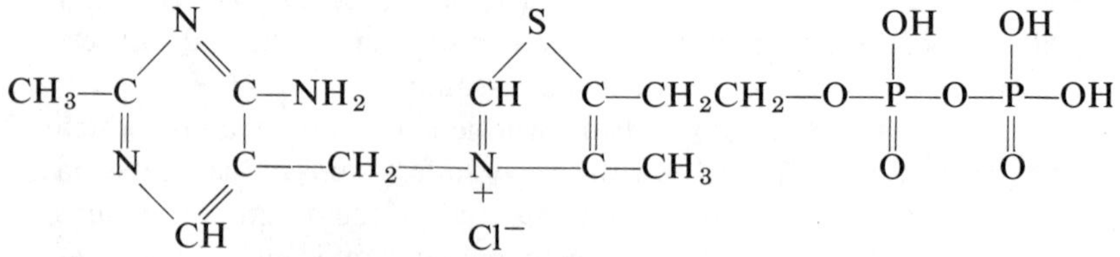

$$CH_3-C \qquad C-NH_2 \quad CH \qquad C-CH_2CH_2-O-P-O-P-OH$$
$$N \qquad C-CH_2-N-C-CH_3 \qquad O \qquad O$$
$$CH \qquad\qquad Cl^-$$

Thiamine hydrochloride pyrophosphate

Vitamin B$_2$ (riboflavin) is an orange-yellow, crystalline compound widely distributed in nature. It is found in milk, lean meats, liver, fish, eggs, and leafy vegetables. A lack of riboflavin in the diet causes an inflammation of the lips, dermatitis, and a dryness and burning of the eyes, accompanied by a sensitivity to light.

The structure of riboflavin is shown.

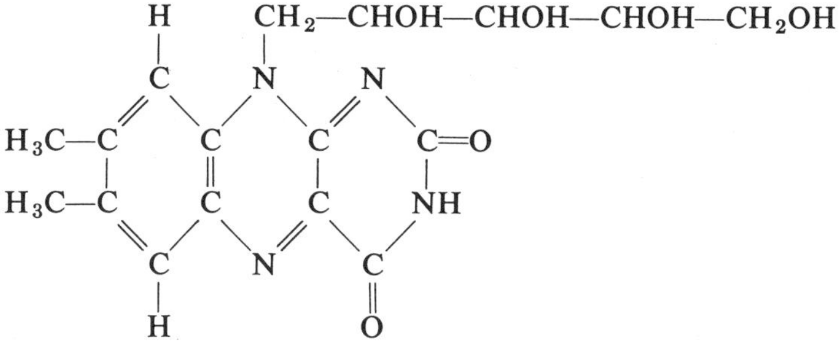

Riboflavin

Niacin (nicotinic acid), another of the B vitamins, is the anti-pellagra factor. Pellagra is a disease characterized by dermatitis, a pigmentation and thickening of the skin, and soreness and inflammation of the tongue and mouth. Niacin may be found in most of the same foods that supply riboflavin. Especially rich sources of niacin are lean meats and liver. Although present in whole cereal grains, niacin is lost in the milling process. The niacin structure is part of the enzyme NAD (Sec. 17.5). The structural formula of niacin, shown below, is relatively simple when compared to those of other vitamins. The oxidation of nicotine (Sec. 17.7) or β-picoline (3-methylpyridine) produces nicotinic acid, or niacin.

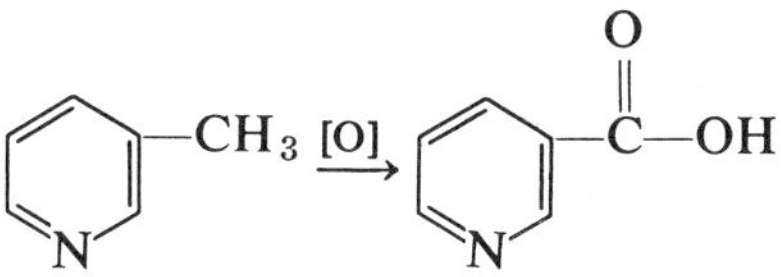

β-Picoline   Niacin

Vitamin B$_6$ (pyridoxine) is a vitamin whose function appears to be intimately related to the proper metabolism of fats and amino acids. Meat, fish, egg yolk, and whole cereal grains are rich sources of vitamin B$_6$. The exact requirements of vitamin B$_6$ for adult man has not been established, but a lack of pyridoxine in the diet of experimental animals leads to dermatitis, anemia, and epileptic seizures. The structures of pyridoxine and two of its derivatives which also show vitamin B_6 activity are given below.

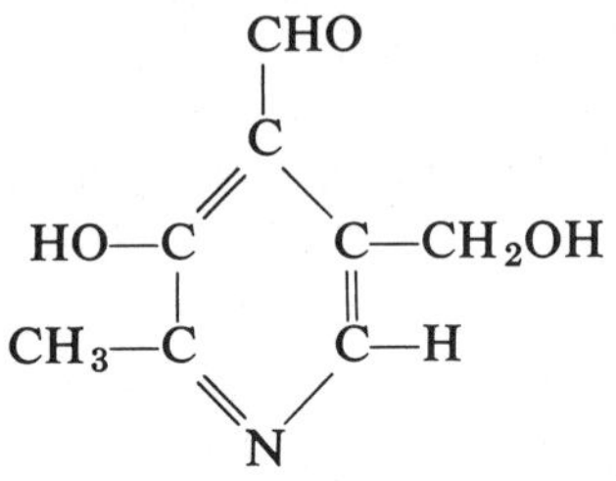

Pyridoxal

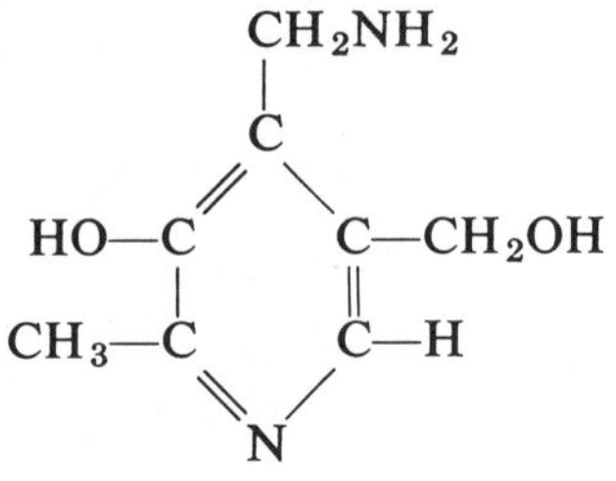

Pyridoxamine

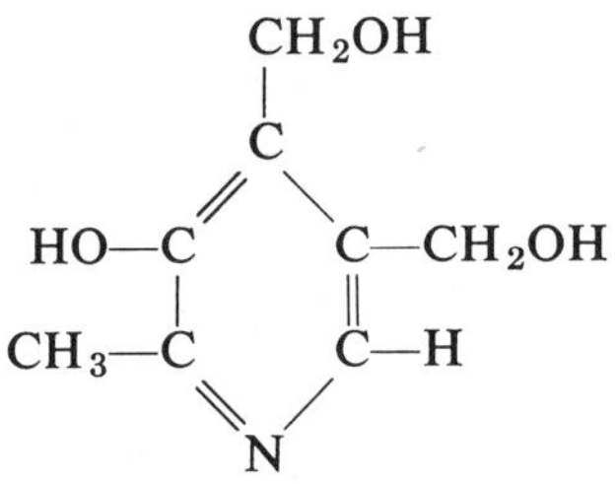

Pyridoxine

Vitamin B_{12} is the vitamin which prevents pernicious anemia. It is a dark red crystalline compound with a complex structure. Like heme and chlorophyll-a, it also contains a porphyrin nucleus, but a unique feature of its structure is the presence of trivalent cobalt. Vitamin B_{12} was the first cobalt-containing organic compound to be found. It sometimes is referred to as *cobalamin*. It is found most abundantly in liver but also occurs in meat, eggs, and sea foods. The structure of vitamin B_{12} is shown on the next page.

Terpenes

17.14   INTRODUCTION

The name **terpene** (Gr., *terebinthos*, turpentine tree) is used to describe, in a *broad* sense, a class of natural products whose carbon skeletons are multiples of the C_5 isoprene unit. The name **isoprenoid** sometimes is used to describe these compounds. Although isoprene itself does not occur naturally, it is apparent that in nature a large

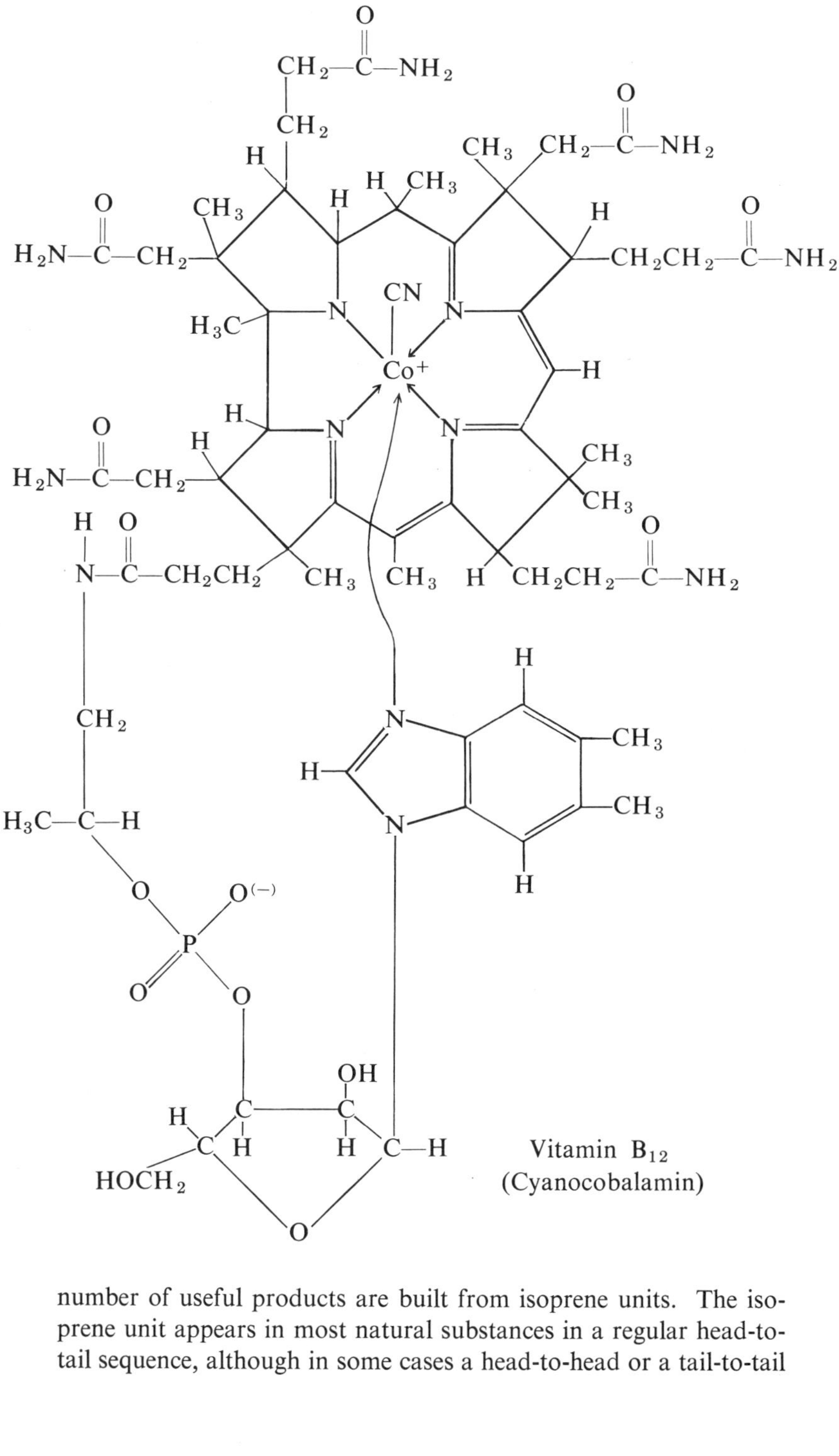

Vitamin B$_{12}$
(Cyanocobalamin)

number of useful products are built from isoprene units. The isoprene unit appears in most natural substances in a regular head-to-
tail sequence, although in some cases a head-to-head or a tail-to-tail

arrangement is found. Recognition of the head-to-tail arrangement as a recurring architectural feature in a number of natural products led to what has come to be known as the **isoprene rule.** This rule simply states that the structure of a terpene most likely to be correct is one that allows its carbon skeleton to be divisible into iso-C_5 units. The rule has been helpful in deriving the structures not only of the terpenes, but also those of a number of other natural products.

$$\text{head (h)} \rightarrow CH_2\!=\!C\!-\!CH\!=\!CH_2 \leftarrow \text{tail (t)}$$
$$\begin{array}{c} | \\ CH_3 \end{array}$$

Isoprene

Many of the terpenes are hydrocarbons while others are alcohols, ethers, aldehydes, ketones, or acids. Terpenes, for the most part, are fragrant compounds and usually can be separated from other plant materials by gentle heating or by steam distillation. A number are classified as "essential oils"[5] and are used in perfumes, in flavoring agents, and in medicinals.

17.15   MONOTERPENES (C_{10})

Terpenes, in a *strict* sense, include those unsaturated hydrocarbons or their derivatives that contain only *two* isoprene units. These two C_5 units may appear in either a cyclic or in an open chain structure. Two very common terpenes are *limonene*, found in the rinds of lemons and oranges, and *α-pinene*, the chief constituent of turpentine. Turpentine is obtained as the steam volatile component of pine tree sap. Pine stumps are another source of this important commercial product. Turpentine is widely used as a solvent and paint thinner. Turpentine, natural resins, and pitch, all essential to the maintenance of early wooden sailing ships, are still referred to as "naval stores." The structures for limonene and α-pinene, and for two other common terpenes, are shown. The junction of separate isoprene units in each is indicated by a dotted dividing line.

---

[5]Essential oils are "oils of essence" — that is, volatile and pleasantly scented.

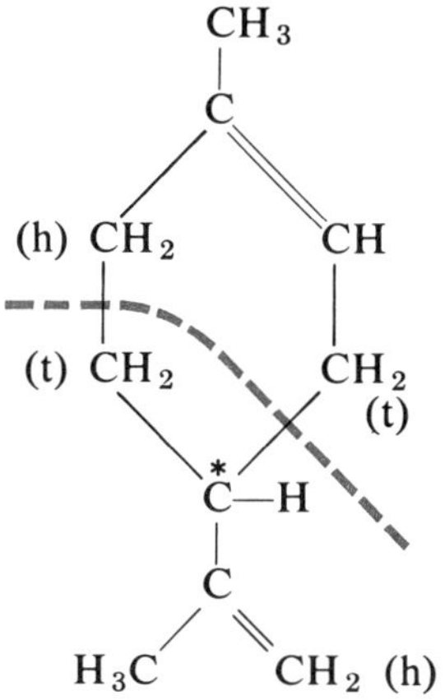

Limonene

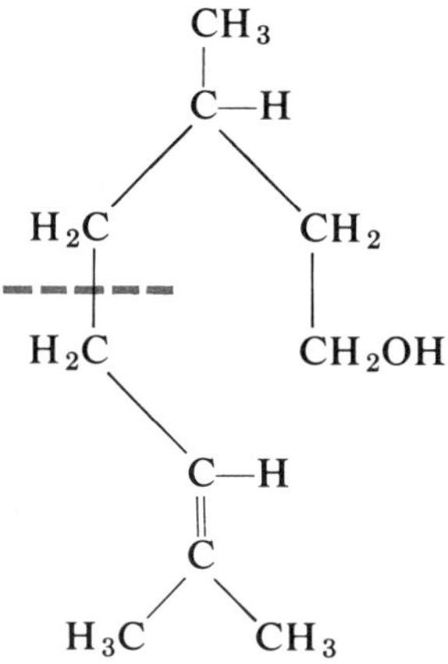

Citronellol

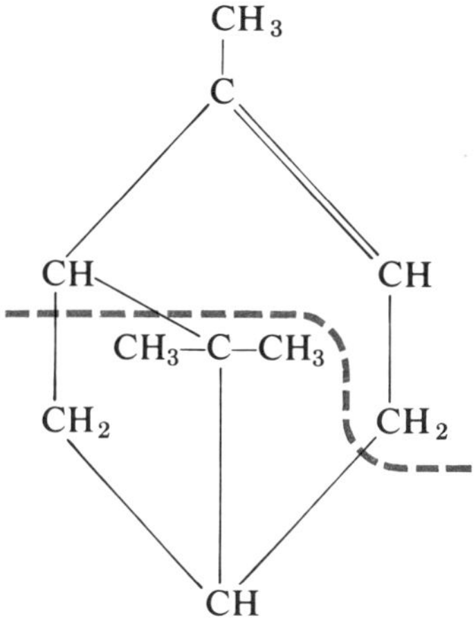

α-Pinene

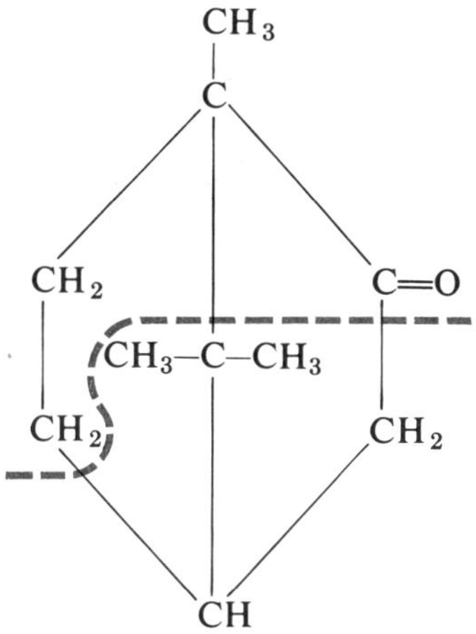

Camphor

17.16   SESQUITERPENES (C₁₅)

Sesquiterpenes (three isoprene units) appear in a number of cyclic and acyclic structures. Many are bicyclic and represent fused ring systems which can be converted into naphthalene derivatives. The structures of *selinene, cadinene,* and *farnesol* are on the following page.

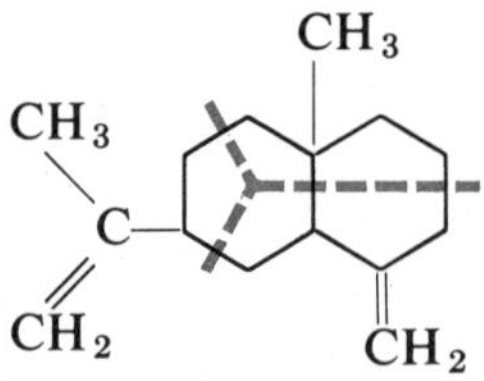

CH$_3$
CH$_3$
CH$_3$

HOCH$_2$

CH$_3$
CH$_2$ CH$_2$ CH

H$_3$C   CH$_3$

CH$_3$

H$_3$C   CH$_3$

C

H$_3$C   CH$_3$

β-Selinene
(oil of celery)

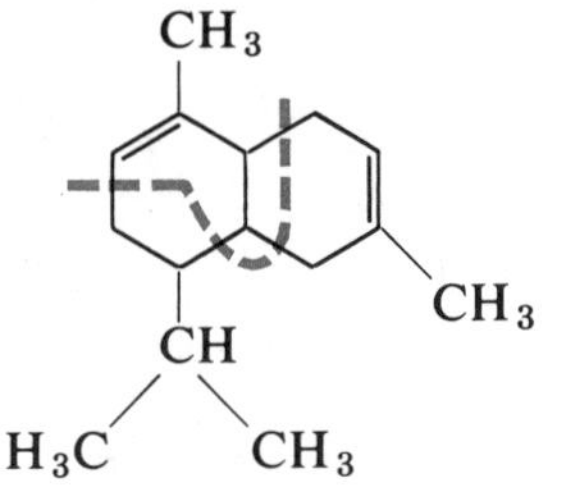

Cadinene
(oil of cade in juniper
and cedar oils)

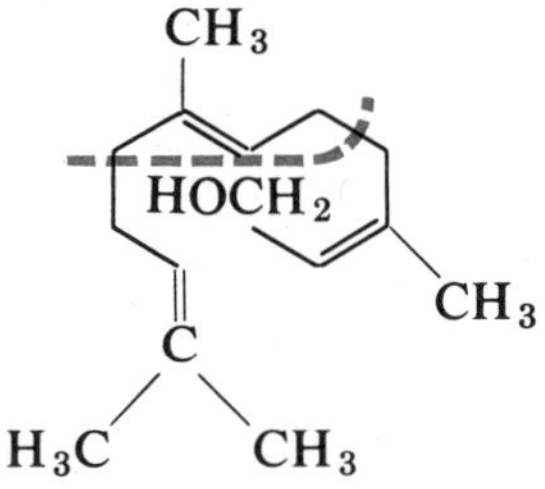

Farnesol
(lily of the valley)

17.17   DITERPENES (C$_{20}$)

Diterpenes (four isoprene units), like the sesquiterpenes, have either cyclic or acyclic structures, or a combination of both. A diterpene alcohol already discussed in some detail is vitamin A (Sec. 17.12-a). The precursor of vitamin A is the *tetraterpene, β-carotene* (Sec. 3.12). The resin acid, *abietic acid,* is a tricyclic diterpene that remains as *rosin* in the residue after turpentine is removed from pine sap. Rosin is an important commercial raw material widely used in the manufacture of varnish, sizing for paper and textiles, and in soaps. Abietic acid is one of the most abundant and cheapest of organic acids. Its structure is shown.

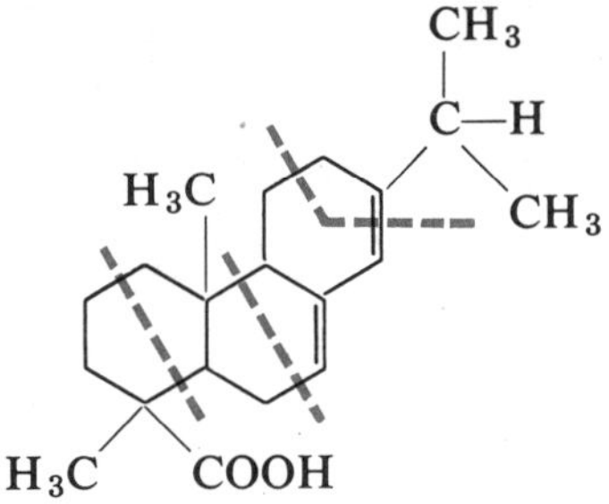

CH$_3$
C—H
H$_3$C   CH$_3$

H$_3$C   COOH

Abietic acid

17.18   TRITERPENES (C$_{30}$)

Triterpenes (six isoprene units) are very abundant natural substances. Of particular interest is *squalene,* a triterpene found in shark-liver oil. Squalene is an acyclic isoprenoid in which two regular C$_{15}$ units are joined tail-to-tail at the center of the chain.

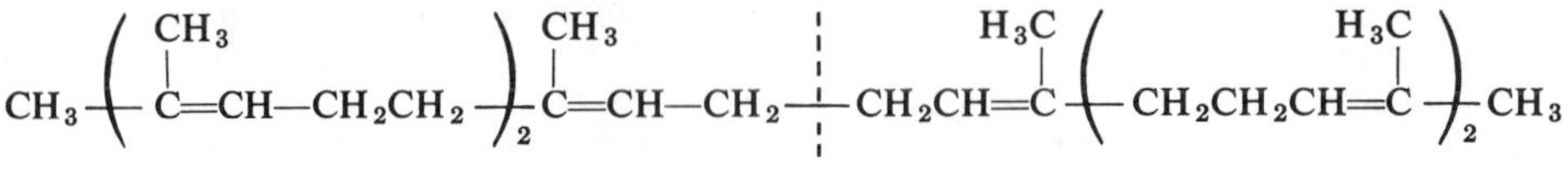

$$CH_3 \left(\begin{array}{c} CH_3 \\ | \\ C=CH-CH_2CH_2 \end{array} \right)_2 \begin{array}{c} CH_3 \\ | \\ C=CH-CH_2 \end{array} CH_2CH=C \left(\begin{array}{c} H_3C \\ | \\ CH_2CH_2CH=C \end{array} \right)_2 CH_3$$

Recent evidence has shown squalene to be a precursor in the biosynthesis of cholesterol (Sec. 17.21).

17.19   POLYTERPENES

Natural rubber, our best example of a polyterpene, is found in the latex of the rubber plant (*Hevea braziliensis*). Approximately 2,000 isoprene units are combined in a rubber molecule to produce a long linear structure. Cross-linking of adjacent chains at unsaturated sites by heating with sulfur (vulcanization) improves the properties of rubber. Natural rubber, when subjected to distillation, produces isoprene.

$$CH_2{=}\overset{\overset{\displaystyle CH_3}{|}}{C}{-}CH{=}CH_2 \; + \; CH_2{=}\overset{\overset{\displaystyle CH_3}{|}}{C}{-}CH{=}CH_2$$

Isoprene   Isoprene

$$\cdots{-}CH_2{-}\overset{\overset{\displaystyle CH_3}{|}}{C}{=}CH{-}CH_2\left(CH_2{-}\overset{\overset{\displaystyle CH_3}{|}}{C}{=}CH{-}CH_2\right)_n CH_2{-}\overset{\overset{\displaystyle CH_3}{|}}{C}{=}CH{-}CH_2{-}\cdots$$

n = 2000   (Unit of natural rubber molecule)

The Steroids

17.20   INTRODUCTION

The steroids are a family of compounds widely distributed in plants and animals. Common to the structure of all compounds of this class is a tetracyclic framework composed of the phenanthrene nucleus (Sec. 4.6) to which is fused at the 1, 2-positions a cyclopentane ring.

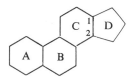

The steroid ring system

The rings in the steroid molecule usually are not aromatic but often contain one or more isolated double bonds. The total structure of one steroid differs from that of another, usually by a variation in the side chain or by a variation in the number and type of functional groups. To the family of steroids with this common ring system belong the sterols, the sex hormones, the bile acids, and other biologically important materials.

For purposes of nomenclature the steroid ring skeleton is numbered as shown.

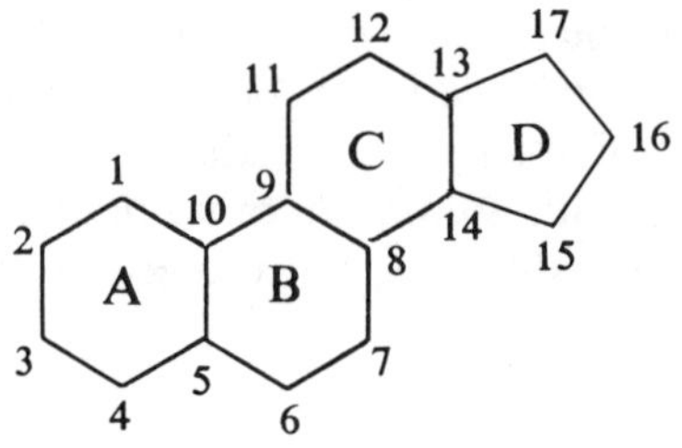

17.21   CHOLESTEROL

The **sterols** are solid alcohols which possess a hydroxyl group at position 3, a double bond between carbons 5 and 6, a side chain on carbon 17, and methyl groups joined to ring carbons numbered 10 and 13. *Cholesterol*, $C_{27}H_{46}O$, one of the most widely distributed sterols, is found in almost all animal tissue but is particularly abundant in the brain, the spinal cord, and in gallstones. Deposition of cholesterol or its derivatives in the arteries (hardening of the arteries) restricts the flow of blood, causes high blood pressure, and leads to some forms of cardio-vascular disease. The structure of cholesterol is shown with asymmetric carbon atoms indicated by asterisks.

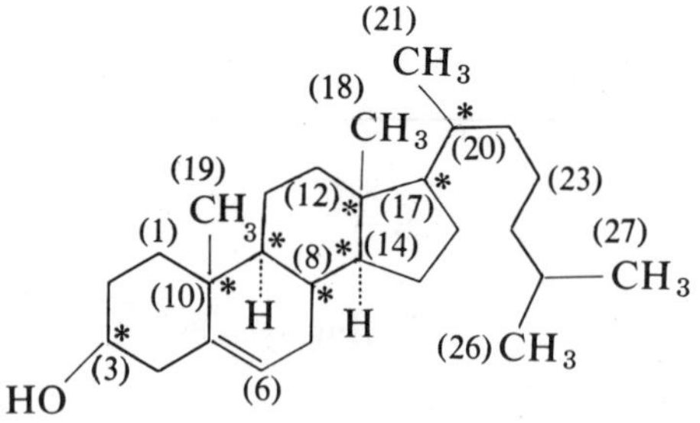

Structure and numbering system of cholesterol

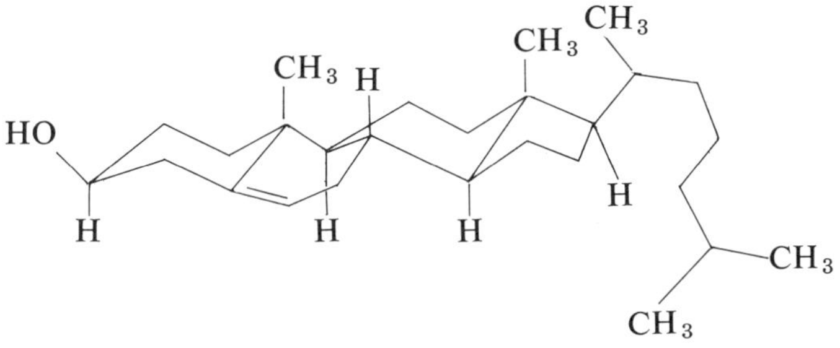

Stereochemical configuration of cholesterol

17.22   ERGOSTEROL

Although cholesterol is found only in animals, a large number of closely related compounds known as **phytosterols** are found in plants. One of these, *ergosterol*, $C_{28}H_{44}O$, is produced by yeast. Ergosterol is of particular interest because, when irradiated, it yields calciferol, vitamin D_2.

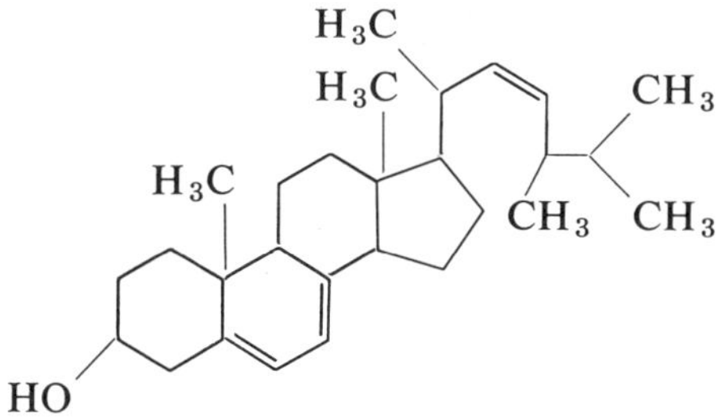

Ergosterol

17.23   SEX HORMONES

The male and female sex hormones are structurally related steroids responsible for the development of sex characteristics and sexual processes in animals. Sex hormones are produced in the gonads (ovaries and testes) when the latter are stimulated by other gonadotropic hormones. The female sex hormones are involved in the menstrual cycle, the changes in the uterus, and in the preparation for and maintenance of pregnancy. The structures and names of the principal female sex hormones are shown on the next page.

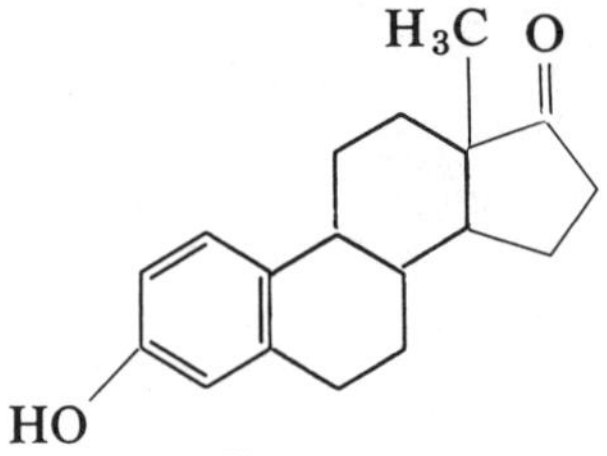

Estrone

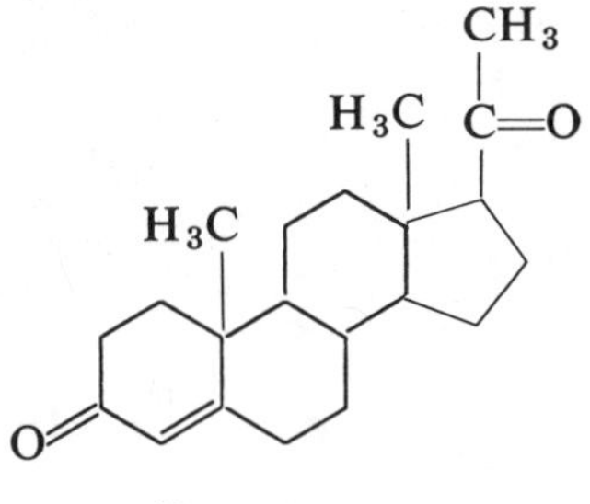

Progesterone

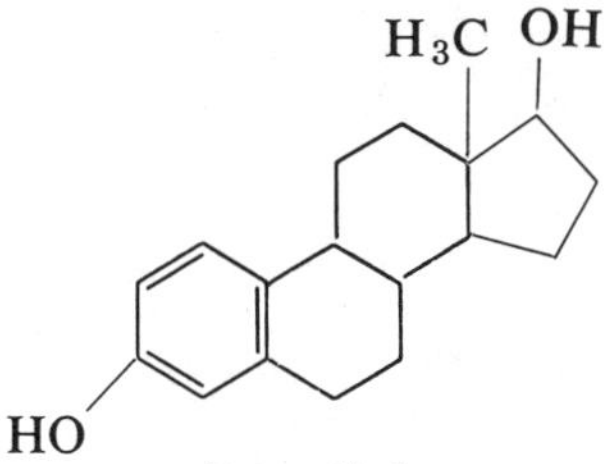

Estradiol

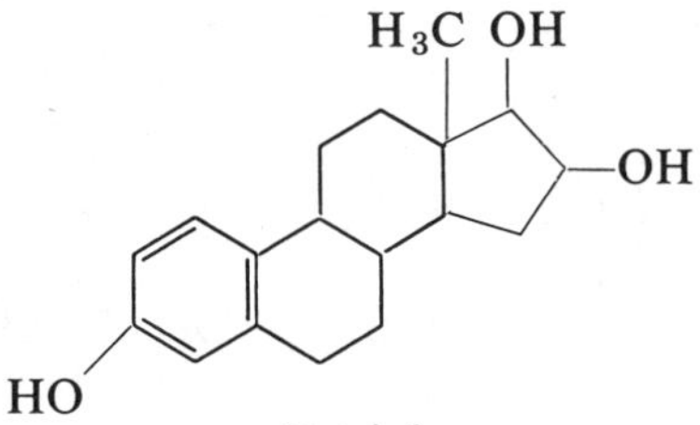

Estriol

Oral contraceptives have been developed that contain synthetic compounds structurally similar to progesterone and estriol but modified chemically to permit easier assimilation into the bloodstream. These synthetic agents, when taken orally, suppress ovulation and mimic pregnancy. The structures of two synthetic progesterones and a synthetic estrogen[6] are shown. Both types of synthetic hormones are used either in combined form or sequentially.

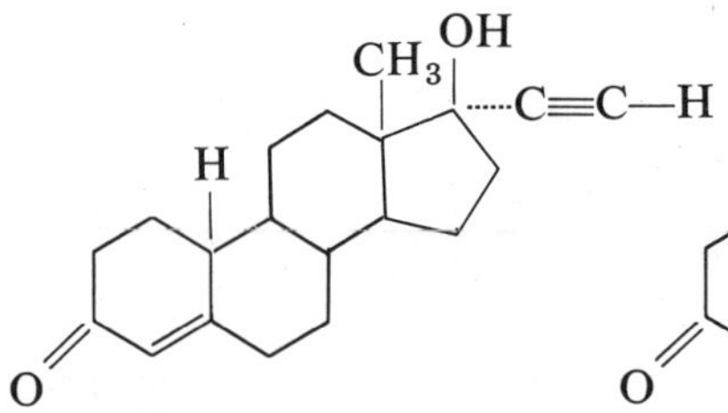

(a)

Norethindrone

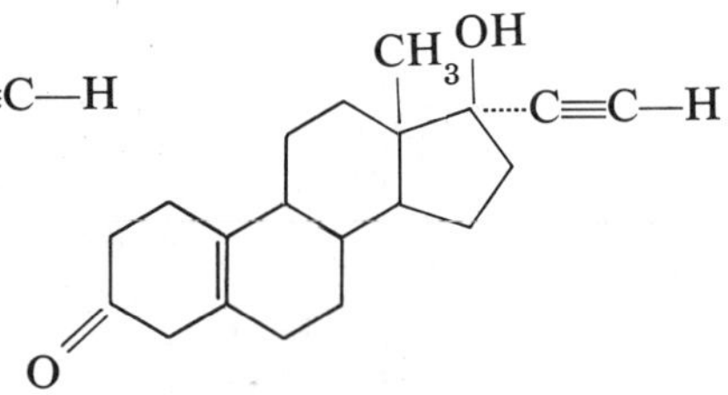

(b)

Norethynodrel

[6]Estrogen is a generic term for a substance that induces estrus—the cyclic phenomenon of the female reproductive system.

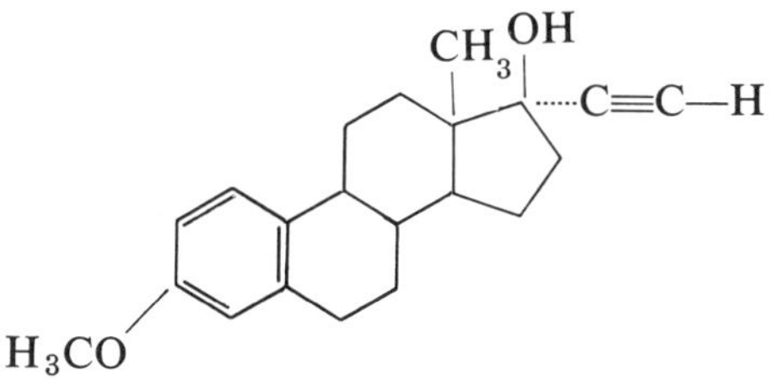

CH₃ OH
C≡C—H

H₃CO

(c)

Mestranol

Orthonovum = (a) + (c)
Enovid   = (b) + (c)

The male sex hormones, called **androgens,** except for the absence of an aromatic ring, are very similar in structure to the female hormones. The male sex hormones control the development of the male genital tract and the secondary male characteristics — e.g., beard, voice. The structures of the principal male sex hormones are shown below.

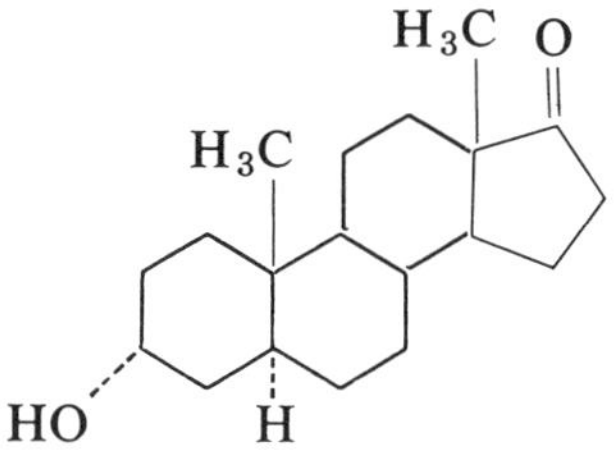

H₃C O

H₃C

HO   H

Androsterone

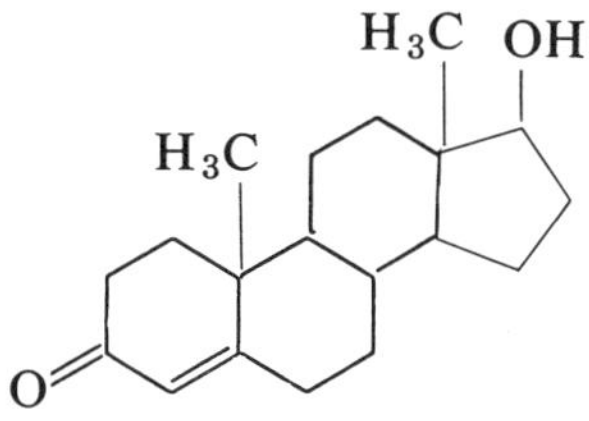

H₃C OH

H₃C

O

Testosterone

17.24   ADRENAL STEROIDS

Cortisone, and its derivative, 17-*hydroxycorticosterone,* are two steroids produced by the adrenal cortex. These compounds have been used with beneficial results in the treatment of inflammatory and allergic diseases. The structures of cortisone and its reduced form, 17-hydroxycorticosterone, are shown on page 482.

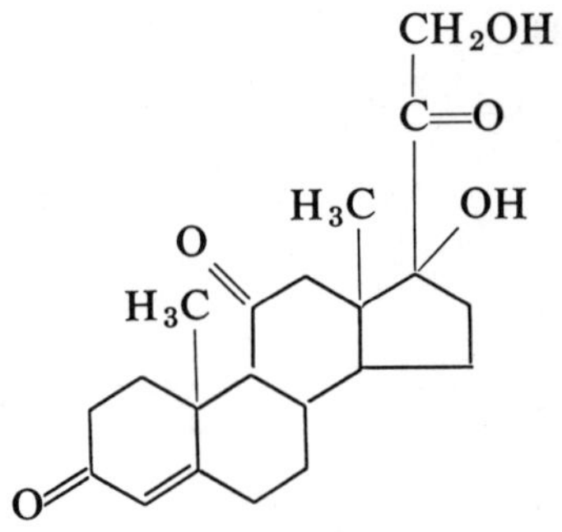

Cortisone 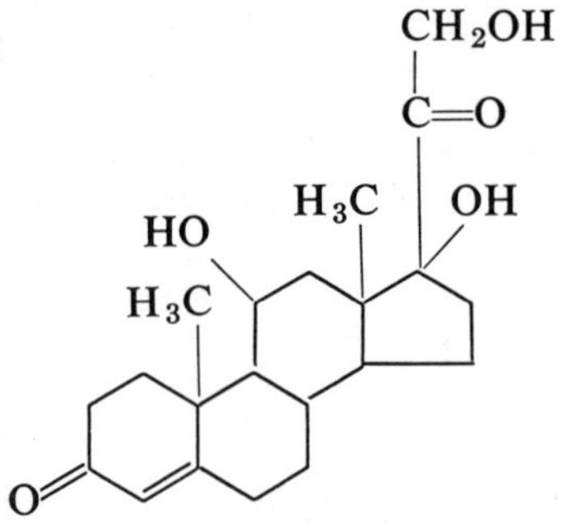   17-Hydroxycorticosterone

Antibiotics

Our discussion of natural products would not be complete without a brief treatment of the antibiotics. These chemotherapeutic agents are potent antibacterials which possess the power to inhibit the growth of, or destroy, microorganisms.

17.25   PENICILLINS

Penicillin, the first antibiotic to be isolated from a mold, was introduced into clinical practice in 1941 with remarkable results. It was found to be active against a number of *Gram-positive*[7] microorganisms of the cocci type and against spirochetes. A number of penicillins have been prepared. Their skeletal structures are the same, but they differ from one another in the character of the side chain R (see formula for penicillin). Commercial preparations of penicillin are mainly penicillin G (R = $C_6H_5CH_2—$, benzyl).

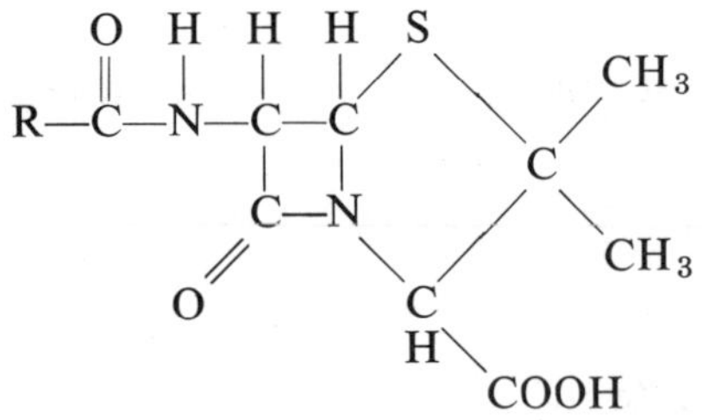

Penicillin

[7]*Gram-positive* refers to organisms which stain "positive" when treated with Gram stain; *Gram-negative* refers to those which stain "negative" to the same reagent. A *broad spectrum antibiotic* is one which may be effective against both Gram-negative and Gram-positive organisms.

17.26 STREPTOMYCIN

A more recent antibiotic is **streptomycin** whose structure is that of a trisaccharide. Streptomycin is active against *Gram-negative* bacteria and is used in tuberculosis therapy. The structure of streptomycin is indicated below.

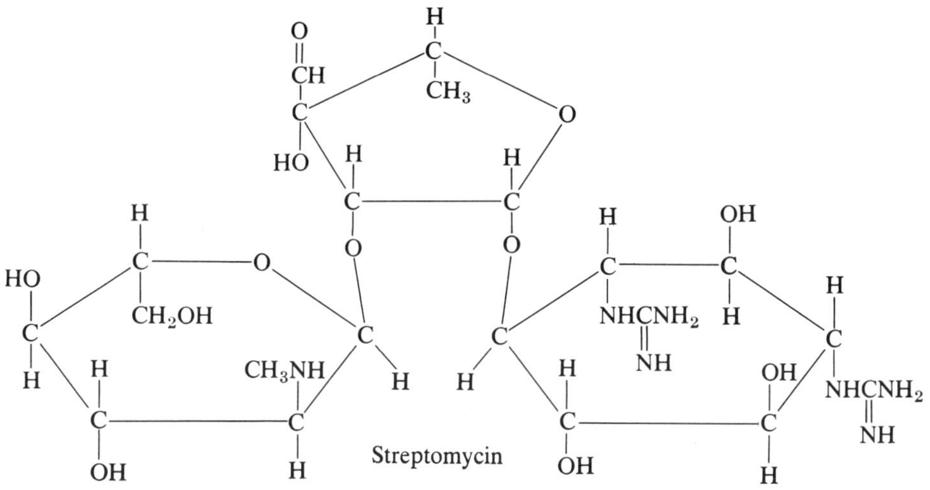

Streptomycin

17.27 THE TETRACYCLINES

The **tetracyclines** comprise a family of compounds, each member of which has a four fused-ring structure. Each member differs from the other only in minor detail. Tetracycline, its 7-chloro derivative, *aureomycin*, and its 5-hydroxy derivative, *terramycin*, are *broad spectrum* antibiotics widely used against a number of bacterial and viral diseases.

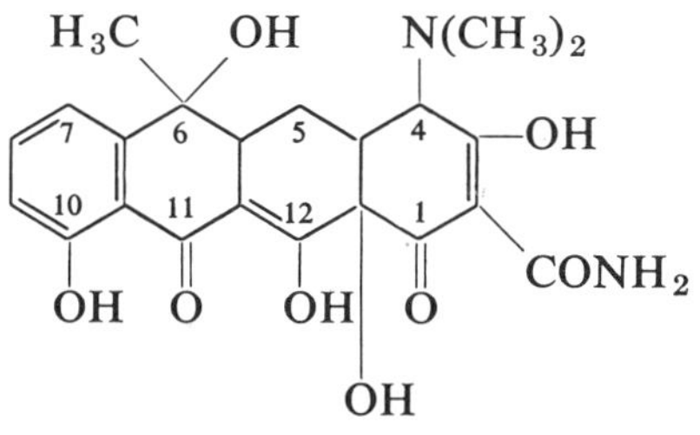

Tetracycline

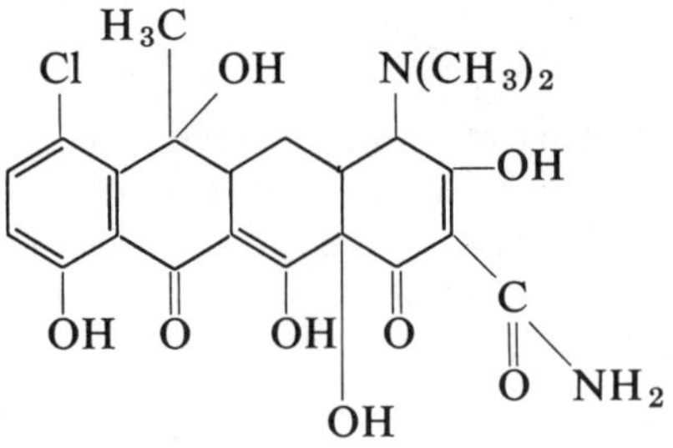

Aureomycin 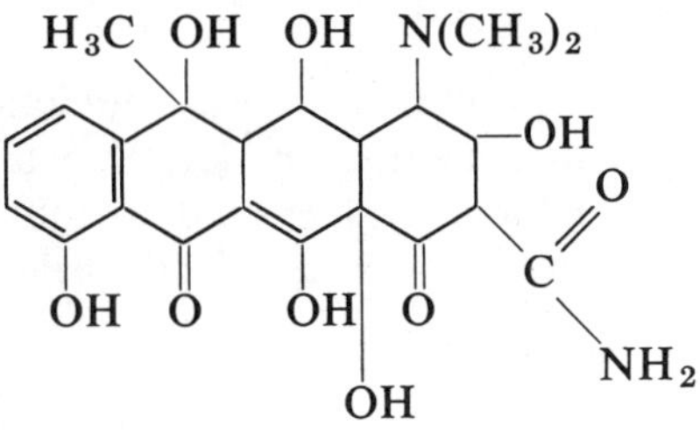   Terramycin

□□ *SUMMARY*

[1]   The heterocyclic compounds are ring compounds containing atoms other than carbon. The most common *hetero* atoms are **nitrogen, oxygen,** and **sulfur.** The hetero atoms appear most frequently in five- or six-membered rings.

[2]   The heterocycles possess *aromatic* properties similar to those of benzene.

[3]   The heterocyclic systems frequently make up all or part of a great number of polycyclic natural products.

Alkaloids

[4]   The alkaloids are nitrogen-containing plant products that possess marked physiological properties.

[5]   Nearly all of the alkaloids are made up of more than one heterocyclic ring. Such rings usually are fused rings — that is, two rings have one or more bonds in common.

[6]   Many of our most valuable drugs are obtained from alkaloids.

[7]   The promiscuous use of alkaloids is dangerous and usually leads to addiction.

Vitamins

[8]   The vitamins are trace nutrients required in the diet of animals for proper growth, development, and good health.

[9]   The absence of sufficient amounts of vitamins in the diet results in deficiency diseases.

[10] Vitamins are generally classified as fat-soluble or water-soluble.

[11] The fat-soluble vitamins are vitamins A, D, E, and K; the water-soluble vitamins are vitamin C and those usually designated B vitamins.

Terpenes

[12] The name terpene is a general term used to describe a large class of natural products with carbon skeletons that are multiples of the C_5 isoprene unit.

[13] Many of the terpenes are unsaturated hydrocarbons. Others possess, in addition to double bonds, the functional groups of the alcohols, carbonyls, and acids. Many are "essential oils" used in perfumery and in flavoring agents.

[14] Terpenes may be branched, open-chain structures; they may be cyclic; or they may have structures that contain both features.

[15] The terpenes are classified according to the number of C_{10} units present. Monoterpenes are C_{10} compounds, diterpenes, C_{20} compounds, etc.

Steroids

[16] The steroids are natural products that have in common the 4-cycle, skeletal structure of 1, 2-pentanophenanthrene.

[17] Steroids with one or more hydroxyl groups may be called *sterols*.

[18] The most abundant steroids of animal origin are cholesterol, ergosterol, the sex hormones, and cortisone.

Antibiotics

[19] The antibiotics are antibacterials used in chemotherapeutic agents to inhibit the growth of, or to destroy, microorganisms. A number are of plant (mold) origin.

[20] Commonly used antibiotics are the penicillins, streptomycin, and those of the tetracycline family — aureomycin and terramycin.

□□ *NEW TERMS*

[1] alkaloid	[7] isoprene rule
[2] androgen	[8] steroid
[3] antibiotic	[9] sterol
[4] essential oil	[10] terpene
[5] estrogen	[11] vitamin
[6] heterocycle	

■ □ SUPPLEMENTARY EXERCISES
▼   AND PROBLEMS

[1]   2-Methylpyridine (α-picoline) and 4-methylpyridine (γ-picoline) both enter into base-catalyzed condensation reactions with benzaldehyde. Suggest a reason why the methyl hydrogen atoms in these two compounds appear to be weakly acidic like those in malonic ester, acetoacetic ester, and other dicarbonyls.

[2]   Refer to the structure of farnesol (Sec. 17.16) and draw it as a horizontal chain. Number all carbon atoms in the longest chain and name the compound according to IUPAC rules.

[3]   To the "stretched out" farnesol structure of exercise [2] add a second molecule of farnesol but set the hydroxyl groups together. If the hydroxyl groups were now removed via reduction and the two carbon atoms to which they were bonded joined, which compound would result?

[4]   Draw the structures of β-carotene and abietic acid (Sec. 17.17). Are all C_5 units in a head-to-tail arrangement? Does either compound contain asymmetric centers?

[5]   Natural rubber (Sec. 17.19, also Exercise 6.1) has a *cis* configuration. Is it likely that β-carotene also has isomers? Could these be geometric isomers, structural isomers, or both types of isomers?

[6]   Cholesterol (Sec. 17.21) is shown both as a planar structure and in its natural conformation. We have been told why cyclohexane rings prefer a chair conformation, but why is the D ring not a planar pentagonal structure?

index

502

Glossary *Continued*

ETHERS	*p. 211 A general class of compounds in which two carbons are joined through an oxygen atom.*
FATS	*p. 296 Solid or semisolid, naturally occurring, long chain carboxylic acid esters of glycerol.*
FREE RADICAL	*p. 43 A highly reactive, short lived atom or group that has an odd, unpaired electron.*
FUNCTIONAL GROUP	*p. 20 A structural feature that identifies a family of compounds and bestows upon its members a common property.*
GLYCOLS	*p. 196 Compounds that contain two hydroxyl groups, usually on adjacent carbon atoms.*
HEMIACETAL	*p. 238 An unstable compound formed by the addition of an alcohol to the carbonyl group of an aldehyde.*
HETEROCYCLIC	*p. 453 A ring compound that contains, in addition to carbon, one or more other kinds of atom.*
HOMOLOGOUS SERIES	*p. 20 A family of compounds in which one member differs from the next by a methylene unit,* $-CH_2-$.
HYBRIDIZED ORBITALS	*p. 11 Atomic orbitals formed by blending orbitals in different subshells.*
HYDROCARBONS	*p. 31 Compounds (usually obtained from petroleum) that contain only hydrogen and carbon.*
INVERT SUGAR	*p. 391 A levorotatory mixture of equal parts of glucose and fructose formed by hydrolyzing dextrorotatory sucrose.*
ISOMERS	*p. 17 Compounds with the same molecular formula but with different structural formulas.*
KETONES	*p. 223 Carbonyl compounds of the general formula* $R_2C=O$.
LEVOROTATORY	*p. 145 A term applied to optically active compounds that rotate plane polarized light counterclockwise or to the left.*
MOLECULAR ORBITAL	*p. 7 An orbital formed by the overlap of two atomic orbitals which encompasses more than one nucleus.*
MUTAROTATION	*p. 385 A change with time in the rotation of a solution of an optically active compound.*
NUCLEOPHILIC REAGENT	*p. 169 A reagent with an unshared pair of electrons to donate, e.g., a base.*